School health practice

Third edition

SCHOOL HEALTH PRACTICE

C. L. ANDERSON, B.S., M.S., Dr.P.H.

*Professor of Hygiene and Health Education and
Chairman of Hygiene and Environment Sanitation,
Oregon State University, Corvallis, Oregon;
formerly Professor of Biological Science and
Health Education, Michigan State University;
formerly Head and Professor of Physiology,
Hygiene and Public Health, Utah State University*

Illustrated

THE C. V. MOSBY COMPANY

St. Louis   1964

Preface to third edition

We know so much more than we *do*. Therein lies the tale of present-day health promotion. Health knowledge expands daily and is disseminated in all directions. Yet, a deplorably small number of citizens, adult and child alike, use health knowledge effectively. One needs but to attend a health convention and observe the legion of heavy smokers, the number of obese individuals, and the disregard of established health principles. If those who are most knowledgeable do not follow scientific health principles, what of the lay individual?

Our health education program in connection with smoking has been at least a 97% failure. Alcohol education has been perhaps a 98% failure. In other areas, health education has been almost equally unsuccessful. New emphases, as well as new methods, are needed.

The need in health is not to place more and more emphasis on the extension and dissemination of health knowledge but to emphasize the day-to-day application of the knowledge we now have. This calls for a retooling of health education to a primary emphasis on *health practice* at all levels and in all aspects. To be even moderately successful will not be an easy task.

Each youngster must be motivated to *want* to promote and maintain his health now and in the years to come. Health may not in itself be a motivating force for a youngster who already has excellent health. He must develop the necessary vision to appreciate health as an asset throughout his life. Other life motives may be used which will promote health as a by-product. This calls for competent teaching by a *dedicated* teacher who possesses the imagination and ingenuity to visualize the many student interests which can be channeled to an interest in health. The student must associate health with himself so that his health learning is always directed to the self, to his own self-interest. This is the focus, or nucleus, in which health practices will find their origin. This spark must be fanned by opportunities for practice of these health principles with continuing motivation through the gratification he receives from self-accomplishment and self-improvement.

A school is not an island unto itself. From the standpoint of school health, a community is an archipelago of many health islands represented by the many health resources of the community. The school wisely uses all of these resources, most particularly the home, in a program to provide an environment favorable to the establishment of desirable practices in the oncoming generations. This requires a lot of doing. Progress in community change is itself a slow process, but a community can grind effectively even though slowly.

The value of a school health program must be appraised in terms of its actual effect upon the health of the students. This effect is the product of practice primarily by the student himself but tangentially by the teacher, the custodian, the school nurse, the parents, the physician, and others. The student and what he does for his own health is the focus of the present-day school health program.

I am greatly indebted to the many individuals who have contributed significantly to this edition of *School Health Practice*. Distinctive acknowledgment is made to certain professional colleagues whose counsel and services have been of special value. Leland M. Corliss, M.D., Director of Health Services, Denver Public Schools, has been most generous in making available his vast professional background and the facilities of his organization. Dr. George J. Sirnio, Director of Health and Physical Education, and Warren LaBounty, Assistant Director, Salem, Oregon, Public Schools, Mrs. Betty J. Owen, Health and Physical Education Consultant, Oregon State Department of Education, and Mrs. Betty Polen, Director of Health Education, Portland, Oregon, Public Schools, have contributed significantly to the preparation of the third edition. Acknowledgment is also made to the legion of students who have taught their instructor so much about themselves and about their needs and their efforts to attain the highest possible level of health.

C. L. Anderson

"Far best is he who is himself all-wise,
And he, too, good who listens to wise words;
And whoso is not wise nor lays to heart
Another's wisdom is a useles man."

—Hesiod (800 B.C.)

Preface to first edition

Health promotion is a recognized component of present-day functional public school education which is designed to prepare each youngster to deal with life's academic, cultural, and practical needs. No phase of the school's activities has more to contribute to the student than does the health program. Closely interwoven with all phases of school life, the health program aims to develop each student in terms of his present and future needs. As an achievement in living, health is integrated with all aspects of school life which contribute to the effectiveness and enjoyment of life for each youngster.

Primary responsibility for the health of the child rests with the parents, but the school is in a strategic position to contribute effectively to the health of every school age child. The school does not assume the role of the parent nor substitute for the parent. Rather, the school health program is planned to fortify and supplement the efforts of the parents.

The *what,* the *how,* and the *why* of the functional school health program are the substance of this publication. Special attention is given to the practical considerations of everyday school life. The approach has been that of presenting a clear, unified, composite picture of school health as represented by the most valuable contributions of the many health educators who have devoted their talents to the school health movement. So far as possible, superfluous material has been discarded and the truly essential substance has been presented. Material of an older vintage has been refreshed to fit the modern school situation. Much of the material is new but nevertheless bears the label of having been tried and found to be effective.

A self-contained textbook designed to serve the optimum preprofessional and in-service health preparation needs of teachers must be based upon actual experienced needs and practices. Successful educators in the field represent a fertile source of information on the health preparation needs of teachers. An extensive survey of the experience and thinking of successful teachers served as one guide in determining the content of this manuscript. College faculties, preparing teachers in health, were further consulted for suggestions on the desirable content of a comprehensive school health textbook. With the recommendations of these various professional groups as a guide, the organization and content of the manuscript were developed.

Because the child is the concern of all school health work, attention is given to an understanding of normal child growth, development, and health. Common departures from health are introduced to enable teachers to understand their proper role in contributing to the needs of the child who falls outside of the normal range. The complete school health program is developed so the material can be applied to the model health program of the large school system or adapted to the needs of the system or school with a minimum health program. Teachers with a modicum of resourcefulness can adapt the instructional materials to their particular classroom needs.

The school health field has attained that level of maturity where it has its own terminology, expressions, picturesque passages, and even shibboleths. Anyone writing in the health field today will use expressions which are the creations of others and the accepted tools of the profession. Maeterlinck, in his essay on *Literary Manners,* commented, "I have at times been twigged for using sentences and phrases that had a familiar ring or were identical with what others had written before me. No writer who loves words, their flair, nuances and beauty can escape such impeachment. We are struck with some beautiful line or paragraph reread many times and lo! later we may find it has popped into our heads as something original. Our only excuse is our utter innocence."

Acknowledgments must begin with an expression of gratitude to that vast number of public school teachers who have expressed their health preparation needs and have thus contributed to the form and substance of the manuscript. These people represent a segment of that legion of unheralded and unsung classroom teachers who are the institution of education in America. An expression of appreciation must be addressed to several individuals: Dr. Rex Putnam, Oregon Superintendent of Public Instruction, for making all of his department's health resources available; Professor Lucille Hall Jones, Walla Walla College, for her work in developing the School Health Program Evaluation Scale; Dr. Helen G. Smith, State College of Washington, for her constructive review and appraisal of the entire manuscript; Dr. Bernice Moss, University of Utah; Dr. Charles J. Hart, Brigham Young University; Dr. Franklin B. Haar, University of Oregon; Professor L. J. Sparks, Willamette University; Professor I. E. Langstaff, Saskatchewan Teachers College; Professor Warren Smith, Lewis and Clarke College; Professor Betty J. Owen, Pacific University; Professor Anna Pavlov and Professor L. J. Carmody, Central Washington College; and Dr. C. F. Shockey, Seattle Pacific College.

CORVALLIS, OREGON   *C. L. Anderson*

Contents

PART 3

School health services

PART 4

Health instruction

PART 5

Healthful school living

PART 6

Appraisal in school health practice

Appendixes

School health practice

*In darkness dwells the people which
knows its annals not.*

—Ullrich Phillips

Chapter 1

Introduction

P araphrasing Ralph Waldo Emerson, "We think the practice of school health
is near its meridian but we are yet only at the cock-crowing and the
morning star." Although man's attempt to promote health is of an an-
cient vintage, only in relatively recent times has the school been
incorporated into the general program of health promotion. Only relatively recently has the school health program developed to a position
where it has had a positive, measurable effect upon the health of citizens.
Yet, the present-day school health program falls far short of realizing
the opportunities afforded it, and many decades now in the future will
have passed into history before the school health program will attain the
status where one could truly say the school health program "has arrived."

Health in the school is an outgrowth of man's constant search for
more effective and more enjoyable living. To live an effective and enjoyable life has been the central, dominant purpose of mankind from
the beginning of recorded history. To attain this goal mankind has
studied the phenomena of the universe, controlled the forces of nature,
developed languages, invented various devices, instituted new practices,
written laws and regulations, established institutions, and even sought
to improve man's basic endowment.

Periods in history in which man has advanced most are those in
which man has made most progress in the promotion of his health. Progress in health has always been associated with advancement in the various
pursuits of learning and with progress in providing for man's material
needs. When health has been neglected, civilization has declined and
mankind has retrogressed.

Mankind's quest for health

Certain periods in the history of the health movement serve as landmarks in man's progress in health promotion. Increased understanding

of health and changing concepts of health promotion are reflected in the pertinent contributions of the various periods. The school became one of the principal agencies for health promotion and has developed a health history of its own. To understand the true role and position of the school in the health field, it is necessary to understand the background from which school health emerged.

Egyptian health practice. Before the year 1000 B.C., the Egyptians stressed personal cleanliness, compounded pharmaceutical preparations, built earth closets, and laid public drainage pipes, all in the interest of better health. In the light of today's knowledge these elementary practices appear to be of negligible health value, but they express the early efforts of man to live effectively and enjoyably.

Hebrew health code. The Hebrews extended the Egyptian health ideas when they formulated the first formal health code in the Mosaic Law. Of interest to the health student of today are nine of the basic areas covered by the law.

1. Personal and community responsibility for health
2. Maternity health
3. Control of communicable diseases
4. Isolation of lepers (*Leviticus,* Chapter XIII, gives interesting account of procedures for control of leprosy)
5. Sanitation of camp sites
6. Fumigation
7. Disposal of wastes
8. Protection of water supplies
9. Protection of food

The Jewish practice of considering pork unclean grew out of the observation that people became ill from eating pork. Trichinosis doubtless existed then as it does today.

Greek approach to health. At the height of Corinthian prosperity and achievement, primary emphasis was placed upon the individual, and secondary emphasis was placed upon the State. In this philosophy the State existed to serve the individual. In consequence, stress was placed upon individual grace, beauty, dexterity, skill, and ability. It was believed that the development of the individual depended on good health and a sound body, which were attained through exercise. Using but the one factor of exercise for the promotion of health, the Greeks attained but a limited level of health. Control of disease, proper nutrition, protection of water supplies, proper waste disposal, and other community health measures were of no concern to them. Each family, or group of families, had its own supply of well water. Because of the lack of a community responsibility, or concept, none of the cities of illustrious Greece was large. Corinth had a population of only 35,000. This civilization produced the renowned Hippocrates (460 to 377 B.C.) whose observations on health and whose teaching and practice of medicine were far in advance of his time. His influence has lived for more

Fig. 1. Hippocrates. His aphorism, "Where there is love for mankind, there is love for the art of healing," is reflected in the face of this revered physician, scientist, and teacher. (Copyright, Parke, Davis & Company and reproduced by special permission of Parke, Davis & Company, who commissioned the original oil paintings for the series, "A History of Medicine," a project written and directed by George A. Bender and painted by Robert A. Thom.)

than 2000 years, and he is still considered to be the Father of Medicine.

Roman health promotion. During the time of Julius Caesar, the State was first and the individual was subservient to the State. The Romans provided public water supplies by constructing aqueducts which carried water from distant points to the cities. Sewerage systems provided for disposal of community waste. Street pavement and street cleaning were regarded as health measures. Their emphasis on the community approach to problems enabled the Romans to build large cities. At the time of Julius Caesar, Rome had a population of about 800,000. Yet, because of their restricted approach to health matters, the Romans did not enjoy a high level of health.

Asceticism. During the Dark Ages, from about 400 to 1000 A.D., the influence of the church caused all emphasis to be placed on the spiritual aspects of life. The physical was neglected. The more one neglected or abused his physical being, the more holy he was thought to be. In such an atmosphere the level of health was indescribably low.

Revival of concept of a sound body. Between the years 1096 and 1248 A.D., during the time of the six great Crusades, the soldiers and followers of the Crusades had to be physically strong to withstand the rigors of the expeditions. For military purposes, the sound body again became the core of health promotion. Disease and malnutrition took their toll, and the period when knighthood was in flower wilts in terms of today's standards of health.

Health from 1500 to 1800. Even with the revival of learning, health progress was slow. The mysticism which previously had surrounded health still survived, and sickness was believed to be of demoniacal origin. Even in the middle of the seventeenth century, in western Europe 75% of the babies born failed to reach the age of 10 years. Pandemics wiped out large segments of the population. In George Washington's time, 90% of the colonists who reached adulthood had been afflicted with smallpox, and the average length of life in colonial America was about 29 years.

Some health progress was made during this era though no concerted, unified program which distinguished this period developed. William Harvey traced the circulation of blood, and Edward Jenner introduced scientific vaccination. The invention of the microscope was to play an important role in the development of the scientific approach to the health of a later period.

Modern era of health (1850 to present). The modern era of health had its beginning in the middle of the nineteenth century. It was ushered in by an awakening of interest in sanitation of the general environment. Although launched on a misconception, it expanded into a program which progressively has reduced the incidence of disease, increased the expectation of life, and extended the general well-being.

The *miasma phase (1850 to 1880),* the first of four phases of the modern era, was based on the erroneous theory that disease was caused by noxious odors. Emphasis was placed on the cleanliness of the general environment. General clean-up campaigns had their beginning in these early attempts of the public to eliminate all noxious odors. Garbage and refuse disposal, street cleaning, fumigation, and cleanliness of home surroundings were considered important to an odor-free atmosphere. The term malaria (ill air) is but descriptive of the original belief that this disease was caused by the damp evening air. Interpreting mere coincidence as a cause-and-effect relationhsip is a frequent mistake of the public in attempting to explain health problems. In the thinking of the period, the fact that the Anopheles mosquito preferred dusk for its flight activities was not associated with the disease.

It is significant that Havana, Cuba, probably was the cleanest city in the world; yet yellow fever was rampant. Though not effective in terms of disease control, measures for general cleanliness of this health phase were not without merit. They laid the groundwork for the more specific measures which were to follow.

The *bacteriological phase (1880 to 1920)* of this era was ushered in by the research work of Louis Pasteur and Robert Koch. The discovery that a specific organism causes a specific disease transferred attention from the general environment to specific things in the environment. It quickly was recognized that spread of disease could be prevented by blocking the routes over which the disease traveled. Emphasis was placed on the sanitation of water and milk and other foods, the elimination of insects, and the disposal of sewage. Sanitary engineers, sanitary inspectors, bacteriologists, and laboratory technicians became essential to the health program.

Control of the ill person, who was the source of the disease, became an established practice. Isolation and quarantine measures were enforced by quarantine officers who dutifully went about putting up nonartistic placards on homes with reported cases of the common communicable diseases. This phase appropriately might be referred to as the tack-hammer stage of public health.

Immunization, as a measure for preventing the spread of disease, was a natural outcome of the interest in bacteriology. In 1883, Pasteur developed the innoculation against rabies. Von Behring's development of diphtheria antitoxin was first put to use in 1894. Wright developed the typhoid innoculations in 1904. Lord Lister's development of the use of carbolic acid (phenol) and Ehrlich's discovery of the value of arsenic compounds in the treatment of syphilis further indicate the progress made during this health phase in the prevention and treatment of infectious diseases. The death rate from communicable diseases declined steadily during these forty years.

The *positive health phase (1920 to 1960)* was ushered in largely as a result of what the physical examination of men for the military services of the United States during World War I revealed. More than 34% of the flower of America's youth were rejected for military service because of health disabilities, most of which were correctable. It was apparent that, although America had been successful in preventing deaths from infectious diseases, the individual quality of health of its citizens had been neglected. To survive is not enough. To build up and maintain a high level of health in each person also is important. This became the rallying point of the nation's health program. While sanitation measures and control measures, including immunization, were still important, the center of interest shifted to the individual, to human beings. This required new services and new types of trained personnel.

During this period, in addition to sanitarians, sanitary engineers, and laboratory technologists, a vast number of skilled health specialists were employed, primarily for the purpose of promoting the health of the individual citizen. Among these were health educators, nutritionists, industrial hygienists, nurses, pediatricians, vision conservationists, audiometrists, epidemiologists, statisticians, and administrators.

The *social engineering phase (1960 to present)* describes today's public health approach. With the vast array of health discoveries and developments emerging in the past two decades, it became increasingly clear that, if these advances in the health field were to be of use to the public, measures must be taken to bring these health discoveries into the lives of the populace. Analysis of the situation in the attempt to bring discoveries and citizens together uncovered a number of significant factors.

As society becomes more and more complex, a greater and greater portion of the public appears to be incapable of adjusting to that increasing complexity. Consequently the public must be prepared if it is to utilize health developments. This means dealing with groups, neighborhoods, and even the entire population of a community. Public health education has become of special importance to prepare the public for the broad programs of sanitation, health promotion, disease prevention, and all other public health services available today. An understanding of human beings is basic to today's public health service. Ethnic backgrounds, neighborhood forces, personal, family and group purposes and values, economic, educational and religious factors, all must be considered if services are to be adjusted to people, and the public in turn is to adjust to the growing health complex.

Modern public health does not seek to control the populace. It seeks to bring together available health services and the people who need these services by making these people receptive to and able to utilize services in a way which would be most beneficial to them. This requires a form of social engineering not previously demanded of the public health profession. It has become the essential ingredient of modern public health promotion.

In man's quest for health the school has been in a strategic position. The school's role has become increasingly important as man has understood the nature of health and the measures that must be taken to achieve it. Recognition of the school as an important agency for the promotion of health has increased as health promotion for the individual human being has been increasingly emphasized. The extent to which the school health movement has grown out of advances in health science, health application, and health advancement is as interesting as it is important.

The school health movement

Health of children has long been a concern of the public, and history is replete with individual and group efforts to improve the lot of children. A century or more ago, a lack of organization and a lack of understanding of the fundamentals of health prevented any semblance of an organized, continuous program directed primarily to the health needs of the child. Yet, some of these early sporadic efforts were forerunners of child health programs which eventually developed into a school health program.

It is logical that the early contributions to the school health movement should come from Europe. Many of the contributors were nonprofessional people who sought to improve the lot of the growing child. In efforts to find a way to promote child health, several of these pioneers recognized the possible role of the school in the promotion of the well-being of the child.

European heritage of school health. As early as 1790, Bavaria provided free school lunches for the underprivileged. This program was fostered by Benjamin Thompson, a transplanted New Englander. The eminent European scientist, Johann Peter Frank (1745-1821), published a series of papers dealing with the general subject of school health. In 1832, Edwin Chadwick was an assistant commissioner to study the operation of the Poor Laws of England. A year later he became Secretary of the Factory Commission. From his studies of the conditions of child employment came reforms which recognized the health needs of children.

In 1833, France passed laws which held public school authorities responsible for the health of school children and the sanitation of school buildings. This law was extended nine years later to require that physicians inspect all schools at regular intervals.

Physicians were placed on public school staffs in Sweden in 1868, Germany in 1869, Russia in 1871, and Austria in 1873. In Brussels, Belgium, the first organized, regular medical inspection system was instituted in 1874. Every three months all schools were inspected by a physician. Later, dentists and vision specialists were added to the inspection staff.

It is significant that all of these early school health activities in Europe were directed toward doing something *for* the child. The concept of preparing the child to do for himself had not yet evolved because the essentials for health education were not in existence. An extensive knowledge of health plus universal education are the essentials for health education.

Modern school health era

The modern era of school health was launched on the fundamental concept that the school can prepare a person to do what is necessary for the protection, preservation, and promotion of his own health. Not only has this era retained the school's responsibility for supervising the child's health and for promoting school sanitation, which it inherited from Europe, but it also has added the all-important objective of preparing each child to make the decisions necessary for his health.

Period of recognition (1850 to 1880). It was no accident that the modern era of public health and the modern era of school health should date from the same year. A consciousness of the need for doing something about the health of human beings brought the natural question, "What can the school do?" A combination of fortuitous developments and certain cause-and-effect relationships account for the twin birth.

Previous to 1850, the schools in the United States were dominated by the church. This type of imposed pedagogy, which prevailed before 1850, did not lend itself to health education. However, in 1850, tax-supported public schools became a living reality in most of the United States, particularly in the northern section.

A second fortunate development of 1850 was the publication of the *Report of the Sanitary Commission of Massachusetts*. The awakening interest in health promotion had led to the appointment of this commission to study and make recommendations on matters affecting the public health. The Report deals with several health topics, but significantly it included a plan for school health instruction. A layman, Lemuel Shattuck, wrote the Report and penned one of the classic concepts of education when he wrote the following:

> Every child should be taught, early in life, that to preserve his own life and his own health and the lives and health of others, is one of his most important and constantly abiding duties. Some measure is needed which shall compel children to make a sanitary examination of themselves and their associates, and thus elicit a practical application of the lessons of sanitary science in the everyday duties of life. The recommendation now under consideration is designed to furnish this measure. It is to be carried into operation in the use of a blank schedule, which is to be printed on a letter sheet, in the form prescribed in the appendix, and furnished to the teacher of each school. He is to appoint a sanitary committee of the scholars, at the commencement of school, and on the first day of each month, to fill it out under his superintendence . . . . Such a measure is simple, would take but a few minutes each day, and cannot operate otherwise than usefully upon the children, in forming habits of exact observation, and in making a personal application of the laws of health and life to themselves. This is education of an eminently practical character, and of the highest importance.*

Because the Report was the most important health pronouncement in that day of health awakening, it commanded the respect necessary for its perpetuation. It gave recognition to the school as an agency for the promotion of health. For the next twenty years this seed of recognition was nourished by the influence of European leaders in education such as Rousseau, Pestalozzi, and Froebel. This influence cannot be over-emphasized because it stressed education as growth from within, not imposed from without, and growth from within is necessary for health education. This influence stimulated an interest in understanding the child and his needs and the means by which these needs may best be met.

Period of exploration (1880 to 1920). Beginning in 1880, pioneer work in the problems relating to the health of the child was inaugurated. A diversity of concepts developed of what constituted school health and what the province of the school was in the health of the child. Although the school health movement was out of its infancy, it showed all of the inquisitiveness and exploration typical of childhood.

The *child study movement* began at the outset of this period in the history of school health. Educators studied the physical and psychological characteristics of child development as the basis for planning the school program. Research was slow and hesitating, but before the end of this period child study was an established basis for all school planning and activities.

---

*From Report of the Sanitary Commission of Massachusetts, 1850, Dutton and Wentworth, p. 178.

Physical education experienced a robust expansion during the first twenty years of this period. In the interest of promoting physical conditioning and efficiency, calisthenics comprised a considerable part of the program. Kansas City, Missouri, had a director of physical education as early as 1885, and during the next ten years physical education was widely adopted by schools in the Middle West. Schools in other sections of the nation were slower in accepting physical education. As early as 1892, Ohio law *required* that physical education be taught in the schools of all first and second class cities.* In 1899, North Dakota law *required* the teaching of physical education in all public schools.

Physical education and health were held to be identical, and, apparently, not until 1910 was there a change in this point of view. In that year the seventeenth meeting of the American Physical Education Association had as the theme, "School Hygiene and Physical Education." Not until 1937 did the American Physical Education Association become the American Association for Health and Physical Education and thus recognize a distinction between health in schools and physical education in schools.

Instruction concerning the effects of alcohol and narcotics was required of all schools in every state by 1890. The drive for this requirement came from the temperance forces, and in more than half of the states the law also required instruction in physiology and hygiene. As early as 1842, Horace Mann had advocated that the schools carry out health instruction, and hygiene had been taught in a few places in the nation. However, the first concerted health instruction in schools grew out of the statutes requiring instruction in physiology and hygiene. Although at the outset the hygiene instruction was heavily weighted with anatomy and physiology, with emphasis on memorization of factual material, it did create interest in the subject of personal health.

In 1904, the National Association for the Study and Prevention of Tuberculosis was formed to combat the greatest single cause of death in the United States. In the absence of a specific treatment for tuberculosis, the Association selected education of the public as its approach. Its success supports the value of health education. In 1915, the Association conducted a program called Modern Health Crusade which made effective use of posters, stories, plays, and ceremonies as motivating devices. Exploration was yielding discoveries.

In 1909, there was formed the American Association for the Study and Prevention of Infant Mortality which developed programs of education for better child care. Later, the Association changed its name to American Child Hygiene Association. The First White House Conference on Child Health and Protection was held in 1910. This pooling of experiences was a forerunner of coming events.

---

*Rogers, J. F.: State-wide trends in school hygiene and physical education, Washington, D. C., 1930, United States Office of Education, Pamphlet No. 5.

The Baltimore, Maryland, school health demonstration of 1914 revealed that health instruction could alter health behavior. During World War I, concern for the health of the nation's children led to the formation, in 1918, of the Child Health Organization to promote health instruction in the schools. In 1920, fellowships in health education were awarded. In 1923 the organization merged with the American Child Hygiene Association to form the American Child Health Association, which was dissolved in 1935.

Health examinations in schools began in 1894 when Dr. Samuel Durgin, Health Commissioner of Boston, introduced the first regular program for medical inspection in the United States. A similar program was instituted in Chicago in 1895, New York in 1897, Philadelphia in 1898, and Massachusetts in 1906. As early as 1899, Connecticut law required teachers to test the vision of school children. Reading, Pennsylvania, employed a school dentist in 1903, and in 1904 the state of Vermont initiated compulsory eye, ear, nose, and throat examinations in the public schools. By 1910, more than 300 cities required medical inspections in their schools.

In 1918, the Commission on the Reorganization of Secondary Education named health as the first of the seven cardinal objectives of education.

These several enterprises were independent efforts to deal with the problem of health through the school. Each effort, in its particular way, contributed to the emerging school health program. Some of the work proved to be of little worth, but much of it had lasting value. The need for combining efforts was becoming apparent.

Period of synthesis (1920 to 1935). In 1920, the childhood period in the development of school health had passed, and the youth period had been reached. The need for a positive approach to personal health was recognized nationally. Mere survival was only a part of the problem. The quality of a person's health also was important. To contribute its share to the nation's health, the school must combine the various phases of the school health activities into a synthesized program. Synthesis is never easy, and to combine the various segments into a unified program posed many difficulties. The special role of the school in the nation's program for health was not simple to delineate in precise terms. There was general agreement that the school was one of many agencies contributing to health and that its activities must be synchronized with the over-all program. Yet, its unique contribution was that of preparing citizens to make the necessary decisions relating to their health. The questions of the responsibility of the school for the present health of the child and the role of the school in the correction of physical defects were to receive intensive study and were eventually crystallized into accepted policies at the close of this period.

School health personnel had many staves with which to construct the school health barrel, but some of the staves were of questionable value. The final selection had to include only staves which fit together.

The test which had to be made was whether the barrel did its intended job when it was completed. Such a test would reveal the defective staves. A barrel with one defective stave can be virtually worthless.

Field research in school health during this period provided the foundation on which the school health program in the United States was to be built. Application of the scientific approach to the problem gave stature to the findings and to the recommendations which resulted. Setting up a demonstration type of study in the field is equivalent to setting up a laboratory study in a social situation. In dealing with social phenomena, precise measurement is not often possible, nor is it always necessary. Observable data which lend themselves to comparison can be highly meaningful. The less precise the data in research, the more important the interpretative skill of the investigator becomes.

In Malden, Massachusetts, in 1922, under the direction of Dr. C. E. Turner and supported by the Massachusetts Institute of Technology, a two-year school health demonstration program was conducted. Incorporating what was considered the best activities in school health, Dr. Turner developed a relatively complete program. At the termination of the demonstration, a critical analysis of the results showed that not only had the health behavior of the youngsters been improved tangibly, but also the health, growth, and development of the children had been affected favorably.

From 1922 to 1925, under the sponsorship of the American Red Cross, a similar demonstration with similar results was conducted in Mansfield and Richland counties, Ohio. In Fargo, North Dakota, the Commonwealth Fund conducted a school health demonstration from 1923 to 1927. With the Milbank Memorial Fund assisting financially Cattaraugus County, New York, conducted a school health demonstration program. Each of these studies contributed to the school health movement by pointing out strengths and weaknesses, suggesting methods and techniques, explaining the procedures which could and could not be used, and showing the results to be obtained from a school health program.

In 1930, the Second White House Conference on Child Health and Protection grappled with the task of synthesizing the various aspects of child health and its concomitant problems. The report of the conference served as a guide for two decades, though the Midcentury White House Conference on Children and Youth, in 1950, submitted a further report.

Developments between 1920 and 1935 are most appreciated by those who examine the school health program critically. Persons in school health work can always do well to go back to a study of this third period in the development of the school health movement in the United States. Therein lies wealth for those who would prospect for it.

Period of integration (1935 to present). By 1935, the school health movement was moving into adulthood. It had become mature, with characteristic stability. The principal task before it was that of integration—of the school health program itself, of health with the entire school program, and of school health with the over-all health program of the home, the community, the state, and the nation.

Integration of health activities was inevitable in the development of the school health program. In the process of integration, school health has merged from a multiphased program of seven or more divisions to an integrated program of three phases. In 1935 the program included health examination, health guidance, prevention and correction of physical defects, control of communicable diseases, study of mental health, health instruction, and maintenance of school sanitation. As the program matured, it was integrated into the three phases of health services, health instruction, and healthful living. With integration, the program became more functional in terms of actual life needs, procedures, and situations. Promotion of each child's health and emphasis on functional health knowledge resulted. As school health became more functional, the static concept of sanitation evolved into healthful school living in which all aspects of environmental interaction were incorporated. Such a program naturally became an integrated part of the total school program, not an isolated segment of it.

Throughout the nation, school health programs are evolving. New methods, procedures, and techniques are constantly being developed. School personnel in the field are finding solutions to the various health problems which arise. No established pattern is designated in detail as *the* school health program, but definite objectives and basic fundamentals of a school health program have been developed.

Integration with home and community resulted. It was apparent that the school health program could not be wholly effective unless it was integrated with the home and the community and the forces in both which contribute to the health of the school child. Services of the personnel of public health departments and staff members of voluntary health agencies were utilized as a regular part of the activities of the school.

In 1941, the Joint Committee on Health Problems in Education of the National Education Association and the American Medical Association developed a complete volume titled *Health Education* which, with revisions, has been a standard reference for the school health profession. This book, plus other joint publications of the two associations, presented the current practices in school health.

Beginning in 1942 and continuing for six years, a school-community health project sponsored by the W. K. Kellogg Foundation extended to several hundred schools in twenty-four states. This project established the value and importance of cooperation of professional personnel of the school and community health agencies. It demonstrated that effective health education requires community understanding and support.

In 1944, the American Council on Education issued objectives of general education in its publication, *A Design for General Education*. Special attention was given to health objectives.

The National Committee on School Health Policies, formed in 1945

77244

by the National Conference for Cooperation in Health Education, presented a charter for school health which was titled, *Suggested School Health Policies.**

An outstanding problem that continues to challenge the leaders of the school health program is the *professional training* of personnel. National conferences on professional training in health education were held in 1949, 1953, and 1955 in Washington, D. C., in Jackson's Mill, Weston, West Virginia, in 1948, and in Pere Marquette State Park, Illinois, in 1950. All of these conferences considered the functions, the necessary competency, and the adequate preparation of personnel for work in school health education. Information from the reports of the conferences was used as a basis for recommended procedures and for establishing standards of achievement for teachers' colleges, for certification agencies, for school administrators in hiring personnel, for health educators, and for classroom teachers.

Thus far, the training of school administrators and special personnel in health education has been given but little attention. However, the maximum effectiveness of a school health program can be attained only when all the personnel related to the program have an adequate understanding of school health in general and their role in particular.

The health program in the schools in the United States has had a century of development and in that time has evolved into an effective aspect of school and community life. Its general significance can be understood by an overview of today's school health program. Its true import can best be appreciated by a study of the program in action.

Today's school health program

It is essential to view the present-day school health program in the light of the over-all change in American education. Because the American concept has been changing from a traditional, classical education to a functional education which deals in terms of life requirements, health has become a natural concern of the school. Health is a functional activity. It deals with the process of living and its needs. It thus has an obvious place in a curriculum based upon a functional philosophy.

When America undertook to convert its long-established classical education to one based upon a philosophy of function, no one connected with the transition had any delusions about the magnitude of the change. Yet, what at first appeared to be a revolution in education is by an evolutionary process gradually emerging into an increasingly effective program which provides youth with opportunities for wholesome living today and prepares them for effective lives in the years to come. The transition is a continuous process in our present-day, vital education, which is by necessity dynamic and not static. In developing functional education, educators have demonstrated their capacity to find solutions

---

*American Medical Association, 10th printing, Chicago, Ill., 1950.

to the problems which have confronted them. Mistakes and inadequacies have been recognized, and the program and approach have been modified accordingly. That which contributed to the child's preparation for the life he is to live has been retained, developed, refined, and extended. School health, with its wealth of life values, flourishes in the soil of functional education.

The school is but one of several agencies which contributes to the health of the people of the nation, but it is in a strategic position to play an important role in the health program. The school health program is not indispensable to the nation's health program, but it is *irreplaceable*. It has a unique contribution, a particular service to give, which no other agency can quite duplicate. That unique contribution is recognized by school administrators, parents, and professionally trained health personnel.

Philosophy. Primary responsibility for the health of the school-age child rests with the parents, but the school should assist the parents in building up and maintaining the highest possible level of health in each child and in developing the necessary competence in each child to deal with the health problems of life. The proper role of the school is to supplement the efforts of the parents in furthering child health. Such supplementation includes consultation with the parent.

Although legally the school has the authority of a parent, a school would err to assume the complete role of a parent. The classical decision of the Supreme Court of the State of Nebraska in 1933 is considered the legal authority on the principle of the school *in loco parentis* (in place of the parent) in matters of school health.

> During school hours general education and control of pupils are in the hands of school boards, superintendents, principals and teachers, which control extends to health while parental authority is temporarily superseded.*

Yet, a school health program based on the ultimate of legal authority is suspect. Not legal authority but child needs, parental support, and professional service are the bases of today's school health program. Although the school accepts the responsibilities of the parent during school hours, it does so in the spirit of service, not in the role of an enforcement officer.

The school health philosophy of today is more realistic and challenging than the philosophy expressed in 1918 when the Commission on Reorganization of Secondary Education named *health* as the first of the cardinal principles of education. Today's interpretation is that almost all children who come to school are healthy. It would be presumptuous to give a child something he already has. Today's school health program places its emphasis on building up and maintaining a high level of health in each child. Its primary concern is with the normal, well child, and

---

*From Richardson v. Braham, 249 N.W. 557, 125 Neb. 142. Haffner v. Braham, 249 N.W. 560, 125 Neb. 147

fully 90% of its effort is directed to the child who has good health. The school rightly assumes responsibility for watching a youngster during the school hours and, in teamwork with the parents, taking action essential to his welfare. Thus, children who are ill or have defects are not neglected. The school initiates the action necessary to assure the child the professional services he should have.

The health program is not something apart from the general school program, but an integrated phase of it. Health activities are interwoven with all phases of the school program in doing everything practical to develop each child to the fullest possible extent in terms of his basic endowment. Health is an integral part of education.

Such a philosophy should be examined in the light of the recognized objectives of general education. Perhaps the best statement of these objectives is contained in a report entitled *A Design for General Education* issued by the American Council on Education. The report states:

> In the committee's judgment, general education should lead the student:
> 1. To improve and maintain his own health and take his share of responsibility for protecting the health of others
> 2. To communicate through his own language in writing and speaking at the level of expression adequate to the needs of educated people
> 3. To attain a sound emotional and social adjustment through the enjoyment of a wide range of social relationships and the experience of working cooperatively with others
> 4. To think through the problems and to gain the basic orientation that will better enable him to make satisfactory family and marital adjustment
> 5. To do his part as an active and intelligent citizen in dealing with the interrelated social, economic and political problems of American life and in solving the problems of post-war international reconstruction
> 6. To act in the light of an understanding of the natural phenomena in his environment in its implications for human society and human welfare, to use his scientific methods in the solution of his problems, and to employ useful nonverbal methods of thought and communication
> 7. To find self-expression in literature and to share through literature man's experiences and his motivating ideas and ideals
> 8. To find a means of self-expression in music and in the various visual arts and crafts, and to understand and appreciate art and music as reflections both of individual experience and social patterns and movements
> 9. To practice clear and integrated thinking about the meaning and value of life
> 10. To choose a vocation that will make optimum use of his talents and enable him to make an appropriate contribution to society*

From a survey of the general outcomes, it may seem that the committee omitted one of the most important aims of general education, the ability to think rigorously and critically. The committee took the position, however, that this ability should be developed and applied as an integral aspect of the learning process throughout the educational program.

---

*From American Council on Education: A design for general education, Washington, D. C., 1944, American Council on Education.

It is significant to note that the committee placed the improvement, maintenance, and protection of health as the first of the objectives. Equally significant is the committee's further elaboration on the implementation of this first objective when it states:

In order to accomplish this purpose, the student should acquire the following:
A. Knowledge and understanding
   1. Of normal body functions in relation to sound health practice
   2. Of the major health hazards, their prevention and control
   3. Of the interrelation of mental and physical processes in health
   4. Of reliable sources of health information
   5. Of scientific methods in evaluating health concepts
   6. Of the effect of socio-economic conditions on health
   7. Of community health problems, such as problems related to sanitation, industrial hygiene, and school hygiene
   8. Of community organization and services for health maintenance and improvement.
B. Skills and abilities
   1. The ability to organize time to include planning for food, work, recreation, rest and sleep
   2. The ability to improve and maintain good nutrition
   3. The ability to attain and maintain good emotional adjustment
   4. The ability to select and engage in recreative activities and healthful exercises suitable to individual needs
   5. The ability to avoid unnecessary exposure to disease and infection
   6. The ability to utilize medical and dental services intelligently
   7. The ability to participate in measures for the protection and improvement of community health
   8. The ability to evaluate popular beliefs critically.
C. Attitudes and appreciations
   1. Desire to attain optimum health
   2. Personal satisfaction in carrying out sound health practices
   3. Acceptance of responsibility for his own health and for the protection of the health of others
   4. Willingness to make personal sacrifices for the health of others
   5. Willingness to comply with health regulations and to work for their improvement.*

The philosophy of the present-day school health program is not one of impractical idealism. It is a decidedly realistic philosophy which deals in terms of the present and the future. Its test is in its final product. That product should be youngsters who have attained the near-potential of their physical, mental, and emotional capacities, who live effectively and enjoyably, and who are prepared to meet the many health problems they will encounter in their life's journey. Living is very much a matter of solving one problem after another. An understanding of health helps in solving problems related to it, but, of itself, is an asset of infinite value.

Evaluation of health. An old adage goes, "The healthy know not their

*American Council on Education: A design for general education, Washington, D. C., 1944, American Council on Education.

health, only the sick." Of all their physical possessions, normal people would perhaps rate health as the most important. Certain nonphysical values such as friendship, honor, reputation, and integrity may be rated ahead of health, but health is the tangible possession man rates most highly. The cardinal challenge to the school health program is to develop in healthy children a lasting appreciation of this magnificent asset. If emphasis is placed on health in a positive way, there need be no fear that hypochondriac children will develop. Rather, there will be a wholesome respect and appreciation of excellent health and a determination to make the most of one's excellent health.

One's state of health determines his capacity for performance, endurance, and even interest. Efficiency in accomplishment is determined both by interest and endurance. Accomplishment is the true source of enjoyment. Performance and enjoyment during childhood and youth set the pattern for an effective and enjoyable life—the dominant purpose of normal persons. A pleasant disposition, wholesome attitudes, and radiant personality are the products of effective and enjoyable living which good health makes possible.

General objective. Well-adjusted, physically vigorous children free from remediable defects, with practices, attitudes, and knowledge which will assure them a high level of well-being and the ability to make the necessary decisions which affect their own health is the goal toward which all school health work is directed.

Specific objectives. To an educator, the general objective of the school health program is like a star to a mariner—it sets the direction and the destination. To chart the navigation requires an orderly, planned, definite course. Such a course is laid out by setting specific markers, or objectives, which will lead to the desired goal when they are attained.

It is possible to list at least one hundred specific objectives of the school health program, but such an extensive list is neither necessary nor desirable. Such a listing would include minutely detailed aspects of the definite, basic aims of school health. The purposes of today's school health program can be stated by eighteen specific objectives.

1. Continuing appraisal of each child's health status
2. Understanding of each youngster's health needs
3. Supervision and guidance of the health of the children
4. Development of the highest possible level of health for each child
5. Prevention of defects and disorders
6. Detection and correction of all defects and disorders
7. Special health provisions for the exceptional youngster
8. Reduction in the incidence of communicable and noncommunicable diseases
9. Positive health awareness and a desire for a high level of health in each child
10. Development of wholesome health attitudes
11. Development of healthful personal practices

12. Acquisition of scientific and functional knowledge of personal and community health
13. Development of an appreciation of esthetic factors related to health
14. Development of a high level of self-esteem in each youngster
15. Effective social adjustment
16. Hygienic mental environment at school
17. Establishment and maintenance of sanitary practices and surroundings
18. Provision of emergency measures

To serve the particular needs of its students and the community, a school may find it advisable to set up other objectives than those listed, but it would be difficult to visualize an effective school health program which rejects any of them. This listing is presented as an optimum, and in matters of health the optimum should be the minimum.

Essential terminology

A definition is a concise statement of the essentials of a word or a term. Being but a framework, it does not include all the connotations, shadings, and variations inherent in the term. Yet, as a framework, a definition provides a common structure from which each person builds his concept. The final concepts of different persons may vary, but not so greatly. They will have certain basic elements in common.

Since words are the media by means of which we convey ideas to each other, effort should be exercised to make primary terminology as meaningful as possible. Despite the most earnest efforts in the interest of clarity, misunderstandings will occur. To improve understanding, certain key terms in school health work should be explained. These will be the most important tools of expression with which the person deals as a health instructor.

Health is that quality of physical, emotional, and mental well-being which enables one to live effectively and enjoyably. In appraising the possible health value of an activity one can employ the criterion, "Does it contribute to a person's effectiveness and enjoyment in living?" Quality is a relative term, and youngsters in the normal range of health can vary in terms of the quality of well-being. The noun *hygiene* has fallen into disuse, but the adjective *hygienic* is employed quite extensively in health literature.

Normal is that which is regarded as the usual, not in terms of an absolute, but in terms of a range. Though each child in a classroom is unique, different from all others, all of the children may be normal— within the usual range as accepted by society.

Education comes from the Latin *educo,* meaning to lead out. It can be applied to the institution which, through organization and the utilization of experience, provides the opportunities and the stimulation for individual learning. Education as an institution illuminates knowledge and develops the science and art of utilizing knowledge. It deals in academic and cultural explorations as well as in practical and vocational experience. It gives a child knowledge, concepts, techniques, and esthetic appreciation, each illuminated by the other. Perhaps most important is the influence of an instructor's personality upon the personality of a child.

Applied to the student, education is a process of self-growth and is a process within the student, not something imposed from without. It is the leading out of self-growth. Education implies the ability to utilize knowledge and apply meaning and value to it. Education is an expression of a person's capacity to penetrate and deal relevantly with significant problems. It relates what we know to what we need and want. It is represented in our capacity for reflection and analysis and in our ability to examine basic assumptions and make valid distinctions and interpretations. It enables us to discriminate, to appraise, and to evaluate people as well as material things and concepts. This ability to discriminate is highly important because life is rarely a matter of black or white; it usually is shades of gray. Thus, a teacher is not just a conveyor of knowledge, but an expeditor of learning and a tiller of dreams.

Public health program encompasses all of society's organized efforts to deal with the problems of prevention of disease, extension of life, and the promotion of well-being. This concept was first advanced by C.-E. A. Winslow,* one of America's revered leaders in public health. This definition conceives organized, voluntary health work as an integral part of the public health program.

School health program means the prepared course of action taken by the school in the interest of the health of the school child and school personnel. It includes health services, health instruction, and healthful school living.

School health services include all school activities and procedures designed to affect the present health status of the youngster. This encompasses appraisal of student health, prevention and control of disease, prevention and correction of physical defects, health guidance and supervision, and emergency care.

Guidance is the organized process of helping children to understand and direct their abilities into the channels of life which will be most fruitful in terms of their interests, abilities, and opportunities.

Health guidance is concerned with acquainting a person with the various ways in which he may discover and use his natural endowment so that he may live to the best advantage for himself and society. Guidance means accepting each pupil as an independent personality.

Guidance services consist of an analysis of individual students, availability of information service and counseling, and follow-up. As members of the school guidance team, health personnel can contribute effectively to these services. Organized health guidance makes health instruction

---

*Winslow, C.-E. A.: The untilled fields of public health, Science 51:23, 1920.

more effective through focusing the student's interest upon the appraisal of his own health status and thus making health knowledge personally identifiable and more meaningful to him.

Counseling is a guidance procedure which is a mutual deliberation consisting of an exchange of ideas which will aid a child to comprehend his problem and understand its solution. Whether directive or nondirective, counseling is essentially a matter of mutual advisement, of deliberating together.

Health instruction is the planned and incidental imparting of formal and informal health knowledge. It may be a lecture, a class discussion, a laboratory situation, or individual tutoring. It carries the connotation of something from the outside directed to the child for his understanding. Instruction is made difficult in America because traditionally children come to school to be taught, rather than to learn.

Health education means the growth within a child of his ability to understand health knowledge and to utilize and apply meaning to it. Health education implies the growth of a child's ability to discriminate, appraise, and evaluate health knowledge and experience. The best health instruction in the world can result in education only when there is a candle of interest in the child which can be ignited. Motivation sparks education.

Correlation means mutual relationship, and the task of health instruction in school health is to connect those various aspects of the school curriculum which have a relation to health. Home economics, biological science, social studies, and other disciplines have health contributions which should be utilized.

Integration denotes the unification of different elements into a whole. Ideally, there should be but one subject in school—life itself—but man has not yet devised the procedure nor developed the skill for a complete integration of the school program. Yet, integration is possible to a considerable degree. Many activities include health aspects as well as other factors, and opportunities for experience in health are afforded in many of the daily school experiences of children. Health is usually more than a by-product, but even as a by-product the health experience can be valuable.

Sanitation denotes the health of the physical environment. Its derivation from the Latin *sanitas* (health) has always left the aura of the emphasis the Roman's gave to environmental health. Formerly, sanitation was limited largely to the prevention of the spread of disease. Today, sanitation goes beyond water purification, sewage disposal, and insect control and includes positive factors such as lighting and ventilation, as well as esthetic factors such as attractive school premises and community housekeeping.

Healthful school living means conditions and manners of existing and experiencing which permit effective accomplishment and joy in the experience. It means a safe, sanitary, esthetic, and wholesome physical environment in which children can participate in normal activity with a minimum of interference, disturbance, and frustration.

Hygienic mental school environment is one in which every child is at ease, has a high level of self-esteem, feels his classmates and instructor hold him in high regard, feels he can succeed, does succeed, and enjoys his success.

Selected readings

American Academy of Pediatrics: School health policies; report of the Committee on School Health, Pediatrics 24:672-682, 1959.

American Association for Health, Physical Education, and Recreation: School health practices in the United States, Washington, D. C., 1961, The Association.

American Association of School Administrators: Health in schools, twentieth yearbook, ed. 2, Washington, D. C., 1951, The Association.

American Council on Education: A design for general education, Washington, D. C., 1944, The Council.

American Public Health Association: A half century of public health, New York, 1951, The Association.

Beyrer, Mary K.: The significance of current trends in school and college health programs (doctoral dissertation), Columbus, Ohio, 1959, Ohio State University.

Calder, R.: The lamp is lit, the story of WHO, Geneva, Switzerland, 1951, WHO Division of Public Information.

Chisholm, B.: International health; the role of WHO, past, present, and future, American Journal of Public Health 41:1460, 1951.

Conant, J. B.: Modern science and modern man, Garden City, 1959, Doubleday & Co., Inc.

Fredericksen, Hazel: The child and his welfare, ed. 2, San Francisco, 1957, W. H. Freeman.

Garrison, F. H.: An introduction to the history of medicine, ed. 4, Philadelphia, 1929, W. B. Saunders & Co.

Graduate study in health education, physical education and recreation (Pere Marquette State Park, Ill.), Chicago, 1950, The Athletic Institute.

Grout, Ruth E.: Health teaching in schools, ed. 4, Philadelphia, 1963, W. B. Saunders Co.

Joint Committee on Health Problems in Education of the National Education Association and the American Medical Association (Bernice R. Moss, W. H. Southworth, and J. L. Reichart, editors): Health education, Washington, D. C., 1961, National Education Association.

Langton, C. V., Allen, R. L., and Wexler, P.: School health organization and services, New York, 1961, The Ronald Press Co.

Leff, S., and Leff, Vera: From witchcraft to world health, New York, 1957, The Macmillan Co.

Leff, S., and Leff, Vera: Health and humanity, New York, 1962, International Publishers.

Means, R. K.: A history of health education in the United States, Philadelphia, 1963, Lea & Febiger.

McCaskill, J. L.: Evolution of federal educational policy from 1785 through World War II, Journal of the National Education Association 41:500, 1952.

National Committee on School Health Policies: Suggested school health policies, ed. 2, Washington, D. C., 1946, National Education Association.

National Conference on the Undergraduate Health Education Minor Program and the Desirable Health Education Emphases for the Physical Education Major Program, American Association for Health, Physical Education, and Recreation, Washington, D. C., 1955.

National Health Assembly: America's health: a report to the nation, New York, 1949, Harper & Brothers.

Paul, B. D. (editor): Health, culture and community, New York, 1955, Russell Sage Foundation.

Rogers, J. F.: State-wide trends in school hygiene and physical education, Washington, D. C., 1930, United States Office of Education, Pamphlet no. 5.

Second Conference on the Professional Preparation of students majoring in health education, Washingon, D. C., 1953, United States Office of Education.

Sigerist, H. E.: Landmarks in the history of

hygiene, London, 1956, Oxford University Press.

Sigerist, H. E.: History of medicine, Vol. I, Vol. II, London, vol. 1, 1951, and vol. 2, 1961, Oxford University Press.

Spiegelman, M.: Health progress in the United States, New York, 1951, American Enterprise Associations, Inc.

Symposium: What is health education, Am. J. Pub. Health 37:641, 1947.

Turner, C. E., Sellery, C. M., and Smith, Sara L.: School health and health education, ed. 4, St. Louis, 1961, The C. V. Mosby Co.

Ulich, R.: Three thousand years of educational wisdom, Cambridge, 1947, Harvard University Press.

Ulich, R.: History of educational thought, New York, 1961, American Book Co.

Wilson, C. C.: Report of the Committee on Terminology in Health Education, Journal of School Health 41:170, 1951.

Winslow, C.-E. A.: Conquest of epidemic disease, Princeton, N. J., 1943, Princeton University Press.

Winslow, C.-E. A.: The untilled fields of public health, Science 51:23, 1920.

World Health Organization: Health education—a selected bibliography prepared by The World Health Organization, published by United Nations Educational, Scientific and Cultural Organization, 1956.

Part 1

The school-age child

Health is a crown on the well person's head
but only the sick seem to see it.

—Arab Proverb

Chapter 2

Health of the normal child

The most important thing on earth is life, the most important form of life is human life, and the most important human life is one's own life. Yet, to the teacher the life of each child can be as precious as one's own life. Certainly to the conscientious teacher, a child's health is as important as the teacher's health. No teaching service can yield greater results nor provide greater personal gratification than what the teacher does to protect, maintain, and further the health of school children. Here is a professional opportunity for the teacher who understands the child and his health and who applies this knowledge effectively.

"Understand the child" is an admonition which applies equally to the prospective teacher and the teacher in the classroom. It is both logical and imperative that the teacher responsible for school health possess a sound understanding of the child, his growth process, his health, and his health problems. It is the health of the child which is the concern of the school's health program, and the child himself is the object of all health activity. More than this, professional preparation should develop in the teacher an attitude toward health which immediately focuses primary attention upon the child and from this point proceeds to evolve an approach to any existing health problem. Just as the law student must develop a certain frame of mind and approach to problems of law, the health educator must develop an approach to problems of health which is founded on an understanding and appreciation of the individual child's health.

Health science is both a collective and an applied discipline. It integrates and utilizes the contributions of several fields of knowledge. There is nothing mystical about true health science though there probably are more misconceptions about health than in any other sphere of human thought. For the person responsible for health in schools, certain funda-

41

mental concepts and essential knowledge can serve as the base of the pyramid of competence in health promotion. The broader and more substantial the base, the higher and sturdier will be the pyramid. College preparation provides the base; growth on the job completes the structure.

A teacher does not have to attain the stature of the final authority—the general of the health army. Rather, the teacher is the frontline officer who comes in direct contact with the situation. The more accomplished the frontline health worker is, the more readily the true problems and situations are recognized and their immediate solution initiated. Extremely difficult or special problems are the responsibilities of the generals, who are available to deal with those problems requiring special tactics and techniques.

To be a competent health educator, the teacher does not need to be an expert. Experience has indicated that certain basic knowledge is adequate for the role the teacher rightfully should serve on the health team. Primarily, that basic knowledge is an understanding of normal growth and development, normal health status, and common deviations from the normal. A study of deviations does not imply that the educator is to be a diagnostician, but rather a "suspecticion." As an officer in the forefront of health, the teacher may well be in the best position to recognize first that a particular child does not appear to be normal in some respect.

In a book on school health, a discussion of the essentials of normal growth, mental development, and health should be concise and cogent, rather than comprehensive.

Concept of normal

Normal is that which is accepted as the usual. It must be conceived as encompassing a range of concepts, rather than a single entity. It includes the average, but extends considerably on both sides of average. No two persons are exactly alike, each is unique. Yet, both persons may be considered within the normal range.

What constitutes the normal, or usual, is easily determined in some instances, but extremely difficult to ascertain in others. To say with assurance that the normal range of glucose in human blood is between 0.08 and 0.14% is quite easy because in more than 99% of analyzed blood samples the glucose content will fall in this range. Many physiological norms are well established; yet the normal range for certain physical measurements is not so easily set down. For example, what is the normal range of height for the American adult male? Should one arbitrarily say it is between 5 feet 4 inches and 6 feet 4 inches? What of the man who is 6 feet 5 inches in height? Should he be considered abnormal? This suggests the need for criteria. Should normal height be that which seems to be all right? Is the outer 10% or the outer 5% on each end of the array of heights for man to be considered as outside the normal? Very quickly it is recognized that for many physiological and physical phenomena there are no definite, prescribed normal ranges. Normal for the same factor may mean one thing at one time and a very different thing at another time.

If normal for physical factors is not a precise quantity, consider how variable it can be when applied to social and psychological phenomena. What is the normal range of emotional responsiveness of junior high school girls in situations involving frustrations such as failure of election to an office or to a group? Thus, standards of normal social acceptance may vary from community to community, from school to school, and from family to family. Yet, determining what is normal usually does not pose too difficult a problem.

In actual school practice, most cases fall definitely in the normal range whether a physical, a psychological, or a social phenomenon is being considered. In the relatively few instances which are borderline, the decision of an expert, or the collective judgment of several competent teachers, can serve the needs of the school for that particular case. Even more important, many deviations from the normal are of little significance in terms of effective and enjoyable living. Every human being has his imperfections, most of which go unnoticed or are accepted by this imperfect world of imperfect people. To be abnormal in some respects, perhaps, is normal.

The healthy child

When health is regarded as that quality of well-being which enables one to live effectively and enjoyably, it must be considered a means to an end. To a person who is ill, health may be an end to be gained, but to the person who possesses health, it is a means to an end—a vehicle for effective and enjoyable living.

It is germane to the best interests of the youngsters in a school room that the teacher be conscious of the health status of every child, whether the child has normal health or is ill or indisposed. The teacher must have a positive attitude or frame of mind and think in terms of the attributes or qualities of health each child possesses. It requires an evaluation of the native constitutional endowment of each child. The constitutional make-up of one child may be such that he has great vitality and almost unlimited energy, endurance, and ability to recover, even though neither he nor his parents follow the accepted practices of good health promotion. Another child may possess a constitution which is adequate for typical living, but so near to inadequacy that every principle of health promotion must be practiced to maintain a normal level of health. Intergrades between these two types require thoughtful discrimination by the teacher who strives to understand the native health capacity of each child, just as she seeks to understand the native intellectual capacity of each child.

Normal health is not to be appraised in terms of physical size nor in terms of muscular strength. The little fellow who appears to be underweight may possess an adequate level of health. Often, these wiry little fellows seem to possess boundless energy, are on the go constantly, and recover quickly from fatigue. It may be desirable to add to his weight, but he may be healthy "for a' that." It is more likely that the level of health of a grossly overweight child is lowered because of the excessive overweight.

In appraising a school child's health in terms of his capacity to carry on the activities he wishes and has a right to engage in, personality dynamics of the individual youngster must be given consideration. A student who is not aggressive, driving, and extremely active physically nevertheless may possess a high level of health, both physical and mental. The studious, industrious, methodical child may possess a level of health as adequate as the athletic child whose activity is so obvious.

It is the over-all capacity of a child to measure up to life's demands that should be the cardinal criterion used by a teacher who attempts to appraise the health of a child. Health is one thing, one over-all condition of well-being, and it encompasses the physical, mental, emotional, and social aspects of well-being.

Outward indices of physical health

A clinical examination by a physician, supplemented by laboratory tests, would be necessary for a thorough inventory of a person's precise status of health, but for practical purposes a teacher can observe certain outward indices as a general gauge of health. These landmarks of health are of special significance in the school situation in which the teacher can observe the child five days a week and get a day-to-day inventory of each child's general pattern of health. Being thus familiar with the child's normal condition, the teacher readily will become aware of any deviation from the normal pattern. The teacher does not deal in the specifics of the diagnostician but in the over-all condition of the child.

When they are observed individually but evaluated collectively, certain outward indices or characteristics can convey a meaning of child health which is adequate for the needs of the teacher in guiding the child. They can also be used to adapt the school program to the child and the child to his school needs. Of necessity, these indices are interpreted in relative terms as follows.

1. *Buoyancy.* The healthy child possesses bounce or a feeling of lightness. Perhaps a concept of this attribute can be attained by visualizing the converse, the lack of buoyancy, which accompanies old age. The aged feel heavy, with which is associated a feeling of chronic fatigue. However, the healthy child conveys the impression that he carries no weight, and he actually feels as though he has no particular physical restriction to movement.

2. *Unaware of his body.* The healthy child is not conscious of the existence of his body. This is somewhat true of the healthy adult, but through various experiences the adult has attained some awareness of his normal bodily existence. However, only in a diseased or disordered

condition does the child display any recognition of the existence of any part of his physical being.

3. *Pleasure in activity.* Every normal child delights in physical action. Restraint, physical or psychological, is both irritating and frustrating to the child. Teachers soon recognize that the solution to most restlessness in the classroom is an opportunity for physical action. A child who prefers not to be active usually suggests a child not well physically and mentally.

4. *Sufficient vigor.* A healthy child possesses the energy to do the things he wants to do and can be expected to do in a normal day. This does not imply a child has a great deal of muscular power, but that he has a feeling of muscular power equal to the normal demands of his regimen of living.

5. *Zest.* A day's activity should be more stimulating than fatiguing. That a child does not want to stop what he is doing though he has been at it for a long time and should be tired out is a very normal situation. He gets tired, but he is so occupied with his very gratifying experience that he is not conscious of any fatigue.

6. *Sleeps well and recovers from the day's fatigue.* Not all children function maximally at nine o'clock in the morning. Some have a constitutional makeup which is slow to accelerate; others have been socially conditioned by the home or other influence to a slow pace in the morning. An alert teacher will quickly identify these types and will aid each child in acquiring a faster tempo of activity.

More serious are youngsters who come to school dragging one foot after the other. These children may come from homes in which they do not go to bed at a desirable hour.

Another type of child goes to bed at a proper hour, but sleeps poorly and comes to school looking and acting like a person who has had no sleep. This child needs the counsel of a physician to determine if there is a physical basis for the condition. Usually, a low level of general function is the basic factor, rather than a specific disorder. The shuttled picture of poor health-inadequate rest, inadequate rest-poor health is frequent in these cases.

Although most children occasionally may show indications of inadequate rest, continued week-by-week indications of inadequate rest merit a study of basic causes and a constructive program of readjustment.

7. *Relaxation.* Being at ease in the school situation is necessary for good health and is an indication of good health. An occasional short-lived display of tension is to be expected in most children, but a child who is constantly tense is not a healthy child of today nor the healthy adult of tomorrow. Tenseness must be displaced by ease and relaxation in the normal channels of life.

8. *Appetite steady and not capricious.* A finicky appetite may be the product of improper or negligent rearing in the home, but more often it is associated with a low level of health. Which is cause and which is

effect are for a physician to determine, but a poor appetite is a symptom of the need for constructive attention by the school.

Occasionally, any normal youngster will have a transitory loss of appetite. It may be the result of such a simple thing as an inopportune sampling of sweets. Or it may be due to fatigue, a cold, other mild infection, or special concern about some situation, real or imagined. However, the teacher should be concerned about a child with a chronically poor appetite.

9. *No appreciable variation in weight.* During his school age years, a child experiences a steady increase in weight. Variation in the rate of increase is to be expected and is normal, but a child whose weight fluctuates appreciably is in need of a thorough physical checkup. Included in this category are children who lose three or four pounds in a week for no discernible cause and may regain the weight just as mysteriously, only to go through the same down-and-up cycle again. Failure to maintain a stabilized body weight is a symptom of a lack of constitutional stability. While the normal body is in a delicate state of equilibrium, constantly shifting slightly away from center then back again, a balance, or homeostasis, is maintained. A small degree of fluctuation in bodily phenomena is normal; pronounced fluctuation is not normal.

10. *Absence of disabling remediable defects.* Freedom from defects which limit the effectiveness of one's activities is essential to optimum health. Some defects are not disabling. Even the loss of a finger or toe may not be disabling. Some defects are not remediable, and thus the health potential of a child must be weighed accordingly. Fortunately, many defects can be corrected or compensated for. Hearing aids can give normal hearing to persons with some hearing defects.

Most defects which are overlooked in school children are minor ones which, in their present state, are not noticeably disabling. However, through the years their cumulative effect can be considerable, even though they do not become more aggravated. The presence of a so-called minor disabling defect lowers the child's health level, perhaps even to subnormal levels.

Attributes of mental health

Since every child is unique, it would seem that an evaluation of mental health would have to be an individual matter, applied to each particular child. Strictly speaking, perhaps this would be true for detailed or specialized purposes, but children, though different, are not so tremendously different. For the purposes of the school certain optimum attributes should be identifiable in every child. Though each child in his normal maturation exhibits variations in emotional responsiveness, the same fundamental attributes provide the framework or timber of mentally healthy persons. By the same token these are the qualities the school should strive to develop in each child to assure him a high level of adjustment during both childhood and adulthood.

1. *High level of self-esteem.* Every child should have a feeling of worthiness, that others regard him highly. A child who knows he has something to live up to rather than something to live down has a first essential for a high level of adjustment.

2. *Obtain self-gratification through avenues approved by society.* Every child is self-centered and seeks to gratify his ego. Society recognizes this desire for self-gratification, but lays down rules by which this gratification may be attained. By precept and example he learns the ways of his world.

3. *Security.* No person attains absolute security, but normal children seek and need acceptance by their own group.

4. *Confidence.* All children have a feeling of inferiority, but through the acquisition of skill and experience much of this feeling can be displaced by confidence.

5. *Courage.* Children with the courage to face new situations and difficult tasks have a valuable asset for effective and enjoyable living. In contrast, fear of failure is a liability in childhood as well as in adulthood.

6. *Stability.* No person is perfectly stable, but mood and conduct should fluctuate within a relatively narrow range.

7. *Orderliness.* Some degree of order is essential for both efficient and gratifying living.

8. *Adaptability.* Life changes constantly, and good mental health requires flexibility to adjust to changes with a minimum of friction and disturbance.

9. *Self-discipline.* Perhaps no one is perfectly self-disciplined, but the mentally healthy person is usually master of his actions, rather than a slave to whim, caprice, or indolence.

10. *Self-reliance.* Although interdependence typifies the complex society of our country, within that framework a well-adjusted person depends on his own resources and relies on others as a last resort. He has both stamina and the ability to mobilize his resources under stress.

11. *Sincerity.* Everyone appreciates and even admires a sincere person.

12. *Emotional control.* When the self is frustrated, negative emotions naturally are aroused, but to attain the highest levels of mental health a person must learn to restrain these emotions and substitute reasoned conduct. Though this practice will not enable one to reach a stage at which negative emotions will never arise, the control one acquires will conceal their existence and display the poise of a well-integrated personality.

13. *Quick recovery from disturbing experiences.* All persons encounter disturbing experiences and even tragedies, but, while he is disturbed emotionally, a well-integrated person recovers rather quickly. A high degree of sensitivity hardly furnishes the child with the necessary timber for this rugged life.

14. *Confidence in the ability to succeed and enjoyment of success.* No

person enjoys a situation in which he is failing. Occasional failure is the lot of all, but constant failure is injurious to mental health. The child who feels he can succeed, succeeds, and fully appreciates and enjoys his success has valuable ingredients for mental health.

15. *Moderation in daydreaming.* Every normal person enjoys the luxury of daydreaming, and in moderation daydreaming can contribute to mental health. The child who is submerged in excessive daydreaming and rarely lives in the world of reality needs to be brought into the world of doing.

16. *Congeniality.* Whereas happiness is a level of elation that a normal person acquires only occasionally and retains but a short period of time, the normal emotional mold or temperament should be cheerful and congenial.

17. *Perception of humor.* A normal child learns that some things in life are incongruous or funny. From these he gets an enjoyable experience whether his laughter is a response to frustration or a feeling of superiority because he sees the unusual aspects of the situation. Humor is an excellent buffer for the rigors of life. To achieve the highest expression of humor in terms of mental health, the child should learn to laugh at himself. A person who can look at himself as objectively as that has the antidote for his inherent egocentricity. It is an attribute of children with the highest level of mental health.

18. *Sincere interest in other persons.* Basic to good social adjustment is an active, sincere interest in other people. A child who likes other persons intensely will experience no self-consciousness, embarrassment, or loneliness. Altercentricity (self-gratification through interest in others) is the key to successful social adjustment because an interest in people telegraphs itself. Persons who know that a particular person likes them would be queer indeed if they did not hold that person in high regard. A sincere liking for persons is an acquired attribute, one which makes conversation more easy and enhances one's social activities.

Levels of health

Almost all of the children in classrooms fall within the range of normal health. Yet, the teacher knows that the quality of these students' health varies. As a practical guide for the teacher and the student, a grading system can be devised to designate various levels of health. Although such a scale does not provide for refined discriminations, like any other appraisal system, it does provide a workable means for evaluating the general quality of a child's health.

A level. A high level of health, but not perfect health, is indicated by this classification. A person with this quality of health may have an occasional cold or other minor infection, perhaps an occasional headache or other mild disturbance. Freedom from disabling remediable defects is an obvious requirement. Youngsters in this category display pronounced vigor and buoyancy and sufficient vitality to carry on the demands of life.

This does not connote great muscular power and endurance, but more than enough strength and endurance for any likely eventuality. It does not include physical size. A child of small physical stature, as well as a child with an average or large stature, can have an A level of health. The child in this health category enjoys life, participates wholesomely in normal activities, and adjusts well to social situations.

B level. Freedom from disabling defects is a primary requirement in this category. Persons in this group do not have quite the vigor and buoyancy of the A level. Many in this classification can attain the higher level of health by conscientious application of health principles.

C level. Persons in this classification pass as well, but lack the vitality for a dynamic mode of living. They go through life functioning at a minimum—not sick, but draggy, rather than buoyant, as are people with good health. Many can attain an A level of health, and most can attain at least a *B* level of health. There should be no school child with a *C* level of health.

D level. Children in this classification attend school regularly, but are not well. A chronic infection or some other apparent or concealed factor or factors is the basic cause of the low level of health. Until the cause is discovered and remedied, the child is not likely to improve his level of health. The teacher or other school personnel should be aware of the state of health of these children and take the proper steps to safeguard their welfare. School obviously is not the place for them. Even children with a low level of vitality, but without specific defects or diseases, should be under the supervision of a physician.

E level. Children in this classification are obviously ill and should not be in school; usually they are not.

Individual variations

That variations exist from person to person and from day to day for a given person are common observations. When the concept of variations is applied to child health, the important task is to identify the particular differences by having a unified, almost cataloged, concept of the status of each child's health. Each child is unique and has a particular constitution with which he functions. The teacher should identify the particular health entity in each child and thus immediately recognize any deviations from the established pattern.

Children with a constitutional makeup of decidedly marked limitations will exhibit more fluctuations in health than other children and may be the cause of special concern to the teacher. Yet, all children are susceptible to variation in their state of well-being—all the way from a slight indisposition to serious disorders. Every child merits the best efforts of the teacher in appraising his health status and any deviation from this health state.

School-age youngsters with chronic disabilities of varying severity may require special measures. It is desirable that these children feel that they are normal members of the class. If the impression that they are abnormal is created, they may feel stigmatized, by both themselves and their classmates. School-age children who have had rheumatic fever or have diabetes mellitus, asthma, or epilepsy do pose problems for the school, but knowledge and planning will enable the school staff to deal satisfactorily with these problems. The school should insist that a physician, preferably the family physician, determine the needs of the child and, in consultation with the school, outline the school's course of action in providing for his best interests.

Building up and maintaining health

For the normal school-age child, the primary health consideration is to build up and maintain the highest possible level of health. No child has a quality of health which could not be improved, nor can any child be expected to maintain the health he has attained without following the course of living necessary for the conservation of the dynamic processes of life itself. A program designed to promote health will both build up and maintain health at one and the same time. Such a program of health promotion is one in which the person adapts established health principles to his specific needs and assiduously applies these principles in everyday practice. This would include principles of nutrition, activity, rest, sleeep, safety, oral health, vision, hearing, cleanliness, control of communicable diseases, prevention of degenerative diseases, and social adjustment.

Because the benefits which accrue from sound health practices are not spectacular, children (and adults) are prone to be doubtful of the value of these practices. The long-range effects are the real sources of health dividends, and long-range vision is needed to see the total results. Although the specific manner in which certain recognized practices promote health is not scientifically established, the general cause-and-effect relationship has been ascertained sufficiently to warrant their use with assurance of health benefits. As more refined aspects of these principles are worked out, or as new principles are developed, they will be profitably incorporated into the matrix of health practices.

Conservation of human resources

The school deals in futures. While it concerns itself with the children of today, it always projects its goals to the young man and woman of tomorrow, the mature man and woman of the following day, on to late adulthood of the next week.

Surely, the most important thing in the universe is life, the most important form of life is human life, and the most important human life is one's own. Man is the most restless living form, is most widely dispersed, and has the greatest adaptive capacity. Man has a remarkable ability to bend nature to his will, but frequently he finds that when he solves one problem he actually creates another. The school must remember that, while it is interested in advancing health practices in the young that will postpone death, it must also consider health problems that relate to the process of aging and the aged, along with measures to promote health during the early years of life. Certainly, the school can play a vital role in the conservation of human resources.

The conservation of human resources means the husbanding of all factors which will help to (1) postpone death, (2) increase the quality of health, and (3) extend the prime of life.

Death cannot be prevented, but it can be postponed. In our present-day complex society, survival is not an individual matter alone. One must rely on the collective efforts of the community to deal with those factors which he, as an individual, cannot cope with alone. In his school experience the child learns the community agencies and forces which exist to aid him in his quest for survival. A well-informed person profits most from the services of community health agencies. Since a reciprocal relation exists between personal and community health, the way in which each person lives affects the community both directly and indirectly.

Fortunately, no normal school child knows what his particular cause of death will be, but from records he can learn which are the most numerous causes of death at various ages. Armed with this knowledge which he should acquire in his school health education, the child can be better prepared to survive. The guiding force in life for a prospective adult is the positive approach of what to do to survive, rather than the negative approach of what causes death.

Not how long one lives, but how well one lives is more important. A high level of health in childhood, based on established sound health practices, is the best possible prologue to a high level of health in adulthood. Proper nutrition during childhood and proper rest and other essential health practices during the early years yield their greatest dividends in later years.

To extend the prime of life is a more recent goal of health science. The normal aging process involves a multitude of changes. Normal for one age or period of life is not normal for another. Normal is a series of variables and changes from age period to age period. The United States has made tangible progress in the conservation of the vigor and efficient function of young adults. The typical 60-year-old person of today possesses about the same health index as did a person 50 years of age at the turn of the century. If during his early years he has avoided health practices injurious to his well-being and followed the principles which conserve and promote good health, a person 60 years of age need not feel old. Studies reveal that chronic, low-grade infections, unattended over extended periods of time, have an adverse effect on the level of health of middle-aged persons. The same effect results from gross over-weight or undue tension. On the positive side, persons who have lived well-regulated, moderate lives and who have relaxed regularly rather than succumbed to the tensions of life are the ones who enjoy a long youth and an extended prime of life. "How well does my motor idle?" is a question young and old alike should ask themselves.

Selected readings

American Association for Health, Physical Education, and Recreation, and National Association of Secondary School Principals: Fitness for secondary school youth, Washington, D. C., 1956, American Association for Health, Physical Education, and Recreation.

American Council on Education, Commission on Teacher Education: Helping teachers understand children, Washington, D. C., 1945, The Council.

Blake, Florence G.: The child, his parents and the nurse, Chicago, 1954, J. B. Lippincott Co.

Children's Bureau: Facts about child health, Washington, D. C., 1946, United States Government Printing Office.

English, O. S., and Pearson, G. H. J.: Emotional problems of living, New York, 1955, W. W. Norton & Co., Inc.

Joint Committee on Health Problems in Education: Health appraisals of school children, ed. 3, Washington, D. C., 1961, National Education Association.

Lindgren, H. C.: Mental Health in Education, New York, 1954, Henry Holt & Co., Inc.

National Education Association and the American Medical Association: Health appraisal of school children, Washington, D. C., 1957, National Education Association.

Prescott, D. A.: Child in the educative process, New York, 1957, McGraw-Hill Book Co., Inc.

Rice, T. B., and Hein, F. V.: Living, ed. 3, Chicago, 1959, Scott, Foresman & Co.

Reeves, Katherine: Children—their wants and needs, New York, 1960, Education Publishing Corporation.

Strang, Ruth: Introduction to child study, ed. 4, New York, 1959, The Macmillan Co.

Stuart, H. C., and Prugh, D. G.: Healthy child, Cambridge, Mass., 1960, Harvard University Press.

Walke, N. S., Droscher, N., and Volpe, M. D.: Health and fitness, Dubuque, Iowa, 1962, W. D. Brown Co.

Wheatley, G. M., and Hallock, Grace T.: Health observation of school children, ed. 2, New York, 1956, McGraw-Hill Book Co., Inc.

White, V.: Studying the individual pupil, New York, 1957, Harper & Brothers.

Wilkes, E. T.: Family guide to teenage health, New York, 1958, The Ronald Press Co.

Growth is the only evidence of life.

—Dr. Scott, cited by Cardinal Newman

Chapter 3

Physical growth and development

Lhe school deals in futures. How the child develops into the mature adult is a concern of the school. Physical growth and development are no less important than other phases of the evolving youngster. Physical growth and development represent a special phase in the maturing process, but are entwined in the total pattern of maturation. Understanding physiological change and the rate of change enables the teacher to understand each youngster in terms of his own particular development and of his relationship to the normal pattern. It is fascinating to watch the development of a child. It is most fascinating when one has a scholarly understanding of the developmental process.

Growth and development are individual matters, each child being distinctive. However there are typical or recognized ranges of growth into which most children fall. A conscientious teacher is eager to understand each child in terms of his patterns of growth and development. Perhaps the teacher should think of the child as a "human becoming." After all, man requires one third of his life to reach maturity, and the school deals in that future.

Growth—cellular and intercellular

Growth consists of the transformation of chemicals present in food into complex protoplasmic and intercellular materials. Essentially, it is the addition of body substance to that which exists.

Cellular growth consists of the addition of proteins, carbohydrates, fat, water, and minerals to the cell substance. This addition may be related to cell division (perhaps a developmental process), but the added substance constitutes growth.

Intercellular growth consists of the addition of organic and inorganic materials between cells. Fat, calcium phosphate, or other substances retained between cells, though having a relation to the cells, must be considered a part of body growth if they are added to the total mass. Intercellular calcium is the principal constituent of bone growth. The noncellular part of tissue undergoes considerable increase in mass during the stage of physical growth of life.

Development or maturation

Development or maturation is an increase in the complexity and effectiveness of bodily functions. It may accompany growth, but properly should be regarded as an entity independent of growth. The biological nature of development is not understood in its totality. It is more than merely the improvement in function of the neuron system or in neuromuscular coordination. Since the various systems of the body develop at differing rates, it is desirable that a teacher have an understanding of the patterns of maturation of the various systems. Their separate, as well as composite, developmental patterns can be the avenue through which the teacher may better understand each child and thus better serve his interests.

Physiological quotient. Knowledge of psysiological development has reached a stage at which norms for various ages are well established. The tyranny of the norm plagues the physiologist as it does other investigators, but the term *physiological age* is applied only to those readily identified and measured characteristics of human change. Further, as in other spheres of human development, a person may be markedly advanced in some phases of physiological development, but may lag considerably in other phases. So the over-all designation of *physiological age* is a composite one which may conceal the fact that some significant function in the maturation process is retarded. Yet, the designation is of value for an over-all assessment of a child's level of maturation. Biometrists have been able to use it effectively in determining the *physiological quotient* of a child.

The *physiological quotient* is obtained by dividing the *physiological age* by the *chronological age* and multiplying by 100, as follows:

$$\text{Physiological quotient} = \frac{\text{Physiological age}}{\text{Chronological age}} \times 100$$

$$\text{Abbreviation: P.Q.} = \frac{\text{P.A.}}{\text{C.A.}} \times 100$$

As a profile or index, the P.Q. is of greater value than mere observation, but not as valid as a detailed analysis of the various phases of development.

Biological determination

Potential biological growth and development are determined at fertilization. The genetic combinations at that moment set the biological potential and limit for both growth and development.

Inheritance. Growth and development are governed or regulated primarily by the hormones of the body, and a child's genetic endocrine endowment is his principal asset for both growth and development. General body size depends upon the output of somatotropin, the principal growth hormone, which is produced by the anterior pituitary gland. Carbohydrate, fat, and water balance are affected by other secretions from this gland. Thyroxin from the thyroid governs the growth of long bones and the rate at which energy is used up and at which the body matures. Sex hormones affect maturation as well as determine secondary sex characteristics. Cortin, the principal secretion of the adrenal cortex which is located at the tip of the kidneys, markedly affects the rate of maturation. An overactive adrenal cortex produces precocious children.

Considering the hormones alone, geneticists calculate at least 40,-000,000 possible patterns of genetic endocrine endowment. The particular combination of factors that a child inherits appears to be a matter of mere chance. Once fertilization takes place, nothing can be done to change the inherited characteristics. Therefore, a teacher who appreciates that there are many possible genetic combinations will likely have a better understanding and appreciation of each child in the class.

Environmental factors

No one attains the absolute genetic maximum in growth and development because environmental factors retard or obstruct normal processes. If man were able to provide the perfect environment for his life processes, he doubtless would develop more rapidly than he does and would attain greater growth. This would entail a better internal bodily environment through scientifically perfected nutrition and respiration, as well as freedom from infection, and an external environment of temperature, humidity, and other factors which best permit processes to function. Man does not know a great deal about this ideal environment, but he does possess some knowledge of it.

A teacher who appreciates the importance of a good health regimen can help children in growth and development. Her efforts may not yield spectacular results or even readily discernible improvement, but a gain of 3% in a child by 10 years of age, accruing at the same rate for the next sixty-five years, will yield a cumulative benefit worthy of every teacher's best efforts. Although the limits for growth and development are set by a child's inherited characteristics, how nearly he realizes his full capabilities depends on the many factors that affect growth and development. Something constructive can be done about these factors. Although our knowledge and procedures are not the most scientific, a combination of that which is truly scientific and that which has borne fruit through practical experience gives us some assurance that probably a teacher can affect the growth and development of a child positively.

Full-term infant

If the normal gestation period is estimated at 280 days after the beginning of the last menstruation, it is interesting to note that 35% of all births occur within one week on either side of this estimate and 65% of births occur within two weeks of it. A child who is born at thirty-seven weeks of gestation (within three weeks of the 280 days) is considered a full-term infant.

Though smaller at birth, girls physiologically are about one month in advance of boys. This advantage increases progressively to 12 years of age. Girls entering school are more mature physiologically than boys. Except for this general group differential, the differences in children entering school will be individual differences. Recognizing that both parental and early postnatal environmental conditions may affect a child adversely, the teacher can proceed with the knowledge that the vast majority of entering students will fit into the normal range of physiological maturation. The few exceptions will command special analysis and assessment. Those below the normal range occasionally mature at an accelerated rate and soon attain the level of their classmates. Others remain a few steps behind their associates until their last two years in school. A few do not attain their normal level of physiological maturation by the time of graduation.

Premature infant

Because of numerous misconceptions, the premature infant is of interest to the teacher who some day may be plagued with the perpetual rationalization that "Junior was a premature infant." A premature infant is one who was born with a gestation period of twenty-eight to thirty-seven weeks. Not lack of size, but lack of maturity is the important factor.

Physiological factors. A premature baby lacks adequate muscle tone, has rapid, irregular, and shallow breathing, lacks endurance in sucking, sleeps for abnormally long periods, and has an immature, inadequate temperature-regulating mechanism. There may be poor excretion of nitrogen wastes, low blood sugar and protein levels, poor liver function, anemia, and a high susceptibility to infection. With modern facilities and methods, 85% of these premature infants can survive; development to the forty-weeks period can be the same whether it takes place in or out of the uterus, though the rate may vary.

Future development. Since most teachers will at some time have in class children who were born prematurely, it is well to recognize that these children take longer to attain normal weight. The smallest do not attain normal weight until 10 years of age, normal height until 9 years of age. In physiological maturation most of these children are in the normal range when they enter school. It must be recognized that they were only about two months retarded at birth. Even if they had not gained on their associates of normal term, they would only be two months in arrears at 5 years of age. Unless the circumstances at birth had caused injury, *every* child born prematurely should be considered in the normal physiological range by the time he attains the third grade in school.

Body types

Constitutional makeup, based upon the relationship of body type to the internal chemistry, has been of interest to investigators through the centuries. That hormone balance and body proportions are related has been recognized, but just how the hormones mold personality still eludes us. Body types which are the result solely of malfunction of the endocrine glands are relatively rare, and the many intergrades make a physical-mental-emotional relationship difficult to chart. However, the classification of body types has been catalogued acceptably. With it has been a recognition that perhaps the hormones which govern body build also affect the basic mold of personality.

Bipolar index and intergrades. The first investigators who attempted to classify body types used a bipolar index of body height and width. It soon became apparent that broad, general classifications, using only these two simple measurements, could not be established because of the intergrades—those that fitted between the types or were combinations of two or more types. Body height and weight were too restrictive to use as a basis of classification to be of value.

Fig. 2. Constitutional types. All are the same age and in the same grade, all are different, and all are healthy.

Kretchmer's classification. Between 1920 and 1925, the European scientist, Dr. E. Kretchmer, classified man into *asthenic, athletic,* and *pyknic* types. Asthenic referred to tall, mentally active, introverted persons; pyknic was applied to thick-set, rotund, extroverted persons; athletic was used to classify ambiverted persons who fell between the other two types. Dr. Kretchmer later added leptosomatic to accommodate the less extreme form of asthenic type. Dr. Kretchmer did offer some evidence for the relationship of body build and temperament, but he found no relation between body build and intelligence.

Sheldon's system. In 1940, Dr. W. H. Sheldon, using Kretchmer's methods, measured students and found an interesting distribution: athletic, 12%; asthenic, 9%; pyknic, 7%; and mixed types, 72%.

Dissatisfied with his results, Dr. Sheldon developed a system based on origin from germ layers. Recognizing that different body structures arise from the three primary layers in the embryo, Dr. Sheldon based his classification on the layer from which a person's distinguishing bodily structures arise. The following three main categories are recognized:

1. *Endomorphic*—Persons with smooth body contours and massive digestive organs which dominate the body economy
2. *Mesomorphic*—Persons with a heavy physique and a firm, rectangular outline
3. *Ectomorphic*—Persons with a linear outline, small bones, slender muscles, and a somewhat fragile general physique, with the body flat, the thorax rather long, the arms and legs more than average length, and the hair and skin distinguishing, dominant features

Dr. Sheldon has used a seven-point rating scale to define the degree to which a person exhibits each of the three sets of characteristics. A person rating a 7 in the endomorphic category and only 1 in each of the other two categories would be a true endomorph with smooth body contours and massive digestive organs. Table 1 gives three examples of how the system is used to determine a person's physical characteristics.

If the ratings are recorded as three-digit numbers (e.g., 711, 444, 515), a *somatotype* can be designated. Although 343 combinations are possible, only seventy-six body types (somatotypes) exist.

Dr. Sheldon's classification is a relatively rough description of the variety of human physiques. The many intergrades among both sexes at various age levels make any such simple device inadequate for more than generalizations. However, the Sheldon scale is of value.

Table 1. Sheldon classification of body types

Endomorphy	Mesomorphy	Ectomorphy	Description
7	1	1	Massive digestive organs
4	4	4	Physique at midpoint of all three scales
5	1	5	Not muscular, slender outline, long limbs, well-developed digestive organs

Height

Teachers have more than an academic interest in the height of their pupils. Besides their personal interest, they will need to help children understand the factors related to growth in height.

Inheritance of stature and size. Height is a multiple factor. The length of the legs, the trunk, the neck, and the head collectively determine the height of a person. Several genes are influential in determining these structures. Genes which affect size also affect other characteristics. The endocrine glands affect both size and other characteristics. Therefore, the genes which affect these glands will also have an effect on multiple other factors.

A child may inherit all of the relatively long or short segment lengths of both parents and thus may be taller or shorter than the parents. Because of the many possible combinations, uniformity is hardly to be expected. Tallness is a recessive trait which represents a high output of the growth hormone, somatotropin, which comes from the anterior pituitary gland and of thyroxin, which comes from the thyroid gland. Shortness is a dominant trait. Thus, tall parents, having only genes for tallness, will have tall children. Short parents may have tall children if both parents have genes for both shortness and tallness. Parents of medium height tend to have children who vary widely in height. Generally speaking, the prospective tallness shows early in the child, and, as will be pointed out later, it is possible to predict in childhood the approximate height a person will be in adulthood.

Dwarfism is usually noninherited, being due to a premature ossification, or closing, of the growth line (epiphysis) of long bones. Why it happens is not understood, and no treatment is known. In a few instances this premature ossification appears to be an inherited condition. When the growth lines ossify early in life instead of at about 20 years of age, the long bones fail to attain their normal length. Short and irregular bones may show some retardation in growth, but not to the extent that the long bones are affected.

Simple gigantism is an inherited condition which is a chance combination of height-giving genes, abnormal endocrine secretions, and other attributes which produces an extremely large stature. Extreme gigantism is an anomaly in which the epiphyses do not close, and the eosinophil cells of the anterior pituitary gland secrete excessive amounts of the principal growth hormone. About 90% of all giants are in this category.

Preschool years. The mean for height is not all-important but does serve as a marker of the midstream of height for various age levels. One standard deviation includes 66⅔% of the total and two standard deviations include 95% of the total.

Children of normal term will be 20 inches long at birth. At one year of age they will have added 10 inches to their height and at four years of age will be twice their height at birth. More precise figures can be tabulated.

Table 2. Height of American children

Age (yr.)	Boys		Girls	
	Mean (in.)	Standard deviation (in.)	Mean (in.)	Standard deviation (in.)
1	30.0	1.0	29.25	1.0
2	34.5	1.0	34.0	1.25
3	38.0	1.25	37.5	1.5
4	41.0	1.5	39.25	1.5
5	43.5	1.5	40.75	1.75
6	46.25	1.75	43.5	2.0
7	48.75	1.75	46.25	2.0
8	51.0	2.0	48.75	2.0
9	53.25	2.0	51.0	2.25
10	55.5	2.25	53.25	2.25
11	57.5	2.25	55.5	2.5
12	59.5	2.75	58.0	2.75
13	62.0	3.0	60.75	25.
14	64.75	3.25	62.75	2.25
15	67.25	3.0	64.0	2.25
16	69.0	2.5	65.25	2.0
17	69.5	2.25	65.25	2.0

School-age children. From Table 2 it is apparent that up to 10 years of age, school-age boys gain about $2\frac{1}{4}$ inches a year. The gain drops to 2 inches a year for the next two years and then increases to about $2\frac{1}{2}$ inches a year to 15 years of age, when the leveling off begins. School girls have a gain of about $2\frac{1}{4}$ inches a year to 11 years of age. The gain steps up to $2\frac{1}{2}$ inches the next year and $2\frac{3}{4}$ inches from 12 to 13 years of age and then begins to level off. Full height is reached by 16 years of age.

Individual variations from this pattern are to be expected; statistics in Table 2 serve merely as an index of the general tendency. Some boys will grow an inch a year for two years after the seventeenth birthday. However, the statistics have predictive value. A boy who is $55\frac{1}{2}$ inches tall at 10 years of age and $57\frac{1}{2}$ inches tall at 11 years of age will not vary appreciably from $69\frac{1}{2}$ inches in height at 17 years of age. The standard deviations can be helpful in charting the likely future growth curve of those children above or below the mean curve.

It is significant that with the onset of biological maturity, height growth slows down because of the decline in the output of the growth hormone from the anterior pituitary gland. It thus is understandable why persons who mature early may have a growth curve which starts to level off sooner than the normal curve.

Weight

From a practical standpoint, for use in the school, weight is not a satisfactory index of growth. Overly obese children would rate highly if weight were used as a sole index of growth.

Indices of growth. When a child is assessed in terms of a table of mean weights, the constitutional makeup of the child must be taken into consideration if weight is to be of any value as an index of growth. Even then, height must be considered in the assessment.

Inheritance factors. Weight is determined by body conformation or proportions as well as by adipose tissue. The person who inherits a conformation of long torso and short legs will tend to weigh above the mean though he appears to be about normal in weight. If a tendency toward obesity is inherited, a sluggish thyroid or pituitary gland doubtless is the inherited factor. Yet, if this person reduces food intake, the obesity need not develop. A person is not a helpless victim of heredity. Medical science can help him, and he can help himself.

The misconception that large bones account for excess weight should be dispelled. In two men 6 feet tall, the skeleton of the one with large bones will not weigh in excess of 3 pounds more than the one with small bones.

Preschool years. At birth the average boy weighs about 7 pounds 8 ounces, the girl, 7 pounds 2 ounces. Negroes are slightly smaller at birth than Caucasians. At 5 months, the weight at birth has doubled and at 12 months it has trebled. In the next four years the child will have an average gain of about 5 pounds a year.

School-age children. From Table 3 we observe that school-age boys gradually increase their yearly gain in weight from 5 pounds to about 14 pounds between 13 and 14 years of age. The annual gain then declines progressively, being only 6 pounds between the ages of 16 and 17 years. Weight gain will continue to 30 years of age. School girls gain from 5

Table 3. *Weight of American children in pounds*

Age (yr.)	Boys		Girls	
	Mean	Standard deviation	Mean	Standard deviation
1	24	2.5	22	2.5
2	30	3.0	28	3.0
3	34	3.5	33	4.0
4	38	4.5	37	4.5
5	43	5.0	42	6.0
6	48	6.0	48	7.5
7	54	7.0	55	9.0
8	61	9.0	62	10.5
9	69	11.0	70	13.0
10	77	13.0	78	14.5
11	86	16.0	88	17.0
12	96	19.0	100	19.0
13	106	21.0	110	19.0
14	120	22.0	120	19.0
15	133	21.0	127	18.0
16	142	20.0	130	18.0
17	148	19.0	133	18.0

to 8 pounds a year until 11 years of age. Then a gain of 12 pounds is followed by a gradual decline in the increment of gain.

Standard deviations of the magnitude indicated in Table 3 suggest a wide range of variation in a group of children. Persons who regularly record the weights of children are surprised at the frequency of children who are below the mean. This contrasts with the fallacy that, in terms of the mean, a higher proportion of children are overweight.

Developmental profiles

Height and weight of themselves are significant, but the busy teacher needs a device which gives her a quick, reliable picture of a child's development. Several practical devices have been produced, a few of which can be of practical value to the school.

Wetzel grid. To assess the physical condition of children objectively, Dr. N. C. Wetzel prepared a growth-development grid.* It is based on the two principles that each child should be considered his own standard of comparison and that the desirable development should be along a channel for a certain body type with an age schedule in keeping with the subject's normal physique. Dr. Wetzel's technique considers physical status in terms of body build, level of physical development, and nutritional status. In addition, it points up the relation between consecutive physical states as defined by a channel and a developmental level *(auxodromic progress).*

If a record of a child's height and weight is kept for several years, points to represent these figures will fall along a certain channel, with some fluctuation. During normal growth and development the child will progress in the same channel at the rate of 12 levels per year. The levels cut across the channels. A persistent trend in one channel would indicate the normal pattern of growth and development for that child's particular physical type. The developmental age is determined by reading the age at which the 67% norm intercepts a given developmental level.

Though considerable computation went into the assembly of the grid, the practical use of the grid is quite simple. It consists in merely plotting the height-weight points and interpreting the resultant graph in terms of the standards which are part of the grid forms.

Meredith physical growth record. Using the two factors of weight and height, Dr. H. V. Meredith has developed a highly practical growth profile chart† for use in schools unable to conduct a comprehensive anthropometric program. The child is weighed with the shoes and jacket or sweater removed. Height is also measured with the shoes removed.

---

*Copies of the grid may be obtained from NEA SERVICE, Inc., 1200 W. Third St., Cleveland 13, Ohio.

†Growth record forms for both boys and girls may be obtained from the American Medical Association, 535 N. Dearborn St., Chicago 6, or the National Education Association, 1201 Sixteenth St., N. W., Washington 6, D. C.

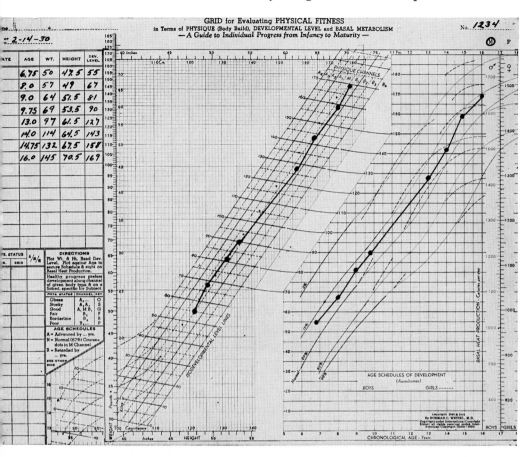

Fig. 3. Wetzel grid. This is the record of a normal boy and was plotted for a period of almost ten years. The development along a channel of a given body type reveals healthy progress. (From Watson, E. H., and Lowrey, G. H.: Growth and development of children; courtesy The Year Book Publishers, Inc.; permission of N. C. Wetzel, M.D.)

As a minimum procedure, each child should be measured in September, January, and May. At each measuring a point is plotted along the vertical age line at the proper weight marker in the weight portion of the chart. Another point is plotted in the height portion of the chart. After successive measurements over a period of two or three years have been recorded, curves of progress can be traced.

The graphs outline five normative zones—tall, moderately tall, average, moderately short, and short. The particular zone in which a child's weight point falls indicates his position with reference to the weights of other children of the same age and sex. The same principle applies to the location of height points. The height and weight points of most children fall in corresponding zone; for example, if the weight falls in the moderately heavy zone, the height will fall in the moderately tall zone.

When a youngster's weight and height points do not fall in corres-

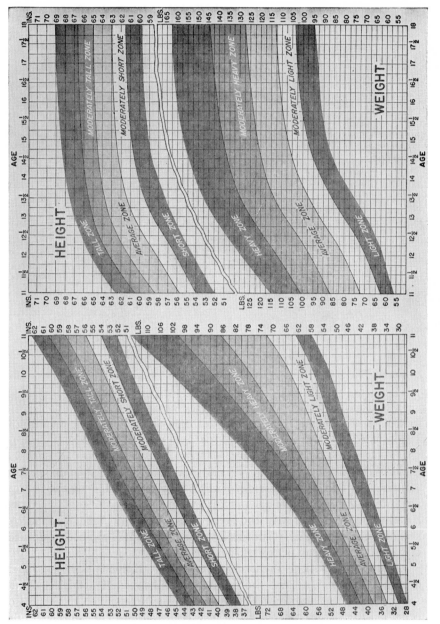

Fig. 4. Physical growth record for girls. Each chart has been reduced from 8 × 11 inch size. This record will indicate the body type and progress in height and weight growth. (Courtesy Dr. H. V. Meredith, State University of Iowa.)

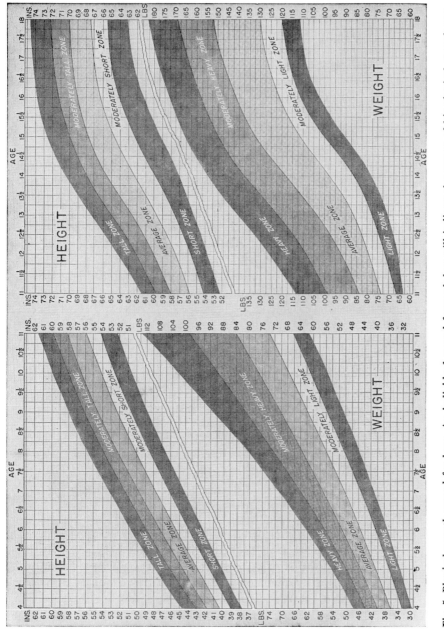

Fig. 5. Physical growth record for boys. An individual record for each boy will indicate the nature of his physical growth pattern. (Courtesy Dr. H. V. Meredith, State University of Iowa.)

ponding zones, two possible interpretations may explain the dissimilarity: (1) It may indicate natural slenderness or stockiness, or (2) it may reflect a poor quality of health. Any child with dissimilar weight and height zones may be in need of further appraisal. Perhaps an examination by a physician will reveal that the child has certain health impairments or that he suffers from malnutrition or overweight. It thus is apparent that the physical growth record can indicate possible health deficiences, as well as portray normal growth progress.

Organismic quotient. In an attempt to represent whole growth in one view, Dr. W. C. Olson and Dr. B. O. Hughes have devised a table to show the longitudinal development of the child as a whole. By taking the mental age, carpal age (ossification of wrist bones), reading age, height age, weight age, and dental age, they arrive at an organismic age. An organismic quotient is obtained by dividing the organismic age by the chronological age, as in the following equation:

$$\frac{\text{Organismic age}}{\text{Chronological age}} = \text{Organismic quotient}$$

This method indicates, and even measures, the central developmental tendency.

Graphs and tables. For practical use in the school, it might be well to consider and appraise the use of graphs and tables in determining physical growth and development.

Advantages of growth and developmental graphs and tables are the following:

1. Implement teacher's observations
2. Aid in understanding a child
3. May indicate the general health level of the child
4. Better parental understanding of a child's status
5. Point up abnormalities
6. Help in making comparisons between groups

Disadvantages of growth and developmental graphs and tables are as follows:

1. May be too complex for everyday use
2. Normal may be misleading
3. Optimums not included
4. Many standards needed
5. May become the end, to the detriment of the child
6. Not a substitute for personal history and physical examination

When the teacher or some other person in the school has an adequate understanding of the Wetzel grid or the organismic quotient, these instruments can be used to advantage. However, the standard physical growth and development tables, used with good judgment, can serve the needs of the vast majority of school children. Perhaps all children rightly should be brought to their family physician for professional appraisal. The school then would be governed by the physician's recommendation.

Motor development

Neuromuscular coordination is necessarily highly important in all human endeavors, and motor skill, perhaps most important of all, is a good index of general neuromuscular development. A person's ability to move about, together with related skills, can be observed and measured satisfactorily.

Preschool years. Whether a child walks at a very young age depends upon physical health, bone development, muscular development, and freedom of action. Delayed walking is not indicative of delayed intellect. It can be due to a variety of physical factors including overweight and also to emotional factors. Accidents may produce timidity. Being hurt in a fall can produce a fear of walking. It is apparent that knowledge of the age at which a child learned to walk is of little value to the school. Rather, the school will need to evaluate the child's motor ability as he displays it in his school activities.

School-age children. No positive correlation between intelligence, athletic ability, and mechanical skill exists. Boys are more competent than girls in motor skills perhaps because of a greater amount of practice. Older, taller, heavier, and stronger grade-school children usually are more proficient in motor skills.

At 7 years of age children tend to become daring, adventuresome, boisterous, and vigorous in their play. Running, chasing, skating, jumping rope, bicycle riding, and swimming appeal to them. Joy, as an expression of self, motivates the child to master a skill which actually becomes a means to an end.

Manipulative skill begins to improve markedly at age 8 years. The child normally becomes progressively stronger and sturdier. Legs lengthen rather rapidly, but the rate of general body growth is slower. Considerable variation in muscular development and coordination occurs. The child fatigues quite easily, but recovers just as readily. At 8 years of age, the smaller muscles begin to be used, though not too skillfully. Marked improvement in manipulative skill and eye-hand coordination results in a surprisingly high level of dexterity.

By the age of 11 years rapid muscular growth has begun, particularly in the girl. At age 12 years a child attains a near-adult level of perfection in control of the shoulder, arm, and wrist muscles. Finger control is slower. Development of large muscle skills first and then small muscle skills is a sound practice. During the period of rapid muscular growth which is ahead, awkwardness, sluggishness, and ineptitude should be expected. More rest appears to be necessary. However, there is a need for physical activity, particularly that which promotes coordination. Laxity in posture is common. Development in girls is ahead of that of boys. In both sexes a certain endocrine instability may produce considerable inconsistency in responsiveness and performance.

Girls begin to taper off in motor performance at the age of 15 years. Boys taper off at about 18 years of age. Although both will develop further skill after these ages, the rate of improvement will be much slower, and the maximum skill attained will not be appreciably higher. Biological maturity is a stage at which motor skill approaches the maximum potential. The girl's maximum potential will be attained at about 20 years of age, and the boy's maximum potential will be attained at about 23 years of age. Girls generally fall far below their potential skill, largely because of inadequate educational programs.

Handedness becomes noticeable by the time the child enters school. Neurologically, most persons are right-handed or left-handed. This marked preference is inherited; right-handedness is a dominant trait and left-handedness is a simple recessive trait. About 7% of all males and 6% of all females are strongly left-handed. About 20% of the members of both sexes are mix-handed and can use either hand about equally well. The hand which is used more depends upon training. These persons can be truly ambidextrous.

In grades four, five, and six, there is no appreciable difference in the manipulative skill of slow and fast handwriters. The one group simply has been permitted to acquire a habit of slow writing. Most children are permitted to acquire undesirable habits of slow motion. Stressing speed in coordination during the early years of life will establish better patterns of action in later years of life.

Special functions

Brief mention should be made of the development of special senses during the school-age years.

At the time the child enters school he should have fair self-control when he is in pain. Sensitivity to pain decreases during the period from 11 to 12 years of age. During adolescence the skin is highly sensitive to pain as well as to other senses with receptors in the skin.

Hearing acuity increases to the 14 to 15-year-age period when it is at its height. Pitch discrimination comes early in childhood and depends somewhat upon training. Perfect pitch is a physiological endowment and may be discerned before the teen-age years. Likes and dislikes for different sounds are predominantly a matter of conditioning and are largely affected by the tastes of associates.

The preschool child usually is farsighted, which he does not outgrow until about the sixth year of age. At this time both the involuntary and voluntary muscles of accommodation mature to give the child the visual apparatus necessary for reading. At the 6-year level of visual maturity, a child can read large type (12 point), but not with sustained effort.

If a child is nearsighted, the condition usually appears early.

Eye strain in school is not necessarily a deficiency in visual acuity, but may be a tendency of the relatively immature muscles of accommodation to fatigue very easily.

The normal eye reaches its maximum growth and acuity at the age of 12 years. It is the first organ to mature.

Skeletal development

Bone or skeletal age is gauged by ossification of the wrist and ankle bones as the index. It is apparent this is not too definite a standard and not too practical for school use since x-ray or fluoroscopic views are necessary. Bone age is merely an expression of skeletal development and does not necessarily indicate any other specific development or general maturity.

Fusion of the growth line, or epiphysis, terminates growth of a bone. Various bones fuse at different ages, thus attaining their full growth at different times. Skeletal growth is complete in the normal girl between 17 and 19 years of age, and in the normal boy between 18 and 20 years of age. Bone age may be delayed by malnutrition, infection, or thyroxin deficiency.

Respiratory system

Though the lungs of the adult are twenty times as large as the lungs of the newborn infant, the number of air pockets (alveoli) is the same, and there is little change in topography. Strangely, the newborn infant can tolerate a longer period of time without air (anoxia) than the adult. The newborn infant may go without breathing for 14 minutes and survive. Few adults can go longer than 5 minutes without breathing and live.

From birth to 7 years of age breathing is almost entirely performed by the diaphragm. At 7 years of age, costal breathing (raising and lowering the chest wall) comes prominently into use. At puberty the conical shape of the adult chest is established, along with the combined diaphragmatic and costal breathing which is characteristic of adults.

The resting respiratory or breathing rate varies from person to person in a given age category, but a normal range is recognized. Likewise, the normal amount of air inhaled and exhaled with each normal breath (tidal air) varies, but normal ranges have been established.

Abnormalities of the respiratory tract are relatively rare. Malformations which do occur are sufficiently pronounced that the child's parents will have consulted a physician and thus are not a problem for the teacher.

Table 4. Respiratory minute volume

Age (yr.)	Breathing rate (per min.)	Tidal air (ml.)	Minute volume (air in liters)
Newborn infant	30 (45)* 60	20	1
6	20 (30)* 35	125	3¾
12	20	250	5
14	18	350	6¼
18 (adult level)	16	500	8

*Mode in parentheses; minimum and maximum outside parentheses.

Circulatory system

Although size of the heart of the adult is twelve times that of the new-born infant, the pattern of operation and the electrocardiograms, or graphs, are similar. When a child is 5 years of age, the heart is four times as large as it was at birth. When he is 16 years of age, the heart may be small in comparison to skeletal muscle because heart growth between 14 and 16 years of age lags behind general muscle growth. Since endurance basically is cardiac output, observation of a child who fatigues (winded) quickly will indicate that probably circulatory capacity lags behind muscular capacity. This frequently occurs in children who are large for their age, but may occur in youngsters of normal stature.

Heart rate. While the minute volume of the heart depends upon both the heart rate and the output per beat, the rate increases as output decreases and decreases as output increases. Thus, if the rate is recorded, it gives a satisfactory index of the heart's capacity and level of functioning.

It must be recognized that the heart rate of a person may be altered by many factors, and a person's state of rest is an important factor. For that reason the pulse rate should be recorded several times if it appears to deviate markedly from the average. Further, a rate within ten beats on either side of the average may well be within the normal range. Usually, a low heart rate indicates a proficient heart.

Blood pressure. Systolic pressure figures usually represent the pressure exerted by the blood against the wall of the main arm (brachial) artery when the heart is in contraction. Diastole is the pressure in the vessel while the heart is relaxed, and pulse pressure is the difference between systolic and diastolic pressures. Pulse pressure indicates the degree of elasticity of the vessels.

Blood pressure is a great deal like a cork in water and can vary considerably in a person. However, a general tendency in pressure can be obtained when a series of readings is taken. Deviations from the average are to be expected, but more than a 15% deviation from the average for

Table 5. Average heart rate sitting at rest

Age (yr.)	Girls	Boys
Newborn infant	140	135
6	100	95
8	95	88
10	90	83
11	86	80
12	83	81
13	79	77
14	80	78
15	78	77
16	77	73
17	76	71
17½	76	71

Table 6. *Average blood pressure sitting at rest (mm. Hg)*

Age (yr.)	Girls			Boys		
	Systolic	*Diastolic*	*Pulse*	*Systolic*	*Diastolic*	*Pulse*
6	98	62	36	98	62	36
8	104	63	41	105	65	40
10	106	64	42	108	66	42
11	107	64	43	110	68	42
12	108	65	43	112	69	43
13	110	66	44	114	70	44
14	112	66	46	116	70	46
15	112	66	46	118	71	47
16	112	66	46	120	72	48

Table 7. *Constituents of blood at various ages*

Age (yr.)	Sex	Red corpuscles (per cubic mm.)	Hemoglobin (per 100 ml. whole blood)	White cells (per cubic mm.)
Newborn infant	Male and female	5.5 million	21 grams	20,000
5	Male and female	4.7 million	13 grams	8,000
10	Male and female	4.7 million	13 grams	8,000
14	Male	5.0 million	14 grams	7,000
	Female	4.7 million	13 grams	7,000
17	Male	5.3 million	15.6 grams	7,000
	Female	4.7 million	13.6 grams	7,000
18	Male	5.3 million	15.6 grams	7,000
	Female	4.7 million	14 grams	7,000

a given age is certainly sufficient indication that the child likely needs medical supervision. The child's physician will provide the school with the information and instruction necessary to promote the best interests of the child.

Blood. From birth to adulthood the blood constitutes about one thirteenth of the total body weight. Since a quart of blood weighs about 2 pounds, one can estimate the blood volume roughly. In persons from 12 to 18 years of age, the rate of increase in blood volume is slightly more rapid in the male than in the female. Final blood volume in the adult is about 4200 ml. in the female and about 5500 ml. in the male.

Quality of the blood, as well as volume, is important. Table 7 shows the average constituents of the blood for persons at various ages.

Antibodies passing from the mother through the placenta to the developing fetus give the child an infantile immunity until about 9 months of age. The immunity may be against diphtheria, smallpox, tetanus, measles, and poliomyelitis. This does not give the child the ability to produce these antibodies. Thus, when the antibodies received from the mother disintegrate, the immunity ceases unless the child, in the meantime, has been immunized by other means.

Lymph system. Man's lymph circulatory system is auxiliary to the blood circulatory system and is important as a transport system and a defense against infection. The number of lymph nodes and the amount of lymphoid tissue increase up to maturity. This increases the defense against infection since the lymph nodes filter out pathogens. Evidence indicates that antibodies are formed by lymphoid cells.

Metabolism

Basal metabolism represents the lowest level of chemical change, or fuel utilization, during the waking state. It is determined by measuring the amount of heat given off (direct calorimetry) or the amount of oxygen utilized (indirect method) during the waking, resting, and postabsorptive states. The postabsorptive stage is reached after a time interval of sufficient length following a meal that the blood is no longer absorbing food from the digestive tract. The usual time interval is twelve hours after a meal. About 75% of the basal metabolic rate is determined by the thyroxin output of the thyroid gland. About 20% of the heat produced under basal conditions is produced by the liver, the warmest organ of the body.

A third method of determining basal metabolism, called the Gale formula, is used in addition to the other two methods which measure the amount of body heat given off or the amount of oxygen used. The Gale formula is as follows: basal pulse pressure + basal pulse rate − 112 = basal metabolic rate.

The number 112 is used for 20-year-old subjects. A factor adjusted to subjects of younger ages can be substituted for the 112: for example, 121 for 10-year-old subjects or 117 for 15-year-old subjects. Thus, the following adaptation of the formula is used for a child 15 years of age: the basal metabolic rate = basal pulse pressure + basal pulse rate − 117.

Until the age of 8 years, there is a slight difference between the basal metabolic rate of males and females. From that age until the age of 20 years, the basal metabolic rate of both sexes is equal. From the age of 20 years onward, a male's basal requirement is 10% greater than a female's of the same height, weight, and age.

Appraisal of growth and development

From the discussion it has been apparent that the term growth and development of the child encompasses changes in many aspects of the child's makeup. Most important, it must be recognized that the standard elongated S-shaped (Sigmoid) curve does not apply to all aspects and that development of one function or growth of one system may be at a rapid rate and another at a more leisurely rate. This phenomenon can be presented by indicating the decade in life in which the various organs attain full growth (Table 8).

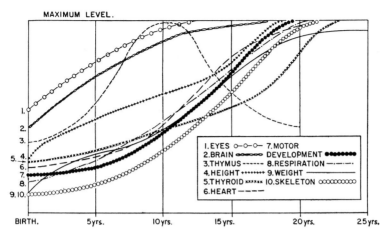

Fig. 6. Growth and development curves. Rates of maturation and growth are more rapid for girls than for boys. A diagrammatic, composite curve of various growth and development patterns is represented here. No one curve applies to all factors. Height, weight, and skeleton are represented as growth curves. For the remaining factors, growth and development run fairly parallel courses.

Table 8. *Completion of organic growth by decades*

First decade	Second decade	Third decade
Eyes	Heart	Thyroid gland
Brain	Spleen	Pituitary glands
	Thymus	Adrenal glands
	Muscles	Lungs
		Liver

It might be pointed out that, while the human brain has completed more than 95% of its growth by the time a person is 10 years old, its development in terms of native endowment does not reach its peak until about age 18 years. Growth patterns also can be illustrated by the use of curves, as in Fig. 6.

Individuality. In the appraisal of the growth and development of a child it is essential to recognize that each child is an individual in his own right, different from all other children. The teacher should give individual attention to each child to obtain a reasonably good understanding of his particular growth and developmental profile. In addition to the over-all appraisal of a child's maturation, the teacher should strive to evaluate the different aspects of development which compose the whole. Comparison with other children is not desirable unless it is of special value in appraising the child under consideration. Comparison with his own previous experience is the basis for relative evaluation.

Deviations from normal. Many children who appear to be normal in all respects deviate from the normal in specific functions or aspects and yet have no particular handicap. Even children who fall outside the normal range in more than one respect can nonetheless fit into the stream of normal childhood and go on to normal adulthood. The teacher whose philosophy recognizes that this is an imperfect world of imperfect people will concentrate on the assets each child possesses and give only necessary attention to deficiencies, which are the lot of humanity.

Prediction of growth and development. Using available standards and by making a detailed study of the developmental history of a child, a teacher can make a reasonably reliable prediction of the child's potential physical growth. A probable error of 5%, from a practical standpoint, is of little significance. Frequently when, in the course of developing an interest in health and general well-being, the teacher challenges a child with developmental data and shows how it can affect his future, it promotes a life-long interest in his general well-being.

Selected readings

Breckenridge, Marian E., and Murphy, Margaret N.: Growth and development of the young child, ed. 6, Philadelphia, 1958, W. B. Saunders Co.

Breckenridge, Marian E., and Vincent, E. Lee: Child development, physical and psychologic growth through the school years, ed. 4, Philadelphia, 1960, W. B. Saunders Co.

Forest, Ilse: Child development, New York, 1954, McGraw-Hill Book Co., Inc.

Gesell, A., Ilg, Frances L., and Ames, L. B.: Youth—the years from ten to sixteen, New York, 1956, Harper & Brothers.

Krogman, W. M.: A handbook of the interpretation of height and weight in the growing child, Child Development Publications, Urbana, 1950, University of Illinois Press.

Larson, L. A.: Health and fitness in the modern world, Chicago, 1961, The Athletic Institute.

Meredith, H. V.: A physical growth record for use in elementary and high schools, American Journal of Public Health **39:**878, 1949.

Meredith, H. V.: Growth, physical, Encyclopedia Americana, 449-502b, 1953.

Meredith, H. V.: Physical growth from birth to maturity, Review of Educational Research **9:**47, 1939.

National Education Association: Growth, development and learning, Washington, D. C., 1955, The Association.

President's Council on Youth Fitness: Youth physical fitness—suggested elements of a school-centered program, Parts I and II, Washington, D. C., 1961, United States Government Printing Office.

Sheldon, W. H., Stevens, S. S., and Tucker, W. B.: The varieties of human physique, New York, 1940, Harper & Brothers.

Shuttleworth, F. K.: The physical and mental growth of girls and boys age six to nineteen years in relation to age at maximum growth, Child Development, Society for Research in Child Development, Urban, 1939, University of Illinois Press, vol. 4.

Stuart, H. C.: Normal growth and development during adolescence, New England Journal of Medicine **234:**666-672, 693-700, 732-738, 1946.

Stuart, H. C., and Prugh, D. G.: Healthy child, Cambridge, Mass., 1960, Harvard University Press.

Tanner, J. M.: Growth at adolescence, Springfield, Ill., 1956, Charles C Thomas, Publisher.

Tuddenham, R. D.: Physical growth of California boys and girls from birth to 18 years, Berkeley, 1954, University of California Press.

Walke, N. S., Droscher, N., and Volpe, M. D.: Health and fitness, Dubuque, Iowa, 1962, W. D. Brown Co.

Watson, E. H., and Lowrey, G. H.: Growth and development of children, ed. 4, Chicago, 1962, Year Book Publishers, Inc.

Wetzel, N. C.: Assessing the physical condition of children. I. Case demonstration of failing growth and the determination of "par" by the grid method, Journal of Pediatrics **22**:82, 1943.

Wetzel, N. C.: Assessing the physical condition of children. III. The components of physical status and physical progress and their evaluation, Journal of Pediatrics **22**:329, 1943.

Wetzel, N. C.: Instruction manual in the use of the grid for evaluating physical fitness, Cleveland, 1941, NEA Service, Inc.

Wetzel, N. C.: The treatment of growth failure in children, Cleveland, 1948, NEA Service, Inc.

Chapter 4

Emotional development

Teachers recognize that the maturation process of the human being involves the development of many factors and aspects of a child's makeup. Knowledge of intellectual and physical deveolpment is vital to the teacher, but knowledge of emotional development is equally important. Many children sufficiently mature physiologically and mentally have difficulty adjusting to their social environment. What commonly is spoken of as mental health is basically emotional adjustment.

An understanding of various levels of emotional maturation enables a teacher to understand each child more fully. The informed teacher not only will know what to expect in emotional responses from children, but will also be able to interpret unusual emotional behavior in terms of the level of emotional maturity it represents.

Concept of emotions

Emotions are intense feelings accompanied by bodily reactions. A person gets angry physically as well as mentally. He experiences joy physically as well as in other conscious respects. Emotions are highly complex and vary in degrees of intensity. They represent patterns of interaction between neurons, endocrine glands, and other parts of the body. While they arise from a conscious experience which originates in the central nervous system, they produce a reaction of the glandular system which in turn affects neural function and practically all of the rest of the body.

Some authorities maintain that there are only two emotions, the negative emotion of anger and the positive emotion of love. Such a broad, even rough, classification is not satisfactory for the practical needs of the teacher. Therefore, a further classification of the negative and positive emotions is in order.

Negative emotions. Feelings which are unpleasant or disagreeable are not entirely distinct, tending to have certain things in common. There is the further difficulty that words must be used to express the feeling, and words themselves can be an obstacle to understanding since they convey different things to different people. However, for practical use a classsification of negative emotions can be made as follows:

1. Anger—fury, rage, hate, annoyance, irritation, and displeasure
2. Fear—fright and alarm
3. Distress—helplessness and futility
4. Envy—jealousy
5. Humility—submission, inferiority, and insecurity
6. Loneliness—isolation

Positive emotions. Feelings which are pleasant or acceptable are even more subtle than others, and grades of distinction necessarily are difficult to classify. A classification of positive emotions includes the following:

1. Tenderness—love, affection, and kindness
2. Elation—pride, mastery, confidence, and assertive self-feeling
3. Possession—security and ownership
4. Amusement—jollity and relaxation

Physical bases of emotions

All overt human conduct arises from a physical source, the protoplasm of the body's cells. Each person possesses a particular constitutional endowment from which emotions arise. When stimuli from the external environment produce an emotional response, virtually all of the body is involved, but two systems, the neural and the endocrine systems, play major roles. These systems function in all coordination and adjustment and are particularly involved in emotional responsiveness. The responses of the neural system are immediate and quick acting. Endocrine functions are slower. A relationship between the two may be visualized by picturing the endocrine hormones as the soil in which the neuronal impulses function. Neurons function in an endocrine soil of a particular kind, perhaps affected by the internal secretions as natural soil is affected by fertilizers.

Since a person is conscious of emotional states, the cortex of the brain, where consciousness is located, obviously is involved. Original external stimuli reach the cortex of the brain and are relayed to the thalamus, from which autonomic nerves originate.

Autonomic neuron system. The autonomic system is particularly important in emotional responses. It is often referred to as the vegetative system since it maintains the functions necessary to sustain life. It is an involuntary system and has two divisions, the sympathetic nervous system which tends to speed up action and the parasympathetic nervous system which has the opposite effect. All organs of the thoracic and abdominal cavities have a dual supply of autonomic nerves, sympathetics, which speed up the function of the organ, and parasympthetics, which will have the opposite action. Thus balance of function is maintained. During emotional states these nerves are stimulated, at times the sympathetics arousing the organs, at other times the parasympathetics reducing the activity of the organs.

The emotional center is in the thalamus, a large ovoid mass of gray matter located toward the center and base parts of the brain. It also is the location of the pain and temperature-regulating centers. That some people are emotionally highly responsive and others much less so is understandable in biological terms. Sensitivity may be inherent in the nerve structure and may be further sensitized by particular endocrine influences. However, social conditioning must not be discounted, nor should training possibilities be discarded. Perhaps all degrees of biological response can be affected by training of the right type.

Endocrine nature of temperament. Generally, temperament is regarded as the emotional mold which distinguishes a person. Each person's temperament is greatly affected by his particular endocrine endowment. Most endocrine influences are rather subtle, but there are some manifestations which are more definite. Irritability, fatigability, apathy, enthusiasm, depression, indifference, and aggressiveness are all understandable in terms of the endocrine secretions.

The term *endocrine type* presumes a great deal. Persons whose basic makeup is due entirely to extreme or true endocrine malfunction are rare, but examples do exist. Persons with an overproduction of thyroxin (hyperthyroidism), in addition to a tendency to lose weight and be thin, are restless, energetic, active, impatient, easily upset, impulsive, and alert. At the other pole are persons with an underproduction of thyroxin (hypothyroidism). For persons of this type it is an effort, almost, to live. They go along at a low level of function, react slowly, fatigue easily, are usually behind in everything, rarely enthuse about anything, are not easily disturbed or upset, and are usually easy going and easily pleased.

Most persons represent various intergrades of endocrine balances. Yet, in school practice, a teacher must recognize that a child reacts as he does, at least in part, because of his particular biological makeup. He can be changed some by training, but perhaps some children can be changed but little. A wise teacher will try to understand a child's conduct in terms of his basic constitutional makeup.

Genesis of emotional responses

What motivates human conduct? What gives force and direction to what one does? Why does a person become angry or elated? Through what channels are emotions mediated and in what manner? These are questions of significance to all persons. They are of special importance to teachers who, if they are to be of the greatest value in guiding children in self-development, must understand why a child acts as he does.

A human being is biologically self-centered, self-interested, and selfish. Knowingly and unknowingly he seeks to gratify this self. His ego requires gratification. He seeks status. So it is necessary that the teacher, observing overt behavior in a child, go behind the scene and understand just *why* the child acts as he does.

Physiological patterns. A child is born with certain physiological patterns such as hunger, thirst, and pain. A newborn child is a biological being and not a social being. His self is gratified by satisfying such physiological patterns as hunger and thirst, by relieving pain, permitting activity, and eliminating discomfort. If the infant is in pain, or hungry, or restrained, it responds emotionally by exhibiting the negative emotion of anger. The newborn infant seems to exhibit no positive emotions.

All through life, gratification of these physiological patterns is a factor in the emotional responsiveness of a person. However, as one matures emotionally, his control over the emotions rises accordingly. Though the teen-aged child may not cry or show the intense emotional response of an infant, his responses are different when he is hungry than when he is not hungry, different when he is not active than when he is active.

Universal socially conditioned motives. Although the child is born a biological being, he becomes a social being and learns to get self-gratification through certain socially conditioned motives which are universally accepted. Every normal person wants attention, affection, approval, applause, praise, and security. He seeks mastery, superiority, and achievement. When he displays positive emotions, he is getting the attention or approval the self seeks, or he has achieved a goal which has been a source of gratification. If negative emotions are displayed, he has failed to achieve his goal or has not had the approval or praise he sought. Or the little self has been thwarted or hurt.

Individualized patterns of motivation. Teachers should be aware of the fact that some children get special gratification through interests or means that are neither universally practiced nor accepted. A child who is gratified by playing harmful pranks is in need of special attention. Perhaps he is not getting attention from the normal, more wholesome avenues of school life. He needs to understand which avenues of self-gratification our society recognizes. Somewhere in the school program there must be means and opportunities for wholesome self-gratification for every child.

Preschool years

By the time a child first appears at school, his emotional mold already has been subjected to many influences. What has happened to his emotional makeup is of extreme importance to the school. While the 6-year-old child is pliable and can be modified, the task of the school in rehabilitating a child with marked emotional deviation is an assignment to frustration for the teacher who does not have an understanding of the factors which characterize normal emotional function and maturation.

Egocentricity. The preschool child is selfish, self-centered, and demanding. His training should be a compromise between too much expression and too much repression. The child who has learned to deny himself and consider the wishes of others, yet who has not been repressed to a state of timidity and reticence, is likely to have the balanced emotional responsiveness of normal children entering school. Preschool children exhibit jealousies and tantrums, but the child who has obtained neither status nor attention through these expressions will find more acceptable means for obtaining self-gratification. Yet, most children enter school life with a handicap because they are entering a life in which they share the stage with thirty others and are coming from a life in which they are the center of all activity and the world revolves about them. It is true that the home has the primary responsibility for guiding a child in his emotional development, but the school gains little by pointing to the shortcomings of the home training.

Early elementary school years

Social influences have modified the child by the time he arrives at school; nevertheless he is still very much an *individualist*. He will play with others for only brief periods of time. It is an ideal time in which to develop self-reliance and the ability to fulfill responsibilities, an attribute of value throughout life.

Emotional expression. The primary school child is cheerful and happy. He is curious and will take a keen interest in new experiences. He enjoys play and can amuse himself. He is friendly to others, but does not sustain an interest in another child. He is not excessively timid or afraid and exhibits self-confidence.

At this period of life the child may display contrasting and even conflicting emotional traits. He may be exuberant, eager, overactive, assertive, aggressive, adventuresome, and daring. He may be overly dramatic. He can be unduly sensitive and will exhibit pronounced negative emotions, such as anger and jealousy. However, the same child can be most sympathetic in his concern for the misfortunes and trials of others. His emotions are usually of short duration, however pronounced they may appear to be.

Evidences of emotional maturation. During the primary years the child should be learning to accept disappointments and disagreeable tasks. He should be learning to control anger, fear, and other negative emotions. He should forget anger and grudges. He respects others and refrains from interrupting and quarreling. He learns to control or reduce possessiveness. He learns to obey rules and wait his turn, as a kindness to others. He learns to do his work promptly and shows reasonable persistence.

Too often the teacher assumes that the child will learn by observation conduct which is not accepted. However, explanation of accepted and unaccepted conduct and the reasons will usually hasten the maturation process.

Later elementary school years

During the fourth, fifth, and sixth grades of a child's school life, he shows the maturing effects of socialization. Actually, emotionally he is much more stable and mature than is generally recognized.

Emotional patterns. The individualistic child in the 9- to 11-year age span is acquiring orderly habits of work and play. He assumes increasing responsibility and self-reliance. He adjusts quite well to frustration and conflict, and, though he occasionally is upset emotionally, he recovers quickly. He is not prone to brood or worry. He has a more lasting interest in friends and shares his pleasures and possessions. He has learned to respect the rights and property of others and conforms to the social and moral requirements of his group.

Although the child's interest span is increasing and his self-control is improved, he is sensitive to failure and he is easily discouraged. In his intense desire to achieve and even excel, this youngster may appear to be argumentative and antagonistic. However, a better interpretation would be that this merely expresses a combination of boundless vitality and extreme competitiveness, a product of the modern American culture.

Many children in this age group do considerable daydreaming. All normal people do some daydreaming, but this age level is the high point for daydreams. Not ridicule, criticism, or punishment, but tasks that interest and keep the child occupied in gratifying accomplishment will reduce daydreaming.

Some of these children are boisterous and noisy, not with asocial tendencies, but as a manifestation of physical vitality and self-expression. Timely counseling will help the child to acquire the insight essential to the necessary adjustment.

Some children in this age level are still quite shy, and teachers frequently overlook them. After all, the boisterous child is more easily remembered. The shy child is usually a lonely child, perhaps with exaggerated feelings of inferiority because of insecurity, poor home environment, lack of specific skill, or other factors, real or imaginary.

Junior high school years

During the period when a child is 12 to 14 years of age, his interest in self is transposed to interest in the group. The tendency of youngsters to gang together at this age is a common observation. No biological reason accounts for the phenomenon. It is a social attraction to the members of the same gender, hence is called the homophiliac period. It is not a homosexual phenomenon. Perhaps the grouping is due to the tendency for girls to be almost two years in advance of boys in physiological and social development and for their interests to be both more advanced and more diverse.

Group loyalties. Attempts to break up a group are met with determined resistance and usually are unsuccessful. Directing the group into wholesome channels usually proves profitable. The intense loyalty of the individual self to the group identity can be the most potent force motivating a child. To him it is more important that he have the approval of his peer group than that he get approval elsewhere. Teachers and parents find that when the standards of the group conflict with those of the school or home, the group will exert the greater influence. Guiding the group, rather than competing with it, can be effective.

Emotional patterns. The marked individualism of previous years is displaced by a cooperative approach. Self-gratification comes from the praise and approval of the group. Status within the group is the primary goal. New interests of the child do not tend to appear except as they are accepted and fostered by the group. Reliance on the support of the group doubtless avoids some personal frustrations and conflicts and can be of value unless the standards and mores of the group range outside of social norms. Leadership exerts itself in the groups, and, if it is directed into proper avenues, the training opportunities are valuable. Ability to lead asserts itself in many forms, from the very highest to the browbeating level.

Many youngsters at this stage of life may be inordinately self-conscious and painfully shy. This in itself can leave its mark on the personality, but the greatest scars occur when this shy self-conscious youngster develops serious doubts that he is normal. Assurance that all normal people, especially those at this age, experience the discomforts of shyness and self-consciousness can relieve his concern and fears.

A child who can fit into no particular group finds himself a person who walks alone. From it may develop the beginning of a tendency to be a lone wolf. Patterns of emotional adjustment acquired at the junior high school level often determine the direction of the emotional mold throughout life. In appraising the child's emotional behavior, the teacher might well ask, "What will be the significance of this tendency twenty years hence?"

Puberty

Precisely considered, puberty refers to the age at which the reproductive organs become functionally mature. It occurs at some time between the ages of 12 and 17 years. In the female, menstruation occurs and she takes on the typical secondary female characteristics of body contour, breast growth, and pelvic enlargement. In the male, seminal discharge and a change of voice are indices of the climacteric called puberty.

In its practical, broader sense, puberty is considered the complete change which occurs at the time of maturation of the reproductive organs. It is more than a physical change. It involves social, emotional, and mental change, as well as physical change. From the standpoint of school practice this is an important concept because some children experience a *negativism* at this stage of life. Negativism is characterized by withdrawal, reticence, and marked timidity. The child is somewhat perplexed by the changes through which he is passing, and, as with all persons, something he does not understand is disturbing to him. He will recover from the negativism in about six months, even without counseling, but he can be helped measurably by being told that he is going through a transition which all normal persons experience.

Senior high school years

Adolescence, the period of youth, is not a pathological state. It does involve special problems related to emotional development which result in frustrations and conflicts. The adolescent finds himself in a social environment considerably more complex than anything he has encountered previously. A combination of inexperience and immaturity may find him unequal to the situation, and thus he makes improper or inadequate adjustments. Adolescence is not a sudden, overnight change. It runs a course of about five years and includes the ages from 15 to 20 years, when the adult level is attained.

Heterosexuality. Adolescence is characterized by an interest in the opposite sex. To the boy the girl becomes physically and socially attractive. The self obtains gratification from the attractiveness of the sexes; emotional responses rise to the highest level on the positive side, yet also may go to the extreme in negative responses. Intense emotional responses of this phase of life may be of fleeting duration—an index of the level of emotional maturity.

Transition to adulthood. This is a period of transition from childhood to adulthood and is characterized by marked inconsistency. At times a youth may act as mature as a 30-year-old adult, but the next hour may exhibit the emotional pattern of a 10-year-old child. It is a period of emancipation in which the youth wishes to be recognized as an individual in his own right. Parents who still think of him as a child may insist on childish standards and requirements, a source of frequent parent-youth conflict. Youth resents restraints and orders. Though the youth lacks experience, he possesses considerable ability. Therefore, both teachers and parents need to consider the viewpoint of the student and provide such compromises and counsel as the situation merits. Suggestions, not orders, are the effective instruments.

Some youth, girls as well as boys, in expressing their desire for emancipation go to the extreme of revolt against their parents, teachers, school, community, and even society. They are students of high intelligence as well as of average mentality. These are the "youth in revolt" of our time. Defiance of the established patterns and order of things seems to give them a certain self-gratification. They appear to obtain a feeling of identity or individuality. With rare exceptions they pay dearly for their revolt for many years to come when they find they are not readily accepted by those who normally would accept them, and they find themselves going down the road of life alone.

Youth needs guidance to avoid this tragic role. To express individuality but within the range of social requirements and with respect for the rights of others must be learned. As an attention-getting device, revolt can exact a high price in future years. This the teen-ager must be helped to understand.

Social conflict. Youth lives in an adult world, made to adult order, and controlled by adults. He possesses a high level of self-esteem. Yet, failure and frustration are frequent, with both deep and superficial scars.

Emotional maturation consists of adapting demands of the self to the demands of the social world. A child matures as he learns that some problems of social conflict have no ready solution, but are something we have to live with; therefore we must not permit them to cause too great an emotional reaction. During maturation, a youth learns that problems which disturb him extremely today will become, with the mellowing of time, of little consequence. Intently, he should strive to develop social traits of sincerity, congeniality, courtesy, tact, fairness, industry, and thoughtfulness.

Emotional patterns. An adolescent is idealistic and sensitive. He is insecure and seeks assurances from his own peer group. Yet, he is eager to be approved and accepted by older people. Hence, the disturbance he suffers when he must choose between the conflicting demands of his peer group and those of older people. The cliquishness and group loyalty of youth doubtless serve to provide some degree of social security. Students of high school age are concerned about their masculine and feminine roles. They may be demonstrative, even border on exhibitionism, in order to obtain the attention and recognition they seek. Yet, though they are anxious about their status, they are seeking a mature set of values. Perhaps the best single index of the emotional maturation of the high school student is to be found in the maturity of the values he is acquiring.

An interesting phenomenon which is not new but is more pronounced than in past generations is the frequent conflict between high school girls and their mothers. This conflict arises partially from the girl's desire to be emancipated from the dependence of childhood to the independence of adulthood, to be recognized as an individual in her own right. The mother, on the other hand, still considers her daughter a child and tends to treat her accordingly. Overprotection, however well intended, interferes with the daughter's style and is resented. Contradictory respect for and antagonism toward the parents also may be extended to teachers and other adults. Though this conflict dissolves, the dissolution can be hastened by honest adult attempts to understand the youth's position and make reasonable compromises between youth demands and adult edicts.

Each high school student should acquire a philosophy of life, as well as day-to-day goals. He should develop confidence, courage, self-esteem, self-reliance, self-discipline, orderliness, humor, adaptability, and an interest in people. He should learn to accept monotonous tasks, gain satisfaction from doing things well, and accept criticism and facts about himself. He should strive to obtain the maximum benefit from his various experiences to assure himself of at least optimum social maturation.

Individual differences

No templet conveniently outlines the pattern of emotional maturation. Every person is unique, the product of an interaction of constitution and environment. Every student can be expected to have assets and liabilities of varying degrees. The teacher who can recognize each child's good qualities and give them proper recognition is truly a great teacher. A greater teacher is the one who can also recognize each child's deficiencies and help him set up a program of constructive readjustment.

Selected readings

Almy, Millie C.: Child development, New York, 1955, Henry Holt & Co., Inc.

Amly, Millie C.: Ways of studying children, New York, 1959, Teachers College, Columbia University.

Bernard, H. W.: Mental hygiene for classroom teachers, New York, 1961, McGraw-Hill Book Co., Inc.

Dalton, R. H.: Personality and social interaction, Boston, 1961, D. C. Heath & Co.

Dennis, W.: Readings in child psychology, ed. 2, Englewood Cliffs, N. J., 1963, Prentice-Hall, Inc.

English, O. S., and Pearson, G. H. J.: Emotional problems of living, New York, 1955, W. W. Norton & Co., Inc.

Frank, L. K., Harrison, R., Hellersberg, and others: Personality development in adolescent girls, Urbana, 1953, University of Illinois Press.

Havighurst, R. J.: Human development and education, New York, 1953, David McKay Co., Inc.

Hurlock, Elizabeth B.: Adolescent development, ed. 2, New York, 1955, McGraw-Hill Book Co., Inc.

Hurlock, Elizabeth B.: Child growth and development, ed. 2, New York, 1956, McGraw-Hill Book Co., Inc.

Hymes, J. L.: A child development point of view, New York, 1955, Prentice-Hall, Inc.

Hymes, J. L.: Behavior and misbehavior, New York, 1955, Prentice-Hall, Inc.

International Symposium on Feelings and Emotions: Feelings and emotions, New York, 1950, McGraw-Hill Book Co., Inc.

Joseph, H. and Zern, G.: Emotional problems of children, New York, 1954, Crown Publishers.

Kanner, L.: Word to parents about mental hygiene, Madison, 1957, University of Wisconsin Press.

King, F. W.: Emotional maturity, its nature and measurement, Cambridge, Mass., 1951, Harvard University Press.

Lehner, G. F.: Explorations in personal adjustment, ed. 2, Englewood Cliffs, N. J., 1957, Prentice-Hall, Inc.

Lippman, H. S.: Treatment of the child in emotional conflict, ed. 2, New York, 1962, McGraw-Hill Book Co., Inc.

Martin, W. E., and Stendler, Celia B.: Child behavior and development, New York, 1959, Harcourt, Brace & Co., Inc.

Menninger, W. C.: How you grow up, New York, 1957, Sterling Press.

Midcentury White House Conference on Children and Youth: A healthy personality for every child, Raleigh, N. C., 1951, Health Publications Institute.

Mussen, P. H., Conger, J. J., and Kagan, J.: Child development and personality, ed. 2, New York, 1963, Harper & Row, Publishers, Inc.

Rand, Winifred, Sweeney, Mary E., Vincent, Edna L., and others: Growth and the development of the young child, ed. 6, Philadelphia, 1958, W. B. Saunders Co.

Redl, F.: Understanding children's behavior, New York, 1957, Teachers College, Columbia University.

Ridenour, Nina: The children we teach, New York, 1960, Mental Health Materials Center.

Riesman, D.: How different may one be? Child Study **28:**6, 1951.

Rogers, C. R.: On becoming a person, Boston, 1961, Houghton-Mifflin Co.

Saul, L. J.: Emotional maturity, ed. 2, Philadelphia, 1960, J. B. Lippincott Co.

Spence, K. W.: Behavior theory and learning, Englewood Cliffs, N. J., 1960, Prentice-Hall, Inc.

Strang, Ruth: Introduction to child study, ed. 4, New York, 1959, The Macmillan Co.

Strang, Ruth M.: The adolescent views himself, New York, 1957, McGraw-Hill Book Co., Inc.

Trapp, E. P.: Readings on the exceptional child, New York, 1962, Appleton-Century-Crofts, Inc.

United States Children's Bureau: Guiding the

adolescent, Washington, D. C., 1946, United States Children's Bureau, Publication no. 225.

Walker, R. N.: Body building and behavior in young children, Lafayette, Ind., 1962, So-ciety for Research in Child Development.

Warters, Jane: Achieving maturity, New York, 1949, McGraw-Hill Book Co., Inc.

White, V.: Studying the individual pupil, New York, 1957, Harper & Brothers.

When any calamity has been suffered
the first thing to be remembered is,
how much has been escaped.

—Samuel Johnson

Chapter 5

Departures from normal health, growth, and development

Every school can expect to have children who deviate from the normal. Some deviations will be minor and affect the youngster little or not at all. In other instances the deviation may be of a nature which so markedly limits the child that special provisions must be made. Whatever the deviation, there are correct ways and incorrect ways to deal with the situation. There are ways to make it possible for the child to make the most of whatever endowment he has and to make him feel he is an accepted regular member of the group. Handled incorrectly, the child with a deviation can be made to feel that he is an outsider, with resulting harm to mental health.

Generally speaking, normal children are eager to accept and assist the child who has some deficiency. It is essential that all children understand the various aspects of the total situation and what their proper role is in the best interest of their classmate with a deviation. Nothing in all of a teacher's experience will be more rewarding or more gratifying than to make a normal, or near-normal, school life possible for the child who has some departure from the normal. Sometimes the opportunity or even the demand of the teacher may be great; at other times it may be small. Perhaps the need is that of aiding in having the child directed to a physician, perhaps in helping the child to help himself to better health, or perhaps in assisting the child to do the best with what he has. Whatever the situation, the teacher's present contribution may well benefit the individual through all the years of his life.

Teachers are eager to do everything reasonable for children who deviate from the normal range of health, growth, and development, but are hesitant to act because of a lack of confidence in their knowledge of such conditions. No teacher, neither elementary classroom teacher nor secondary school health educator, should be considered an expert on any of these conditions, but the teacher can have a fundamental understanding of the essentials of these conditions. Such knowledge gives the teacher the confidence to participate actively in a program for the betterment of the child.

Responsibility of the school

Schools do not have a recognized legal responsibility for the correction, or even the improvement, of health defects in any child. The responsibility is recognized as a professional obligation of the teaching profession to do everything reasonable for the health and well-being of every child in school. This professional obligation can be fulfilled in various ways. (1) It may simply be a matter of bringing a child's condition to the attention of his parents. (2) It may be a follow-up of such a referral. (3) It may require counseling with the parents on means for obtaining necessary professional services. (4) It may mean seeking outside financial or other aid to obtain the corrective services the child needs. (5) It may require that the teacher carry out certain instructions from the child's physician or other practitioner. (6) It may be a matter of adapting the school program to the needs of the specific child. (7) It may mean helping the child to help himself in solving health problems which are not directly under the supervision of any practitioner. (8) Most important of all, it may simply mean that the teacher fully understands the child's condition, appreciates his problems, and is able to make his school life more enjoyable and effective because she does understand the condition and its various implications.

A teacher need not have the technical background of a Sir William Osler. Her province is neither diagnosis nor therapy. What her role requires is an understanding of how and why various deviations affect the individual child in his pursuit of school life. She needs to know what factors in the school can affect the child favorably as well as unfavorably. Above all, she should have an appreciation of what she as a teacher can do for the best interests of the child.

Low vitality

A teacher's attention is quickly drawn to a child who seems to lack the vitality of other children. This child seems to function at a low level. To move appears to be an effort for him. Other than his general sluggishness, no symptoms distinguish the child. He may be of normal height, weight, and general growth.

While many of these children exhibit no pronounced disorders, a thorough examination by a physician usually will ferret out a combination of minor deficiencies which produce the low vitality. Low thyroxin output, anemia, chronic low-grade infection, malnutrition, and visual fatigue account for the sluggishness, and the physician will readily diagnose these conditions. He will undertake treatment of the child for these disorders and notify the school of its responsibilities in rejuvenation of the child.

Many times the causes of low vitality are not basically organic, but are primarily functional. Children with low vitality seldom are taken to a physician, and, unless the school makes concerted efforts to help him, the child goes through school dragging around, disinterested in everything about him, and destined to be a social liability.

Inadequate rest is more frequently a cause of sluggishness in a child than is generally recognized. Some homes lack any semblance of a regular schedule, and the children get to bed at almost any hour of the night. In addition, sluggishness becomes a habit with some children. A child who has been permitted to loaf through childhood is a neglected child. It is more important that a child acquire effective practices for applying his ability than it is that he acquire the usual classroom factual information. The school has both an opportunity and an obligation to develop the best possible work practices for a child in keeping with his ability and vitality.

In practice, the school should have a true evaluation of the capacities of a child with low vitality. Further, the school should plan a definite program for improving his general vitality. Such a program should include a regular routine of living, activity sufficient to stimulate muscle tone and circulation, no excessive tension, no excessive fatigue, adequate rest, balanced diet with midmorning and midafternoon lunches, and immediate medical care for illness, whether infectious or organic. Spectacular results are not the rule. Steady, gradual improvement should be the goal. The teacher's personal gratification in being of tangible value to such a child is one of the finest rewards of teaching.

Malnutrition

Severe or pronounced malnutrition is relatively uncommon among the children in America today, but moderate and mild malnutrition is far more prevalent than is commonly known. A teacher can easily recognize pronounced obesity and underweight, but children with the usual type of vitamin deficiency and lack of sufficient protective foods are not readily detectable. While the general school health program should be planned to promote the nutrition of every school child, certain children merit special attention because of recognized or suspected nutritional needs.

Obesity. Children more than 10% overweight for their height and age are considered obese. In some children overweight of more than 10% may not visibly affect the health adversely during childhood, but the long-time effect may be to lower the level of health. Though no physical effect may be discernible, obesity will reduce both the effectiveness and enjoyment of living. A child who carries around an excess weight of 15 pounds is likely to fatigue easily. Although the added burden may not tax a normal heart, a slightly defective heart may be burdened seriously. The obese child is handicapped in play and in muscular reactions. He frequently is the object of taunts and ridicule and may be considered different by his associates. Being classed out of the normal category is not conducive to the best mental health for the developing child.

Obesity can result only from eating more food than one burns. Even when a glandular disorder in which organic substances readily turn to fat exists, the organic compounds must come from what a person eats. The remedy for obesity is to eat less or burn more food or both. Any child who is obese has been eating too much. He has established dietary practices which lead to caloric excess. Long-established family dietary customs, perhaps of foreign national origin, patterned to the needs of people who work in the fields or at other manual labor may well produce obese children who become conditioned to excessive eating. Once this psychophysiological pattern is established, the obese child finds it progressively more difficult to reduce his intake. His problem is both physiological and psychological.

Hunger is basically physiological and is governed essentially by the sugar level of the blood. When the blood sugar level is low, a person experiences sensations of hunger. Immediately after a meal, the blood sugar level is high. This high level affects the output of insulin from the pancreas. Insulin converts excess blood sugar to stable glycogen, which is stored in the liver. This results in a low blood sugar level and hunger. It is apparent that consuming carbohydrates (e.g., sugars) to relieve hunger may shortly cause a reaction of high insulin output—low blood sugar and increased hunger. For this reason reducing diets are high in proteins and low in carbohydrates. Proteins satisfy hunger without an appreciable increase in insulin output.

A child who can reduce his caloric intake by 600 calories a day should lose a pound a week. This is a wholesome weight-reduction rate. Cutting down on portions and using proteins to allay between-meals hunger are the two points that must be emphasized. If at all possible, dieting should be done under medical supervision. Encouragement from the teacher and cooperation from the home complete the picture.

A low calorie and high protein diet is one which includes grapefruit, eggs, steak, lamb, chicken, fish, lettuce, tomatoes, combination salads, dry toast, and nonfat milk. Salt is ruled out of the diet and no fried foods (e.g., eggs) should be eaten. The child need not suffer from hunger so long as he uses proteins to satisfy his hunger. Once he has reduced his weight to the desired level, his teacher should help him establish permanent dietary practices which will keep his weight within the normal range.

When there is a combination of underweight and illness or even a low level of health, it is the province of the medical profession to find the underlying causes. Yet, the observant teacher can initiate the chain reaction which brings the child and physician together. Eliminating the obstacles to good health is more important than bringing the child's weight up to that of the group norm. Putting weight on some of these young bean poles is beyond the ability of the pediatrician. Some underweight children gain a few pounds on a high calorie diet, supplemented by emulsions and a routine of reduced activity and extended rest. Yet, those who remain thin in spite of this special program may well be as healthy and live as long and vibrantly as any of the others.

In practice, the school correlates its efforts with the home and family physician. As a minimum, the teacher should confer with the parents when she is concerned about a child's weight. Usually, the parents, too, are concerned and express the wish that something could be done. Proposing a health examination is in order. From the examination may come a recommended program to which the school may be asked to contribute. Or it may elicit this sage advice from the physician, "The child is healthy and normal in all respects, including weight for his particular constitutional type."

Specific nutritional deficiencies. It obviously is not the role of the teacher to diagnose deficiency diseases. She may suspect that a specific condition is the result of a nutritional deficiency. Perhaps if, as a health project, each child records the family menus for a week, the suspicions of the teacher will receive further support. Yet, in the absence of medical diagnosis and direction, the teacher's province is primarily that of education which results in desirable knowledge, attitudes, and practices. A teacher with ingenuity and a sincere interest in the child can utilize the school lunch, the home, and self-interest to achieve a gradual yet tangible improvement in his general condition. A well-thought-out plan to assure the child of the necessary quality foods is basic. "Drug store vitamins" should not be taken without a physician's prescription.

Endocrine disturbances

Neither the classroom teacher nor the director of the school health program is expected to be an expert on glandular disorders. Yet, an understanding of some of the disorders which may likely be found in a school population can be of value to the teacher and to particular children. Parents and the teacher's school superiors hold in high regard the teacher who understands children with special problems.

Diabetes mellitus. Although it is generally considered a disease of later life since the average age of the more than 1,000,000 diabetic persons in the United States is 55 years, diabetes mellitus does occur among school-age children and occasionally among preschool children. Medical authorities point out that for every four known cases, three unrecognized cases of diabetes exist.

Most persons who have diabetes can keep well and lead healthful and useful lives. Careful attention to the physician's instructions can safeguard the subject's health. In this respect the school can be of appreciable service to the diabetic student.

Diabetes mellitus is usually due to a deficiency in the insulin output of the Islands of Langerhans in the pancreas. It also may be due to a deficiency of the glycogenic hormone of the anterior pituitary gland. A deficiency of these hormones results in a high level of blood sugar (hyperglycemia) and sugar in the urine (glycosuria). Lassitude and weariness result; there is a pronounced thirst after meals, and, with the subsequent consumption of water, there is frequent urination. Increased hunger, a drawn expression, and loss of weight may occur. The mouth is dry; the tongue red and sore. Dry skin, itching, eczema, and boils occur. The eyes are affected, and neuritis, numbness, and tingling of the hands and feet occur. Marked weakness results from the inability of the muscles to use available fuel.

Some diabetic students may be on a restricted diet, which may be sufficient to control the condition. The physician or parents should inform the school of the prescribed diet and routine for physical activity. The teacher should guide the child in adherence to the prescription. In the absence of such information, the teacher will have to regard the child as any normal member of the group.

A child under insulin treatment will probably receive his injection at least an hour before coming to school. The peak of the effect may occur a short time after he arrives at school. Or it may appear late in the afternoon, and a low blood sugar level (hypoglycemia) may result. The condition is commonly spoken of as insulin shock and is characterized by trembling, faintness, palpitation, unsteadiness, excessive perspiration, and hunger. Orange juice, which contains carbohydrates, produces recovery in a few minutes. Some children carry a supply of carbohydrates and begin to ingest them immediately upon the appearance of symptoms. The other children soon accept the procedure, and it becomes part of the school life. It is indicative of a mentally hygienic school environment.

Hyperthyroidism. A youngster with a basal metabolic rate above plus 10 may be considered to have a hyperthyroid condition. During childhood the child is healthy, thin, but strikingly robust, active, energetic, high-strung, and perhaps nervous and highly excitable. He never seems to tire and seldom is ill. As an adolescent he may be a restless, energetic person who is a perpetual doer and worker. He may be impatient and impulsive. Life is at a maximum function for this person from early in the morning until late at night. To be idle is his biggest trial.

The need for a routine or plan for everyday living is urgent with some of these children. In this, guidance from the teacher can be helpful. To harness this energy and direct it into productive channels is the objective. Routinization of the day helps to slow down the dizzy pace.

Persons with excessive hyperthyroidism obviously need medical supervision.

Hypothyroidism. Children with extreme hypothyroidism (cretinism) do not attend school, but children with marked thyroxin deficiency are present in our classrooms. They are disinterested and slow, need constant coaxing and forcing, are chronically late, and do poorly in their school work. They perspire very little, have a slow reaction time, fatigue easily, sleep heavily, and are often accused of being lazy loafers. Life is a real effort for these children. In practice, teachers should exercise patience and strive to understand the child's limitations. A duty-possessed teacher who lacks understanding could do infinite harm by harassing such children every hour of the day.

Endocrine therapy can do much for these students. Frequently treatment transforms them into alert, energetic, active, and bright-eyed children who for the first time, as expressed by one of them, "Really know what it is like to live." Sometimes at puberty, nature brings about this sudden reversal from a dull, lackadaisical child to a highly colored, vivacious adolescent.

Rheumatic fever

Rheumatic fever is an insidious disease which overtakes a child stealthily. Though it undoubtedly is infectious, the causative agent is not known. However, physicians generally agree that certain types of infection are forerunners of rheumatic fever. These are the streptococcal infections such as scarlet fever and infections of the throat. From this primary infection two additional phases can be delineated in the evolution of rheumatic fever.

1. Middle phase—dormant phase which lasts two or three weeks after the sore throat and during which no visible symptoms appear; child seems to be completely recovered from sore throat
2. Final phase—acute rheumatic fever which lasts from two or three weeks to several months

Although most afflicted children have the services of a physician and the condition diagnosed, some children appear in the classroom without the benefit of medical advice. It is not the province of the teacher to diagnose rheumatic fever, but the teacher who recognizes certain danger signals can contribute immeasurably to the child's welfare by bringing the matter to the attention of the parents. Early detection may prevent the most serious complication—rheumatic heart disease.

Specific symptoms for every case of rheumatic fever do not exist, but enumeration of the various symptoms which have been observed will encompass the symptoms of any specific case. They include fever, irritability, undue fatigue, nosebleeds, pallor, pain in the joints, arms, and legs, jerky and twitching motions, poor appetite, loss of weight, and a lack of interest in school activities. The teacher will make no mistake in contacting the parents of a child with various of these symptoms because there obviously is something wrong with the child and he should not be in school.

Prevention of rheumatic fever. Rheumatic fever is not communicable; therefore prevention is directed toward the conditions which are forerunners of it. Prevention of the spread of throat infections in the school indirectly should have an effect on reducing the incidence of rheumatic fever. Prompt medical treatment for any throat infection may prevent it from becoming the forerunner of rheumatic fever.

Since rheumatic fever tends to run in families, members of the patient's family should be informed of the need for a well-balanced diet, adequate rest, early treatment of respiratory infections, and regular medical supervision. A child with rheumatic fever will receive long-term medication from his physician to prevent repeated attacks.

Classroom adjustment. When the child who has recovered from rheumatic fever returns to the classroom, the teacher will be guided by the instructions of the family physician. If the disease has impaired the heart, a well-planned program will be proposed to the school, but, if no cardiac complications have occurred, the child should be made to feel that he is a normal member of the group. Participation within his limits is imperative for the child. Overprotection produces feelings of dependence and anxiety. Confidence of the child in his ability to live normally is worth cultivating.

Cardiovascular disorders

Approximately 1% of school children in the United States have a diagnosed cardiac disorder. Together, rheumatic fever and its accessory, rheumatic heart disorder, cause more disability than any other disease of childhood. A second important cardiac disorder of childhood is congenital heart defect. In both congenital heart defect and rheumatic heart disorder, the everyday management or supervision of the child is all-important. A teacher who knows what should and can be done is in a position to make an invaluable contribution to the well-being of the child.

Congenital heart defects. A child may be born with a defective heart. Some defects are so severe that the child does not survive to school age. Others are of such a nature that the child can attend school. Some congenital heart conditions can benefit from surgery; others cannot be helped by methods now known. Some congenital heart disorders are so minor that they can almost be ignored. Others are not serious enough to prevent a child from attending school; yet he is in need of everyday supervision and management. From this range in degree of defect, it is apparent that some knowledge of these defects will enable the teacher to cooperate effectively with the child's physician and fully understand his instructions.

Many cardiac patients can participate in the regular classroom activities. Restriction or limitation should not be imposed except upon instruction from the child's physician. Many of these children limit their own activity when necessary because of the distress of fatigue. A physician may rule out competitive sports for a child because in the excitement of competition he may be oblivious of fatigue. Restrictions imposed by the physician are only those which must be imposed because, for him to be mentally healthy, it is desirable that the child live as normal a life as possible. It is essential that the child develop a wholesome, positive attitude toward his capacities and abilities. His teacher should emphasize what he can do and give less emphasis to what he cannot do if he is on a restrictive regimen.

Rheumatic heart disease. Two out of three rheumatic fever patients suffer damaged hearts. A single attack may cause minor damage, but recurrence of the disease will likely cause further damage to the heart. Regular medical supervision can prevent attacks from recurring.

During the acute stage of the infection the heart muscle may be affected. This muscle inflammation (myocarditis) may weaken and enlarge the heart. At times the outer heart covering is inflamed (pericarditis). As the infection declines, the heart tends to return to normal size. Permanent injury usually is due to the inflammation of the valves of the left half of the heart. During the healing process, scar tissue forms, which prevents the valves from opening or closing properly.

About a third of the children with rheumatic fever show no evidence of heart damage; about one third more show signs of cardiac injury, but can lead practically normal lives.

In practice, the school should be governed by the instructions of the physician in charge of the case. No limitations should be placed upon the child except those advised by the physician. From the physician's advice the teacher makes such classroom adaptations as are indicated. Such adjustments may include permission for the child to be late to school, special transportation, restricted recess and physical education activity, minimum of stair climbing, between-meal lunches, and rest periods. So far as possible, the child should be made to feel that he is not abnormal but can, with some exceptions, participate in the regular work of the classroom.

If the child should experience a cardiac crisis, the teacher should allow him to assume a comfortable position. He may find it comfortable to lie flat, but, if the child has difficulty in breathing, he should be permitted to sit up. Giving him plenty of air and loosening his clothing may be of help. The poise of the teacher while waiting for the physician will be important in effecting composure in both the subject and his classmates.

Hypertension. High blood pressure is not frequent among children of school age, but it does occasionally occur among boys of high school age. Among girls of this age the condition is extremely unusual. High blood pressure (hypertension) is not due to a disorder of the walls of the arteries, but perhaps to overstimulation of the vasoconstrictor nerve fibers which govern the contraction of the arteries. This excessive contraction of the vessels indirectly produces an elevation in blood pressure. Certain renal, endocrine, vascular, and cerebral disorders may also account for hypertension.

Even in a normal person systolic blood pressure may vary considerably, but in hypertension the systolic pressure consistently will be above 160 mm. Hg. Sometimes the condition is functional, being due to mental and emotional tensions. If their tensions are relieved, these persons improve considerably. Sometimes the condition is organic, perhaps due to a substance produced in the kidneys which affects the vasoconstrictor center of the brain. It is from this center that impulses which travel along the vasoconstrictor nerve fibers originate.

In practice, the school should rely upon the student's family physician for guidance in making any necessary provisions for students with hypertension. Some physicians forbid participation in vigorous athletics, but otherwise approve the normal activities of a typical high school. With this prescription the student enjoys a normal existence. Often, the vascular pressure returns to normal.

Anemia

Anemia literally means without blood (Gr. *an,* without; *haima,* blood), but in its practical sense anemia means a condition in which the red corpuscle count or the hemoglobin content of the blood is low or both deficiencies are present. Actually, anemia is not a specific disease, but a symptom which may arise from various causes.

Skin color is not an index to the condition of the blood. Pallor, of itself, does not denote anemia. Pale lips and fingernails may be somewhat indicative, and a pale inner lining (conjunctiva) of the eyelid may be associated with anemia. A better general indication is the lack of vitality and endurance of the child. Since oxygen available for the tissues depends upon adequate red corpuscles and hemoglobin content, the anemic child becomes breathless quickly and is unusually fatigued and uncomfortable. Surprisingly, some anemic children will not be denied in physical contests and will exert themselves to the limit to keep up with the group. Anemic children frequently are missed until a physician makes a count of the red corpuscles and a hemoglobin determination.

Anemia occurs most frequently among girls. Perhaps biologically girls are more prone to anemia, but usually the condition is preventable.

Several classes of anemia are recognized, but two of them are most likely to be found in children of school age. Other types occur rather infrequently.

Chlorosis, which is the anemia of preteen-aged children, occurs among girls and results in a sallow complexion. It occurs less frequently than formerly because of improved nutrition. In most girls with this type, the anemia is due to poor nutrition although sometimes it is due to the inability of the red marrow cells to produce sufficient red corpuscles.

The most frequent type of anemia which occurs in school-age children is *nutritional anemia* due to dietary deficiencies or the inability of the body to utilize the constituents of the diet. Iron, proteins, and copper are essential for the production of red corpuscles. Yet, the human male needs only about 0.006 to 0.010 grams of iron daily since the iron fraction of hemoglobin is used over and over again. A female needs four times as much iron as a male. Too much milk in the diet may displace such valued sources of iron and protein as egg yolk, liver, and other meats.

In the school, anemic children may be helped by supplementary feedings, reduced activity, and extra periods of rest. However, primary supervision of the child should be by the physician who likely will prescribe medication to stimulate the production of red corpuscles and formation of hemoglobin. If a child who lacks normal vitality is not under medical supervision, the teacher performs a service by arranging for a thorough health checkup for him.

Deviations of the respiratory system

Some noninfectious chronic conditions of the respiratory system are of minor consequences. Others are significant in terms of reducing the effectiveness and enjoyment of life. Occasionally, life itself may be threatened.

Nasal congestion. All persons experience some congestion of the nasal passages, but usually it is a temporary condition due to an excessive production of mucus associated with coryza or other respiratory infection. While it is temporarily distressing, the accumulation of mucus is not serious, being a natural response to irritation of the mucous tissue. A chronic or permanent congestion may be caused by mucus or can be a mechanical obstruction such as a stemmed growth (polyp) of mucous tissue. Except for the inconvenience, some of these congestions are not too serious; whereas others need constant medical care or to be corrected by surgery.

Sinusitis. The sinuses of the skull are air cavities lined with the same type of mucous tissue which lines the nasal passages. Two frontal sinuses, one above each orbit, and two maxillary sinuses, one in each upper jaw bone beneath the orbits, have narrow passageways, or ducts, which empty into the nasal passages. Exhaled and inhaled air passes into the ducts and sinuses. These structures properly are considered part of the respiratory tract. Even normally the mucous tissue lining the sinuses secretes a small to moderate amount of mucus. Mechanical or bacterial irritation can produce an excessive amount of mucus (ozena), with resulting congestion. Until the irritation is removed, the overproduction of mucus is likely to continue. Persons with constricted ducts may have sinus congestion, with devastating pain.

To use home or patented remedies to deal with excessive mucus is fraught with considerable danger. Nasal sprays that contain astringents may constrict blood vessels and, for a while, reduce mucus output. However, these sprays in time will be highly irritating to the sensitive tissue, and serious damage may result.

In practice, the school should identify children with chronic sinusitis and set into action the chain of events which will bring the child into the office of a physician. If a cure is not possible, the physician at least will relieve the child of much of his distress.

Deviated septum. At least half of the adults in the United States have some degree of deviation of the partition which separates the nares, but most deviations are of no particular significance. Deviation can occur without a nasal fracture.

In children, only when the deviation is so pronounced that one of the nasal passages is closed will surgery be advised by the physician. When the condition is so markedly pronounced, the teacher will observe that, though the youngster has no difficulty in breathing under ordinary conditions, slight exertion requires mouth breathing. Closing the open nares by pressure with the finger and asking the child to exhale forcibly will indicate the degree of obstruction in the other passage. Mouth breathing is not necessarily objectionable, but the chronic condition which produces it usually requires correction.

Enlarged turbinate bones. On the lateral surface of the nares, the scroll-shaped turbinate bones may be sufficiently enlarged to obstruct breathing. It is an infrequent condition in children, but, if present, is discovered in the typical health examination of school children. Excessive production of mucus, as well as any obstruction in the nasal passage, is a discomfort, if not a hazard to well-being.

Allergy. Hypersensitivity can affect the respiratory tract in a variety of ways. Hay fever, bronchial asthma, bronchitis, and croup are end products of allergies which affect the respiratory system. While some of these conditions exist when the child enters school, others do not show up until the child is in his teen years. Sometimes, allergies do not appear until adulthood. Because of the factor of inheritance, a child with a family history of allergy should be considered to have a possible respiratory allergy if he displays chronic respiratory disturbances while in school. Unwittingly, some teachers, suspecting an infectious condition, exclude a child from school only to discover that he has an allergy. Had they studied the health record form of these students, they might have avoided this embarrassment.

Under medical supervision, a child with a respiratory allergy usually carries on the normal activities of school life. An asthmatic attack in school may appear dramatic, but should not be alarming. Usually the student himself knows what action to take. A sitting position is usually more comfortable than any other. For many children, exhalation is the more difficult mechanism, and a siege may leave them near exhaustion. Poise and assurance on the part of the teacher may help the student to relax.

Disorders of the oral cavity

Disorders of the oral cavity are not an urgent life-and-death matter; yet they play an important role in the quality of health, the length of the prime of life, and life expectation. Early detection and correction are dictated if the child's present and future well-being are considered.

Caries and cavities. The process of dental decay is called caries; the end result of decay is the cavity. The process is initiated by the *Lactobacillus acidophilous* (L.A.) organism and can be expressed in the equation

L.A. → enzyme + carbohydrate = acid. Disintegration of the enamel occurs as the acid dissolves it.

Dental cavities occur more frequently than any other disorder that school children experience. Yet, of itself, a simple cavity may have no effect upon health. However, it may progress to a point at which the tooth is destroyed or must be extracted. Loss of several teeth, without compensating dentures, can affect a person's dietary practices. More serious, the cavity can be an avenue of invasion for disease-producing organisms which can pass, via the pulp cavity, to the apex of the tooth root and produce an abscess.

It is not the province of the teacher to examine children's mouths. To prevent the children from having caries, she can carry on a program to encourage effective practices of dental care, including a visit to the dentist at least twice a year. Whenever a child with a special dental health problem comes to her attention, counseling an immediate visit to the dentist is the minimum service she owes to the child.

Abscess. An infection in the gum or at the apex of a tooth root may be painful or virtually painless. Toxins produced at the abscess can travel about the body and cause serious impairment of vital tissues. Any gum involvement, including the familiar gum boil, which is an abscess, is a warning of the need for immediate professional attention. Prompt action may save the tooth and prevent injury to the general health.

Pyorrhea. Pyorrhea is an infectious or mechanical irritation of the periodontal membrane which attaches the tooth to the gum and bone. A red margin of the gum around the neck of the tooth is indicative of this irritation. If permitted to continue, the irritation may seriously damage the membrane. Since the periodontal membrane does not have the capacity to rejuvenate itself, the tooth becomes permanently loosened and may have to be extracted.

Gingivitis. Any inflammation of the gum may be termed gingivitis, but in its general usage the term designates infection by two known pathogens, *Bacillus fusiformis* and *Borrelia vincenti*. Commonly called trench mouth, or Vincent's disease, the condition is characterized by inflammation and even ulceration of the gums and other parts of the mouth, bleeding, excess salivation, and considerable soreness.

Gingivitis does not often occur in the healthy child. Malnutrition, poor general health, inadequate rest, and poor mouth care predispose to gingivitis. The infection can be treated successfully by the dentist, but improvement in general health also should be sought.

Malocclusion. Marked overbite or underbite or poorly aligned teeth should be considered mental health problems primarily. For children with these conditions, the services of an orthodontist is a necessity, not a luxury. Before their school days are over, by some means, these children should have the services of an orthodontist. Once the teeth are permanently set, as in adulthood, it may be too late. Correction of these conditions when a child is 15 years of age or younger means a possible 70 years of benefit. A conscientious teacher will do everything possible to see that the child receives the necessary service. The child is not the only one to benefit. Nothing in the teacher's professional experience is more gratifying than to watch the change in a child who has benefited from the wonders of orthodontal science.

Disorders of vision

With a function as complex as vision and a structure as remarkable as the human eye, the wonder is that the incidence of defective vision is not greater. Every school expects to have children whose vision is not normal. Standard screening tests usually detect children with more pronounced vision disability, and a professional practitioner's examination will locate even the slightest disability. Teachers who observe their students closely can be helpful in detecting a child whose posturing, squinting, inattention, or poor progress may be due to his inability to see normally.

Myopia. Nearsightedness is a heritable tendency and is usually due to elongated eyeballs. The image falls in front of the retina unless the object is close to the eye. Thus, close objects can be seen quite clearly, but distant objects are blurred. Fortunately, concave lenses will compensate for the extra length of the eye bulb. Though the nearsighted child may be able to read without glasses, he will become less distressed and fatigued with proper glasses. He also will see better at various ranges.

Hyperopia. Farsightedness is due to an eyeball so short that the image literally falls behind the retina. With a great deal of effort, a farsighted child can see near objects by overworking the delicate muscles of accommodation. Visual fatigue sets in very quickly with such strain. A tendency to become cross-eyed is possible. Convex lenses can compensate for the farsightedness so that the child can read with a minimum of strain and fatigue.

Astigmatism. Irregularities in the curvature of the cornea and lens prevent a true focus of the eye, and a blurred image with discomfort results. Astigmatism requires carefully prescribed glasses and, in some instances, frequent renewal of the prescription. Contact lenses frequently prove highly satisfactory. For effective and enjoyable living, the child with astigmatism needs glasses of accurate prescription.

Amblyopia. Dimness of vision without known cause can occur in people of all ages. No discernible lesion in the eye structures is present. A disturbance in the optic nerve is a possible cause. It is known that certain metallic poisons, certain toxins, alcohol, tobacco, and uremic conditions can be responsible for the disturbance, but in children usually no specific cause can be identified.

Amblyopia may begin with a central or peripheral spot where there is little vision. The condition may enlarge slowly and will progressively interfere with vision. Visual disturbance will be more pronounced **in bright light.**

Fortunately, amblyopia in children usually clears up spontaneously, but every child with dimness of vision should be under the supervision of an ophthalmologist for periodic checkups.

Strabismus. Cross-eye, not cross-eyes, is descriptive of strabismus because only one eye is crossed, due to a shortened extrinsic muscle which turns the eye inward. Ophthalmologists can correct many conditions of strabismus by treatment or by surgery or a combination of procedures. Early attention to the condition is essential. The accommodation or acuity of one or both eyes may be affected in some children if the condition is untreated. Such children exhibit posturing and other signs of difficult vision. The alert teacher will call this difficulty to the attention of the child's parents.

Ptosis. A drooping of one or both upper eyelids is usually an inherited condition in which the nerves which stimulate the elevating muscle do not conduct impulses. Paralysis of the muscle may come on gradually during the school life of the child. Nothing now known to medical science can be done to prevent or correct the condition. If the paralysis is bilateral, the child will naturally tilt his head back in order to see through the small apertures formed by the backward tilt of the head.

Hearing disability

Most children who have some hearing loss acquire it gradually. The whisper test or the audiometric test will detect hearing disabilities, but the teacher can observe indications that a child has hearing difficulties. Children who cannot hear will often posture, are inattentive, copy, and make poor progress. Faulty pronunciation and an unnatural voice are hints that the child does not hear well.

Conduction deafness. Almost all hearing loss in children is due to disturbances of the outer and middle ear which interfere with the conduction of sound. Excessive wax (cerumen), ruptured or rigid tympanic membrane, rigidity of the ligaments of the bones of the middle ear (ossicles), mucus congestion of the middle ear, and rigidity of the oval window of the spiral shell (cochlea) all can interfere with sound conduction. Some of these conditions can be corrected, and most are amenable to treatment.

In addition to letting the parents know that a child has a hearing defect, the teacher can be of further service by helping children to understand that wearing a hearing aid is a sensible thing and not a stigma. How fortunate the child is to have a disability for which science has a relatively simple solution rather than to have some disability for which nothing can be done.

Neurological disorders

Two neurological disorders, epilepsy and chorea, from which occasional students suffer and which cause the uninformed teacher considerable concern, are worthy of discussion. An understanding of the two conditions and the proper care of the afflicted children gives a teacher the assurance necessary for dealing with any episode involving these children.

Epilepsy. From its Greek derivation, the word epilepsy literally means a seizure. Being merely descriptive of clinical symptoms, the term is not satisfactory, but it usually is used to designate recurrent fits and periods of unconsciousness.

The more serious type of epilepsy is called grand mal and essentially is a convulsive seizure with the following characteristics:

1. Aura, or sensory disturbance, e.g., light or taste, sometimes precedes and gives warning of the attack
2. Shrill and startling cry sometimes
3. Sudden loss of consciousness and falling backward
4. Pupils dilated; eyes open at beginning of seizure
5. Tonic spasm—drawing up limbs in rigid, flexed position
6. Clonic spasm—intermittent contraction and relaxation with thrashing about of arms and legs
7. Spasm of respiratory muscles—no breathing and blueness of the face
8. Spasm of the jaw muscles—biting the tongue results in bloody foam
9. Relaxation, prolonged stupor, and profound sleep

The active convulsion lasts less than a minute and terminates in exhaustion. During the seizure an attempt should be made to protect the child from injury. It is sometimes possible to catch him before he strikes the floor. Moving the child out into a clear space away from hot and sharp objects may prevent injury. The seizure should not be resisted.

Typical minor attacks (petit mal) are characterized by a transitory (3 or 4 seconds) loss of consciousness without falling and only minor, if any, muscular twitching.

Children with petit mal attend school without any particular incidents. Children with grand mal who have only two or three seizures during the school year usually continue school attendance. When seizures become so frequent as to disrupt the school, serious consideration should be given that the child remain at home until medication can control the seizures somewhat. The cause of epilepsy is unknown, but sedatives can reduce the severity of seizures and increase the length of time between seizures.

Chorea. Commonly called St. Vitus' Dance, chorea is characterized by convulsive twitchings, especially of the facial muscles. Grimaces and arm and body jerking occur, with some remission from time to time. The disorder usually follows a siege of rheumatic fever or other infection, which sometimes has gone undiscovered. Toxins appear to affect one of the motor control centers of the brain and the incoordination results. Most of these children can be treated very effectively.

Because of the effectiveness of modern treatment, children with chorea are not encountered as frequently in school as in former years.

Yet, they do appear. After ascertaining that the child is under medical care, the teacher should try to treat him as a normal member of the class. It may be helpful for the child to avoid undue excitement and fatigue. If a child with chorea is not under treatment, the school should takes steps necessary to make medical care available to him.

Delayed maturation and growth

A typical school population will have children who are retarded in either or both maturation and growth. Most of these children show little concern over their delayed growing up, and there is no reason why the teacher should be concerned and thereby disturb the child. So long as he possesses a good level of health, the teacher should accept the child as a normal member of the group. In all likelihood, the child's physician will have nothing to offer which might hasten growth and maturity and will not deem any action on his part necessary. Eventually the child will mature into adulthood. Though the student may never attain average adult height and weight, growth will take place. To assure a disturbed child, especially a boy, that his final level of growth and development will be within the normal range is a service which the teacher can contribute to the children concerned about delayed growth and development.

Accelerated maturation and growth

Whereas boys show most concern about delayed growth and development, girls are more likely to be disturbed by acceleration of maturation and growth. Yet, girls can be assured that there are many illustrious women who have travelled the same road. To adapt to her situation is the girl's goal. To despair is to take an emotional approach. If the precocity is due to an overactive adrenal cortex or other physical cause, usually little or nothing can be done. Sometimes the accelerated maturation and growth level off while the child is relatively young, and she attains adult physiological maturity and growth at 15 years of age. A person who understands his assets and places primary emphasis on these will usually make a wholesome adjustment. Indeed, many make these assets the springboard to outstanding achievement.

Deviations in mental health

Major and minor mental disorders are the province of the medical profession, but the teaching profession is in a most strategic position to give wholesome, positive assistance to the child who exhibits personality deviations. Most of these deviations are not serious, but they do detract from the child's effectiveness and enjoyment in life and may become serious if nothing constructive is done to correct the deviation.

In undertaking to aid a child with a personality deviation, the teacher must obtain as complete an understanding of the child and his background as is practical. Then the teacher must strive to answer the cardinal question, "What motivates this conduct?" Any constructive program of readjustment is certain to yield the child some benefit and in many cases will produce the optimum of readjustment.

Undue shyness. A shy child is a lonesome child. The shyness may be an expression of too marked a feeling of inferiority. It may be a fear of failure or embarrassment. It can be mere habit. It may be a lack of preschool opportunities to associate with children of the same age. It can be a reaction to imaginary guilt.

A teacher with ingenuity will contrive situations in which the child will associate closely with one, two, and then several of the group. If the shyness is to be overcome, it is essential that a child be brought gradually into the activities of the group. It is most helpful for the teacher to express high regard for the child and to point out that his classmates regard him highly, too. The solution is gradual readjustment, not medical treatment.

Tendency to be a lone wolf. The child who seeks to be alone, to do everything on his own, may never have learned to play or work with others. He may not feel equal to the group or may feel that the group does not accept him. Perhaps his home background or an imaginary deficiency is the genesis of the tendency.

Constructive readjustment would require opportunities for group participation, perhaps indirectly at first. Self-esteem must be bolstered, particularly in terms of contributions to the class and school.

Restlessness and easy distraction. A thyroid disorder, malnutrition or inadequate rest may be the cause of restlessness. Uneasiness may be due to a feeling of inadequateness. Lack of success and subsequent gratification may lead to disinterest.

If physical disturbances have been ruled out, a child should be motivated to take an interest in school activities by assistance in attaining success and learning to enjoy his success. If the child has a short attention span, a reshuffling of his daily schedule may be helpful.

Excessive daydreaming. Physical health may be of significance in accounting for this state. Inadequate rest, visual fatigue, and a low level of vitality may be present. A lack of success, with a resulting escape into phantasy, may be the primary factor. A child who gets self-gratification entirely in a dream world must be brought out into the world of reality through assigned tasks which require that he take attention away from himself.

Anxiety states. An overanxious, tense, apprehensive child shows an inability to relax. Fear of censorship, fear of punishment, or fear of failure may underlie the state. Identification with an older person who is tense and unrelaxed can be the source of the child's tenseness.

Helping a child to assess his own abilities and success can yield tangible results. These children need to be assured of the importance of their role in the home, in school, and with their associates. That he is held in high esteem by those about him can be helpful. Readjustment usually is a slow process.

Sitting on sidelines. Frequently from mere habit, some children have been conditioned to be spectators, not participants. The busy elementary school teacher unintentionally permits children to slide into this mode of life. In other children, fear of failure or embarrassment can be primary factors. The child who likes to be coaxed is usually seeking attention in a manner society does not approve.

Devising situations in which the child is naturally a participant is not difficult. If the new practice is associated with success, it will likely become habitual.

Hysteria. Occasionally a child of school age will display hysteria. This type of person usually is highly unstable and has a tendency toward explosive conduct. Adjustment generally is inadequate. In true hysteria a person may become unconscious or semiconscious, with an absence of sensation. A form of functional paralysis may result. The whole episode is an unwhosesome escape from reality. Paralysis is imaginary and can be removed merely by the suggestion that the paralysis is gone. The great need of this person is insight into his real motives, with guidance in learning to adjust wholesomely to frustration and conflict.

In pseudohysteria a person may go into a tantrum or a violent display of temper. Helping him to see himself as others see him is essential. The first step in readjustment is for others to disregard the tantrum or display. Rebuilding his ability to adjust to the trials of life may be a long process.

Some pseudohysteria is passive. As an attention-getting device a child may feign that he has fainted. The less attention given to him, the sooner recovery will occur. This child will abandon this form of behavior as soon as it becomes apparent that others know why he does it.

Chip on the shoulder. The belligerent, pugnacious, quarrelsome youngster is the defensive youngster. Perhaps an exaggerated feeling of inferiority, a feeling of rejection, or a defensiveness because of a lack of status can account for this personality mold. Perhaps the youngster cannot find success in his school life and other activities and resorts to the one superior attribute he has—physical force. There is some suggestion that inward physiological tensions may underlie belligerent behavior. Whatever the underlying cause, this type of youngster is in need of help to understand himself, to attain status in his group, and to find success in the normal pursuits of childhood.

Suspiciousness. Occasionally, a child may be overly suspicious, exhibiting a marked distrust of others, even to the point of suspecting everyone of taking advantage of him or her. This defensiveness may express an extreme insecurity and perhaps inadequateness. The home situation may be reflected in the attitudes and general conduct of the child.

Selfishness. A youngster who lacks consideration for others and is possessive particularly in relation to material things even to the extent of being greedy may merely have acquired a distorted set of values. Insecurity can account for the egomania expressed in extreme selfishness. Such youngsters can acquire new values under a regime which emphasizes respect and consideration for others and the importance of other than material things.

Excessive moodiness. The depressed or moody youngster usually lacks incentive or purpose in life. A child coming from a home in which life is a terribly gloomy affair may reflect this in school life. Perhaps a physiological basis does exist, but, whatever the youngster's physiological endowment, he can be challenged through worthwhile purposes. He can attain and receive desirable self-gratification from accomplishment.

Exaggerated emotionalism. An overly responsive child, even the overly dramatic child, expresses a pattern outside of the normal. The child who is ecstatic one moment and in the depths of sadness or depression in the next exhibits an unhealthy emotional instability. Whether this expresses an attention-getting attempt or other motive, the child can be benefited by helping him or her to understand that such extreme emotionalism is neither usual nor acceptable.

Hypochondria. The child who finds he or she can get attention by having a pain or other physical complaint may resort to this ruse whenever an uncomfortable or trying situation is encountered. Expression of an imaginary pain can be an escape mechanism or an attention-getting device. Perhaps the school has failed to give the child the recognition he or she should have from normal acceptable accomplishment or performance. However, distinguishing true pain from pseudo pain is not always a simple task. To make too big an issue of the matter, whether in error or in truth, can compound the problem. When there is little doubt that the pain is imaginary, then obtaining a statement from a physician that no physical disorder exists is a desirable first step. A matter-of-fact approach suggesting the pain is leaving can produce a surprisingly effective acceptance by the younger. On the impressionable child the effect of suggestion may not be spectacular, but suggestion can help to produce the desired wholesome outlook of the normal child.

Mental health promotion

Education accepts as both a professional obligation and a privilege the opportunity to promote the mental, emotional, and social, as well as the physical, growth of the child. All children can be helped in their total growth. The normal child can attain an even higher level of mental, emotional, and social growth with effective supervision. Those children with minor mental and emotional disabilities can overcome their difficulties when understanding and dedicated teachers give these children the necessary insight and guidance. Many of the lesser behavior problems can be managed in the classroom. Even the children with marked or gross emotional difficulties can be helped by direct and indirect action by the school.

Mental health programming in the classroom usually is not formally structured. Yet, a recognizable program usually is in operation in schools in which there is an awareness of the opportunity to make the greatest possible contribution to the over-all development of each youngster. Such a program logically has four basic aspects.

First is a mentally hygienic environment in which each child feels he has status, is accepted by classmates and teacher, is challenged to develop his abilities, and succeeds to a gratifying degree. A teacher cannot create a perfect environment, but can create one which, though not perfect, can provide for a high level of emotional, mental, and social development for most, if not all, students. This situation is not attained by chance. It results from planning and application.

Group social interaction can be used to the benefit of all youngsters in the classroom. It means tailoring the school life to the patterns of living which provide opportunities for varieties of human interaction.

There are certain things that rightfully can be expected of the teacher in the role of an educator.

1. Understand his or her own behavior
2. Separate personal problems from the classroom and school life
3. Respect each youpngster
4. Understand individual differences
5. Understand the cause-and-effect relationship of deviant behavior
6. Maintain an atmosphere not too rigid or severe, nor too permissive
7. Strengthen desirable behavior through recognition and even praise
8. Deal with behavior problems not serious enough for professional care
9. Substitute acceptable behavior for deviant behavior

Second is the individual guidance the teacher gives individual youngsters. An able, discerning, understanding, conscientious teacher who seeks to know each child, his strengths, his weaknesses, and particularly his needs can guide into the proper channels those youngsters who have special problems in emotional and social adjustment. This implies a person-to-person, or a one-to-one, approach. It requires some degree of ability in counseling, in understanding the child, and in assisting the child to understand himself. Mutual deliberation enables the child to develop his ability to deal with his own problems.

Third is the organized, cooperative, total guidance program of the school or the school system which is designed to deal with gross emotional or mental health difficulties. It begins with the general observation of the classroom teacher and his or her recognition of the problem. Staff conferences, discussions with the nurse, doctor, principal, school counselor, and parents may lead to the necessary action to deal with the problem of the child under consideration. Fortunately, more people are being prepared to aid the classroom teacher in working with problems of deviant behavior in students.

Fourth is the use of consulting services other than those in the school. Referral is through the parents to the professional services a particular youngster may need. Public schools generally have not accepted the use of outside professional mental health services, preferring to leave entirely to the parents any decision in this sphere which should be made. Schools must reconsider their reluctance to recommend that the services of a professional mental hygienist be obtained for a grossly maladjusted child. The stigma of mental and emotional deviation has dimmed in recent years, and the school should not be reluctant to recommend the employment of available community professional services when the school has exhausted its own resources or recognizes its own inability to be of value to the child. A youngster with 60 or more years of life ahead of him is entitled to the best possible start on this long journey.

Appraisal

The age-old aphorism, "Know the child," should be extended to, "and know what might befall the child." A teacher has no acknowledged final legal responsibility for a child's health, but educators recognize a professional responsibility for the welfare of each school child. This obligation is most fully discharged when the teacher understands deviations as well as the normal. This basic understanding translated into action through continual alertness cannot but resound to the benefit of every student under the supervision of a teacher with this competence. Transposed into numbers represented by an entire staff of teachers, it is easy to visualize the possible impact on human health which can be exerted by teachers well prepared to fulfill their school health obligations. Here is opportunity for those who will prepare themselves for this role.

We have seen in this chapter that we are not dealing with something mystical, bewildering, or totally obscure. We deal with those things we can understand, with some conditions in which the teacher can be of primary assistance, and with other conditions in which the knowledgable teacher can play a secondary contributing role. From a modest beginning of basic knowledge, the teacher can continue to extend and expand that knowledge through a combined program of study and practical experience.

Perhaps special emphasis should be given to the likelihood that today children will be in regular attendance in school who but a few years ago would have been invalids at home. This is a result of the phenomenal advances of recent years in the medical field. Physicians may prescribe school attendance for pupils with what appear to be extreme deviations from normal. Yet, as the teacher becomes familiar with the capabilities of these pupils, she or he soon accepts the child as one of the group and easily makes whatever adjustments are indicated. Most important, this growth or maturation in the teacher reflects itself in increased confidence and in a more meaningful service to pupils.

A teacher who feels inadequate to deal with a particular problem in mental health should seek assistance. To disregard the problem or to take a fatalistic point of view is to neglect her professional obligation to help each child attain the highest possible level of effective and enjoyable living.

Selected readings

Children's Bureau: Facts about child health, Washington, D. C., 1946, United States Government Printing Office.

Children's Bureau: Research relating to children, Washington, D. C., 1950, United States Government Printing Office.

Holland, Dorothy F.: The disabling diseases of childhood, Public Health Reports 63:69, 1948.

Hathaway, Winifred: Education and health of the partially seeing child, ed. 4, New York, 1959, Columbia University Press.

Licht, S. H. (editor): Therapeutic exercise, ed. 2, New Haven, Conn., 1961, Physical Medicine Library.

Lippman, H. S.: Treatment of the child in emotional conflict, ed. 2, New York, 1962, McGraw-Hill Book Co., Inc.

Maxwell, C. H., and Brown, W. P.: The age-incidence of defects in school children, their changing health status, Journal of School Health, March, 1948.

Mykelbust, H. R.: Auditory disorders in children, New York, 1954, Grune & Stratton, Inc.

National Health Education Committee: Facts on the major killing and crippling diseases in the United States today, New York, 1961, National Health Education Committee, Inc.

National Office of Vital Statistics, Public Health Service, United States Department of Health, Education and Welfare: Health statistics, Washington, D. C., 1959, United States Government Printing Office.

National Office of Vital Statistics, Health and Demography, Washington, D. C., 1962, United States Department of Health, Education and Welfare.

Teicher, J. D.: Your child and his problem, Boston, 1953, Little, Brown & Co.

Turner, C. E., Sellery, C. M., and Smith, Sara L.: School health and health education, ed. 4, St. Louis, 1961, The C. V. Mosby Co.

Ullman, C. A.: Identification of maladjusted school children, Washington, D. C., 1952. United States Department of Health, Education and Welfare, Public Health Monograph no. 7.

Wallin, J. E. W.: Children with mental and physical handicaps, New York, 1949, Prentice-Hall, Inc.

Wolff, G.: Childhood mortality from rheumatic fever and heart diseases, Washington, D. C., 1948, United States Department of Health, Education and Welfare, Children's Bureau Publication no. 322.

Part 2

Organization of the school health program

All are born to observe order,
but few are born to establish it.

—Joubert

Chapter 6

Basic plan of the health program

basic plan or blueprint is essential to any important undertaking, particularly one such as the school health program which is expected to deal with the diversity of factors and situations related to human well-being. Although the plan for school health must have a basic pattern or framework, it should be sufficiently flexible to adapt to any situation or need. To be functional it must be practical. It should be adjusted to the needs of the students and must be in harmony with the background of both the school and the community.

There is no such thing as the only school health program. Many plans have their merits. However, in the interest of clarity and emphasis the discussion here will deal only with one basic master plan for a school health program. It is a program which has been highly effective in a diversity of schools and school situations. It is not a visionary paper program, but a realistic one which achieves the objectives of school health work. It can be adapted effectively to schools of various sizes, of different means, and in various situations. It can be used in its entirety, or, as circumstances may require, certain phases can be used while other phases may be omitted. It has the essentials for the most ambitious program as well as for the most elemental or limited program.

Authorization of school health programs

Inherent in the American system of schools is the principle that the local board of education is responsible for the schools of its district. This principle acknowledges that the closer a governmental agency is to the people, the more likely it is to be in tune with the situation in which it functions. Accordingly, extensive authority and responsibility have been delegated to the local school board. However, state governments, through legislation, have made certain requirements of school districts. In addition state departments of education, through regulation, have set standards which local school districts must meet. Such legislative and regulative requirements have applied to school health programs.

State legislation. Some states have passed permissive or recommendatory legislation which recognizes health promotion as a school function and encourages school health programs. Other states have enacted legislation which requires that each school district provide a health program in order to develop and maintain optimum growth, health, and physical fitness at all age levels. Statutes may further indicate the areas of health instruction and charge the state superintendent of instruction with responsibility for providing materials and advisory services for the schools throughout the state. The state department of education in cooperation with the state department of health may also be required to prescribe a program of health examinations of students in the elementary and secondary schools. The state superintendent of public instruction is charged with the implementation and enforcement of these statutes. Enforcement is exercised through school standardization requirements.

Among other requirements, in order to qualify as standard, the school district must meet the state standards for health services, health instruction, and school sanitation. Failure to meet these requirements may place the district in a probationary status for a specified period of time. Failure to meet requirements within this time period may disqualify the district from participation in certain state school aid funds.

Advocates of legislation to assure health protection and promotion for *every* school child in the state assert that many school boards have very little understanding of school health work. The thinking of board members and administrators is conditioned by the old classical education they received. The practical value of health in the school may not be fully appreciated. State recognition of the importance of health in the school will assure *every* school child of at least a minimum of health promotion and health understanding.

State education department initiative. Some states seek to achieve the same goal through prescription by the state board of education. The state board sets up standards for school health services, health instruction, and sanitation. Districts failing to meet these requirements may be declared nonstandard and ineligible for certain state financial aid.

In practice these provisions are not carried out ruthlessly and dictatorially. Great leniency is granted by giving ample time for the development of health programs. Only in those districts in which the school board or administration actually resists the development of an adequate school health program will the ultimate in enforcement be exercised. The important thing is the health of the students, not the state aid or the prerogative of school boards and administrators.

Responsibilities of the local board of education. Sovereignty or ultimate authority rests with the people. Except such authority as the states have granted to the federal government through the federal constitution, the people have vested their authority in the fifty states to exercise within their own borders. Local governmental units have only such authority as has been granted to them by the state legislature through specific legislation and accepted practice. Unless otherwise specified or prohibited local school boards have broad authority to make such provisions for their schools as they deem necessary to discharge their responsibilities to the school-age children of their districts. From common practice certain authority and responsibility of the school for health promotion have become generally accepted.

1. School health promotion is vested in the board of education. In practice, although the superintendent and his professional staff propose the program, such proposal is merely a recommendation to the board. Only as the board approves the plan can the program have official status. The board can make the program as extensive as it sees fit. It can appropriate such funds as it deems necessary for the health program.

2. All phases of the school health program must comply with state laws and their implementing regulations. In practice the state provisions serve as minimum standards. A board of education properly may set standards or requirements higher than the state provisions, but not lower. If a state statute provides that all students participating in interscholastic athletics must have a health examination before the season in which they are to compete, the local board on its own initiative may also require such an examination of all who participate in intramural sports. What a prudent and far-sighted board that would be!

3. A board of education has the authority to require every child to have a health examination before entering school and at such other times as it deems reasonable. Some boards have made provisions for exceptions on religious grounds. Other boards have made no exceptions, contending that a health examination does not constitute medication. The Washington State Supreme Court has upheld this point of view.

4. A school board can require immunization against a particular disease as a condition for admission to school. Here religious rights definitely do enter in, and provisions for exceptions should be made. In the event of an epidemic or threatened epidemic, the board may exclude those children from school who refuse immunization on religious grounds.

5. The school can pass rules governing school attendance. It can extend this authority to include provisions for exclusion and readmission in control of communicable diseases. Although legal isolation and quarantine are functions of the health department, the school can assert control of communicable diseases so far as they are part of the school program.

6. A board may require daily inspections for indications of communicable disease.

7. A board may require all elementary school teachers to test the hearing and vision of all pupils under their supervision.

8. School boards may specify the areas of health instruction, going beyond any requirements of the state, but including the state requirements in the program.

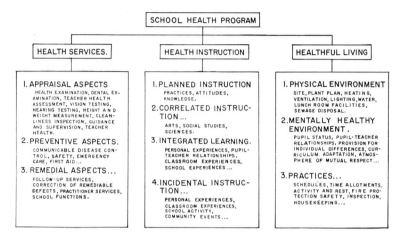

Fig. 7. Organization of the school health program. For purposes of planning and administration, three distinct phases of the program are recognized, but in actual function the three phases constitute a cohesive integrated contribution to the total school program.

Basic divisions of the health program

In a world which gets progressively more complicated, it is refreshing to find a group, especially an education group, which is striving to simplify its program. Two decades ago the school health program in general use consisted of seven phases or divisions. Repeated reassessment and realignment have sifted to the following three basic divisions: (1) school health services, (2) health instruction, and (3) healthful school living.

In a well-integrated school health program no pronounced demarcation of the divisions exists. They are interdependent and support and supplement each other. In actual operation the divisions do not exist; they are essentially creations for organizational and administrative convenience. There is *one* school health program with three different aspects. Whether a particular activity belongs under one aspect or division is primarily academic. How effectively it functions is the significant consideration.

School health services

School health services constitute those school activities directly concerned with the present health status of the school child. It is only natural that the school should concern itself with the health condition of the children because the health of the students and the type of education program in which they participate are interdependent. The child can do his best work only if his health condition will permit him to participate to the extent the school program requires. A child with low vitality will have little interest in any school program. A school program in turn must be adapted to the physiological and emotional health levels as well as the intellectual level of the child. More than this, the program should be designed to develop the highest possible level of physical and emotional health in the child.

In the area of health services the school should be considered the agency which objectively supplements the efforts of the parents in safeguarding and promoting the health of the child. From a vantage point the parents do not enjoy, the school is able to focus daily attention upon the child and trace his health progress as well as detect any obstacles to that progress. To the busy subjective parents this service can provide added insurance that their children's health is given the attention necessary to assure each child of optimum health during his exceedingly important developmental years.

As important as present child health is, well-functioning health services will project their influence into the future years of the child as a mature citizen. The healthy adult whose preadult years were marked by proper supervision of health, growth, and development enjoys a high level of well-being built upon a solid foundation of two decades of planned health promotion. An accumulation of twelve years of organized school health services will have a beneficial effect upon a person's health for the remaining years of his life. The healthy well-educated student in school becomes the effective and happy adult citizen of the community, freely giving of his services and influence to his neighbors and his nation.

Scope. In actual practice, though accessory to the home, the school concerns itself with all phases which affect the child's health. The degree to which the school supplements the efforts of the parents depends upon the circumstances of the home and the child involved.

Some mothers and fathers are highly capable parents with adequate educational, social, and economic backgrounds and are able to guide the health of their children with but little assistance from the school. These parents usually have an understanding appreciation of the efforts and success of the school in safeguarding and promoting the health of their children. Other mothers and fathers are incapable of being parents in the complex social matrix of modern America, and the school necessarily plays the major role in the protection and promotion of the health of their children.

A school board and staff which provide only such health services as states laws and regulations require fail in their obligations to the children of the school. At best, state requirements are only minimum standards, and in some states virtually no health service requirements are specified. A school board has a moral and civic duty to provide the best possible school health program consistent with the situation prevailing in the community. A school staff has a professional obligation to do everything reasonable toward the health of every child in the school. Acting upon staff recommendation the board should approve a health services program which includes appraisal, health guidance and supervision, prevention, and remedial measures. Provision also should be made for facilities for health services.

Appraisal. Complete evaluation of each child's health includes health examinations by a physician, dental examinations, health assessments and observations by the teachers and nurses, screening of vision and hearing by the teachers, weighing and measuring, and inspection of cleanliness.

Health guidance and supervision. In a well-conducted school health program provision is made for aiding the student in directing his own health. It includes all processes necessary to acquaint a student with his health status and with the sources and channels for developing his health assets. It aims to help the student in health self-direction. The school supervises the child's health while he is in school much as the parents supervise his health at home. Such supervision must be planned, be well organized, and have recognized spheres of responsibility.

Prevention. Control of communicable diseases, safety promotion, first aid, and emergency care are not only opportunities for school service, but also responsibilities for doing everything reasonable to prevent disasters of all proportions.

Remedial measures. The school has no legal responsibility to remedy defects and disorders, but it does have a professional opportunity for service to the students by bringing together children who need professional service and the professional service they need. Correction and rehabilitation within the school can be extremely important for certain students.

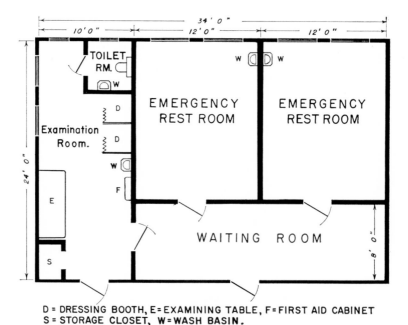

D = DRESSING BOOTH, E = EXAMINING TABLE, F = FIRST AID CABINET
S = STORAGE CLOSET, W = WASH BASIN.

Fig. 8. Health services facilities. A simple yet efficient plan for complete health services needs which permits a variety of arrangements.

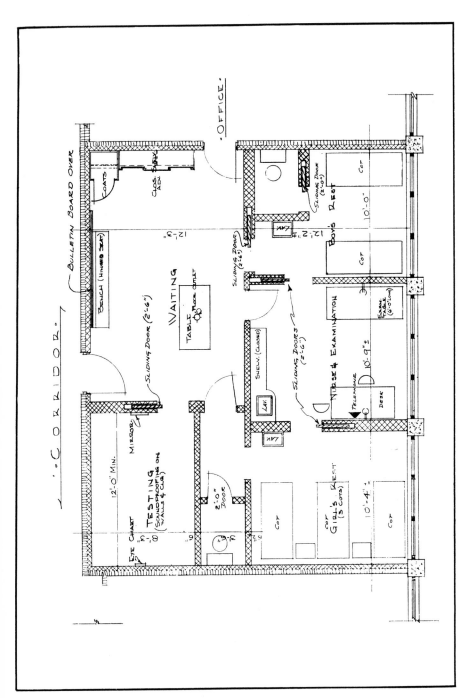

Fig. 9. Clinic floor plan. Complete and more elaborate facilities should be standard when finances and other factors permit. These facilities properly could be regarded as optimum for health services. (Courtesy Denver Public Schools, Denver, Colo.)

Facilities for health services. From both necessity and recognition of the importance of health services, well-planned adequate health facilities should be provided. Various plans have proved satisfactory. Existing rooms can be remodeled satisfactorily. Necessarily plans must be adapted to needs and available space.

A suite of four rooms can be arranged to provide the necessary quarters. Such a plan provides a waiting room, examination room, and two emergency rest rooms, as illustrated in Fig. 8. The examination room can be used for a variety of purposes—health examinations, dental examinations, x-ray examinations, hearing and vision testing, first aid, and conferences. Equipment will be determined by the requirements of the physician, the dentist, and the nurse. One emergency rest room for girls and one for boys can prove invaluable. Space devoted to facilities for health service is well invested. The director of the health program, the nurse, or other suitable person should be in charge of the health rooms.

Health instruction

Formal planned classroom health teaching is designed to prepare students to make the proper decisions throughout their lives on matters affecting their health. The very nature of health allows for a great variety of approaches in instruction. Diverse methods, techniques, and combinations have been effective in health instruction. In the final analysis any program of health instruction must be appraised in terms of the extent to which it modifies persons in their understanding and practice of health principles. Instruction that favorably directs the students' attitudes, understanding, and practice into a pattern of living which promotes and maintains the highest possible level of health meets the true goal of all health teaching.

Elementary school. During the early years of school life health instruction is directed primarily to the establishment of recognized health practices and the inculcation of desirable health attitudes. Health knowledge may be used as a vehicle for promoting health practices and health attitudes. Elementary school children will acquire valuable health knowledge which may be associated with pleasant experiences, but health knowledge should always be considered a means to an end—better health. As such, health knowledge should be regarded as secondary to health attitudes and practices in promoting an effective elementary school health instruction program.

Junior high school. The idealism and group tendencies of junior high school students make an ideal setting for the promotion of community health interests and ideals. Interwoven with the concept of respect for the welfare of one's neighbors are the interrelationships which exist between personal and community health. Practices and attitudes are fortified with further knowledge.

Senior high school. Health attitudes and practices developed in the previous years are fortified by established scientific knowledge in the high school. Since most of the students will never again have an opportunity to receive organized health instruction, high school health teaching should be conceived of as the last opportunity the school has to prepare the student for self-directed study in problems of health. Sources of health knowledge, health services, and health products are of particular importance in high school health instruction.

Healthful school living

From the beginning of public school education in the United States communities have shown a special pride in their new up-to-date school buildings. The school building denoted a monument to the culture of the community and the people's concern for their children. With this concept was the connotation that the school environment consisted of the physical plant, and a costly building per se constituted an ideal environment for learning. It was a static concept.

The present-day dynamic concept of the environmental factors in the school is well expressed in the designation, *healthful school living*. It denotes a social situation in which the child develops his potentialities in effective and enjoyable living. The child's educational, emotional, and physical development will have the stimulation and motivation essential to their fullest attainment. It is expressed in the atmosphere of the classroom, the corridors, the gymnasium, the playground, and every other place about the school. It incorporates factors which affect both the physical and mental health of the child. In so doing it includes the physical plant, its equipment, and the practices within the school.

If an atmosphere of wholesome living is to be created, all plans and activities must be focused on the child and his needs for wholesome development. The physical, esthetic, cultural, moral, emotional, social, and all other aspects of the experiences and needs of the child must be met by the school. It properly should create in every child a pride in being a part of the school, an elation in the level of living in which he participates.

The physical plant with its site, proper living conditions, ideal sanitary equipment, and general attractiveness represents a first essential in healthful school living. How the teaching staff utilizes and incorporates these assets into the life of the student will determine whether the school is truly a place of healthful living. To have a lunchroom with adequate space and sanitary equipment is not enough. The practices in the lunchroom and the general atmosphere are equally important. Children need guidance in learning to appreciate and live fully, even in the most ideal physical environment. Out of this appreciation should evolve the social values so important to the present and future citizen.

When the physical plant is not of an acceptable standard, the intrepid teacher can instill in the children a desire to better the conditions under which they are learning. Even to appreciate what is and what is not com-

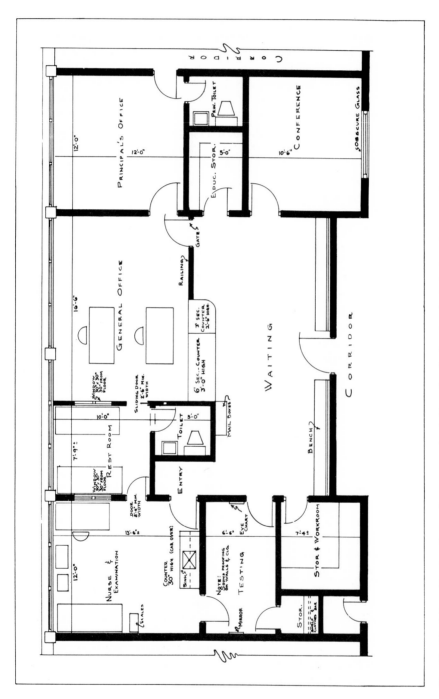

Fig. 10. Administrative area in an elementary school. Functional planning includes health services facilities in the administration center. (Courtesy Denver Public Schools, Denver, Colo.)

mendable in the school is an achievement in personal growth. Out of these experiences can come improvements in school, home, and community.

After all, the most important thing in the school environment is the people we find there. The quality of these people can be noted in their values, attitudes, activities, and attainment. Healthful school living is simply an effective way of life.

Responsibility for environmental health. Parents, school board members, architects, administrators, teachers, custodians, lunchroom personnel, and students are responsible for the environment of the school. United responsibility, combined with collective effort, produces the environmental conditions conducive to the atmosphere necessary for healthful school living.

Factors influencing environmental health. The attitude of the school patrons constitutes the all-important background for environmental health. What the parents hold as standards and put into effect by their own contribution and interest set the pattern or mold for a healthful school environment. Through the board of education this attitude will project itself into attractive functional school buildings, which are safe, efficient, sanitary, and commodious. It will lay the groundwork for an effective school program which will assure the children of an opportunity to develop their potentialities. This community support makes it possible for the school staff to create an atmosphere in which children can live effectively and enjoyably.

A second factor is a well-planned, well-constructed sanitary school plant. This implies a suitable site, functional architecture, adequate heating, ventilation, and lighting, safe water supply, approved disposal facilities, and essential accessory school equipment.

A third factor is the practices of the school. From custodial housekeeping, to lunchroom decorum, to group courtesy, to opportunities for self-status, one can enumerate the many practices which contribute so vitally to healthful school living. Capable teachers can utilize fully the available facilities and opportunities to create a mentally and physically healthy environment.

Healthful school living can be reduced to a rather simple equation: Functional school plant + wholesome practices = healthful school living.

School health personnel

In the organization of the school health program an essential consideration is the role of the various members of the school staff. The health responsibility of each staff member and the correlated functions of the staff as a whole should be well defined and understood. That overlapping and duplication should exist is inevitable and frequently desirable. Needless duplication should be avoided, especially that which adds nothing to the effectiveness of the program and may appear to be at cross purposes and even lead to confusion. If each member of the school staff conscientiously and competently discharges his or her health responsibilities and cooperates with others who are capably discharging their duties, the ingredients of a balanced effective school health program are provided.

Administrator. There can be no greater obstacle to a first-class school health program than an administrator who knows little or nothing about school health and cares less. Conversely there can be no greater asset to a school health program than an administrator who has a thorough understanding of the school health program and appreciation of the contribution of the school to child health.

Some administrators, reared in the classical tradition, do not accept health promotion as a responsibility of the school and look upon health instruction as a come-lately upstart intruder. They may resist vigorously any attempt to develop a health program. Or they may develop a passive resistance which may discourage even the most enthusiastic health educator. In some cases the obstinate lethargy of the administration is an anchor the school health program must drag along. Every ship should carry an anchor, but a school is a far cry from a ship.

In every state there is an expressed need for the education of school administrators in the fundamentals of school health. Some states require work in health education as a qualification for an administrator's certificate. With knowledge of the health program many administrative skeptics go through successive stages of acceptance, increasing interest, enthusiasm, and finally missionary zeal. The confidence which knowledge fosters asserts itself in a positive leadership in matters of school health. In three or four years some of these administrators will regard their health programs as one of the most effective and important phases of the life of the school. School health is entirely in keeping with today's philosophy of functional education.

Both the superintendent and the principal have responsibilities in the health program. However, in practice it is the principal who deals directly with the program. Any listing of administrator's health responsibilities inherently lists those of the principal, though the superintendent may be concerned in a sanctioning role.

1. Emphasize health promotion as a basic objective of education
2. Formulate and supervise the school health program
3. Obtain adequate funds for the health program
4. Inform the school patrons of the program and its functions
5. Maintain channels of communication between the school and community agencies
6. Cooperate with health agencies
7. Provide services of trained health personnel
8. Arrange for regular nurse-teacher conferences
9. Provide effective screening to locate child health needs
10. Provide time and opportunity for teachers to observe the health status of the children and to record these observations
11. Possess knowledge on health problems of all children

12. Work with parents and community leaders to secure adequate treatment for all children
13. Establish an adequate functional system of health records
14. Set up a cooperative program for controlling communicable diseases
15. Set up and promote a safety program
16. Coordinate school health services and health instruction
17. Provide elementary classroom teachers with necessary facilities, materials, and time for health instruction
18. In the secondary school provide time and facilities for health teaching
19. Assign only qualified teachers to teach health
20. Arrange an in-service program in health education for staff members
21. Through mutual agreement arrange for teachers to stay home when they are ill
22. Provide a healthful physical environment for children and staff
23. Have food handling checked for transmission of disease
24. Provide a hygienic mental environment
25. Provide an organized plan to meet emergencies

During the past twenty years school administrators have experienced increasing difficulty in obtaining medical services for schools. Physicians in private practice have had less and less time and inclination to serve the school, except to examine athletes or others for activity programs. A standard of 250 medical service hours per academic year for each 1000 students is a recognized but unattainable goal for many schools. The smaller and medium-sized school systems have been forced to operate without the services of a school physician or have been obliged to provide makeshift arrangements for the occasional service of whatever physician could spare a morning for a clinic or some special health problem.

School physician. Only a few metropolitan school districts with large enrollments have full-time physicians. Even among large school districts a full-time school physician is decidedly the exception rather than the rule. Several factors account for the small number of full-time school physicians.

First is the limited supply of physicians interested in the position. A school physician properly should have an interest and training beyond that of the general practitioner. A qualified school physician must be interested in the normal growth and development of children. He must be interested in mental health and health promotion. An interest in and knowledge of public health, public relations, and factors in the community and home which affect child health are basic for the school physician. Immunization and special problems in child health are fundamental to school medical service. Though school health conceivably should be a challenge, few physicians are attracted to the field.

A second factor in accounting for the small number of full-time school physicians is a lack of interest on the part of school boards and school administrators. Perhaps this merely reflects a lack of interest by the public. There has been no general public acceptance of the proposal that schools have a full-time physician. Doubtless the element of cost enters in. However, a full-time physician could mean an excellent investment in child health rather than a school expense. School boards have the authority to hire a physician either on a full-time or a part-time basis.

Part-time or fee-basis school physicians have been accepted more readily and are far more commonly employed. The board of education arranges with a practicing physician or physicians for specified medical services in the school. The physician may be scheduled to appear at certain school buildings at a given time each morning for work in control of communicable diseases. He may also be scheduled to conduct examinations or immunization clinics. A set pay schedule is prearranged. An interested properly prepared physician can be a wonderful asset to the school.

Some schools arrange for physicians' services through the local medical society. Not all member physicians will be interested, but some will be. If properly administered, this type of program can be satisfactory. It is a modified part-time medical service.

Whatever the administrative arrangement, there are certain recognized functions of the physician who serves the school.

1. Participate in the planning of the school health services program
2. Conduct health examinations
3. Provide medical consultant service in the school
4. Advise the administration on problems of school health
5. Advise parents of children with defects or disorders
6. Assist in exclusion and readmission in the program for control of communicable diseases
7. Provide necessary health services in-service training of school personnel
8. Provide emergency care
9. Coordinate health services with the health instruction program
10. Coordinate the school health program with the public health program
11. Assist in informing the public of the operation of the school health services
12. Serve as adviser on medical aspects of the school environment

It must be emphasized that the school physician does not correct defects or provide treatment for children except in an extreme emergency. His service is primarily in the appraisal and preventive fields. In a consulting capacity he does function in the corrections program by advising parents of the need for professional services for children with disorders. The school physician is a guardian of the school child's health.

Director of the school health program. Terms such as director, supervisor, and coordinator are used to designate the same or various aspects of the same thing, depending upon the section of the country, legal designation, adoption by state education departments, terminology of particular schools, or just convenience. For the present purpose the term *director* will be used. It will designate the person who has immediate responsibility for the direction of the school health program. As such, he may be school health director for the entire system. Or he may be director of the elementary school health program or director of the secondary school health program. Whatever the expanse of his jurisdiction, he is the administrator of the school health program.

A school health director, first and foremost, should be an educator. In addition to his education background he should have a special interest and preparation in school health work. Because he must of necessity work with children, teachers, custodians, and other school personnel, he should be a well-adjusted person who is able to get along with people.

Large school systems employ full-time health directors with full-time and part-time assistants. Different plans are in effect. One plan has a full-time director with a full-time assistant who directs the elementary school program and part-time assistant director in each high school building. The part-time directors teach health classes as part of their duties. The elementary school assistant health director serves the elementary teachers in promoting their health programs. Modifications of this plan are in vogue and usually are adapted to the particular needs of the system.

Medium and small school systems may engage a full-time school health director who administers the entire health program and has no other duties. Some systems divide his duties between health and physical education or health and some administrative assignment. Most often the school health director devotes about half of his time to classroom health instruction in either the junior or senior high school. He thus is able to integrate health instruction and the rest of the health program in the high school. In addition he can be of service to the elementary schools in planning, organizing, promoting, and implementing their health programs. Here is a plan which with some modification should be considered a minimum for any school system, regardless of how small it may be.

To have one person in charge of school health is sound educationally and administratively. If that person has a deep interest in health and is prepared professionally, he may be a principal, a home economics teacher, a science teacher, a physical educator, or any other staff member. She could be a nurse with a background in education. The important thing is that the person be qualified. This was superbly expressed by a school superintendent who said:

> I am looking for someone to take charge of health work in our high school. I want someone who has more than just a superficial knowledge of health. If the extent of a health director's knowledge is to urge a student to go to a dentist twice a year, or take a bath, or have his eyes tested if he has visual difficulties, I will not need him. The run of classroom teachers knows that much.
>
> When I engage a person to direct instrumental music, I expect him to know far more in that field than any other member of the faculty. I do not expect him to be an Arturo Toscanini. Neither do I expect a health director to be a Sir William Osler, but I do expect him to be trained so that he has more than a superficial knowledge of health.

Certainly a person with a baccalaureate degree and a teaching major in health could be qualified to direct a health program. Further on-the-job growth supported by advanced preparation leading to a master's degree in health education could produce a first-class school health director, eminently qualified to assume the recognized duties of the position.

1. Formulate an over-all school health program for the consideration of the administration
2. Assume direct supervision over the health program
3. Assume the role of coordinator between the school, the home, and individuals and agencies in the community which may contribute to the health of the child
4. Keep all school personnel thoroughly informed on all aspects of the school health program, particularly the role of each person
5. Make arrangements for health examinations, dental examinations, and special clinics
6. Arrange for the necessary facilities for health services
7. Provide channels through which referrals may be made easily and effectively
8. Arrange for screening of hearing, vision, and posture early in the school year
9. Establish a systematic program of teacher observation for deviations from normal health.
10. Confer with teachers, nurses, attendance coordinator, and others regarding students absent excessively
11. Assess the health status of students when special occasion requires
12. Assume over-all direction of the follow-up program in securing correction of defects
13. Assume responsibility for health records
14. Issue health notices and announcements
15. Supervise activities for control of communicable diseases, including exclusions and readmissions
16. Arrange necessary in-service health preparation of the teaching staff
17. Coordinate health instruction from grade to grade
18. Obtain health instruction materials for the teaching staff
19. Serve as health counselor for students with health problems or health needs
20. Serve as adviser for student groups or committees participating in activities of health programs
21. Assume responsibility for the promotion of the sanitation of the school plant
22. Plan and supervise a program of safety promotion
23. Organize a program to care for emergencies
24. Assume responsibility for first aid and other emergency care
25. Provide special programs for exceptional children
26. Accept responsibility for special health problems which may arise in the school
27. Provide for evaluation of the school health program

Not enough school systems have recognized the role of the school health director. Those which have a competent health director are strong advocates of the principle of having a definite person responsible for the school health program. Administrators, especially, value the services of a school health director. The cost is relatively low and actually is an investment in better health for the children of the school.

School nurse. Perhaps the ideal is a school health nurse, prepared in education and public health as well as nursing, who devotes full time to school work and is on the school payroll. She properly is a teacher-nurse. Many school systems have nurses who meet these specifications. Other schools have the services of nurses on the staff of the county or city health department. In the latter case the nurse divides her time between the school and her public health duties. The two responsibilities do not necessarily conflict. Budgeting the nurse's time is frequently difficult, but whatever time is made available to the school will yield a valuable contribution to the school health program. Some phases of school health services are distinctly the nurse's province. In other areas she assists or supplements what is being done by others. To list her duties will suggest the possibilities of her services.

1. Assist in the formulation of the school health program
2. Assist the physician and dentist when examinations are conducted in the school building
3. Assess the health of specific children when requested by the teachers
4. Recheck children with questionable vision and hearing defects and interpret findings
5. Help administer follow-up program by explaining examination findings to parents and assisting in obtaining corrections of defects found
6. Assist in control of communicable diseases through inspections, exclusions, and readmissions
7. Participate in a program for the prevention of handicaps and the care and education of handicapped children
8. Conduct classes or give demonstrations such as care of the sick, practices for communicable diseases, and first aid
9. Assist teachers in health instruction
10. Assist in accident prevention and emergency care
11. Assist in promoting a healthful school environment
12. Coordinate school activities with all of the health forces of the community and state

Some school districts financially unable to employ a school nurse have relied on the school health director to assume many of the tasks usually performed by the nurse. Moderate-sized systems have found that a double team of health director and school nurse has been the formula for a dynamic effective school health program.

Dentist. In the United States between the years 1925 and 1935 a considerable number of schools and local health departments had full-time dentists on their staffs. Duties of the dentist consisted essentially of dental examinations of elementary school pupils, although some health department dentists did corrective work for children whose parents were unable to pay for the services of a dentist. Today few schools employ a dentist, even on a part-time basis. In some schools the local dental society provides annual free dental examinations for all elementary school pupils. Such a program works simply and effectively.

The first essential of such a program is a September meeting between school representatives and representatives of the dental society. A schedule is drawn up in which each dentist is to give specific half days to school examinations. Through various media the parents are informed of the program. A dental record card for each child is supplied by the school, but the dentist supplies his own instruments for the examinations. All examinations are done at the school, and the dentist makes out a record card for each child. After making a duplicate for herself, the teacher mails the original to the parents who thus are informed of their child's dental health status.

Even when the dentists are paid on a clinical fee basis by the school board, this type of program serves only as the first step in assuring every youngster the benefit of a thorough dental examination. Yet, it is an important first step. However, a well-planned, persistent dental education program can be effective in getting parents to take their children to the family dentist before the fall opening of school. The same education program is likely to carry over into corrective measures by parents, which is a further goal of the dental health program. Final evaluation of any school dental health program must be made primarily on this basis. It can be done as effectively by educating parents to take children to the dentist as by expecting the school to bring dentists to the children.

Elementary classroom teacher. An elementary school with teachers well prepared in health has the foundation for an effective school health program. The elementary classroom teacher has both an opportunity and an obligation to aid youngsters in building up and maintaining a high level of health. Nothing the teacher does will give her more gratification than what she does in behalf of the health of the children under her supervision. Most of the health duties of the elementary teacher are integrated with the normal routine of classroom life.

1. Appraise the health of every child in her room and make continual observation for deviations
2. Support and advance the school health services by utilizing the results of examination and surveys in promoting the best health interests of each child
3. Screen vision, hearing, and posture during the first month of the school year
4. Make inspection for cleanliness, neatness, and symptoms of disease
5. Detect symptoms of communicable disease, isolate the child, and assist him in understanding the need for isolation
6. Weigh and measure each child three times a year
7. Observe and refer to the health director or nurse those children who appear to need special attention
8. Refer such children to their parents in the absence of a director or nurse
9. Encourage treatment of disease and correction of defects which have been discovered
10. Observe health practices of children
11. Encourage children to evaluate their own health and health behavior and to take responsibility for its improvement
12. Motivate children to establish good health practices
13. Prepare children for medical and dental examinations as learning experiences
14. Be familiar with basic health principles
15. Integrate daily experiences into health education opportunities
16. Provide direct health instruction
17. Provide a healthful environment
18. Take care of first aid and emergency situations
19. Keep herself in good health as an example
20. Evaluate the school health program

Physical educator. A physical educator is in a strategic position to offer much to the health of the school child. The responsibility of the physical educator is definitely to promote physical and mental health in children rather than to develop muscular power.

1. Constant observation of the health status of children and detection of deviations from normal
2. Exclusion of students from classes when an apparent indication of communicable disease exists.
3. Motivate and assist students in establishing good health practices
4. Develop understandings and practices relating to cleanliness and the prevention of infection
5. Develop an appreciation of the role of community health services in safeguarding health
6. Develop an appreciation of the relationship of diet to health
7. Create an interest in skill as an attribute for more effective and enjoyable living
8. Promote safety practices
9. Provide first aid and emergency services
10. Develop an appreciation of the nature of fatigue and the need for rest
11. Adapt student activities to the capacities of the students
12. Promote wholesome boy-girl relationships through co-recreation
13. Promote mental health as expressed through emotional control
14. Cooperate with physicians and parents in providing special activities
15. Rehabilitate students who have recovered from illness or defects
16. Assume responsibility for good posture
17. Assume responsibility for excellent grooming
18. Maintain a healthful school environment in cooperation with the students

Secondary school classroom teacher. All secondary school classroom teachers have a contribution to make to the school health program. Certainly opportunities for health discussions arise in every class. Home economics classes especially provide repeated opportunities for health instruction. Nutrition, family life, and homemaking encompass health aspects. More than just imparting health instruction, all secondary school teachers have an opportunity to observe students daily and thus be concerned directly with the health condition of the students. The health responsibilities of the high school teacher are not many, but they are important.

1. Observe students continually to note any deviations from the normal
2. Report to proper administrators when a student appears to be in need of health counseling
3. Cooperate with the administration in preventing the spread of communicable diseases
4. Maintain sanitary, safe, and congenial environmental conditions in the classroom
5. Note the kind of questions students ask regarding health and assume some responsibility for helping them to find accurate answers
6. Recognize requirements and activities which may jeopardize health
7. Assume responsibility for first aid and emergency care
8. Analyze particular area or areas of subject matter for the purpose of making the content more functional in terms of the health needs and problems of the students

Custodian. The custodian is concerned with a healthful physical environment—cleanliness, ventilation, lighting, heating, water supply, sewage disposal, safety factors, floors, exits, walks, and fire equipment. He also has a direct responsibility for pupil health and should be regarded as a member of the school health team. A qualified custodian is one with the proper training to meet the present requirements. Health protection and promotion are two of his most important functions.

Other personnel. Lunchroom workers, clerks, bus drivers, and other school employees can make contributions to the health program. A first essential is that they understand that they are part of the program to promote health. Secondly, they should be made to feel that their role is an important one. Thirdly, they should have specific instruction in performance of their tasks in the light of health protection and promotion. It is the composite contribution of everyone in the school community that builds the complete school health program.

Selected readings

American Association for Health, Physical Education, and Recreation: School health practices in the United States, Washington, D. C., 1961, The Association.

American Association of School Administrators: Health in schools, twentieth yearbook, Washington, D. C., 1951, The Administrators.

American Medical Association, Bureau of Health Education: Physician participation in school health services, Chicago, 1950, American Medical Association.

Bathrust, Effie G.: Petersburg builds a health program, Washington, D. C., 1950, United States Government Printing Offie, Office of Education Bulletin no. 9.

Children's Bureau: Priorities in health services for children of school age, Washington, D. C., United States Government Printing Office.

Davis, R.: Quality in school health administration, National Elementary Principal **39:** Feb., 1960.

Dukelow, D. A., and Hein, F. V. (editors): Physicians and schools, report of the Third National Conference on Physicians and Schools, Chicago, 1952, American Medical Association.

Foord, A.: Health services for children of school age. In Maxcy, K. F. (editor): Rosenau Preventive medicine, ed. 8, New York, 1956, Appleton-Century-Crofts, Inc.

Grout, Ruth E.: Health teaching in schools, ed. 4, Philadelphia, 1963, W. B. Saunders Co.

Haag, Jesse H.: School health program, New York, 1958, Henry Holt & Co., Inc.

Handbook for School Administrators: A story about the National Conference for Cooperation in Health Education and its 62 member agencies, Raleigh, N. C., 1952, Health Publications, Inc.

Irwin, L. W., Humphrey, J. H., and Johnson, W. R.: Methods and materials in health education, St. Louis, 1956, The C. V. Mosby Co.

Joint Committee of Minnesota Department of Health and State Department of Education: School health manual, ed. 2, St. Paul, 1950, prepared by the Joint Committee.

Kilander, H. F.: School health education, New York, 1962, The Macmillan Co.

Langton, C. V., Duncan, R. O., and Brightbill, C. K.: Principles of health, physical education and recreation, New York, 1962, The Ronald Press Co.

Massachusetts Department of Education: Health in school, Boston, 1951, Massachusetts Department of Education.

National Committee on School Health Policies of the National Conference for Cooperation in Health Education: Suggested school health policies, ed. 3, Washington, D. C., 1956, National Education Association.

National Conference for Cooperation in Health Education: The school administrator, physician, and nurse in the school health program, New York, 1947, Metropolitan Life Insurance Co.

North Carolina Department of Public Instruction: Health education, Raleigh, 1953, North Carolina Department of Public Instruction.

Oberteuffer, D.: School health education, ed. 3, New York, 1960, Harper & Brothers.

Sellery, C. M.: Duties and functions of the health coordinator at the secondary level, Journal of School Health **16:**282, 1946.

Smith, L. M.: A survey of the status of school physicians, Journal of School Health, **19:** 201-205, 1951.

Strang, Ruth: Techniques of counseling in regard to health problems, American Journal of Public Health **39**:886, 1949.

Turner, C. E., Sellery, C. M., and Smith, Sara L.: School health and health education, ed. 4, St. Louis 1961, The C. V. Mosby Co.

Tyler, E N., and Morgan, L. S. (editors): Health educators at work, Chapel Hill, 1952, University of North Carolina Press.

Wisconsin Cooperative School Health Program: Administrator's outline for study of the school health program, Madison, Wis., 1946, Department of Public Instruction.

Wishik, S. M.: Administrative jurisdiction of school health service, American Journal of Public Health **41**:819, 1951.

Yankauer, A., Jr.: A further evaluation of the Astoria plan of school medical services in New York City elementary schools, American Journal of Public Health **41**:383, 1951.

Part 3

School health services

The preservation of health is a duty.

—Herbert Spencer

Chapter 7

Appraisal aspect of health services

For planned understandable advancement one must know the point or milepost from which one proceeds. A necessary corollary is that, as one progresses along his journey, he must take readings from time to time if he is to have a measure of where he is at a given time as well as how much his progress has been. This applies to one's health history in terms of health promotion as well as protection.

There is much that health appraisal has to contribute to a student's welfare. It can give assurance to the child, his parents, and his teachers that his present health is at a satisfactory level. Or it can give a warning that the health status is not satisfactory and perhaps thus provide a forewarning of possible danger ahead. It can indicate where strengths and weaknesses exist and where special attention might profitably be applied. It can give an accounting of progress or lack of progress in the health program of each child. It can serve as an experience which motivates a child to take pride in his health. It can motivate the child to maintain and, so far as possible, to improve his quality of health.

An appraisal of health is an evaluation or assessment of the present health status of a person. It is more than a static inventory since it deals with the relationship of a person's health attainment to his basic endowment and with his adjustment to his life needs. Appraisal of health denotes a positive approach in which major emphasis is placed upon the health assets of a person, and deviations and deficiencies are appraised in terms of the degree to which they obstruct or interfere with effective and enjoyable living.

Health appraisal properly is a continuing process. From the entrance health examination, to the observations by the class room teacher, to the last health examination or other health evaluation in the final year of high school, the appraisal of health traces the course of each child's health status throughout his school career. However, in the final analysis the appraisal of health is not an end in itself. It is a means to an end, a means to better health for the student. Its value comes in its use, and the appraisal of health will thus contribute to the general well-being of the youngster.

Fundamental objectives

Although the improvement and maintenance of the health of the student is the ultimate object of the health appraisal program, several immediate objectives are the avenues through which the final goal can best be reached.

1. Develop in the student an understanding interest in his health status
2. Establish a life-long practice of having one's health status evaluated at regular intervals
3. Establish the basis on which to construct a life program of health promotion
4. Help the parents to understand the health status and needs of their children
5. Enable the school to understand the health endowment of each pupil so that the child and school program will be adapted to the best interests of the student
6. Establish a wholesome physician-child relationship
7. Establish a wholesome dentist-child relationship
8. Develop in each child an appreciation of the value of professional services, methods, and techniques.
9. Discover deviations from normal
10. Assess changes in individual health status

Health examination

A health examination is a means to an end, and potentially it is perhaps the most effective single instrument mankind possesses for elevating the general standard of health. In keeping with the present-day positive approach, the physician's examination of the child is designated a *health examination,* not a medical examination or physical examination. The physician looks for evidences of health. While he points out defects, these are considered obstructions to the true goal of health. The first consideration of the physician is evaluation of the health status of the child. Determination of specific conditions which interfere with the best possible health of the child is the second consideration.

Purpose. The importance of the health examination is reflected in the multiple purposes it serves.

1. To make a comprehensive, meticulous appraisal of the child's status
2. To be sufficiently informative to be of value to parents and to school personnel
3. To discover defects
4. To provide professional counsel for any existing deviation
5. To indicate the extent to which the school program should be modified to benefit the child
6. To secure medical supervision and corrections as indicated
7. To provide a valuable health experience for the child
8. To determine the fitness of the child to participate in the school program

Legal requirements. In some states the legislature specifically has provided that the state board of education shall prescribe a program of health examinations for pupils. Under this provision the state board of education sets examination requirements to which local education districts must conform.

In some states the local education boards specifically are granted legislative authority to provide a program of health examinations for pupils. However, in the absence of any such specific legislative authorization courts have held that a board of education has the authority to specify that a health examination is a requirement for admission to school. This authority can be extended to include health examinations for other purposes, such as participation in athletics. However, courts stipulate that the exercise of this authority shall be *reasonable*.

Usually exceptions are made on religious grounds although a question arises as to whether a health examination constitutes medication. The Washington State Supreme Court ruled that the University of Washington Board of Regents was within its authority in requiring that all students matriculating at the university have x-ray pictures of the chest. The court further ruled that the board acted properly in denying exceptions for religious reasons because an x-ray examination is not a form of medication.

In practice the state board of education establishes a pattern for a health examination program which guides the local education board in the exercise of its legal responsibility and authority.

Examination schedule. An annual health examination for every school child might be ideal, but in practice is hardly attainable. Cost, scheduling problems, time consumed, and parental objections to apparently unnecessary repetitions have combined to make the annual school health examination an academic question. Actually, from the standpoint of practical health protection and promotion, modifications can be made which will yield approximately the same end result as the annual examination.

One modification is to give the child a health examination when he enters school, another when he is in the fourth grade, and a third when he is in the eighth grade. Supplemental examinations are made as indicated by screening by the teacher or nurse and for participation in athletics. Even this relatively modest program did not gain wide acceptance. As a result a further modification was inevitable, even though it appeared that anything less would be inadequate. Yet, a recent modification has been practical and effective and each year appears to be gaining wider acceptance. This program is described in the following discussion on the various groups of pupils to be examined, which are listed in order of priority.

1. *Pupils entering school for the first time.* Entering children who are to begin school in September should be examined sufficiently early to permit an adequate follow-up on recommendations of the examining physician. June has been found to be the most satisfactory month for the preschool examination.

2. *Pupils referred through screening by the teacher or nurse.* Alert teachers and nurses frequently are the first to detect that a child is not up to his normal health status. Both minor and serious deviations are recognized by the informed and observant teacher who has an excellent opportunity to observe the child during the many hours of close association each day. Referral by teacher or nurse means referral to the parents or guardian of the child. Parents refer the child to a physician. When the school has a nurse available for consultation, referral should be a teacher-nurse referral channeled through the school principal's office. If a nurse is not available, the classroom teacher should channel all referrals through the principal although the teacher may make the actual contact with the parent. Even though the teacher is doubtful about the need for having a pupil examined, it is prudent in this case to err on the side of caution and speak to the parents about the advisability of having the child checked by a physician.

3. *Students participating in vigorous athletics.* Any student participating in interscholastic athletics should be examined just before the beginning of the sports program in which he is to participate. The physician's certification of the student's fitness to participate in athletics will indicate any limitations or restrictions. A physician's certification of fitness for every participating athlete should be on file in the school before the students are even permitted to practice for an interscholastic sport. Following an injury, illness, or other incapacity, the student should be permitted further participation only on the recommendation and under the supervision of a physician. Students participating in vigorous intramural sports should also be examined before the season of participation.

4. *Pupils new to the system.* If an acceptable health record is received from the school the pupil previously attended, an examination may be deemed unnecessary. If there is no health record or a doubtful health condition exists, a health examination is in the best interests of the child.

5. *Pupils entering seventh or ninth grades.* In schools organized on the 6-3-3 basis, examination as a requirement for admission to junior high school is both sound and easy to administer. In schools on the 8-4 plan, this requirement will apply for admission to the high school.

A few school districts have inaugurated the plan of giving all graduating seniors a health examination four to eight weeks before graduation. Thus, in addition to an evaluation of the academic status of the student at the time of graduation, the school also provides a record of the health status of the graduate. In some communities service clubs have made the health examination a gift to the graduating seniors.

Preparing the students. A health examination should be considered a valued opportunity and the physician a valued friend. This positive attitude can be developed only by planned effective health instruction, fortified by an exchange of individual experiences among the students and the utilization of incidental events and incidents which provide opportunities for appraising and evaluating the health examination. A positive attitude, supported by knowledge and wholesome personal experiences, is the equation for proper preparation for the health examination for child and adult alike.

Methods for obtaining examinations. A variety of methods and combinations of methods are used by various school districts in obtaining health examinations of school children. The particular method best suited to conditions in the community should be used. This particular method or plan should be worked out jointly by the school and representatives of the parents, the health department, and the medical society. The final plan may include the parts of several methods or may be limited to one of the recognized methods.

1. *Examination in the family physician's office.* Since the family physician frequently knows the background of the child and family, he is in an excellent position to make a more comprehensive appraisal of the child's health. A commendable physician-student relationship exists. Ideal conditions for examination usually prevail, and laboratory facilities are available for tests indicated by the clinical examination. Parents frequently accompany the child to an examination by the family physician, and a highly profitable physician-parent-child conference can be held. An additional benefit is the likelihood that families without a recognized family physician will select a physician who serves subsequently as physician for the family. A concept of parental responsibility for health services is always worth cultivating.

Three disadvantages are possible in conducting the examination in the family physician's office. First is a lack of uniformity both in the examination and the reporting. This can be reduced by using a standard examination form. Second is the failure of the physician to use the opportunity for effective health instruction. Third is the possibility that only a small percentage of school children will have an examination.

A common difficulty encountered in using this method for obtaining examinations is the reluctance of some parents to pay for a health examination. Education of the parents would be a solution, but at times such education is not effective enough to produce the desired health examination. In such cases other means should be found. Certainly the child should have the benefit of the examination if there is some reasonable way of making it available.

2. *Examination by health department physician.* In some districts the health department staff conducts all, most, or a few selected health examinations. Clinics for preschool examination, prejunior high school examination, and athletic examination may be held in the health department office or in a school building. This method has special value for small or isolated school districts.

3. *Examination clinics held in the school building.* These clinics are conducted by practicing physicians selected through arrangement with the local medical society. Most of the advantages of the examination in

the private office are retained, and the convenience appeals to many parents and some physicians. Parents can be present at the examination although some physicians prefer not to have parents present when examinations are being conducted on a clinic basis. Some parents monopolize too much of the physician's time, and occasionally unfortunate incidents occur. When parents are not present, the school nurse later visits the home to explain the examination findings to the parents. In unusual cases the physician himself may have a conference with the parents to explain certain aspects of the child's health status.

4. *Examination by the regularly appointed school physician.* These examinations constitute a principal function of the school physician.

Payment. The method by which the physician is paid for his examining services is determined by local practices, by the method used to obtain examinations, and by individual circumstances. Any one or all of the four common methods of payment may be in use.

1. The parents pay the family physician.

2. The board of education, as prescribed by law, makes a contribution to the budget of the health department. In turn, examinations and other services are given to the school.

3. The board of education pays practicing physicians for conducting health examinations of school children. A board of education legally can pay a physician for an examination of a school child whether the examination is conducted in the physician's office or elsewhere.

4. The school athletic department pays for examination of athletes. Separate arrangements frequently are made for providing for the examination of those who intend to participate in interscholastic athletics. Students participating in athletics frequently are examined many times during their high school years. Certainly these examinations should be conducted, but should not deplete funds for the examination of other students and thereby deprive them of the benefit of health examinations.

Occasionally community service clubs pay for the health examination of school children but usually on a selective basis—hardship cases, athletes, seniors—rarely on a school-wide basis.

The examination. Techniques for conducting an examination are the province of the medical profession, but various factors relating to the examination are of interest and importance to all school personnel.

Whether the preschool examination is conducted in the physician's office or elsewhere, the family history and child history parts of the examination form should be filled out by the parents in advance of the examination time. It should be logical for the parents to be present at the preschool and referral examination though there may be some question of the necessity for the parent to be present at junior high school or athletic participation examinations. At the preschool examination the physician will include tests for vision and hearing.

For children who are in school and are scheduled to be examined, the school may test vision and hearing and record height and weight on

Fig. 11. Thorough health examination by the school physician. Although it is a means to an end, the health examination is perhaps the most important of all school health activities. (Courtesy Denver Public Schools, Denver, Colo.)

Fig. 12. Functional health education. The health examination provides an ideal situation for motivation and education in the area of personal health. (Courtesy Denver Public Schools, Denver, Colo.)

the examination form. In addition the school can assume responsibility for having the parents complete the history portion of the form if such information is not on record.

Optimum time for an examination is 15 minutes, and 10 minutes should be regarded as minimum. Every phase of the examination should be thorough. A superficial examination may be worse than none at all if it gives a false feeling of security. It is recognized that in 7 minutes one physician may conduct the actual medical aspects of the examination just as thoroughly as another physician who takes 15 minutes for the entire examination. The difference comes in the amount of health instruction which is included. An examination is a magnificent opportunity to impress a youngster with the importance of his health. To get a person to appreciate the value of his own health is the most difficult single task in health education, and here is the best possible teaching situation for that purpose. Informing the examinee of his health assets and complimenting him on his best points can create a wholesome *health-esteem,* an essential to a high level of lifelong health promotion.

In addition to the history of health behavior and experiences a standard health examination usually includes an evaluation of the following:

1. Height and weight
2. Vision and hearing
3. Posture, gait, and feet
4. Muscular and skeletal systems
5. Nutrition and skin
6. Head and neck, nose and throat, mouth and teeth, and eyes and ears
7. Heart and lungs
8. Abdomen and genitals
9. Endocrine and neuron systems
10. Laboratory tests as indicated by clinical findings

When examinations are held at the health department or school, a nurse may serve as recorder for the physician, which conserves time and energy for the physician. If there is no nurse, some physicians appoint a teacher to record their findings as they call them off.

All examination records should be considered confidential. "Keep confidences inviolate" is an ethical principle of all honored professions.

Examination record form. Medical societies, public health societies, and public health departments have developed model health examination forms. The particular form adopted by any school district should be one approved by the local medical society. Usually, in practice the state department of education, state department of health, and the state medical society jointly develop a form for use by schools throughout the state. In the absence of such a form the local school board should ask the local health department and local medical society to recommend a form for use by physicians examining school children.

One such health examination form is reproduced in Appendix B and is titled *Health Examination.* It is a concise practical form. This is not to be looked upon as *the* model form. It conforms to most requirements for such a recording, but modifications of this form have been found to be highly satisfactory. Forms that are too long or too short have obvious disadvantages.

If the form is to be used for day-to-day reference, a lightweight cardboard (index Bristol) should be used rather than sheet paper. However, if data from this form are to be transferred to a school record card for everyday use by the teacher, sheet paper (20 pound bond) is adequate.

When the health department cooperates in the school health program, the school health administrator should furnish the department with a duplicate report for each child examined within the district served by the health department. The original copy should be kept by the school the child attends. A separate form is used for each health examination the child has during his school career. Examination records should be available for use, not filed in an inaccessible cabinet. An effective plan for the elementary school is to file the examination form, filled in by the physician, in the office of the principal and give the teacher a *health record card* with pertinent health information copied from the examination form. In the high school the original examination form can be kept in the principal's office and the health record card can be in charge of the director of health education, the health educator, or another interested competent person.

Health record card. The health record card brings together in one record essential health information supplied by the parent, physician, nurse, and teacher. It may be a light cardboard (index Bristol) card 8 × 10 inches. One side will record personal and family histories, height, weight, results of vision, hearing, and susceptibility tests, annual health summary, immunizations, and physician's recommendations. On the reverse side records of the child's illnesses as well as the regular observations by the teacher can be made. The health record form presented in Appendix B illustrates one type of form which has proved to be highly satisfactory.

A card is provided for each pupil when he enters school for the first time. The card goes with him from grade to grade, precisely as the academic record goes with him, and at the close of his senior year in high school is filed with his academic record. If the student transfers to another school system, the original health record form should accompany his scholastic record. A duplicate health record card is retained by his original school.

Each teacher should have a filing case conveniently located for use by her, the nurse, the principal, or any other proper person. Data should be filled in under specified headings as soon as they are available. This holds for observations as well as for vision and hearing testing and weighing and measuring. Colored tabs can be clipped to cards of children who need special referral or attention. At the close of the academic year or when the pupil goes from grade to grade or school to school, the health record card is transferred by the school principal.

A health record card is a means to an end, not an end in itself. It is there to be used. It can be used in conferences with the nurse, the parent, and the physician or in a conference of the teacher with all three. It is a means of sharing information and can quickly point up the health status of each child in the school. It can indicate desirable or attained health advances. It can tell the teacher what is happening in relation to the health of the child.

Report to parents. When parents are present at the health examination, it is logical that the attending physician verbally inform the parent of findings of special significance. When parents are not present at the examination, a routine report can be sent to the parent on a formal report form if nothing of special importance has been discovered. This form can be mailed by the health department. In the absence of a health department the school nurse, the director of school health, the principal, or the teacher can mail the report or send it home by the child. When some condition which merits immediate attention has been discovered, an early home visit by the nurse, the health director, or the teacher is in order. Even when the examination reveals no special problem or a very minor health problem, a person-to-person conference with the parents has many possible values. The follow-up to any examination program is an index of the vitality of the whole school health program. As a phase of the remedial aspects of health services, the follow-up is given special consideration in Chapter 10, Remedial Aspects of Health Services.

Dental examination

Although both the physician's and dentist's examinations are designed to evaluate, protect, and promote the student's health, the two examinations have basic differences which have led to different administrative practices. Some schools provide for a record of the dental examination on the health examination form. This section of the form is thus filled out by the dentist since the physician is not qualified to make the dental examination. Most schools use separate record forms for the dental examination and keep the dental examination program distinct from, yet correlated with, the general health examination program. Dental examinations are far more frequent than the general health examination, which further justifies a special dental examination program.

Purpose. Dental cavities are the most prevalent of all defects in America's school population. A simple dental cavity may have no demonstrable effect on health. Yet, if it is permitted to progress, a simple cavity could result in a loss of the tooth, with possible indirect effects upon health. Most important, an apical abscess may develop as a consequence of the cavity, and vital structures of the body may be affected by the toxins formed at the abscess. The dental examination thus is primarily a preventive measure. It is also an appraisal measure and is important in health promotion.

Since mankind does not have a specific absolute preventative for dental caries and early detection of defects is so vital, health education is of paramount importance in the program for dental health examination. Although prevention is an important phase, the dental examination should be considered in terms of health appraisal because it does provide an assessment or evaluation of the child's dental health.

A minimum of two dental examinations a year, supplemented by referrals by the teacher or nurse, is an acknowledged standard. Every school child should have a dental examination before the beginning of the school year. The examination should be completed sufficiently early to permit any necessary corrections before fall classes begin. When the dental examination is conducted in the school, examination clinics should be scheduled for the two weeks immediately following the opening of school. A second regular dental examination should be scheduled for the beginning of the second semester. Here an admirable opportunity for health education presents itself in preparation of the pupils for the examination and in review of the experience after the examination has been completed.

Methods for obtaining examinations. To meet the ideal that every child should have a dental examination every six months, some school boards have engaged dentists who examine every elementary school pupil. Some of these school dentists are on full-time appointment, others on a part-time or fee basis. Some school boards pay practicing dentists on a clinic basis for examining elementary school pupils. The usual method now is to have the family dentist examine children although some local dental societies promote free examination clinics in the elementary schools.

Examination by the family dentist does not always result in all school children being examined every six months. Yet, this method can be highly satisfactory if an effective school dental health education program is promoted and supplementary means are employed for children unable to pay for dental service. A health education program planned to educate pupil and parent to the importance of dental health and the dental examination are the foundation of any dental examination program.

A school health instruction plan properly includes dental health, provides knowledge, and establishes attitudes and ideals for the pupil which should motivate him to want good dental health. A realistic positive approach is one in which the child is taught to recognize that dental services may necessitate some temporary pain and discomfort, but the gains in better teeth and better health far outweigh the discomfort of the hour.

Education of the parents in dental health can be promoted through school bulletins, pamphlets, conferences, newspaper articles, radio pro-

grams, and addresses by dentists, dental hygienists, nurses, or other qualified speakers.

Although the goal is a dental examination for every school child at
least twice a year, the goal does not justify some of the means that are
employed. Particularly vicious is the practice of setting standards in
which all rooms must attain 100% in examinations or corrections. To
reach the 100%, unjust pressures may be exerted on some hapless children
whose parents cannot or do not have the examination provided. Children can be cruel to each other if some highly fancied goal is at stake.
This is particularly true if banners or other awards are given to rooms
for dental health records.

Generally at least 75% of the pupils will be taken to the family dentist for a check-up. The teacher can counsel each of the remaining children individually. A private conference with each child will often point
the way to the youngster's dental examination. The dental profession
does not permit any child who needs dental care to go without such care
because his parents actually cannot afford the service. A teacher truly

Fig. 13. Dental examination in the school. Note the facilities, even though limited, which every
school in the nation can provide. (Courtesy Oregon State Board of Health, Portland, Ore.)

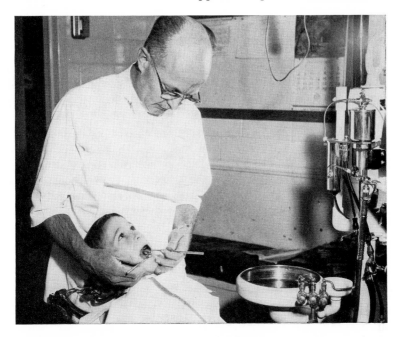

Fig. 14. Ideal dental facilities for a school. Some students are privileged to attend schools which provide both complete facilities and professional services for dental examinations. (Courtesy Denver Public Schools, Denver, Colo.)

interested in the dental health of a child can always find some way to provide dental treatment for him.

A second method for obtaining dental examinations is to hold examinations in the elementary school buildings on a clinic basis. On a schedule worked out between the school and the local dental society dentists are scheduled for a half day at a time to examine children in specific grade rooms. All of the grade school rooms thus have a dentist assigned to them. Examinations may be conducted in the examining room of the health services facilities or in some other suitable room. A regular dentist's chair is not needed. One can be improvised from an ordinary chair. The dentist examines each child in the grade room and makes a report of his findings on each child's record chart. The teacher copies the data from the card onto the child's health record form, and the card with the report of the dentist's findings is then sent to the child's home. If defects are found, the report advises the parents to take the child to the family dentist. Some dental societies give this service to the schools without charge. At times the dental society and the school board agree upon a clinic fee, the fee being paid by the school board.

In the promotion of the school clinic examination method, explanatory advance announcements to the parents are especially important. Parents should be advised of the program and asked to notify the school if they do not wish their child to be examined at the clinic.

Examination record form. When all examinations are done by the family dentist, the dentist obviously will have his own examination record form. When the clinic method is employed, the participating dentists design the record form. It may be a simple form with only a section for recording cavities or other defects, or it may give a more detailed designation of particular teeth in need of attention. It may be a general statement.

Follow-up. Since the dental examination is merely a means to an end, it is important that emphasis be placed on having dental repair work done. Establishing the practice of having dentists give school children a card certificate that all dental corrections have been made serves both the child and the school. It motivates the child to want good dental health, and it promotes pride in his attainment. It gives the school a record of the child's status and an indication of the effectiveness of its program of dental health promotion. The only danger comes when the contest or competitive idea of 100% attainment of corrections is introduced into the program. Group interest and motivation can be valuable. It also can be harmful.

Health assessment by teacher or nurse

A competent teacher who has charge of a group of children for a year strives to understand each individual child as fully as possible. Surely the health status of the child is as important to the teacher's understanding of him as is the academic ability or any other aspect of this intriguing person we designate the student. During the course of the school year every teacher, intentionally or incidentally, develops a general concept of each child's overall physical makeup, emotional pattern, and social adaptation. A more definite evaluation of each child's health status would benefit both teacher and child. Such evaluation is not difficult if one recognizes that it is a judgment based on outward observable indices, not a detailed examination. However, such an evaluation is better than a guess or rough estimate, because it can be based on a well worked out inventory of factors which enter into the attainment of health.

Properly used, the term *inspection* does not apply to the teacher's appraisal of the child's health. *Evaluation* and *observation* are better terms. Inspection connotes masses of fingers and an aura of investigation. Inspection applies when a check-up for communicable disease is made, but not for appraisal. Evaluation of a child's health denotes a quite thorough systematic appraisal and should be made at about the end of the first month of school. This evaluation should be supplemented by observations from day to day to note any deviations from the acknowledged health pattern of the youngster.

Purpose. It is important that the school know the academic status of each child at a given time. It is equally important that the school know each child's health status. A child's success in school and his health status are related. The school program and the health of the child must be in adjustment. To enable the child to obtain most benefit from his school experience, the teacher should know his health endowment, his limitations, and his possibilities. Once the teacher has a unified concept of a child's health status, not only will she have a better understanding of the child's performance and behavior, but she also will be quickly aware of any deviations from his normal condition. The health evaluation made early in the year will serve as a marker or landmark from which to judge the child's subsequent status or changes in status.

Any certified classroom teacher should be capable of making an acceptable child health evaluation. There is nothing mysterious about it since it is a general over-all appraisal based on several observable factors.

HEALTH EVALUATION

Name _____ Date _____ Health rating A B C D

Parent _____ Family physician _____

Muscle tone _____ Posture _____ Coordination _____

Vitality _____ Endurance _____ Nutrition _____ Skin _____

Eyes

Inflammation _____ Styes or crusted lids _____ Squinting _____

Ears

Inflammation _____ Discharge _____ Wax _____ Earache _____

Nose and throat

Nasal discharge _____ Nose bleed _____ Mouth breathing _____

Sore throat _____

Oral cavity

Lips _____ Gums _____ Oral hygiene _____

Behavior

Restlessness_____Drowsiness_____Twitching_____

Tenseness_____Instability_____Timidity_____

Cooperation_____Industriousness_____Orderliness_____

Height _____ Weight _____ Hearing: R _____ L _____

	Both eyes	Right	Left
Vision:	W 20/	W 20/	W 20/
	WO 20/	WO 20/	WO 20/

Health assets _____

Deficiences _____

Attention needed _____

Comments:

In some instances the nurse may assist in making the evaluation; in other cases the nurse may make an independent evaluation.

Evaluation record form. A school health record card, such as illustrated in Appendix B, has points the teacher can observe and which can serve as an evaluation record form for the teacher. If she uses these points, the teacher can get a practical evaluation of a child's health. She might supplement this evaluation with a classification of the child's health as A, B, C, or D, for her own guidance.

When no such health record form is available to the teacher, she easily can devise a form to serve her purpose. This form can be simple and easily scored and understood. A form should be completed for each child.

In scoring the evaluation form, the teacher uses the designations most meaningful to her. Words, symbols (o, x), and check marks can be used. Blue pencil marks to designate meritorious points and red marks to designate deficiencies help to point up health assets and liabilities. Although this evaluation is an assessment of the present level of a child's health, it could have further value if a follow-up plan for day-to-day health improvement is instigated with the child. Occasionally the evaluation brings to the teacher's attention a condition which should be referred to the parents.

Daily observation. In addition to the more comprehensive evaluation the health-minded teacher will observe both positive and negative indications of the child's health at any given moment on any given day. Outward indices of changes in health are not generally pronounced, but the teacher becomes so well acquainted with the pupils that she will observe minor changes in a child's condition. Most gratifying to the teacher is the gradual improvement in health which many of the pupils will display.

Report to parents. Normally the evaluation is for the teacher's own use. When a child has no particular health deficiency and appears to be in normal health, the teacher makes no special report to the parents as a consequence of the health evaluation. Occasionally a child will show a pronounced deficiency which should be reported to the parents. At times a child may show a sudden pronounced decline in health. Referral to the family is in order because any acute change in health can be serious. Likewise any chronic condition which appears to lower a child's effectiveness and enjoyment in living should be discussed with the parents. All referrals should be followed up, because for the best interests of the child it is important to know what has been done and what is being done.

Conservation of vision

Vision is a priceless heritage, and professionally the school accepts the responsibility of doing everything reasonable to conserve and protect that heritage for every school child. A child with normal vision for school purposes is fortunate. Perhaps equally fortunate is the child with a slight defect which is detected early in its course. Not only is the efficiency of the child's sight involved, but also his personality may be affected.

A child who is farsighted (hyperopia) may sit and stare out of the window, relaxed and contented, and perhaps watch every detail of a bird building a nest. To look in the distance relaxes the eyes and is restful. The child who is nearsighted (myopia) does not stare at the bird building a nest. Perhaps he does not even see the tree. Instead, he may be buried in a book, no bother to the teacher or anyone else, whereas the hyperopic child may be a worry to his teacher because of his apparent inattention. The farsighted child will likely develop into an active, outdoor, extroverted person, interested in athletics and vigorous activities. A nearsighted child is more apt to be a recluse, buried in reading and related interests.

From 2% to 5% of school children will have amblyopia, a dimness of vision. These youngsters will have difficulty in the standard Snellen vision test. In screening these youngsters, the school does not diagnose the condition as amblyopia. Diagnosis or identification of the condition is the province of the certified professional eye specialist.

A school's vision conservation program logically can be divided into four phases: (1) vision screening tests, (2) observation, (3) health record, and (4) follow-up.

Vision screening tests. A vision screening test is not a selective diagnostic test, but is a process of separating those who are most likely to need further examination from those who are less likely to need further examination. Some children who need further examination may be missed, and some who do not need further care will be selected. Indeed, whether the deficiency revealed by the screening is serious or even significant is for the professionally trained practitioner to determine. Thus the teacher is not a vision-testing expert. Rather she is an aid in sifting out those children who have difficulty in distinguishing the symbols which experimentation and experience have demonstrated are reliable and valid measures of visual distinctness. Defects in visual acuity are due to hyperopia, myopia, and astigmatism. Children in the first and second grades tend to be farsighted. Nearsightedness in children develops at about the level of the fourth grade. Most children who need glasses will show the need by the time they are in the seventh grade.

Schools do not test for color vision except for some unique purpose.

Test schedule. In the elementary school every child should have a vision screening test during the first month of the school year. Thereafter, any child who squints, strains to see, tilts his head in trying to look at something, or fatigues easily might profit by an additional screening test. Surprisingly a minimum schedule of a test in the second grade and in the sixth grade will identify over 80% of the children who need further examination.

In the high school, vision screening of all students in health classes as

Fig. 15. Snellen test group practice trials. A separate card or the top line of the chart can serve equally well for group instruction. (Courtesy Oregon State Board of Health, Portland, Ore.)

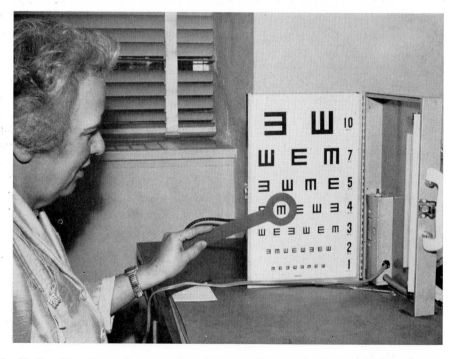

Fig. 16. Tumbling E test. Demonstration of the simplicity of the Snellen vision screening test and the use of a special portable case. (Courtesy Oregon State Board of Health, Portland, Ore.)

a learning experience can be helpful in identifying children who need a thorough eye examination. An observant staff of teachers who note those students exhibiting visual fatigue or other visual difficulty will refer them to the health director or nurse. Actual screening is done by the health director or the nurse. Few high schools give a vision screening test to all its students. Yet the time would be well invested.

Test procedures. The best known and most widely used test for vision screening is the *Snellen test.* Though apparently simple, this test has been found through experience to be extremely reliable and valid in identifying loss of visual acuity. Experience indicates that the "tumbling" E chart is as effective as the multiple letter chart, whether readers or non-readers are being tested. The test is a valuable educational experience. Procedures can be enumerated in a series of steps.

1. Explain the purpose of the test to the children in the classroom.
2. Show the chart to the children as a group and conduct group practice trials until they understand the test thoroughly.
3. Demonstrate how to cover the eye not being tested by holding a 3 x 5 inch card by the corner in front of the eye so that the eye is open and is not disturbed.
4. Do testing in a room where there are no distractions. The classroom is usually unsatisfactory for obvious reasons.
5. Hang a clean chart vertically in an uncluttered space so that all possible glare is eliminated.
6. Place the child being tested so that the light comes from the side, rear, or overhead; he should not face the light.
7. Focus an intensity of light of eight to twelve footcandles, whatever the source, on the chart.
8. Be sure that the 20-foot reading line on the chart is at the child's eye level when he is standing.
9. Draw a chalk line or make a tack line on the floor 20 feet from the chart so that the child may toe this mark as he stands and reads the chart.
10. Test each child individually.
11. Have the child toe the 20-foot mark and give him a 3 x 5 inch card to cover his eye (each child should have a fresh card which he holds close to the eye).
12. Begin with the 50-foot line on the chart and let the testing proceed from left to right. Using a card with a 1-inch hole, expose only the letter you wish the child to see. Proceed from line to line downward to include the 20-foot line. If a child reads three out of four symbols successfully, it is evidence of satisfactory vision at a particular level.
13. Check for possible farsightedness by including the 15-foot reading line and even the 10-foot line if indicated.
14. If the child wears glasses, first test him with glasses, then without glasses. Test both eyes first, then the right and left eyes separately. Record in the same order.
15. Note any unusual actions such as tilting of the head, blinking, scowling, or squinting.
16. The numerator which denotes the distance from the chart is always 20.
17. The denominator is the lowest line the child can read successfully.
18. If the child correctly reads the 20-foot line with the right eye, the score is right 20 over 20 (normal).
19. If he can read only the 50-foot line at a distance of 20 feet, the record is 20 over 50.
20. After the tests are completed, keep the chart out of sight until the next time for testing.

These instructions should be followed as closely as a housewife follows the directions for a recipe. Some practice is necessary to gain skill.

Interpretation of the test is not difficult in most cases. For school purposes 20/20 is normal. Occasionally a child with 20/20 vision may have a vision defect, but the teacher cannot be expected to ferret out every conceivable irregularity of the eyes. A child with 20/30 vision is probably nearsighted though the teacher determines merely that the child has difficulty in seeing, not that the child is nearsighted. A child with 20/10 or 20/15 vision is probably farsighted. For jet pilots 20/10 vision is normal; good hitters in baseball find 20/15 vision to be an advantage, but for the schools 20/20 is normal.

Another test is designed to identify farsightedness in pupils who pass the Snellen test and are not wearing spectacles. It is administered by having the subject wear a pair of spectacles with convex, or plus sphere, lenses of 1.50 to 2.50 diopters refractive strength. Each eye is tested separately, and the subject reads the 20-foot line of the Snellen chart. The convex lenses will distort the vision of the child of normal vision, but will make the necessary refractive correction for the farsighted or hyperopic individual. Thus the person who fails the test has normal vision whereas the person with hyperopia can read the line.

This test can be of value in verifying possible hyperopia as indicated by the Snellen test. However, it must be pointed out that any vision testing done by the teacher or nurse in the school is a screening test. If the Snellen test or just observation indicates the child's vision may not be normal, through the parent the child should be referred to an eye specialist. It is of some interest that a combined survey and experiment in Oregon public schools indicated that the plus sphere test screened out very few cases of vision difficulty which the Snellen test had not identified. This study indicated that discerning observations, competent screening with the Snellen test, and an effective referral and follow-up program will fulfill the obligation of the school in vision conservation.

Observation. An observant teacher who knows what to look for can identify children who have vision trouble before she ever conducts a Snellen test. The signs of eye trouble in children listed by the National Society for the Prevention of Blindness, Inc.* are the best guide for the teacher to use.

Behavior
Rubs eyes excessively
Shuts or covers one eye, tilts head or thrusts head forward
Has difficulty in reading or in other work requiring close use of the eyes
Blinks more than usual or is irritable when doing close work
Stumbles over small objects
Holds books close to eyes
Is unable to participate in games requiring distance vision
Squints eyelids together or frowns

---

*From Signs of eye trouble in children, New York, 1959, National Society for the Prevention of Blindness, Inc.

Appearance

Crossed eyes
Red-rimmed, encrusted, or swollen eyelids
Inflamed or watery eyes

Complaints

Cannot see well
Dizziness
Headaches } following close eye work
Nausea
Blurred or double vision

Any suspicion of vision trouble should be followed up to protect the valuable heritage of sight.

Follow-up. After conducting the Snellen test, the teacher should follow definite steps.

1. List pupils needing further vision examination
2. List pupils to be checked by the school nurse
3. Arrange conference with the nurse
4. Record results of the conference
5. Refer to parents, using a special form
6. Follow-up visits by nurse or teacher if parents take no action following original referral
7. Record results of Snellen test made with new glasses child is wearing

REPORT ON EYE CONDITION

Date _____

Pupil _____

Address _____

_____
            Parent or Guardian

Symptoms which may indicate vision difficulty have been observed in your child ____

_____

The school urges you to consult a doctor at once for professional advice.

_____ Signed _____
            School   **Teacher**

_____

EXAMINING DOCTOR'S REPORT TO THE SCHOOL

Visual acuity

Without glasses   **With glasses**

Right _____ Left _____   Right _____ Left _____

Explanation of condition _____

Time of next examination _____

Restrictions on eye work _____

Other recommendations _____

Date _____ Signed _____
                                                Examiner

Actually this program is relatively simple; yet the dividends are considerable in terms of sight saving and effective and enjoyable living. Here are both an obligation and an opportunity for service to the school child which the truly professional teacher will fulfill.

Conservation of hearing

The first obligation of the school in the conservation of the hearing of children is the prevention of hearing loss. In this role the school can serve in several spheres. It can educate children on proper action to prevent injury to hearing. It can inform parents on measures to avoid possible hearing loss in their children. Equally important, the school can follow established practices to prevent hearing loss in children enrolled in the school.

Prevention of hearing loss. Most hearing defects are preventable, and the school, through understanding and an effective approach, can contribute directly to the prevention of hearing loss. Several factors can be involved in hearing loss, and various measures can be taken to protect the hearing of children. The school and the home, with full understanding, working together in a common purpose, can best serve the interests of any child whose hearing may be threatened. Several factors can be involved and should be given necessary consideration:

1. Any foreign object in a child's ear canal may cause hearing loss and even lead to infection. Usually it is wise to have a physician remove the object.
2. Hard packed wax in the ear canal can be softened by warm oil and then removed, but when the wax is soundly embedded it should be removed by a physician.
3. A discharging ear should have the immediate attention of a physician.
4. Some of the common infectious respiratory diseases such as measles, scarlet fever, and diphtheria can develop into a complication of middle ear infection and result in damage to the hearing apparatus.
5. Frequent colds can affect hearing, and, when there is a possibility of this happening, the services of a physician should be enlisted.
6. Blowing the nose hard, particularly through one nostril, can injure the hearing apparatus.
7. A child with a ruptured ear drum should have a physician's approval before swimming.
8. No child outgrows a hearing loss. He may adjust to the condition, but medical service is necessary to assure improvement or complete recovery in hearing.

Nowhere does a "stitch in time" apply more aptly or with more certainty than in measures directed toward alleviating a condition threatening hearing. *Action Now* should be the school motto in matters of hearing conservation.

Discovery of hearing impairment. Loss in hearing acuity is frequently so gradual that it is imperceptible to the person concerned. Unconsciously a person adapts to a gradual loss of hearing. People with normal hearing do a certain amount of lip reading, and the person whose hearing is declining relies more and more on lip reading. Often the teacher will observe behavior symptoms of hearing difficulty such as posturing, inattention, faulty pronunciation, unnatural voice, poor academic progress, and copying.

However, many children with a hearing defect do not show behavior changes, and a hearing screening test is a more reliable device for the discovery of hearing defectiveness than is the child's outward behavior.

Hearing screening tests. Many adults with markedly defective hearing could have normal or nearly normal hearing if the defect had been discovered when it first began to develop. Youngsters with a small hearing loss, by ingenuity, can compensate for the deficiency, and neither the child, the teacher, nor the parents will ever observe the deficiency in the early stages. A hearing screening test will identify the child who has a hearing loss. In addition to being the first stage in the prevention of further hearing loss, the test may be a step to more effective hearing in the immediate future.

It must be recognized that the hearing screening test is but the first of six steps.

1. Screening test
2. Evaluation of school progress
3. Preliminary medical screening
4. Parent interview
5. Examination and care by family physician
6. Adjustments based on recommendations

Test schedule. Ideally, early in each school year every school child should be given a hearing test. Next best would be a yearly hearing test for every elementary school pupil and tests for high school students whom classroom teachers report as having possible hearing trouble. A minimum program would be a test of all first-grade pupils, supplemented by tests of other children who appear to be having hearing difficulties.

Test procedures. Even a screening test should be as accurate and reliable as possible. If the tests are to be completely accurate, instruments should be available, but the teacher or nurse is obliged to use available equipment.

Whisper tests are not the most accurate, but in the absence of an audiometer the whisper test may be of some value. Its usefulness is determined largely by the skill of the person who administers the test. The tester can gain experience in obtaining the correct whisper volume by practicing with children who are known to have excellent hearing. A room for the test should be reasonably quiet, and only the tester and the child being tested should be in the room. Procedures are simple.

1. The child should be placed 30 feet from the tester and faced in the opposite direction, with his left ear stoppered by his finger. The tester then whispers names of cities, numbers, colors, and other familiar words.
2. If the child is unable to hear at 30 feet, the tester should move up to 25 feet and the child remain stationary. The tester should move up 5 feet and repeat the words until the child is able to hear them. If at 10 feet the child is unable to hear the words, the examiner should move a man's pocket watch slowly up behind the child's ear and ask him to indicate as soon as possible what he can hear. Obviously a child whose hearing is so defective that he cannot hear a whisper at 10 feet needs immediate medical attention. The child who cannot hear a whisper at 30 feet also has sufficient hearing loss to need medical attention.
3. The test is repeated for the other ear.
4. A child with normal hearing should be able to hear the whisper at 30 feet.

Audiometer tests are most reliable and should be used. A pure-tone audiometer is simple to operate. A person need not have a master's degree in speech pathology and ear disorders (audiologist) or even have a baccalaureate degree in speech and hearing (audiometrist) in order to operate the pure-tone audiometer. A brief training session is usually adequate. The manual of instructions clearly explains the operation of the instrument.

In some states the state department of health provides the services of audiometrists and audiometers for all of the school districts in the state. It is an excellent service for school districts which do not feel disposed to buy an audiometer.

Fig. 17. Pure-tone audiometer group test. If the eyes of the children are closed, the test can assume the value of an individual test. (Courtesy Oregon State Board of Health, Portland, Ore.)

A quiet room should be used for the test. All the children in a group of ten can be tested at the same time. At various frequencies from 250 to 6000 per second, sounds are sent into the earphones of each child. Instrument controls send the sounds into either the right or left phone for each child. The operator increases the volume, and each child raises his hand as soon as he hears the sound. To eliminate the possibility that the child might be influenced by other children raising their hands, the operator can cut out any one earphone. Or the children can be asked to keep their eyes closed. A loss up to 15 decibels is within the normal range. As shown in the audiogram in Fig. 18, the subject had normal hearing in the left ear, but had a loss of 20 decibels at 1000 frequencies, 30 decibels at 2000, 30 decibels at 3000, and 20 decibels at 4000 frequencies in the right ear. This degree of loss is outside of the normal. Yet, this child could hear adequately in the classroom since it is the loss in the better ear which is important, and the child had normal hearing in the one ear. However, the other ear is important, too. Perhaps the defect can be corrected. About 8% of elementary school pupils fail the group pure-tone audiometer test. That is, they will show more than 15 decibels loss. These students should be given individual tests, using the same audiometer. This individual testing will indicate that 5% of the elementary school pupils have a hearing loss. Further steps are followed for these children.

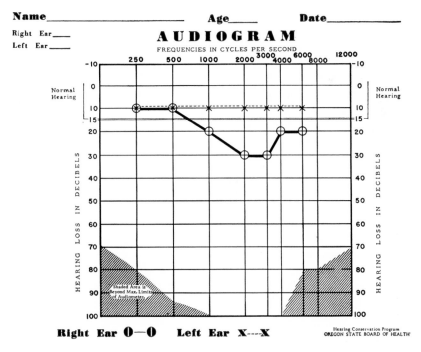

Fig. 18. Audiogram. The diagram indicates normal hearing in the left ear, but in the right ear a loss of 20 decibels at frequencies of 1000, 4000, and 6000 per second and a loss of 30 decibels at frequencies of 2000 and 3000 per second.

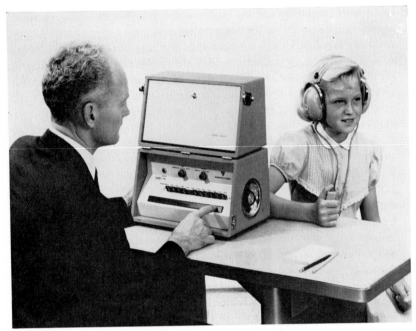

Fig. 19. Audiometer test of individual pupils. Those pupils in a group test who appear to have a hearing difficulty can be tested individually. In some school situations all pupils are tested individually. (Courtesy Focus, vol. 1, no. 1, May 1963, Bausch & Lomb, Inc., Rochester, N. Y.)

Follow-up. The next step is to review the child's progress in school and look for a possible relationship to hearing acuity. Following this review of his school history the child might profitably be given an examination of the ears, nose, and throat by the health officer or school physician if one is available. The next step is an interview with the parents. After explaining the findings, the nurse or other school representative obtains a history of ear trouble and related disorders. The parents are then urged to refer the child to a physician. All information obtained up to this point is made available to the physician. A physician's examination and recommendation for care are the logical outcome of the previous attention given to the child. It now is a problem for the medical profession, but the school may be called upon to contribute to the final step—adjustment.

Many persons and even organizations may work together to help a child with defective hearing make the necessary adjustment. The program may include special classroom seating, tutoring in academic subjects, instruction in lip reading, guidance, speech therapy, and auditory training.

Height and weight measures

Perhaps the practice of weighing and measuring has been the most firmly established aspect of the school health program. At one time teachers literally worshipped at the shrine of the height-weight-age tables, but fortunately that delusion has vanished.

Purpose of the measures. The primary purpose of recording the height and weight of children is to interest them in their own growth and well-being. As a health education project it is invaluable. Emphasis should be placed upon interesting a child in his own condition, not in comparing him with a standard table or with other children. Each child is an individual in his own right. No two are alike. One may be tall and heavily built; another may be short and slender. An effort should be made to interest each child in his own condition and in that which is best for him.

Procedures. A group discussion and an analysis of the signification of height and weight should precede the weighing and measuring. Other aspects of health can be incorporated into the discussion to develop a desirable interest in each child.

Formal records should be made three times a year—the first week of school, the first week of the second semester, and the final week of the school year. On a card (e.g., one shaped like a milk bottle) the child will keep a record along with that kept by his teacher on his health record card. Children can be taught to weigh and measure although the little ones will need considerable help. The children keep their shoes on during both weighing and measuring, and proper deductions are made for them (e.g., 1 pound for weight and 1 inch for height). Scales should be available at all times for children interested in weighing and measuring between the class projects.

Evaluation. Weighing and measuring are not without merit. Ingenious teachers make weighing and measuring a stimulating group and individual experience. Even the location of the scales can be significant. To complete the picture, an extensive group discussion should grow out of the experience. Individual teacher-pupil conferences may be indicated. No child should lose status as a result of the weighing and measuring. Every child should "gain." If a child is in good health, the fact that he is shorter and less heavy than others is of minor significance. The child may have a father who is barely 5 feet tall and a mother even less than 5 feet tall. Height and weight, as a part of a total picture, may have significance. In this light, weighing and measuring is an aspect of health appraisal. Extreme underweight or extreme overweight may present opportunities for the teacher to be of service to the child.

Inspection for cleanliness

In the elementary school perhaps no problem is more delicate than that of personal cleanliness. Few teachers have the frankness to tell parents that their children are not clean. Teachers are reluctant even to tell a child outright that he is not clean. Yet, personal cleanliness and cleanliness in the classroom are important.

Purpose. Cleanliness is primarily an esthetic attribute rather than a health factor. However, washing the hands with soap and water may be significant in preventing the spread of communicable diseases. General personal cleanliness also has mental health values. A pride in personal appearance can well be the avenue to important personal health practices.

An assessment of cleanliness on a classroom basis can be an impersonal approach to a very personal matter. It utilizes group participation, acceptance, and influence. It can be positive if cleanliness, not a lack of it, is emphasized. A highly efficient and completely satisfactory program to assess cleanliness has been developed.

Procedures. In this program, soap, water, towels, and other essentials must be available in the school. Toothpicks to be used for cleaning fingernails can be of value. Cleanliness must be attainable at school if children are to be afforded the necessary experience of learning by doing. Yet, the program is relatively simple.

1. All children in the room must be prepared by means of a preliminary class discussion so that each child understands the what, why, and how of cleanliness standards.
2. Each classroom is provided with a 6 x 9 inch score card (Fig. 20).
3. The nurse or teacher makes the first inspection. Children are asked to spread their fingers and rotate their hands as the nurse or teacher passes up the aisle.
4. The nurse or teacher observes cleanliness of the skin, nails, ears, hair, and clothes.
5. If in a class of 40 children, 36 are tidy, the class gets a score of 9/10 of 60 or 54.
6. Then, in turn, desks, floor, walls, and cloakroom (or locker area) are inspected for tidiness and scored.
7. Inspections are made at irregular intervals, usually just before the recess period.
8. Later the children assume the task of inspection by electing one of their number to make the inspection.
9. The score card is placed in a prominent place in the classroom.

Evaluation. Since the unclean children are at no time identified, possibility of stigma is reduced to a minimum. Children will have a fairly good idea who brought the score down. Experience has shown that these erring children themselves will recognize their deficiency and, if facilities are available, will strive to correct the condition. Thus, with a minimum

CLEANLINESS RECORD _____ School _____ Grade Year_____	POSSIBLE SCORE	Date							
Child Cleanliness	60								
Desks and Seats	10								
Floors	10								
Walls	10								
CLOAKROOM OR LOCKER AREA....	10								
Total	100								

Fig. 20. Cleanliness record card. If the children keep records, too, it will add to the effectiveness of the record card.

of hurt feelings, a class group can attain a high level of personal cleanliness. Every opportunity should be given the group to improve its score, but the value of personal cleanliness should be given major emphasis. Although some educators may question the method, self-competition can be wholesomely motivating. Each room competes with itself, not with another room.

Health guidance and supervision

What happens to a student's health status is important today, and the school traditionally has accepted the role of supervising the health of the child during school hours. In practice such supervision at school corresponds to the type of immediate supervision the conscientious parent would exercise in the home. More than just the protection and maintenance of the child's health are inherent in the school's health supervision.

Any school health program must be appraised in terms of its effect upon the health of the individual student. No phase of the school health program has a more direct effect upon the immediate health of the student than does guidance and supervision of his health. The effect will be reflected in the health of the student in future years if the guidance and supervision have been effective in developing the student's ability to guide his own health. This phase must be a carefully planned, integrated program which is centered on the student's health.

School administrators have experienced increasing difficulty in obtaining medical service for the school. Physicians in private practice have had less and less time and inclination to serve the school, except for special purposes. Small and medium-sized school systems have been forced to proceed without the services of a school physician or have been obliged to provide makeshift arrangements for occasional service of a physician who can spare a morning for a clinic on some special health problem. In consequence, except in metropolitan schools, health guidance and supervision by a physician do not exist.

Absence of a school physician does not eliminate an effective program of health guidance and supervision. It makes that supervision even more necessary. Indeed proper use of available private medical services depends upon an effective school guidance program. Such a program not only guides the health of the student, but also aims to develop the student's ability to guide his own health.

Basic concepts. Guidance is a matter of aiding the student in the direction of his own affairs. It encompasses all the processes of acquainting the student with his endowment, the sources from which he may draw benefit in developing his talents, and the channels through which his endowment may best assert itself. The Education Policies Commission stated, "Guidance is a way of helping boys and girls to plan their own actions wisely, in full light of all the facts that can be mustered about themselves and about the world in which they live and work."

Health guidance is concerned with the process of acquainting a per-

son with various ways in which he may discover and use his natural endowment so that he may live to the best advantage to himself and to society. Guidance means accepting each pupil as an independent personality. Effective guidance means developing the student's ability in self-
guidance. If the student continues to lean heavily on the guidance person, the guidance has not been effective. As revealed diagrammatically in
Fig. 21, page 174, the guidance person should play a diminishing role and
the student an increasing role in the guidance. Development of the student's self-direction is the goal.

Responsibility. That the school health program and the school general guidance program experienced a parallel growth in America is not a
mere coincidence. Both health and guidance grew out of the transition to
functional education. Both are concerned primarily with the student as
an individual and with his over-all well-being. Because of the direction
in which education is now developing, guidance is no longer incidental,
but is an integral part of the total education process. Leaders in education support the view that all teachers have a role in guidance. These
leaders also recognize that people in the school health program are in a
strategic position to make a unique contribution to the school guidance
program and consequently to the fullest development of each student.
The 1951 Annual Report of the American Association of School Administrators lists the health educator's duties as a counselor-specialist as follows:

1. To convey to pupils a clearer understanding of their growth and health
   problems.
2. To help pupils develop a sense of responsibility in meeting personal and family health problems.
3. To interpret to parents the significance of health appraisal findings and to
   assist them in obtaining appropriate health care for their children.
4. To contribute to the health education of both pupils and parents by utilizing the potentialities for education that are inherent in all health appraisal
   and counseling activities.
5. To assist all pupils with non-remediable defects to obtain programs adapted
   to their interests and needs with due consideration for their disabilities.
6. To work with community groups to assure the availability of treatment facilities for all children.*

Although health guidance has long been accepted as an essential
school service, how the health guidance program should be organized,
how it should be administered, what it should encompass, who should
participate, and what professional training for health guidance is necessary have never been clearly delineated. Some school districts in the nation have established health guidance programs in response to existing
local situations. This pragmatic pioneer approach is commendable, and
the experiences of these independent and widely dispersed districts have

*From American Association of School Administrators: Health in schools, Twen-
tieth Yearbook, Washington, D. C., 1951, National Education Association, p. 261.

served as pilot studies to guide those who follow. What is needed is a synthesis of that which experience has already demonstrated to be functional and an integration of the best of all these programs into a practical, workable, well-defined program of health guidance

In a study conducted by H. E. Petersen in 1954 and 1955, a group of seventy-five nationally recognized guidance specialists, a group of seventy-five nationally recognized health education specialists, and a group of one hundred secondary school health educators agreed on the guidance functions of health educators in the public school program. These three groups agreed on the responsibilities in which the health educator had a major role. Just as any other member of the school staff, the health educator has an incidental role in other areas. However, the guidance responsibility of the health educator can be well portrayed by listing the areas in which health educators have a major responsibility as agreed upon by the three groups of educators.

I. Home and family problems
   1. Parent-student relationship
II. Boy-girl relationships
   1. Adjustments to other sex
   2. Dating
   3. Going steady
   4. Marriage
   5. Sex problems
III. Personal-social problems
   1. Appearance
IV. Mental health problems
   1. Conflicts
   2. Frustrations
   3. Fears
   4. Depressions
   5. Insecurity
   6. Marked inferiority feelings
   7. Personality clashes
   8. Oversensitivity
   9. Daydreaming
   10. Overcompensation

V. Physical health problems
   1. Vision
   2. Hearing
   3. Speech
   4. Orthopedic disorders
   5. Skin
   6. Posture
   7. Feet
   8. Nutrition
   9. Overweight
   10. Underweight
   11. Fatigue
   12. Diabetes
   13. Epilepsy
   14. Cardiac disorders
   15. General health
VI. Vocational and placement problems
   1. Health requirements
   2. Health assets and liabilities

Perhaps the most significant result of Dr. Petersen's study was the revelation that the guidance specialists almost unanimously maintained that secondary school health educators have an extremely important role to play in the guidance program which they thus far have failed to fulfill. These guidance specialists from outside the field of health have pointed out to those in the health program that health educators have been derelict in their responsibilities and need to make a critical self-appraisal of their guidance role.

With guidance specialists in virtual unanimity that school health personnel should participate actively as members of the school guidance team, it is most unfortunate that the same guidance specialists feel compelled to criticize school health personnel for not participating in the organized guidance program. Health educators particularly, they contend, tend to be too isolated and to play a lone hand and generally do not see the complete picture. Health educators who see secondary school students every day of the school week are in a position to acquire an understanding of each child's capabilities, interests, needs, and liabilities. Health personnel develop a desirable rapport with these children which can be of enormous value in the general guidance program. These functions, plus the knowledge that a member of the school health staff has, make it possible for health personnel to make a distinct contribution to the over-all school guidance program. Although some independent health counseling will be both necessary and justified, school health personnel must begin to think of their contribution as part of the larger program, not as an isolated island in the sea of education.

Health educators must begin to think less of health as an academic subject. Health instruction is but a means to an end, and the over-all goal is the fullest possible development of a student's endowment. It is represented in the quality of well-being the student maintains and in his ability to make the necessary decisions relating to his own health. These are important outcomes of the health program, but health personnel also contribute to other aspects of the student's personal development. By participation in an organized school guidance program, school health personnel can offer the broader more valuable services which are effective in terms of service to the student.

Counseling is a procedure of guidance and is a form of mutual deliberation which consists of examination of the items which will aid a child in comprehending his problem and understanding its solution. The school counselor does not make the final decision. He may aid the student or the parent to arrive at a solution, but the final decision rests other than with the counselor. Counseling may be helping a child to see his health needs and to find the medical or other service he needs. It may be a matter of working out a pattern of living to attain a maximum level of health. Counseling also can be an instrument to help each child develop a full appreciation of the valuable asset he has in good health and to inculcate a determination to promote and protect that asset. It may be an avenue through which a student visualizes his future needs and accomplishments.

As a sequel to Dr. Petersen's study, I attempted to determine the specific guidance responsibilities of secondary school educators as recognized by college health education specialists and guidance specialists. The intended purpose of this study was to identify the specific functions of secondary school health educators in the guidance area. College health education specialists and guidance specialists were in agreement that there are specific guidance functions with which secondary school health personnel should be concerned. Both groups contend that these functions must be considered a part of the over-all guidance program, even though individuals in the school health program may be immediately responsible for certain of these functions.

1. To assist the guidance services program in the secondary schools as a resource or referral person or health counselor
2. To be a member of the guidance team or council and assist the other members in dealing with students' personal, mental, and physical health problems
3. To arrange necessary in-service training programs as they relate to health for the teaching staff
4. To assist in arranging for the promotion of medical and dental examinations of students
5. To share appropriately in recording, filing, and maintaining health records
6. To keep the school staff suitably informed about pertinent health problems and needs of individual students as reported from professional and other sources
7. To serve as a member of the health team in the appraisal of student health status
8. To assist the student and others concerned in determining the student's health assets and liabilities for vocational and placement purposes
9. To assist in arranging for and conducting hearing and vision screening tests
10. To play a major role in sight and hearing conservation practices and in correction of posture and foot disorders
11. To participate appropriately in conferences with parents on student health problems
12. To prepare and submit appropriate phases of the student's health history at case conference
13. To assist in analyzing and evaluating pertinent case data
14. To assume suitable responsibility for referrals
15. To plan meetings of the health education staff and teacher-health education conferences
16. To promote parent group conferences on health
17. To serve in a coordinating role among school, home, and community health resources
18. To correlate health teaching with other fields of instruction
19. To promote proper first-aid procedures when sudden illness or accidents occur
20. To stimulate, direct, and implement results of research projects

A logical corollary of these two studies was a third study to determine the roles of the health educator and nurse in those secondary schools of the nation with excellent relatively complete health programs. To obtain an acceptable sample, directors of health education in the various state departments of education were asked to submit the names of high schools in the state which had outstanding school health programs, with health guidance as an important phase. Subsequent survey returns showed that 657 secondary schools had health educators and a school or public health nurse who participated in the health program. Every state in the United States and Alaska and Hawaii, which were still territories, were represented in the 657 schools. Responsible administrative heads were asked to report specific information. It is significant that 95% of the schools which reported had a general organized guidance program. In addition in 70% of the schools the health educator was a member of the guidance team, and in 72% the school nurse was a member of the guidance team. These administrators were also asked to report whether the health educator, the nurse, or some other person had first, second, or third responsibility for certain guidance functions. A condensed portion of these data is both interesting and revealing (Table 9).

Table 9. *Per cent of responsibility for health service functions for specific duties*

Health services functions	First responsibility		
	H.ed.	*Nurse*	*Other*
Counseling in the area of			
Boy-girl relationships	.397	.171	.432
Personal-social problems	.300	.122	.577
Mental health problems	.310	.160	.529
Physical health problems	.368	.487	.145
Moral problems	.265	.112	.624
Health assets and liabilities	.433	.406	.161
Individual physical capacities	.420	.316	.264
Vocational health requirements	.305	.189	.506
Parent conferences			
Student health appraisal	.207	.564	.229
Counseling on referral defects	.167	.638	.195
Health appraisal			
Appraise health status	.305	.466	.230
Appraise health attitudes	.535	.314	.151
Administer vision and hearing tests	.194	.571	.234
Remedial measures			
Sight conservation	.207	.568	.225
Hearing conservation	.210	.527	.263
Posture correction	.458	.244	.298
Foot correction	.351	.429	.221
Prepare health histories	.154	.673	.173
Referrals to determine nature of defects	.156	.637	.207
Coordination			
School and home	.153	.529	.318
School and community resources	.276	.420	.304
Organizing and planning			
Staff health progress meetings	.428	.289	.283
In-service health preparation	.424	.306	.271
Parent group conferences	.289	.367	.344
Health classes for parents	.314	.443	.243
Responsibility for health records	.168	.677	.155
Composite	.299	.407	.294

Second responsibility			Third responsibility		
H.ed.	*Nurse*	*Other*	*H.ed.*	*Nurse*	*Other*
.250	.375	.375	.282	.487	.231
.426	.382	.191	.390	.463	.146
.316	.456	.228	.375	.475	.150
.325	.260	.415	.162	.081	.757
.525	.328	.147	.233	.667	.100
.344	.410	.246	.212	.030	.758
.283	.533	.183	.226	.194	.580
.338	.523	.138	.313	.406	.281
.459	.246	.295	.355	.065	.581
.317	.183	.500	.515	.030	.455
.383	.450	.167	.214	.036	.750
.153	.559	.288	.152	.212	.636
.341	.439	.220	.083	.083	.833
.413	.326	.261	.263	.053	.684
.413	.326	.261	.333	.056	.611
.180	.660	.160	.318	.182	.500
.321	.491	.188	.167	.111	.722
.395	.209	.395	.364	.045	.591
.452	.193	.355	.267	.100	.633
.397	.270	.333	.500	.071	.429
.288	.407	.305	.433	.167	.400
.178	.555	.267	.320	.240	.440
.211	.684	.105	.250	.125	.625
.235	.500	.265	.500	.050	.450
.250	.333	.417	.300	.100	.600
.333	.125	.542	.455	.045	.500
.353	.388	.277	.311	.202	.487

From these data it is clear that the health educator has a highly significant role in the sphere of health counseling in those programs which have the services of a nurse as well as other personnel. Evidence is unmistakable that, in the secondary schools with a relatively full complement of health personnel, the health educator is playing a prominent role. In many guidance services he has primary responsibility. In others he plays a secondary or lesser role. The inference is also clear that in those secondary schools without the services of a nurse the health educator will be called upon to assume an even greater guidance responsibility than is manifest in the programs studied here.

In view of these data some basic conclusions can be drawn.

1. The health educator is already called upon to provide health guidance.
2. It is logical to assume that the scope of his services will be extended.
3. The health educator's training in basic health science must be fortified.
4. Health educators need sound preparation in the guidance field. Perhaps a graduate minor in guidance is in order.
5. Continuing studies must be conducted to determine the direction health guidance in the school must take.
6. Studies must be conducted to determine the most effective methods and techniques for health guidance.

The school health program is destined to grow. The profession must grow with it and can grow with it only by becoming competent in the services it is expected to give. Health guidance will become an increasingly more important function of the health educator, and the health educator will have an increasingly more important role in the secondary school general guidance program.

Primary responsibility for the health of the child must always rest with the parent, but the school is in a strategic position to complement and supplement the efforts of the parents by dealing with the expressed and observed health problems of the individual students. Nothing in their teaching experience will give teachers more satisfaction and gratification than what they do in behalf of the physical, mental, and emotional health of children. A small improvement in a student's health today can be reflected in better health for 60 or even 70 years more. After all, the best and fullest development of each child is the cardinal objective of the school. Subject matter and other learning are important, but only as a means to an end—the development of the student. It would be incongruous to teach a child about health and disregard his existing health problems. The extent to which a person can succeed, the height to which he can rise, is conditioned by the quality of his health. It is incumbent upon everyone in the school health profession to do everything within his means to assure each child the fullest possible development of his native endowment as a vehicle for effective and enjoyable living today and in the unpredictable years ahead.

Except for those problems peculiar to a child of high school age the elementary school teacher should accept responsibility for guidance in the areas here specified. Both the opportunity and responsibility for guidance rest with the elementary classroom teacher.

It is not intended that the elementary school teacher nor the secondary school health educator be experts in the various areas listed. Their guidance role is to help the student understand his problem, to see a possible solution, and to understand which professional people and agencies may be of service to him in solving his problem and meeting his needs.

Organized health guidance makes health instruction more effective by focusing the students' interest upon the appraisal of their own health status and thus making health knowledge personally identifiable and more meaningful.

Student appraisal of personal health. If he is to develop the ability to guide his own health, the student must have a tangible understanding interest in his own health. In the final analysis the student's own health is the concern and object of the whole program and is the logical vehicle by which the program is promoted and his self-guidance is developed.

Whether health is a required or elective course, an effective arrangement is one in which all students take a half year of health during their first year in high school. In the 8-4 plan it would be in the ninth grade and in the 6-3-3 plan in the tenth grade. The final half of the course is deferred until the senior year.

At the outset of the first term all of the study in the health class is an appraisal of personal health and the development of a health inventory. Although it is recognized that a thorough technical health examination is necessary for a precise evaluation of a person's health, nevertheless various outward indices which the student can appraise do exist.

Emphasis is on the positive aspect of health. Interest is in health evaluation, not diagnosis of disease. Wise use of medical service is an obvious corollary. Following this rather extended discussion of appraisal of personal health each child, using a health inventory approach, makes an evaluation of his own health status. The health teacher-counselor then schedules individual conferences with each member of the group.

Because of the time consumed by these conferences, the counselor may find it necessary to use actual class periods for appointments, which necessitates assignments which the other class members work out in their class time. Yet, these conferences are of sufficient importance to justify any improvisation necessary.

Counseling is a matter of mutual advising. Ideally the health counselor should be qualified to counsel the student in all aspects of living, not just in the area of health. The well-prepared health counselor can be an effective school counselor.

Before each appointment an effective counselor assembles and studies all available data relating to the health of the next counselee. Personal history, health examination records, dental records, inspections, vision tests, and other data are appraised in advance of the consultation.

At the conference the counselor establishes rapport as soon as possible to place the student in the most favorable situation for presenting his evaluation of his health. The counselor incorporates those findings he deems pertinent in arriving at a joint appraisal of the student's health status. Together, a future course of action is planned which will enable the student to make the most of his native endowment and to live most effectively and enjoyably. Health goals are made definite and practical. Few people attain anywhere near 100% of their health potentialities, partially because there is no definite lifetime plan for health promotion.

Out of this conference a confidential relationship between counselor and student which will be effective throughout the high school years should develop. Out of it should come a student-centered health program, in and out of the health class.

At the outset of the student's new program in health the counselor provides a considerable portion of the health guidance, but the aim should be to reduce the counselor's contribution and increase the student's ability to guide himself. The object is to develop the student's ability. His growth in self-guidance is an important index of the effectiveness of the teacher's work.

Should a woman guide the girls and a man guide the boys? Should the health counselor have no teaching responsibilities other than health? Ideally, perhaps the answer to both questions should be in the affirmative. Yet, practical administrative considerations make modifications necessary. In one four-year high school of 520 students a man who serves as health counselor for boys also teaches biological science, whereas the woman who serves as health counselor for girls also directs physical education for girls. In another high school a woman has charge of the entire secondary school health program.

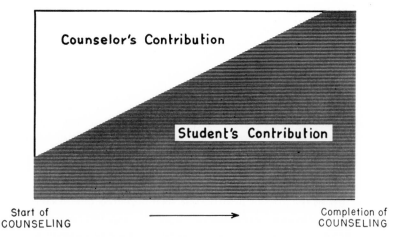

Fig. 21. Counselor and student contributions in health counseling. At the outset the counselor makes a considerable contribution, but reduces his role as the student increases his contribution. The final objective is to develop the student's ability to rely on his own resources.

As an outgrowth of the student's interest in his own health the alert health educator will ensure that all materials used in health classes are functional in terms of possible value to each student's health interest and promotion. The student-centered concept will be projected to all student experiences which might have personal health implications.

During the senior year the half unit of health provides opportunities to crystallize the student's health interests, experiences, and problems into an integral part of his attitudes, practices, and knowledge which will result in graduates with a definite functional health outlook, lifelong in its effectiveness.

Guidance which follows this pattern will logically encompass preventive and remedial aspects of health. Need for immunization or the correction of defects, by their very nature, suggests the value of guidance.

Teaching and counseling. In many respects teaching and counseling are similar. Many of their objectives are the same. Teaching attempts to obtain these objectives through classroom situations. Counseling seeks these objectives through counseling relationships. This distinction is admirably aligned by the Michigan State University Institute of Counseling, Testing and Guidance.

Teaching	Counseling
1. The teacher needs to know pupils so that educational objectives are attained and normal growth processes encouraged.	1. The counselor needs to know pupils in terms of specific problems, frustrations, and plans for the future.
2. The subject matter outcomes (or objectives) to be attained are known to the teacher.	2. The subject matter of the interview is unknown to the counselor and sometimes unknown to the counselee.
3. The teacher is responsible for encouraging growth toward objectives partially determined by the social order (citizenship, honesty). The teacher has a responsibility for the welfare of the culture.	3. The counselor is responsible for helping the counselee resolve his own personal problems. The counselor has a responsibility for the welfare of the counselee.
4. Teaching starts with a group relationship and individual contacts grow out of and return to group activities.	4. Counseling starts with an individual relationship and moves to group situations for greater efficiency or to supplement the individual process.
5. The teacher is responsible for the welfare of many children at one time.	5. The counselor is responsible for only one person at any one time.
6. The teacher carries on most of her work directly with children.	6. The counselor works with and through many people. Referral resources and techniques are of considerable importance.
7. The teacher uses skill in group techniques with great frequency—whereas interviewing skills are used less often.	7. The counselor uses interviewing skills as a basic technique.

Continued on next page.

Teaching—cont'd	Counseling—cont'd
8. The teacher uses tests, records, and inventories to assist the instructional (educational) process.	8. The counselor uses tests, records, and inventories to discover factors relating to a problem. The results are used for problem-solving (therapeutic) purposes.
9. The teacher has many tools (curriculum outlines, books, workbooks, and visual and auditory aids) to increase her effectiveness.	9. The counselor has no tools which are used with all the counselees. She must first help the counselee discover problems and their causes and then the individually appropriate sources of assistance.
10. The teacher needs to increase her information relating to instructional activities.	10. The counselor needs information not frequently used by teachers; information about occupations, training institutions, colleges, apprenticeship programs, community occupational opportunities, placement, referral resources, social service agencies, and diagnostic and clinical instruments.
11. The teacher has a "compelled" relationship. Children are required to be there.	11. The most effective counseling comes from a voluntary association. The counselee must want help and must feel that the counselor can be helpful.
12. The teacher deals with children, the majority of whose adjustments are happy and satisfying.	12. The counselor's clients are disturbed by frustrations. They are often characterized by emotional tensions, previous disappointments, and lack of confidence.
13. The teacher is much concerned with the day-to-day growth of pupils and with their general development.	13. The counselor is concerned with the counselee's immediate problems and choices, but she is also interested in helping the counselee develop workable long-term plans.
14. The skillful teacher tries to develop many abilities which increase her instructional effectiveness.	14. The skillful counselor tries to develop many of the abilities used by a wide variety of highly technical specialists; psychiatrist, clinical psychologist, test technicians, occupational information specialists, social workers, visiting teachers, juvenile delinquency workers, placement officers, etc.

Health and the teacher

Too frequently the teacher's health is considered merely in terms of the teacher being a possible reservoir of disease. In consequence many programs of teacher health deal essentially in terms of the prevention of the spread of disease from the teacher to the children. That the teacher can be a source of spread of communicable diseases is readily recognized, and appropriate action should be taken to prevent this. However, from the more positive approach promotion of good health for teachers should yield returns in a better school program. Teachers with a high level of health usually will do a more effective teaching job than those who have a low level of health. School boards, school administrators, and parents should concern themselves with those factors which are most likely to ensure the highest possible quality of health in the teachers so that they can give a high level of teaching. The responsibility for the teacher's health does not rest entirely with the teacher.

Health examination of the teacher. Some school districts require a health examination certificate of every teacher employed by the district for the first time. The examination usually includes a test for tuberculosis. Other districts require an annual x-ray examination of the chest, but no general examination. A third approach requires an examination every third year and an annual test for tuberculosis, supplemented by additional examinations following illness or as otherwise indicated. From a practical standpoint this plan has merit. It is a standard any school district can attain, and it will assure a good appraisal of each teacher's health. A few schools achieve the ideal of an annual health examination including a test for tuberculosis, supplemented by additional examinations as indicated.

There is no legal question of the board's authority to require that all teachers have health examinations. Usually the state department of education and the state health department, with the cooperation of the state medical society, develop a standard examination form. Local school districts may have their own health certificate forms or may accept the report used by any practicing physician. Logically the board of education which requires a health examination of its teachers should pay for the examination. This has been the practice of private industry and should be followed by school districts. A test for tuberculosis is usually obtained without cost, and some physicians perform the health examinations without charge to the teacher. Yet, the school, which benefits by the examination, should assume all or at least part of the costs involved.

Promotion of teachers' health. Many conditions and factors in the school can contribute wholesomely to the promotion of the health of the teaching staff. None of these factors is novel or unique; some or all of them exist in many schools today. Further they place no great burden on the school administration or the school patrons. An investment in these factors is an investment in a better school, with an end result of students who are better prepared.

Teaching loads not to exceed forty hours a week with midmorning and midafternoon breaks yield a better quality of work in school as in industry.

Rest rooms for teachers provide the opportunity for necessary relaxation away from the pressing tasks of the classroom.

Lunch hour should have a minimum of responsibility. If the responsibility for supervision of the lunchroom and noon-hour activities is divided among the teachers, all will have some lunch hours that are free for relaxation.

A healthy emotional environment in the school is one in which tensions are resolved as soon as possible and in which the teacher knows her status, feels she is appreciated, is reasonably secure, succeeds, and knows she can rely upon the support of her administrators in solving special problems.

Sick leave of ten days a year with pay and an accumulation of sick leave up to sixty days help to assure the district that only well teachers are in the school. The implications are clear although some school boards fail to appreciate the economy of the plan.

Medical and hospital insurance is always available, and the teacher should expect to pay the premium. However, group programs often offer a better policy and should be encouraged by the school administration.

Tenure may prevent the discharge of a teacher merely on the whim of one administrator. Terms of tenure should be stated in the teacher's notice of appointment. No person is totally secure, but tenure does make a teacher somewhat more secure professionally. However, tenure is not a license to neglect professional duties and do slipshod work. It is a reciprocal agreement.

Retirement provisions have health implications, especially when a teacher may retire voluntarily before 65 years of age because she feels she no longer can do an adequate job. All measures designed to aid the teacher carry with them obligations on the part of the teacher to give the students the best possible education. Students, teachers, and parents benefit from the school's efforts to promote the highest possible level of health for the teaching staff.

Selected readings

American Medical Association, Department of Health Education: Physicians and schools, report of the Eighth National Conference on Physicians and Schools, Chicago, 1961, The Association.

American Medical Association: Physician participation in school health services, Chicago, 1950, The Association.

American Public Health Association, School Health Section: Suggested standards for health services in secondary schools, American Journal of Public Health Yearbook, 1951-1952.

Blum, H. L., Peters, H. B., and Bettman, J. W.: Vision screening for elementary schools, Berkeley, 1959, University of California Press.

Committee on School Health: Priorities in health services for children of school age, Washington, D. C., 1950, United States Department of Health, Education and Welfare.

Dukelow, D. A., and Hein, F. V. (editors): Physicians and schools, report of the Fifth National Conference on Physicians and Schools, Chicago, 1956, American Medical Association.

Foord, A. M.: Guiding the pupils physical and emotional well-being, National Elementary Principal 34:102, 1954.

Gardner, W. H.: Instructions for conducting audiometer tests, Washington, D. C., 1940, American Hearing Society.

Geyer, M. A.: Counseling for physically impaired students in high school, Personnel and Guidance Journal 32:214, 1953.

Joint Committee on Health Problems in Education of the National Education Association and the American Medical Association (Bernice R. Moss, W. H. Southworth, and

J. L. Reichart, editors): Health education, Washington, D. C., 1961, National Education Association.

Keene, C. H.: School health services, Journal of School Health **23**:23-24, 51-59, 88-96, 1953.

Massachusetts Department of Public Health: The Massachusetts vision test, Auburn, New York, The Welch-Allyne Co.

Maxwell, C. H.: School health examinations, Journal of School Health **20**:140, 1950.

National Education Association and American Medical Association: Health education, Washington, D. C., 1961, National Education Association.

National Education Association and American Medical Association: Health appraisal of school children, Washington, D. C., 1957, National Education Association.

National Society for the Prevention of Blindness: An eye health program for schools, New York, 1943, The Society.

National Society for the Prevention of Blindness: Screening, eye examinations and follow up. New York, 1945, The Society.

National Society for the Prevention of Blindness: The Snellen eye chart, New York, The Society.

National Society for the Prevention of Blindness: Vision screening in schools, Pub. P257, New York, 1961, The Society.

Rogers, J. F.: What every teacher should know about the physical condition of her pupils, Washington, D. C., 1945, United States Office of Education, Pamphlet no. 68.

Rosencrance, Francis, and Hayden, Velma: School guidance and personnel services, Boston, 1960, Allyn & Bacon, Inc.

Schlesinger, E. R.: Health services for the child, New York, 1953, McGraw-Hill Book Co., Inc.

Strang, Ruth: Techniques of counseling in regard to health programs, American Journal of Public Health, **39**:886, 1949.

Troester, C. A., and Avery, Elizabeth S.: Legislation for school health services, Journal of Public Health, Physical Education and Recreation, January, 1950.

United States Public Health Service: Planning for health services: A guide for states and communities, Washington, D. C., 1949, United States Public Health Service, Public Health Bulletin no. 304.

Washington State Board of Education: Guide for the school health service program, Olympia, 1947, Washington State Board of Education.

Waters, Jane: Group guidance: Principles and practices, New York, 1960, McGraw-Hill Book Co., Inc.

Wheathley, G. M., and Hallock, Grace T.: Health observation of school children, ed. 2, New York, 1956, McGraw-Hill Book Co., Inc.

Willey, R. D.: Guidance in elementary education, rev. ed., New York, 1960, Harper & Brothers.

Tis an odious kind of remedy to owe your health to disease.

—Ben Jonson

Chapter 8

Preventive aspects of health services—control of communicable diseases

T he school today is concerned with the prevention of all possible diseases and defects. Yet, in day-to-day practice its primary attention is directed to the prevention of communicable diseases even though the incidence of infectious diseases in the school population continues to decline. Perhaps this very decline is but a reflection of the school's attention to the problem.

Communicable disease

Disease is a harmful departure from the normal state of health. A communicable disease is one which can be transmitted from one person to another or from other animals to man. It involves parasites which are pathogenic to man. Most of the organisms involved are microscopic although some of the worms and even mites which affect man are visible to the unaided human eye. Of the microscopic pathogens bacteria cause the greatest number of communicable diseases. However, true fungi and protozoa are serious offenders also.

Infection and disinfection

Infection is the successful invasion of the body by pathogenic organisms under conditions which permit them to multiply and harm the body. The mere presence of organisms in the body does not comprise infection. At a given moment a high percentage of persons harbor pneumococcus bacteria in the lungs without having pneumonia, and all of us have billions of *Streptococcus albus* on the skin without having acne. Harm to the body usually is due to the toxin (biological poison) produced by the organism though some organisms invade and damage tissues directly. To multiply and thrive the pathogens of man require a temperature of about 98.6° F. (37°C.), moisture, alkalinity, darkness, and nutrients. Man's body provides these optimum conditions.

The body reacts to infection by an increased production of white

Table 10. *Incidence of acute and chronic illness by sex per 1000 persons 5 to 14 years of age, 1957, State of California**

Diagnosis	Boys	Girls
Common cold, sore throat, cough, nasopharyngitis	1776	1774
Accidents	1010	848
Bronchitis and chest cold	254	175
Asthma and hay fever	223	133
Intestinal influenza	209	270
Indigestion	205	213
Common childhood diseases	240	190
Allergies (other than asthma and hay fever)	169	118
Diseases of ear and mastoid, including deafness	120	100
Migraine and headache	98	128
Chronic tonsillitis or sore throat	93	152

*Courtesy California State Department of Public Health, Sacramento, Calif., Health Survey, 1957.

blood cells, elevation in body temperature, inflammation caused by blood gorged in the localized area, and pain. These body defenses may be sufficient to overcome the infection.

Disinfection is killing or removing the pathogens of infection or arresting their activity so that the defense mechanisms of the body can overcome the invader. Disinfection mechanisms are:

1. Oxidation of the organism
2. Dehydration (dessication) of the organism
3. Hydrolysis (hydration)
4. Coagulation of cell proteins
5. Destruction of enzymes

Chemical disinfectants are generally used for infections. Tincture of iodine, Argyrol, gentian violet, Mercresin, Metaphen, Merthiolate, Zephiran, and alcohol dilutions are examples. A disinfectant must be effective without causing damage to living tissues.

Contamination and decontamination

Contamination is the presence of pathogens of man or nonpathogenic organisms *(Escherichia coli)* of man's alimentary canal on inanimate objects, which cannot react. Thus, one speaks of a contaminated handkerchief, glass, water supply, or quart of milk, but one speaks of an infected finger, tonsil, or intestine. Water is said to be contaminated if it contains *E. coli* because it is assumed that discharges from human beings are infesting the water since these nonpathogens inhabit the human colon. Milk is a good medium for the pathogens of man, but other inanimate objects are poor media because pathogens live but a matter of seconds in light, dryness, and low temperature. Inanimate articles, other than milk, water, and solid foods, which harbor pathogenic organisms are called fomites.

Decontamination is killing or removing the pathogens and *E. coli* in or on inanimate objects. Severe methods, such as burning, heat, drying, ultraviolet rays, and highly concentrated chemicals such as Lysol can be used.

Causative agents

Knowledge of the classification and nature of organisms causing diseases in man is esstential to a working understanding of the nature of infectious diseases. Most pathogens of man belong to the plant kingdom, as shown in Table 11.

Classification of communicable diseases

Many different systems have been devised for classifying communicable diseases. Each system has a particular basis for classification. Some systems combine several factors. A simple, yet comprehensive, classifica-

Table 11. Classification of pathogens of man

Plants		Animals	
Bacteria (split fungi)		*Protozoa (one cell)*	
Bacillus (rod-shaped)	Diphtheria	Ameba	Dysentery
	Bacillary dysentery		
	Pertussis (whooping cough)	Plasmodium	Malaria
	Tuberculosis		
	Typhoid	Spirochete (spiral)	Syphilis
Coccus (spherical)	Furunculosis (boils)	*Metazoa*	
	Gonorrhea	Round worm	
	Scarlet fever	Tapeworm	
	Streptococcus throat infection	Trichinella	Trichinosis
Spirillum (spiral-shaped)	Cholera		
	Rat bite fever		
Rickettsia (small bacteria)	Rocky Mountain fever		
	Typhus fever		
Virus (ultramicroscopic)	Chickenpox		
	Cold		
	Influenza		
	Measles		
	Mumps		
	Poliomyelitis		
	Rabies		
	Smallpox		
True fungi			
Mold	Tinea (ringworm)		
	Mycosis		
Yeast	Blastomycosis		
	Dermatophytosis		

tion accepted by many people in the health field is one which recognizes four different classes of communicable diseases. Each class title is descriptive of the diseases in the group and incorporates a suggestion of the mode of transmission.

The four classes and some of the more common diseases in each class will indicate the nature of this classification.

I. Respiratory diseases
1. Chickenpox
2. Coryza (head cold)
3. Diphtheria
4. Influenza
5. German measles (rubella)
6. Measles (rubeola)
7. Meningococcus meningitis
8. Mumps (parotitis)
9. Poliomyelitis
10. Rheumatic fever
11. Scarlet fever
12. Smallpox
13. Streptococcal sore throat
14. Tuberculosis
15. Whooping cough (pertussis)

II. Alvine (intestine) discharge diseases
1. Amebic dysentery
2. Bacillary dysentery
3. Typhoid fever

III. Open-lesion diseases
1. Furunculosis (boils)
2. Gonorrhea
3. Impetigo contagiosa
4. Syphilis

IV. Insect-borne diseases
1. Malaria
2. Rocky Mountain fever
3. Tularemia

In the normal school situation the respiratory diseases constitute by far the greatest problem in control. A teacher rarely will encounter the other diseases.

Transmission of infectious disease

Man himself is the great reservoir of organisms which cause disease in human beings. Although other reservoirs exist, the great problem in the control of communicable disease is the prevention of the transmission of organisms from one person to another. The increase in population, the increase in travel, and the congregation of the populace in large cities have made the problem of control increasingly difficult. Yet, technical advances in disease control have kept ahead of the difficulties which have been created.

Transmission of pathogens is by direct or indirect contact or by an intermediate host.

Direct contact is the most common means of transfer of infection. Three conditions are necessary for transfer of disease by direct contact—the infectious material must be fresh, the distance traveled must be short, and the elapsed time must be brief. Material may be transferred through handshaking, kissing, coughing, or sneezing. Normal air does not contain enough virile pathogens to cause infection by inhalation, but sneezes and coughs containing water droplets or sprays may provide a means of transfer. Respiratory diseases are transferred by direct contact. Most of the respiratory diseases we acquire by carrying the organisms to the mouth via our own hands. Open-lesion diseases also are transmitted by direct contact.

Indirect contact involves an intermediate vehicle between the reservoir and the prospective new host. The infectious material may be old, the time interval long, and the distance great. Alvine discharge diseases are usually transmitted indirectly via water, milk, or foods. Respiratory diseases may be spread by indirect contact via handkerchiefs, towels, and eating utensils though the usual method of spread of respiratory disease is by direct contact.

An *intermediate host,* the third method of transmission, accounts for the transfer of insect-borne diseases. A specific insect or other intermediate host acquires the organism from an infected person or lower animal and transfers the organism to some person. In some instances the organism spends part of its life cycle in the intermediate host, but in other cases the transmission is a mechanical transfer.

Blocking routes of transmission

If one visualizes a person as the original reservoir of infection and another person as a prospective new host, then the organisms must travel by one of several routes from the reservoir to the new host. If these routes can be blocked, the new host will be protected from contracting the disease. First, the organisms must escape from the reservoir. Their ability to travel is practically zero; therefore they must rely upon vehicles of transmission. Conditions outside of the human body are decidely unfavorable to pathogens; hence the organisms must enter the new host shortly after leaving the reservoir. Several means are available for blocking the routes of transmission of disease.

Early diagnosis is essential to all methods for blocking the routes of transmission. Since diseases vary in their mode of transmission, identification of the disease makes it possible to concentrate on blocking the specific routes over which the organisms of that disease may travel.

Control of the social contact route is the most difficult to handle effectively. In a democratic society the citizens enjoy a personal freedom which makes both voluntary and compulsory restrictions difficult to establish. An informed citizenry, willing to undergo some personal inconvenience for the protection of others, is a primary necessity in control of disease. In addition citizens who practice sound principles of personal and community health may aid measurably in controlling disease spread by social contact.

Isolation of persons with diagnosed cases can be an effective means of controlling the social contact route. Also helpful is quarantine of exposed susceptible persons during the period in which they might transmit the disease should they be infected. These are legally enforced measures, but persons who are ill can go into voluntary isolation and by thus avoiding social contact prevent the spread of disease. This is citizenship of the highest order.

Control of the air route is based upon an understanding of the three principle ways by which infection may be spread via aerial contamination—droplets, droplet nuclei, and dust. *Droplets* are the fine drops of moisture composing the spray of coughs and sneezes. Moisture sustains the bacteria for several seconds so that inhalation could carry virile organisms into the respiratory tract of a susceptible host. However, the droplets settle to the floor rather quickly. *Droplet nuclei* are minute particles from the evaporation of droplets and, being small and light, may float in the air for minutes. *Dust* can become contaminated from droplets and droplet nuclei and thus be a vehicle for the transmission of disease.

Control measures of airborne infection are in need of further analysis. Evidence does not warrant the general use of ultraviolet irradiation and glycol vapors. Ventilation and oiling of floors and other objects may be helpful in the control of transmission, but the evidence is inconclusive. The old admonition, "Cover that cough and sneeze," is still the very best measure. Bacteria exhaled during normal breathing are not a danger.

Control of the water route is highly effective through community water treatment plants, sewage treatment, and the prevention of stream pollution. The same procedures apply to private and semipublic water supplies.

Control of the milk route is possible through testing of herds for tuberculosis and brucellosis, pasteurization of milk, inspection of dairies, and examination of dairy employees.

Control of solid food route is focused upon sustained inspections and sanitary safeguards for the cultivation, production, distribution, and preparation of food. Special attention is given to those foods, such as products from truck farms, which are consumed raw. Supervision of sanitation in restaurants and establishments for the production or preparation of foods, such as canneries and bake shops, has been fruitful.

Control of the insect route depends upon a knowledge of the pathogen, the insect, and the disease itself. Control measures are directed toward the destruction of the intermediate host. Elimination of breeding places and the use of insecticides and larvacides are direct means which are highly effective. Theoretically insect-borne diseases can be controlled completely.

Resistance and immunity

Resistance is the general ability of the body to ward off pathogens. Several factors in the body act as barriers or defenses against all organisms pathogenic to the human being. These mechanisms are nonspecific in their action, attacking all foreign organisms with varying degrees of effectiveness.

Man's skin serves as a mechanical barrier, and its moderate acidity provides an unfavorable medium for pathogens. Mucous secretions of the respiratory tract interfere with pathogens which the hairlike cilia of the mucous cells propel outward. The acid of the stomach and high alkalinity of the intestines are defenses against pathogens. Salinity of the tears protects the eyes and eyelids against infection. Fever is the body's response to disturbance by the invading parasites. Since most pathogens are inactivated at temperatures above 100° F., a fever makes easier the body's task of destroying organisms.

Perhaps the most important defense mechanism is *phagocytosis,* the process of enveloping, dissolving, and absorbing microorganisms. White blood cells (leukocytes) and fixed (endothelial) cells of the liver, spleen, and lymph nodes are phagocytes, capable of destroying pathogens.

Immunity is complete resistance to a disease and is specific for a particular disease. Immunity to one disease does not ensure immunity to any other disease because immunity is due to specific chemical substances (antibodies) which neutralize a particular toxin or cause bacteria to stick together or to precipitate.

Active immunity exists when a person's own body has produced the antibodies either through an attack of a disease or by inoculation with an antigenic substance which stimulates the body's lymphoid cells to produce antibodies. The length of time active immunity lasts varies with different diseases. Second attacks are common in coryza, influenza, and pneumonia and are rare in chickenpox, measles, mumps, poliomyelitis, scarlet fever, and smallpox. Inoculation during infancy against smallpox, diphtheria, pertussis, and tetanus may produce lifelong immunity. Artificial active immunization is available for diphtheria, measles, mumps, poliomyelitis, rabies, Rocky Mountain fever, scarlet fever, smallpox, tetanus, typhoid fever, and whooping cough.

Passive immunity is attained when antibodies preformed in lower animals or human beings are injected into another person. Passive immunity is of short duration; the borrowed antibodies tend to exhaust their cycle and disappear as the blood is renewed. An example of passive immunity is the *infantile immunity* of the first six months of life. Antibodies from the mother diffuse through the placenta into the blood stream of the fetus. Another type of passive immunity is the injection of horse serum containing diphtheria antibodies (antitoxin) into a susceptible child who has been exposed to diphtheria. The injection of serum (convalescent serum) from a person who has had measles into a susceptible child who has been exposed to measles is another use of passive immunization. Convalescent serum should be injected within three days after exposure to the disease if the serum is to be effective. Passive immunization is used but little today because of effective active immunization and treatment.

Cycle of respiratory infectious diseases

Respiratory infectious diseases follow a characteristic cycle of six stages or periods—incubation, prodrome, fastigium, defervescence, convalescence, and defection.

Incubation is initiated by the invasion of pathogens. During the incubation period organisms are multiplying, but the infected person dis-

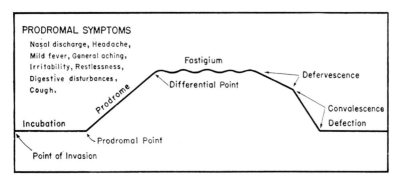

Fig. 22. Course of an infectious respiratory disease. All respiratory infections follow the course indicated on this graph. In the school the prodrome and convalescence periods pose the greatest problems in disease control because the infected person may be well enough to be up and around and thus will expose others.

plays no symptoms. The incubation period varies from one disease to another and from one person to another with the same disease. Usually the disease is not communicable during the incubation period although measles and chickenpox can be transmitted during the last three days of the incubation period.

Prodrome is initiated by the first symptoms of illness. Symptoms of the prodromal period are the same for all respiratory infections and are those of the common cold—nasal discharge, watery eyes, mild fever, headache, general ache, irritability, restlessness and perhaps a cough, and digestive disturbances. This period lasts about a day, and a definite diagnosis cannot be made. Since the person often thinks he has just a cold, he may continue his usual mode of life and expose many people during this highly communicable stage. Teachers should be alert to observe prodrome symptoms in children as the signals of impending danger.

Fastigium represents the height of the disease. It is initiated by the differential point at which characteristic signs of the specific disease make diagnosis possible. Since the person is now home or in a hospital, not many people are exposed although this period is a highly communicable one.

Defervescence is a decline in the severity of the disease. A new disease may produce a *relapse,* but usually the case proceeds to convalescence.

Convalescence or recuperation represents a difficult problem in control of the spread of disease. The disease may still be transmissible, and, if the patient mingles with other persons, he may communicate the disease.

Defection is a casting off of organisms and may coincide with convalescence. Recovery from a disease does not imply the end of communicability. Isolation time is based on the termination of defection, which is when the person has cast off all organisms.

Infectious respiratory diseases

Although the list of known infectious respiratory diseases is extensive, certain of them affect the school population and are of particular interest to the teacher. An understanding of the characteristics, mode of transmission, and control measures for these diseases can be of value to the teacher in her efforts to prevent the spread of disease. Though the teacher at no time will attempt to diagnose a particular ailment, knowledge of the various diseases will enable her to have the necessary confidence to take effective action.

Chickenpox. A fairly prevalent, though not serious, disease among school children, chickenpox can become widespread.
1. *Infectious agent:* unidentified virus
2. *Source of infection:* respiratory discharges; lesions of the skin of infected persons
3. *Mode of transmission:* directly from person to person; indirectly through objects with fresh respiratory discharges from the mucous membranes and skin of infected persons.
4. *Incubation period:* 14 to 16 days

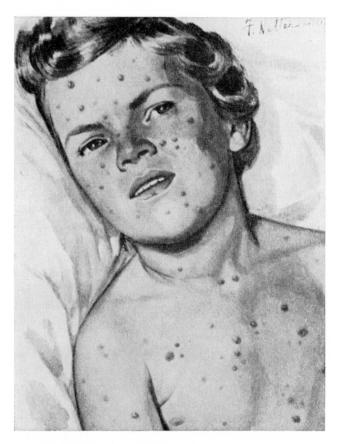

Fig. 23. Chickenpox. Fully developed eruptions with lesions at various stages of development are shown. (From the Sharp & Dohme *Seminar* vol. III, no. 2.)

5. *Description:* mild constitutional symptoms; slight fever; few eruptions and mostly on covered surfaces; eruptions at various stages of development in the same area

6. *Control measures for the school:* exclusion for minimum of 7 days

Coryza (head cold). Typical coryza merits more attention than usually is given. It can be a forerunner of other diseases.

1. *Infectious agent:* unidentified viruses

2. *Source of infection:* nose and mouth secretions of infected person

3. *Mode of transmission:* directly by sneezing and coughing; indirectly from objects with fresh respiratory discharges of infected person

4. *Incubation period:* 1 to 3 days

5. *Description:* nasal discharge; watery eyes; mild fever; headache; general aches; irritability; cough

6. *Control measures for the school:* exclusion for 3 days

Diphtheria. An entirely preventable disease, diphtheria still appears in school populations.

1. *Infectious agent:* Klebs-Loeffler bacillus

2. *Source of infection:* secretions from throat and nose of carrier or active case; also skin lesions

3. *Mode of transmission:* person to person or objects (including milk) contaminated with discharges from throat and nose of carrier or infected person

4. *Incubation period:* 3 to 5 days

5. *Description:* early symptoms not striking; onset insidious; temperature not high; illness greater than symptoms indicate; throat sore and has gray membranes; blood-tinged nasal discharge

6. *Control measures for the school:* exclusion of suspected case until released by health authorities following successive negative nose and throat cultures. Preventive measures: reimmunization of all students entering school for the first time

German measles (rubella). Often referred to as three-day measles, rubella is a distinctive disease in its own right and appears among primary school pupils.

1. *Infectious agent:* unidentified virus

2. *Source of infection:* nose and mouth secretions of infected persons

3. *Mode of transmission:* directly from person to person; indirectly from objects contaminated with fresh discharges from nose and mouth of infected person

4. *Incubation period:* 16 to 18 days

5. *Description:* mild symptoms; slight fever; eruptions varied but often deep pink and small; lymph nodes on neck behind the ear swollen and sensitive

6. *Control measures for the school:* exclusion merely for sake of infected child; isolation of no practical value.

Hepatitis, infectious. Infectious hepatitis is an acute involvement of the liver which occurs sporadically or epidemically. It occurs most frequently in autumn. Poor sanitation and overcrowded living conditions appear to increase its spread. An uneventful recovery after seven or eight weeks of illness is usual. Mild symptoms and malfunction of the liver may persist for more than a year. About 12% of the patient suffer a relapse, usually because of overactivity or other indiscretions.

1. *Infectious agent:* heat resistant virus

2. *Source of infection:* usually milk or other food contaminated by fecal discharges of an infected person; feces and blood may be infectious before, during, or after the occurrence of hepatitis.

3. *Mode of transmission:* both sporadic and epidemic types usually transmitted from feces of infected person by way of the hands which come in contact with milk, food, water, etc.; infection from direct contact or fomites and direct fecal contamination of water possible; transmission via blood from transfusions, medical instruments, or biologicals possible

4. *Incubation period:* 15 to 35 days

5. *Description:* Prodromal signs include fever, headache, lassitude, nausea, anorexia,

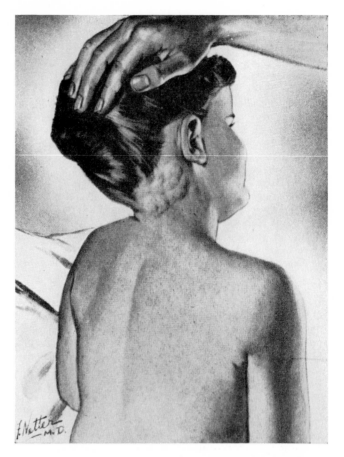

Fig. 24. German measles. The fine macular eruptions are rose pink in color. Note the marked enlargement of the lymph nodes, characteristic of German measles. (From Sharp & Dohme *Seminar* vol. III, no. 2.)

fatigue, and marked tenderness and pain in the liver; jaundice appears about the fifth day and then fever subsides. Not all patients develop jaundice.

    6. *Control measures for school:* recognition of disease; exclusion from school until readmitted by attending physician or health department; improve sanitary and hygienic practices in food handling, handwashing, and disposal of sewage. Food handlers in school cafeteria should be checked for possible latent infectious hepatitis.

    Measles (rubeola). A highly communicable disease, measles occurs in three-year cycles.

    1. *Infectious agent:* unidentified virus

    2. *Source of infection:* secretions from nose and mouth of infected person

    3. *Mode of transmission:* directly by sneezing and coughing from person to person; indirectly from objects contaminated with fresh respiratory discharges of infected person

    4. *Incubation period:* 10 to 12 days

    5. *Description:* nasal discharge; eyes red and sensitive to light; eye lids swollen; irritability; moderate fever; hacking cough; Koplik spots on buccal surface of mouth; dusky red skin eruptions which tend to coalesce

6. *Control measures for the school:* exclusion for not less than 5 days after appearance of rash; exclusion of contacts only if symptoms appear

Meningococcus meningitis. One of the most feared of the respiratory diseases, meningococcus meningitis can now be treated successfully if it is discovered early.

1. *Infectious agent:* meningococcus (spherical bacterium)
2. *Source of infection:* nose and throat discharges of carrier or person with active case
3. *Mode of transmission:* directly from person to person; indirectly from objects contaminated with fresh discharges from nose and throat of carrier or person with active case
4. *Incubation period:* 6 to 8 days
5. *Description:* acute onset; intense headache; fever; nausea; stiff neck; irritability
6. *Control measures for the school:* exclusion until recovery, usually minimum of 14 days, or until released by health department following negative laboratory tests; exclusion of contacts in same household for 7 days from last exposure

Mononucleosis. This disease is an acute infection which occurs in epidemic form

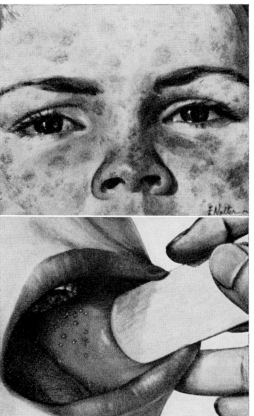

Fig. 25

Fig. 26

Fig. 25. Measles. Characteristic appearance of the eyes in measles showing puffy eyelids, lacrimation, and swelling of caruncula and mucous lining of eyelid. (From Sharp & Dohme *Seminar* vol. III, no. 2.)
Fig. 26. Koplik spots. These red and white pinpoint eruptions on the buccal mucosa are one of the most important signs of measles. (From Sharp & Dohme *Seminar* vol. III, no. 2.)

among children and youth, but more often is sporadic. It usually lasts from 1 to 3 weeks, but involvement of the lymph system and general fatigue and weakness may last for months. Recurrences are frequent, but usually are short lived.

1. *Infectious agent:* unidentified virus
2. *Source of infection:* probably discharges from nose and throat of infected person
3. *Mode of transmission:* probably by direct contact with infected person
4. *Incubation period:* 5 to 15 days
5. *Description:* fever; sore throat; headache; fatigue; chilliness; malaise; general involvement of lymph system, hence use of name glandular fever; white cell count of the blood varies between 10,000 and 20,000; excessive agglutinins present in the blood
6. *Control measures for school:* recognition of disease; no legal isolation, but pation should not return to school until so advised by attending physician

Mumps (parotitis). Involving the salivary glands primarily, mumps nevertheless is properly classified as a respiratory disease.

1. *Infectious agent:* unidentified virus
2. *Source of infection:* saliva of infected person
3. *Mode of transmission:* droplet spread by direct contact; indirectly from objects contaminated with fresh saliva of infected person
4. *Incubation period:* 18 days
5. *Description:* slight fever; tenderness and swelling over the jaw and in front of the ear; one side or both sides; involvement of ovaries and testes may occur in persons with mature reproduction system
6. *Control measures for the school:* exclusion until the disappearance of swelling and tenderness

Poliomyelitis (infantile paralysis). Long a greatly feared disease, poliomyelitis can now be considered one of the highly preventable diseases.

1. *Infectious agent:* Brunhilde, Lansing, and Leon or types 1, 2, and 3 viruses
2. *Source of infection:* discharges from nose, throat, or bowel of person with active case or of carrier
3. *Mode of transmission:* direct from person to person though history of association with other patients is infrequent
4. *Incubation period:* 7 to 14 days
5. *Description:* abortive form presents characteristics of severe coryza—fever, headache, sore throat, nasal discharge, watery eyes, general ache, irritability; *neurologic* form includes stiff neck and back and muscle tenderness and weakness; *paralytic* phase involves motor neurons and produces paralysis of one muscle or a muscle group of one extremity or muscles used to breathe or swallow
6. *Control measures for the school:* exclusion of suspected case until released by health authorities, usually 7 days or for duration of fever; home contacts excluded at discretion of health authorities. Preventive measures: immunization of all pupils and students

Scarlet fever and streptococcal throat infection. These two diseases are commonly classed together.

1. *Infectious agent:* hemolytic streptococci
2. *Source of infection:* nose and throat discharges of person with active case or a carrier; articles soiled with these discharges
3. *Mode of transmission:* directly by coughing and sneezing from person to person; indirectly via handkerchiefs, clothing, and other objects which reach the mouth; from contaminated milk
4. *Incubation period:* 3 to 5 days
5. *Description:* sore throat; fever, nausea; vomiting; flushing of cheeks; pallor about mouth; if rash occurs, it is on the neck and chest and is a fine scarlet goose-pimple type which blanches when pressure is applied
6. *Control measures for the school:* exclusion for at least 7 days or until all ab-

normal discharges have disappeared; a sore throat is always a signal for exclusion

Smallpox (variola). entirely preventable, yet an occasional case of smallpox among school children is reported.

1. *Infectious agent:* unidentified virus
2. *Source of infection:* lesions of mucous membrane and skin of infected person
3. *Mode of transmission:* directly by person-to-person contact; indirectly through objects contaminated by discharges from lesions of infected person
4. *Incubation period:* 12 days
5. *Description:* two or three days of severe illness with headache, backache, and fever which subside when rash appears; eruptions first occur on exposed surfaces; small elevations (papules) develop into pustules all at the same time
6. *Control measures for the school:* exclusion of suspected case until released by health authorities, usually until scars have healed. Preventive measures: revaccination of children on entering school

Tuberculosis. In the high school population, tuberculosis still remains a serious problem.

1. *Infectious agent:* tubercle bacillus (Koch)
2. *Source of infection:* open lesions of person with pulmonary tuberculosis
3. *Mode of transmission:* direct contact by kissing, from hands, and from droplets from sneezes and coughs; indirectly from contaminated drinking and eating utensils, perhaps contaminated dust; repeated, not casual, exposure is necessary
4. *Incubation period:* minimum 1 month, usually considerably longer
5. *Description:* primary or first infection type involves infection of the lymph nodes along the windpipe (trachea) and bronchi; usually no discernible general symptoms and therefore frequently missed; recovery spontaneous, with infected lymph nodes becoming fibrous and calcified as revealed by subsequent x-ray plates. Primary form always precedes secondary form. Secondary or reinfection type has gradual onset; chest x-ray plates reveal the condition long before constitutional symptoms appear. General symptoms may be fatigue, fever, cough, loss of weight, dullness, and finally expectoration of blood. The condition is now far advanced and should have been detected earlier. Few patients contract secondary type before 15 years of age, but occurs in high school population, particularly among girls.
6. *Control measures for the school:* preventive measures: routine examination of all students exposed to active case; periodic chest x-ray examination of students 15 years of age and older; referral of all students observed to be lacking in usual vitality.

Common skin infections and infestations

Skin conditions which are communicable in themselves are not a life-or-death matter, but they can be a trying problem to the secondary school as well as the elementary school. Much of the nuisance effect can be eliminated by an understanding of the common communicable skin diseases.

A skin infection is a condition in which the pathogen penetrates the skin and causes harm. A skin infestation is a condition in which the parasite remains *upon* the skin and causes harm.

Impetigo contagiosa (gym itch). In elementary schools impetigo may spread quite widely from a single unrecognized case. Early recognition is important.

1. *Infectious agent:* streptococci and staphylococci
2. *Source of infection:* skin lesions of infected person
3. *Mode of transmission:* directly by contact with discharge of skin lesions; indirectly from objects contaminated on such discharges

4. *Incubation period:* 2 to 4 days
5. *Description:* systemic manifestations usually are absent except in infants. Lesions first appear as pink-red stains which are fluid-filled and wet, then fill with pus, and finally form a crust which appears as though it were pasted on. The face (particularly the butterfly area about the mouth) and hands are commonly involved, but other parts of the body may be affected, particularly the scalp. Pressure generally causes pus to escape from beneath the oval-shaped crusts
6. *Control measures for the school:* exclusion from school until the pustules have healed. Preventive measures: encourage prompt treatment which consists of soaking crust until it can be removed and applying 5% ammoniated mercury ointment or sulfa ointment to the infected area. Some schools have ointments available for the student's own use, and in some instances at the request of the parent or student teachers have assisted the student. A physician's services should be obtained if possible. Emphasis on general personal health promotion helps to avoid any wide spread of impetigo

Pediculosis (lousiness). This condition is a classical example of infestation.
1. *Infesting agent:* head or body louse
2. *Source of infestation:* infested person or his personal belongings
3. *Mode of transmission:* directly from infested person; indirectly by contact with clothing of infested person
4. *Incubation period:* ova hatch in 1 week and mature in 2 weeks
5. *Description:* the louse egg (nit), larva, or adult louse on the scalp or other parts of the body or in the clothing; nits attached to the hair shaft; occasionally a severe secondary infection
6. *Control measures for the school:* exclusion not necessary if proper insecticide has been applied to scalp, skin, and clothing. Inspection of possible contacts and use of effective insecticide for infested pupils. Preventive measure: emphasis on bodily cleanliness.

Ringworm (tinea). The term athlete's foot applies only to ringworm of the feet. Ringworm can affect all parts of the body. Common dermatophytes are often present on healthy skin and cause disease only when favorable conditions prevail.
1. *Infectious agent:* several types of fungi
2. *Source of infection:* lesions on body of infected person; objects contaminated by the fungi or their spores
3. *Mode of transmission:* directly by person-to-person contact with lesions; indirectly from objects contaminated by the fungi or their spores
4. *Incubation period:* unknown
5. *Description:* lesions often circular, clear in the center, with vesicular (fluid) borders; not widely distributed; crusting not present; itching common. Foot ringworm (athlete's foot) more common in adults; the body, face, and head forms are more common among children, especially in warm weather
6. *Control measures for the school:* exclusion when lesions of exposed parts of the body are present until treatment has been effective; in foot ringworm exclusion from privileges of swimming pool and gymnasium. Preventive measures: personal cleanliness; through drying of feet after bathing; use of sandals; gymnasium and shower room cleanliness; regular inspections and treatment

Scabies (the itch). The common term seven-year itch is often used to designate scabies. Both male and female mites live upon human skin, but the female burrows into the superficial layer of the skin to deposit eggs. The female can be seen with the unaided eye, but the male, being half her size, is not readily detected. The parasites are short lived, the male dying after mating and the female after she has laid her eggs. Larvae are hatched in 4 to 8 days.
1. *Infectious agent: Sarcoptes scabiei* (itch mite)
2. *Source of infection:* person infected with the mite
3. *Mode of transmission:* directly by contact with infected person; indirectly from underclothing, bedding, towels, and other objects of the infected person

4. *Incubation period:* 1 to 2 days
5. *Description:* itching of the skin often unbearable; frequent locations—the waist, armpit, and crotch; at times, lesions on the face, scalp, and arms; when infection mild, systemic symptoms negligible, but severe infections may result in fever, headache, and discomfort
6. *Control measures for the school:* exclusion from school until successfully treated with an effective miticide, e.g., 5% sulfur ointment. Preventive measures: personal cleanliness

In the consideration of the control of infectious disease the teacher need not be limited to specific detailed symptoms. Any time a child has a sore throat, fever, or watery eyes, the teacher should prudently assume that he has the beginning of an infectious respiratory disease. Skin eruptions which exhibit inflammation will likely be infectious as contrasted with noninflamed skin areas such as occur in eczema.

Although the usual incubation period for each disease has been stated, atypical cases may have an incubation slightly shorter or considerably longer. These deviations from the usual incubation patterns will not alter the general prodrome characteristics of the disorder. A teacher who watches for typical prodrome symptoms will quickly identify the child in the early stages of any of the usual infectious respiratory diseases. Skin disorders will also be recognized early in their development.

Responsibility for control of communicable diseases

In the control of communicable diseases both legal and professional responsibilities must be considered. Responsibilities as written into law or into sanitary codes represent the minimum desirable control essentially in terms of restrictions. Over and beyond these legal responsibilities are the moral or professional responsibilities assumed by individuals and groups. These professional responsibilities add measurably to the effectiveness of the control of disease.

Public health personnel. Health is recognized as a prime essential of a people. Primary authority for the protection and promotion of the people's health rests with the state. The state has taken such measures as have been necessary to protect and preserve the health of those subject to its authority.

Health authority is vested in the police power of the state. Police power is the authority of the people, vested in the government to enact and enforce laws to protect the health and general welfare of society. It is the power to promote public welfare by regulating and restraining the use of property and liberty. It is based on the concept of the greatest good for the greatest number and may operate to the inconvenience of one individual or family in the interests of the common good. Yet, it allows for personal freedom insofar as such freedom does not work to the detriment of others.

State legislatures delegate authority to a state board of health to set up rules and regulations governing the health of the people. Accordingly the health board passes regulations which govern the control of communicable diseases. This includes the imposition of isolation and quarantine, milk control, water treatment, and all other measures necessary to the control of disease. Thus, a state board of health has legislative authority to set up a sanitary code to govern health, which will include control of communicable diseases in the state. The state code specifies the time and terms of isolation, quarantine, and other control measures.

State health boards set up a division of communicable disease control to deal specifically with the immediate problems of the prevention of the spread of disease. Personnel of the division are specialists in specific phases of the control program. These professional workers may deal with any problem of disease control anywhere in the state. Or they may leave the control to local health personnel and will be available for consultation or special services if requested by local health officials.

The state delegates many of its powers to subdivisions of local governments to exercise within their own borders. Through enactment of law the state legislature delegates to counties the power to control diseases. The state also grants charters to cities giving them absolute self-rule (home rule) to exercise within their own borders and within specific limits or fields. Police power thus delegated to the municipalities enables them to control communicable diseases within their own geographical borders.

In terms of direct effect upon the individual citizen, it is the county or city health department which is charged with legal responsibility for the control of communicable diseases. A city or county board of health passes regulations which govern the activities of the control of communicable disease. Standards may not be lower than those of the state code, but may be higher. Thus, if the state code sets the isolation period for a particular disease as seven days, the local code may require nine days, but not six days. In practice the local code usually coincides with the state code.

Local health personnel are charged with legal enforcement of isolation and quarantine and such other provisions as pertain to disease control. However, a health official is a public servant and accepts the professional responsibility of giving every service possible which may aid persons or families with communicable diseases. Professional service is extended to others in the community as well. A particular recipient of public health service is the school, and properly so since in the school population a considerable number of cases of communicable disease will occur in any given year. The school is free to call upon the public health personnel for advice and other control services. A cooperative working agreement between the health department and the school benefits both agencies, but more especially serves the children and community.

At the outset of each year a conference between the health department staff and the school administrators will foster a better understanding of the function of both groups and a better program of control. If possible, the public health nurse should be scheduled for regular visits to the school and be available for special calls from the school. The nurse can thus assist the school in problems of exclusion and readmission as well as advise it on other health problems.

The director of the public health department should be available to assist the school with especially difficult problems which occur in its program for control of communicable diseases. In addition the director has the legal authority and responsibility to make final decisions relating to isolation and quarantine. Termination of isolation by the health department automatically clears a child for readmission to school.

Health departments sponsor immunization programs. When the prevailing local practice is that each family physician performs all immunizations, the health department carries on extensive public health education programs. In addition health department personnel contact homes with children in need of immunization.

Private physician. From time immemorial the practicing physician has been the key figure in the control of communicable diseases. It is he who diagnoses and supervises the case. He is in the best position to advise as to the best interests of the patient. Modern health codes require that he report cases of certain diseases to the local health departments. For his convenience special forms and franked envelopes are available. He can quickly fill out the form and mail it to the health department which then assumes responsibility for enforcement of isolation and quarantine without interfering with the physician's medical supervision of the case. Physicians properly accept responsibility for the health of the public as well as for the welfare of their private patients.

Today's practicing physician advises clients to have their children artificially immunized and does the immunization as a routine part of his medical service to the family. Through this practice the physicians of the nation are largely responsible for the high percentage of children who enter school immune to diseases for which artificial immunization is recommended.

Parents. An obvious health responsibility of parents is to carry out such recognized health measures as will protect their own children and all other children. Parents assume this duty by observing their children for symptoms of disease during the morning of each school day, keeping them home when symptoms of communicable disease are present and following the practices recommended by the school and required by the health department. Parents have legal responsibilities when isolation has been imposed officially. More than this, parents have a moral obligation to go beyond legal requirements and do everything reasonable to prevent the spread of disease. The formula for effective control of communicable disease consists of civic-minded parents who work cooperatively with an alert school staff and a competent health department.

School personnel. Promotion of immunization, early recognition of symptoms of disease, and effective control of exclusions and readmissions are the means by which the school staff carries out its responsibilities in communicable disease control.

Some states, through legislation, have made vaccination for smallpox a prerequisite for entrance to school. Kentucky, Maryland, Massachusetts, New Hampshire, New Mexico, New York, Pennsylvania, Rhode Island, South Carolina, and West Virginia have enacted such laws. Massachusetts also has required diphtheria immunization for entrance to school. In some states the state department of education sets the requirement. However, in general, immunization as a prerequisite for entrance to school has been left to local school boards. Courts have held that a board of education has the authority to require such immunizations as condition for entrance to school. However, provisions of the requirement must be reasonable. Exceptions must be made on religious grounds, and a board could not require immunization for some uncommon disease. In practice, boards require immunization against diphtheria and smallpox.

It is recognized that compulsory immunization was instituted in the interests of the child, and in many school districts it may still be desirable. Where effective public and school health education programs have been operating for several years, voluntary immunization can displace compulsion.

Teachers who are prepared to recognize early symptoms of communicable disease and who make proper inspections, reviews, and observations of children perform a highly valuable service in the control of communicable diseases. Early detection of disease can mean early exclusion, with benefit to the individual affected as well as to the child's classmates. It is relatively simple to exclude children and to refuse readmission until all communicability has passed, and it is highly effective.

Teachers as well as the school nurse can advise children and parents on matters relating to disease control and thus assist children and families to follow the desirable course of action. Knowledge leads to understanding and harmony which will operate to the best advantage of all concerned.

Immunization program

In the best democratic tradition an immunization program should be based upon voluntary participation. Basic to an effective voluntary immunization program is an informed public which understands the importance of preventive measures and the effectiveness of present-day immunization practices. A voluntary immunization program in which more than 85% of entering school pupils have been immunized against diphtheria, smallpox, and poliomyelitis would be successful in preventing all outbreaks of epidemic proportions. Yet, all children should be protected, and all parents should understand the importance of immunization. The most effective instrument for health education is an epidemic, but it is also the most costly, and health officials and schools do not want epidemics in any form. Although the public health agencies assume primary responsibility for public health education, the school has both an opportunity and an obligation to educate parents in the importance of immunization for all children. To be effective, adult health education must be continued over a long period. In the absence of such a long-term program and until such a program can be developed, compulsory immunization may be necessary to assure every child the protection to which he has a right.

Compulsory immunization against diphtheria, smallpox, and even poliomyelitis as a requirement for entrance to school is an accepted concept. When thus required, immunization should be available to all children through the services of the family physician or of a clinic. The school board may legally pay the costs of such immunization on whatever basis the program is organized. Such an appropriation would be an investment in lives saved, health preserved, family and community stability maintained, and education continued without needless interruption.

In the event of an epidemic health authorities may deem it advisable to require immunization as a requisite for school attendance. A conference of school officials and health authorities can formulate a program of emergency immunization. Students who refuse immunization on religious grounds may be placed under quarantine by the public health department until the danger is past. Courts have held this to be a reasonable exercise of the authority of the health department to control communicable diseases.

Smallpox. Vaccination against smallpox can produce immunity which will last for more than five years. The standard schedule for immunization is vaccination for infants by 6 months of age and revaccination when a child first enters school and thereafter at five-year intervals. In a school program, the minimum should be immunization of each child at 6 months of age, revaccination when each child first enters school, and revaccination for the entire school population if the disease appears in severe form.

In the preparation of the vaccine virus, smallpox virus is scratched into the shaved and disinfected skin of a calf. The smallpox virus is attenuated in the calf so that the virus has only a mild harmless effect on human beings. When a pustule forms at the site of a scratch on the skin of the calf, the pus material is collected and put in capillary tubes. This living virus of cowpox is called vaccine (from *vacca,* the Latin word for cow). The United States Public Health Service tests the vaccine for purity and potency.

A modified method of producing smallpox vaccine is to cultivate vaccinia in the living cells of the chick embryo. This culture virus can be kept for long periods without deterioration and leaves very little ulceration or scar. However, the bovine vaccine is the most widely used.

When a human being is vaccinated, a small area of the arm is sterilized with acetone. Alcohol and iodine inactivate the vaccine, and ether is flammable; therefore none of these is an acceptable sterilizing agent.

The ends of the capillary tube are broken off, and a drop of vaccine is placed directly on the sterile skin. A sterile needle, held almost parallel to the skin, is pressed repeatedly until eight to thirty pricks are made in an area ⅛ inch in diameter. No dressing is necessary, but for mechanical protection a sterile gauze pad may be placed over the vaccination. On the third day an elevation (papule) appears, on the sixth day it is fluid filled (vesicle), and on the tenth day it is filled with pus (pustule). Inflammation of the localized area and of adjacent lymph nodes occurs. The pustule heals in about a week, and a small scar may remain.

If only a papule appears, it is an indication of high residual immunity. No reaction at all means improper vaccination, and revaccination is indicated.

Diphtheria; tetanus; pertussis. Combined immunization for diphtheria, tetanus, and pertussis is highly effective and practical. The effectiveness of each seems to be increased by the activity from the others.

Diphtheria toxoid is produced by propagation of the diphtheria bacillus in a broth medium at 37.5° C. Under these conditions the bacillus produces toxin. The bacteria are then killed with phenol, and the

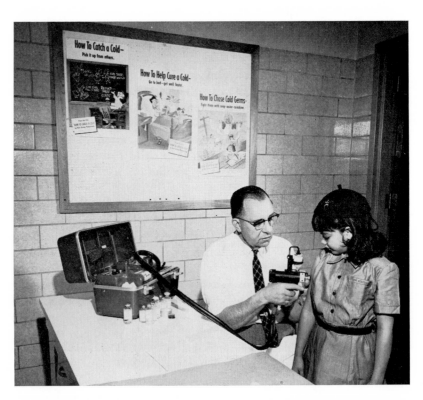

Fig. 27. Hypospray (jet gun) for diphtheria-tetanus shot. No needle or syringes are used and there is no chance for the pupil to get infectious hepatitis when the physician uses this method of immunization. (Courtesy Denver Public Schools, Denver, Colo.)

toxin is filtered out. This toxin is treated with formaldehyde and alum so that it is no longer a dangerous poison. It now is designated alum-precipitated toxoid. Tetanus alum-precipitated toxoid is produced in much the same way. However, pertussis immunizing material is produced by killing Phase I strains of the pertussis organism and injecting the dead organisms into the person to be immunized.

The first inoculation of multiple (trivalent) antigens is an intra-muscular injection into the arm. It usually is given between the third and sixth months of infancy, plus a reinforcement inoculation within three to twelve months. All children entering school for the first time should be reinoculated. This should be a minimum requirement. Reinoculation of the entire school population will be recommended by the health officials if any cases of diphtheria are reported in the community.

The *Schick test* for suspectibility to diphtheria is seldom used today. An injection of 0.1 ml. of toxoid is necessary. Physicians agree that if an injection must be given it should be an immunizing dose, and thus the child is spared a second stab from the needle.

Poliomyelitis. A recently developed immunization procedure, the Salk method of immunizing against poliomyelitis, is successful in about 75% of the persons who receive the inoculation. Active immunity against poliomyelitis is attained from inoculation with a nonliving form of the poliomyelitis viruses. Not all human bodies appear to be capable of pro-ducing antibodies when the antigen of poliomyelitis is introduced into the body.

The immunizing material for poliomyelitis is produced by a fairly elaborate process. The trivalent poliomyelitis vaccine contains types 1, 2, and 3 strains of poliomyelitis virus. Each virus is grown separately in tissue culture on living kidney tissue of Rhesus monkeys. Long periods of time are required for the viruses to multiply in adequate numbers. Tis-sue cultures containing each type of virus are clarified to remove ex-traneous matter. To stimulate multiplication of the organisms, tissue culture fluid containing high concentrations of the virus is then incubated at 37.5° C. The live viruses are later killed by the addition of formalde-hyde. This material of dead viruses is then refrigerated and checked to ascertain that the material is sterile and the viruses are dead. The three vaccines are then pooled in equal amounts to make the final trivalent vaccine.

Various schedules are used, but immunization procedure usually con-sists of an initial intramuscular injection of 1 ml., two to four weeks later the second injection of 1 ml., and the third injection after six or seven months. Since July, August, September, and October are the months of high incidence of paralytic poliomyelitis, immunization should be done considerably in advance of this season though any time of the year ap-parently is acceptable.

Sabin vaccine consists of attenuated live viruses in a medium such as a liquid or a lump of sugar. Type 1 vaccine can be given to a child as young as 3 months old. Six weeks later type 3 vaccine is given, and four weeks later type 2 vaccine is given. For the child in the early months of infancy, vaccine in liquid form is most practical. As soon as the child can take a lump of sugar, the vaccine in sugar lump form can be used.

A newly developed oral trivalent live poliovirus vaccine has the advantage of conferring simultaneous immunization against all three types of poliomyelitis viruses. A dose may be given in a teaspoon or in a paper cup. If a cup is used, a small amount of chlorine-free water is added. This type of vaccine may also be given absorbed in bread, cake, or a cube of sugar. Two doses are given within a period of eight weeks, and the age to begin administration is between 6 weeks and 6 months.

Schedule for immunizations. Various immunization schedules have been recommended, all with merit. Perhaps no standard schedule exists, but most will approximate the one presented in Table 12 although individual physicians may deviate considerably from this pattern.

Special immunization practices. In practice, immunization against certain diseases is not advocated except under special circumstances. When a disease is peculiar to a special area (endemic), health authorities may recommend immunization of all the persons in that area, particularly those who are likely to be exposed. Thus, in the Bitterroot area of Montana, endemic for Rocky Mountain fever, health authorities have recommended that persons living in the area be immunized against that disease.

Normally mass immunization against typhoid fever is not advocated, but, if an outbreak occurs in a community, health authorities and physicians may advise all susceptible people to be immunized. The program is on a voluntary basis, not a compulsory one.

For mumps a killed virus vaccine gives no more than two years' im-

Table 12. *Suggested schedule for immunization*

Disease	Age at start	First series	Boosters
D—diphteria P—pertussis T—tetanus	3 months through 6 years	3 injections	12 months after first series, then every 3 years through 6 years
D—diphtheria T—tetanus, adult type	6 years and over	3 injections	Every 5 years
Tetanus	Adults only when DT is not used	3 injections	Every 4 years and after injury
Polio { Salk Sabin	2 months 3 months	3 to 5 injections 3 administrations	1 year after first series, then every 2 years
Smallpox	3 to 6 months	1 vaccination	Every 5 years
Measles { Killed virus Live virus	3 to 6 months 3 to 6 months	3 injections 1 injection with 1 injection of gamma globulin	At school entrance At school entrance

munity and is not widely used. Better, as a possible preventive for exposed men who lack prior immunity, is a special gamma globulin that will give temporary immunity and thus will prevent possible sterility. High school boys exposed to mumps and who lack prior immunity should have a physician's counsel on the advisability of gamma globulin administration.

Because German measles in a mother during the first three months of pregnancy can cause the birth of defective babies, there exists an urgency to develop an effective vaccine. To date no such vaccine has been developed, and the best available procedure for immunization is to expose little girls to German measles deliberately—however, not while their mothers are pregnant.

No proposed preventive for tuberculosis has been generally accepted in America. However, a tuberculin testing program is being urged by health departments and practicing physicians. The tine test or the patch test can be given at 3 to 6 months of age with a retest as recommended by the administering physician or the department of health. The tine test uses no needle but a disposable gadget with four tiny prongs. The tines are coated with protein from dead tubercle bacilli. If the punctured area

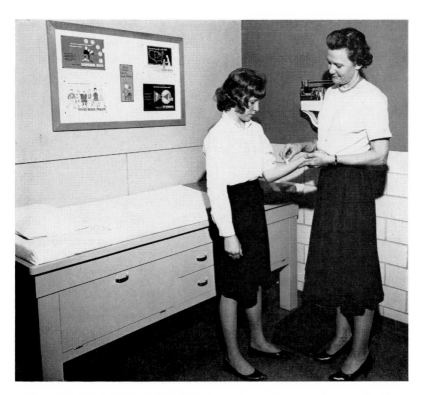

Fig. 28. Tine tuberculin test. Administered by the school nurse, this simple procedure is a reliable indicator of whether there has or has not been tuberculous infections. (Courtesy Denver Public Schools, Denver, Colo.)

becomes inflamed within two or three days, it is then a positive reaction indicating there has been tuberculous infection. A chest x-ray is then taken to determine whether the infection is active or whether it is a past involvement now contained.

When susceptible preschool children are known to have been exposed to measles, diphtheria, or whooping cough, the family physician may advise passive immunization. However, this procedure normally does not involve the school population.

School-parent-health department practices

Any effective program requires teamwork based on complete understanding. Well-informed parents who understand the role of both the school and the health department are essential to effective control of communicable disease. A health department carries on a continuing program of health education, keeping the public informed of the activities of disease control. Logically the health department and school work out a program of joint action in disease control and work hand in hand in administering the program. After all, both are public agencies created to serve the public. Too frequently the school is remiss in failing to make clear to parents just what it seeks to do to control communicable disease and how it proposes to carry out its program.

School bulletin on control practices. To prevent misunderstanding and thus possibly avoid ill feeling, the school should compose a statement of its policy and program for control of communicable disease. Issuing the bulletin on attractive bond paper or cardboard will encourage the

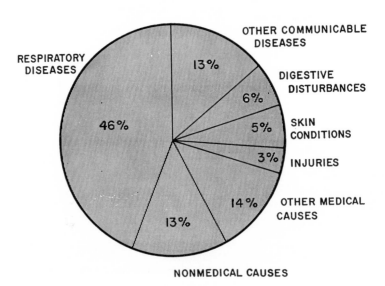

Fig. 29. Chart showing causes of absence from school. All causes of absence must be considered, but respiratory diseases always command major attention. (Courtesy Metropolitan Life Insurance Co.)

parents to keep the bulletin in a convenient place. It should be sent to the home during the first week of the school year. The bulletin should be clear and concise.

Health bulletin

Everyday living brings with it exposure to infection and other dangers to the health of children. Recognizing this the teachers and principals of your schools have organized an intensive program to protect the health of your children during the coming year. The success of the program will depend greatly upon the cooperation of the parents. Knowing that parents are eager to protect the health of their children, teachers propose to parents:

1. If your child appears to be ill before he is ready for school, for his own good keep him home. Any of the following symptoms may indicate illness:

Flushing	Fever
Repeated sneezing	Sick feeling in the stomach
Sniffles	Diarrhea
Red or watery eyes	Skin eruption
eyes sensitive to light	Rash
Nasal discharge	Skin peeling
Sore throat	Pain
Sluggishness	Cough
Irritability	Dizziness
Paleness	Headache

2. If after coming to school your child becomes ill, for his own good the child will be either brought home immediately or given proper care at school until it is advisable to take him home.

This action on the part of the home and the school will protect the health of your child and every other child in school.

Let us remember:

(a) Serious illness appears to be but a trifle at the outset.

(b) A cold is in itself serious enough and often develops into something more serious.

(c) Your child's health is more important than a perfect attendance record.

———————————————

Principal

(Save this bulletin for use throughout the year)

Detection of communicable disease

In an orderly plan for detecting the early symptoms of communicable disease, the teacher utilizes three procedures—inspection, review, and observation.

Inspection for communicable disease on one or two mornings during the first week of school is a means of enabling the teacher to become familiar with the distinctive physical characteristics of each child, as well as to identify any existing infectious disease. Thereafter the inspection is conducted only during an epidemic or threatened epidemic.

A daily morning *review* for detection of communicable disease is followed when no epidemic exists or threatens.

Observation for communicable disease is the continual survey of the children during the school day for any indications of illness.

Table 13. *Communicable disease inspection*

Inspection	Directions to child	Stigmata
	For respiratory disease	
1. General condition	How do you feel?	Facial expression, listlessness, irritability, sneezing
2. Eyes	Move your eyes about.	Watery eyes, inflammation, puffiness, redness
3. Nose	Tilt your head back.	Discharge, inflammation, odor
4. Skin	Do you feel hot?	Flushing, hot, cold, clammy
5. Forehead	Raise the hair from your forehead.	Eruptions along hair line
	For skin infection	
6. Chest	Open your shirt (or dress).	Eruptions, redness, irritation
7. Hands and wrists	Pull up your sleeves and spread your fingers.	Eruptions, redness, irritation

Inspection for communicable disease. Whenever an epidemic threatens or is present, a complete inspection (Table 13) of each child should be made each school day at 9:00 and 11:40 A.M. Experience has proved that if the inspection is made just before lunch, rather than at 1:00 o'clock, the teacher can avoid the awkward situation of returning a child who has just come from home if symptoms of illness are found. Three plans for the inspection are used. In the first method the teacher stands at the door and inspects each child who enters the room. In the second method all the children enter the room and take their seats, the teacher sits or stands in a convenient place, and the children pass by for inspection. In the third and most satisfactory method the pupils remain in their seats as the teacher passes up the aisle and inspects to the right and to the left. Economy of time and a more natural relaxed situation recommended this plan highly.

With practice a teacher develops her own procedures and techniques. She is looking for deviations from the normal and is not making a diagnosis. As she gets to know the normal characteristics of each child, she will quickly recognize any deviations from normal conditions. In making an inspection for communicable disease a teacher is a "suspectician," not a diagnostician.

Daily morning review. Under normal conditions when no epidemic threatens or is present, it is not necessary to make a close inspection of the children. A fairly rapid daily morning review will detect signs of illness or other deviations from the normal. At the opening of the morning session, while the pupils are seated and before classwork begins, the teacher can observe each child as she stands at the front of the room. She looks up one row and down the next, viewing the appearance of each child and noting any deviations from normal. The teacher should note the following points: facial expression, flushing of skin, pallor of skin, catarrhal discharge, watery or red eyes, restlessness, lassitude, coughing, and sneezing.

If it is indicated by the review, a close inspection of a particular child should be made.

Continual observation. A child may be well at the opening of school in the morning and become ill before the noon hour. A teacher with an appreciation of the importance of the control of communicable disease will detect any symptoms of disease children exhibit because she will continually observe children for deviations from the normal. She will be looking particularly for prodromal symptoms of respiratory disease. Children themselves are helpful because they inform the teacher when they do not feel well.

Isolation of child at school

A child with the symptoms of a communicable disease should be segregated immediately. An emergency rest room is ideal for a child who appears to be but slightly ill and may recover in a short time or who possibly may not have a communicable disease. This child should lie comfortably on a cot in a moderately darkened room. He should be kept warm with blankets, and someone should be in attendance or responsible for visiting the child at intervals. This attending person should be an adult, but if this is not possible a responsible sixth-grade child or an older one can serve. The attending child should be sufficiently removed from the ill child to eliminate transmission of disease.

If the isolated child does not seem to improve in a reasonable time, his home should be contacted and arrangements made to take him home. At times it is not possible to get in touch with the parents; in that case the child's interests are probably best served by keeping him in the emergency rest room. If the child should become seriously ill and no contact with the parents can be made, the family physician should be called and his advice followed. Failure to reach the family physician within an hour would justify calling some other physician. Since the call is in the best interest of the child, the parents will be responsible for the cost of the physician's services.

Exclusions

A question of considerable concern to the classroom teacher is her responsibility for the exclusion of children who appear to have a communicable disease. A teacher readily recognizes her professional responsibility to do everything reasonable in behalf of the child's health, but knowledge of legal aspects and administrative procedures gives the teacher the necessary confidence to deal competently with exclusions due to communicable diseases.

Legal aspects. Does the teacher herself have the right to exclude a child for suspected communicable disease? If it develops that the child's condition was not communicable, can the teacher be held legally liable for her act? These two vital questions have been answered with definiteness by the courts. The classical decision was laid down by the court in the case of Stone versus Probst in which parents instituted a civil suit against a public school educator for excluding their child from school because of suspected communicable disease. The key sentence of that decision is this:

> Pupils who are suffering, or appear to be suffering, from a communicable disease may menace the well-being of all pupils and therefore should be denied the privilege of school attendance.*

It is significant that the court emphasized that the mere *appearance* of the symptoms of communicable disease is sufficient basis for exclusion. The court did not require proof that the well-being of other pupils was being menaced, but merely that their well-being *might* be menaced. The court did not assert that the school may exclude the child, but that it *should* exclude the child. This decision means that if a teacher has reason to believe that a child has a communicable disease, she should exclude the child. When she exercises this responsibility, the teacher's action should be reasonable and reflect what a person of ordinary prudence would do. If it is subsequently found that the child did not have a communicable disease, all concerned should be pleased. It is inconceivable that any jury would ever hold the teacher liable for such reasonable actions. Courts recognize that at times the individual must be inconvenienced in the interests of the general good.

Administrative procedures. Various situations require different methods, and typical examples illustrate standard procedures.

1. If the child is not well, but some doubt exists as to whether the condition is communicable, he may be isolated in the emergency rest room.

2. If no doubt exists that the child is quite ill and very likely has a communicable disease, the child should be taken home. First the parents should be called to be certain that someone is home. If someone is at home, an adult, preferably, should drive the child home. One of the child's parents may come after him. If neither of these alternatives is possible and no adult is available, a responsible student may walk home with the ill child. A sixth-grade student can carry out this assignment. Under no circumstances should the ill child walk home alone. All decisions to exclude a child should be channeled through the principal's office.

3. In a doubtful case the teacher should rely on the school physician for a decision and, if no physician is available, rely on the school nurse. If neither is available, the collective judgment of three or four teachers would be in order. If the group of teachers agreed that exclusion was advisable, the principal should be notified and steps taken to transport the child home.

4. When circumstances are such that the ill child rides home

---

*Supreme Court of the State of Minnesota, 165 Minn., 1925, 361, 206 NW 642; appeal from the District Court, Hennepin county.

in a bus, he should sit with the bus driver, away from other children.

Readmissions

The problem of readmisison of children with questionable symptoms after they have had a communicable disease does not occur so frequently as that of exclusion of children with questionable symptoms. However, some of the school's knottiest problems are questions relating to readmission. Yet, by following established authority and procedures the school can find acceptable solutions to the various questions of re-admission.

Legal aspects. In general, courts have held that it is the responsibility of the parent to demonstrate that the child is not in a communicable state and thus should be permitted to attend school. This interpretation is best expressed in the case of Martin versus Craig:

> It is the responsibility of the parents to prove otherwise if the child is not to be denied the privilege of school attendance.*

When doubt exists as to communicability, the parents must resolve the doubt by obtaining a written clearance from the health department or a practicing physician.

Administrative procedures. Schools properly should be reasonable in readmitting a child who has been ill with a communicable disease, but it also has an obligation to susceptible children who are in school. Usually action in the interests of the many are also in the best interests of a child who has been ill. Certain cases and situations are easy to administer, whereas others are difficult, as examples will illustrate.

1. If the child has been under official isolation or quarantine, an official statement of release by the health department is the certificate of readmission to school.

2. If no official isolation has been in force but the child has been under the supervision of a private physician, the school can properly request the physician's written statement that the child is in a noncommunicable state. A standard form makes the physician's reporting task easier.

3. If there has been no supervision by either the health department or a physician, the school has its most difficult readmission problem. In some states the state department of education requires that any child absent from school for illness for five or more consecutive school days must present a statement from a physician that the child does not harbor a communicable disease. A better approach is for each local school board to establish an official policy on readmissions. Details of the policy and procedures should be developed cooperatively by the school administration, the local physicians, and the health department. Thus, a form

---

*Supreme Court of North Dakota, April 22, 1919, 42ND213, 173NW787, Mand. 81. Schools 157.

that includes space for the physician to include the nature of the illness and instructions for the school can be developed.

Normally the requirement of a statement from his physician after a child has been absent five consecutive school days is practical and effective. However, parents may be tempted to send the child to school on the fifth day to avoid calling a physician. If the child appears to be somewhat ill upon his return on the fifth day, or fourth day, or any other day, it should be the policy of the school to require a physician's certificate of clearance. This should apply to any child who has returned after illness if there is any doubt about his being in a noncommunicable state.

In practice when a child has been absent for a day or two, the teacher should attempt to judge whether or not symptoms such as nasal discharge indicate that the child should remain home for another few days. In this case the school calls the parent and diplomatically suggests that for the best interests of the child it might be wise to keep him home for another day or two. With the judgment of the nurse and other staff members, the teacher can make the necessary decisions in the more difficult situations.

Repeated controversy on readmission is an indication of an inadequate program for educating parents on policies and procedures of disease control. Where parents are well-informed and cooperative, children will be kept out of school until there is no doubt that the child should be readmitted. Tact and diplomacy, not high-handed police methods, from school personnel are needed when misunderstanding or controversy develops. After all, the school as well as the parent is concerned with the same thing—the best interests of the child who has been ill and of every other child in the school.

Epidemics and school policies

Experience has demonstrated that during an epidemic it is better to keep the schools in session unless the epidemic is extreme and all public gatherings are prohibited. This is a decision for the health department. When children remain in school during an epidemic, regular inspections and observations result in early detection and segregation of children with a communicable disease. This opportunity for control is important and should not be lost by default.

If the health department recommends that schools be closed, prohibiting groups of children in theatres, recreation centers, churches and other places is properly in order. School personnel can assist by appealing to parents and students to follow health department regulations and remain away from public places.

Occasionally an outbreak of influenza or other respiratory disease in a school population may be so widespread that school officials, for academic and economic reasons, close the school. When more than half of the student body of a high school is absent because of influenza, it may be wise to close the school for the remainder of the week. Most of the school work for that week would have to be repeated for the benefit of those who were absent. Though it is not done in the interest of controlling communicable diseases, it might be profitable academically and economically.

Selected readings

American Public Health Association: The control of communicable diseases, ed. 7, New York, 1950, The Association.

Anderson, G. W., and Arnstein, Margaret G.: Communicable disease control, ed. 4, New York, 1962, The Macmillan Co.

Bauer, J.: Person behind the disease, New York, 1956, Grune & Stratton, Inc.

Bower, A. G., and Pilant, Edith B.: Communicable diseases for nurses, ed 8, Philadelphia, 1962, W. B. Saunders Co.

Burnett, F. M.: Natural history of infectious disease (second edition of biological aspects of infectious disease), London, 1953, Cambridge University Press.

Dubos, R. J.: Communicable diseases, Philadelphia, 1952, J. B. Lippincott Co.

Elkin, I. I.: A course in epidemiology, New York, 1961, Pergamon Press.

Greenberg, M., and Matz, Anna V.: Modern concepts of communicable disease, New York, 1953, G. P. Putnam's Sons.

Krugman, S., and Ward, R.: Infectious diseases of children, ed. 2, St. Louis, 1960, The C. V. Mosby Co.

Maxcy, K. F. (editor): In Rosenau, M. J.: Preventive medicine and public health, ed. 8, New York, 1956, Appleton-Century-Crofts, Inc.

National Office of Vital Statistics, Public Health Service, United States Department of Health, Education and Welfare: Health statistics, Washington, D. C., 1959, United States Government Printing Office.

Pullen, R. L. (editor): Communicable diseases, Philadelphia, 1950, Lea & Febiger.

Stambul, J.: The mechanisms of disease, New York, 1952, Froben Press, Inc.

Stimson, P. M.: A manual of the common contagious diseases, ed. 5, Philadelphia, 1956, Lea & Febiger.

Top, F. H.: Communicable diseases, ed. 3, St. Louis, 1955, The C. V. Mosby Co.

Turner, C. E., Sellery, C. M., and Smith, Sara L.: School health and health education, ed. 4, St. Louis, 1960, The C. V. Mosby Co.

Weaver, Ruth H.: Control of communicable diseases in school, University of Pennsylvania Schoolmen's Week Proceedings, pp. 224-229, 1950.

Winslow, C.-E. A.: Man and epidemics, Princeton, N. J., 1952, Princeton University Press.

In life, as in chess, forethought wins.

—Charles Buxton

Chapter 9

Preventive aspects of health services—safety, emergency care, and first aid

I n modern school life the prevention of accidents has become as important as the prevention of communicable diseases. In terms of their effect upon the school-age population, accidents loom as a greater threat to health and life than do the infectious diseases. Whether one thinks of accident prevention or safety promotion, there is ample justification for considering this activity a phase of the preventive aspects of school health services.

Just as the most effective prevention of communicable diseases is the positive approach of immunization, the most effective prevention of accidents is also the positive approach—safety promotion for effective living. Safety does not mean the elimination of all risk. Some risks are inevitable, even necessary, but needless risks can be eliminated. Safety extends the scope of human experience by anticipating and preventing conditions which would otherwise be injurious and even fatal. If it thus becomes possible for the child to extend his adventures without mishap, the end result will be more effective and enjoyable living.

The child's environment is one of dynamic action and change. It cannot be a totally safe environment, but physical hazards can be reduced if they are recognized and modified. Children's behavior is normally fast moving and vigorous, which in itself may invite injury. Yet, in the interest of safety, no one would advocate that children just sit and do nothing. Behavior necessary for life's demands also may have to be modified to reduce or even eliminate unnecessary risk.

School safety program

It is apparent that safety in the school does not imply that the physical environment be converted into an accident-proof situation nor that children's actions be completely restrained so that an accident cannot possibly happen. Rather, it means pursuit of the normal demands of life in an environment in which hazards are reduced to a practical minimum and the behavior of the pupils is adapted to safe and effective living.

Because of the high accident rate among children of school age, the promotion of safety is both a challenge and an opportunity for all school personnel. Not all accidents which involve school-age children occur on school premises; yet, a high number do occur at school. Although the immediate task is to prevent accidents, today, the school safety program has the further value of turning out safety-conscious citizens better adapted to the hazards of modern life.

School population death rates. To get a perspective of the importance of accidents as a cause of death in the school-age population, it is desirable to review the causes of school-age deaths for a representative year. Complete and final data are available for 1960 and are quite representative of the year-to-year occurrence in the United States. Table 14 gives the

Table 14. *Leading causes of death of children by age groups, United States, 1960 (rate per 100,000 for specified groups)* *

Rank	Cause	Rate
	5 to 9 years of age	
1	Accidents	19.7
2	Malignant neoplasms	7.4
3	Congenital malformations	4.2
4	Influenza and pneumonia	3.2
5	Diseases of the cardiovascular system	1.8
6	Meningococcal infections	0.6
7	Gastritis, enteritis, colitis	0.3
8	Tuberculosis	0.1
	10 to 14 years of age	
1	Accidents	18.8
2	Malignant neoplasms	6.1
3	Congenital malformations	3.0
4	Diseases of the cardiovascular system	2.6
5	Influenza and pneumonia	2.0
6	Gastritis, enteritis, colitis	0.2
7	Tuberculosis	0.1
8	Meningococcal infections	0.1
	15 to 19 years of age	
1	Accidents	50.7
2	Malignant neoplasms	7.7
3	Diseases of the cardiovascular system	6.2
4	Influenza and pneumonia	2.8
5	Congenital malformations	2.8
6	Tuberculosis	0.3
7	Gastritis, enteritis, colitis	0.4
8	Meningococcal infections	0.3

*Data are from the United States National Office of Vital Statistics.

official rate of deaths per 100,000 children in each category of causes for various age groups.

These data reveal that in a year 10,000 children of school age lose their lives in accidents. In the 5- to 9-year age group accidental deaths are about twice as high as the combined total of the next two causes of death, cancer and congenital malformations. In the age group from 10 to 14 years the number of deaths due to accidents is more than twice as high as the combined total of the next two causes of death, cancer and congenital malformations. In the 15- to 19-year age group the accidental deaths are more than three times as high as the combined total of the next three causes of death, cancer, diseases of the circulatory system, influenza and pneumonia. Viewed in another light, accidents caused 40% of all deaths in the 5- to 9-year group, 43% in the 10- to 14-year group, and 55% in the 15- to 19-year group.

In 1960 records of the National Office of Vital Statistics indicate that accidental deaths were much greater for boys than for girls of school age. From a difference of three boys to two girls in the 5- to 9-year age group, the gap widens to three to one in the 10- to 14-year age group and four to one in the 15- to 19-year age group.

For the school-age group of 5 to 19 years, a total of 13,128 accidental deaths occurred in 1959. The distribution is significant.

Motor vehicle	54%	Firearms	6%
Drowning	17%	Railroad	3%
Fires, burns	7%	Other	13%

These data point up the over-all hazard to life encountered by the school-age youngster. The school should extract from these general figures what the relation of the school is to this accidental death picture and what this means to the school in terms of its obligations and opportunities.

School accidents. Studies and surveys reveal that about 43% of accidental deaths among school-age children are connected with school life. Of these accidents about 20% occur in school buildings, about 17% on school grounds, and about 6% on the way to and from school. In school buildings the gymnasium is the most frequent location of accidents and about one third of the fatal accidents occur within the building. Another 20% of the fatal indoor accidents occur in halls and stairs. Shops and laboratories account for about 18% and other classrooms add another 14%. The remaining indoor accidents occur in various other locations. On the school grounds, 41% of fatal accidents occur during organized activities—football, 20%; baseball, 12%; playground apparatus, 9%; and other organized activities, 18%.

The 6% of fatal accidents among school-age children which occur while the pupil is going to or from school are mostly pedestrian-motor vehicle and bicycle-motor vehicle accidents.

Student injuries by location and grade level for 1951 are reported by the National Safety Council. Reports of accidents to school children

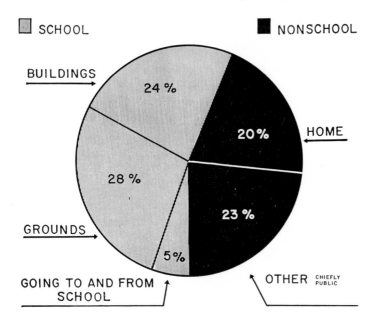

■ SCHOOL   ■ NONSCHOOL

BUILDINGS 24%

HOME 20%

28%

23%

GROUNDS

5%

GOING TO AND FROM SCHOOL

OTHER CHIEFLY PUBLIC

SOURCE: REPORTS TO THE NATIONAL SAFETY COUNCIL FROM SCHOOL SYSTEMS WITH ENROLLMENT OF ABOUT 1,940,000 STUDENTS.

INJURIES REQUIRING THE ATTENTION OF A DOCTOR, OR CAUSING ABSENCE FROM SCHOOL OF ONE-HALF DAY OR MORE.

Fig. 30. Chart shows injuries to students; the breakdown is by location at which the injuries occurred. In buildings about one third of the injuries occurred in gymnasiums and about one fifth in classrooms. On school grounds injuries occurred more during organized activities than during unorganized activities. (Courtesy National Safety Council.)

which occurred in the school environment and elsewhere and caused injuries requiring a physician or causing at least a half day's absence were available from schools having a total enrollment of more than 1,900,000 students. In school buildings most accidents occurred in the gymnasium, and classrooms were second. On school grounds football and unorganized activities in which running was involved caused most injuries. This report of the National Safety Council also indicated injury by grade levels.

All grades have unjustifiably high accident rates. Fourth- to ninth-

Table 15. *Injuries to school-age children by location*

Location	Per cent
School buildings	24
School grounds	28
On way to and from school	5
Home	20
Other	23

grade children tend to engage in vigorous activity, often with an abandon that leads to a high accident rate. The problem is to control and modify vigorous activity, not abolish it.

Through an orderly process of supervision and guidance, children can acquire modes of activity less hazardous than the ones they usually follow.

A tabular presentation of injury rates can be revealing (Table 16).

Table 16. *Injury rates by location and grade level, 1951 (per 100,000 students)*

Grade	All injury rate	School building	School grounds	Going to or from school	Home	Other
All grades	16.6	4.0	4.7	0.8	3.3	3.8
Kindergarten-3	11.2	1.4	3.4	0.8	3.5	2.1
4 to 6	16.3	2.4	5.4	1.0	3.6	3.9
7 to 9	23.7	7.8	5.5	1.0	3.5	5.9
10 to 12	24.1	9.0	7.1	0.6	2.2	5.2

Legal aspects. Teachers and other school employees run the risk of a law suit from injured students because of alleged negligence which causes injury.

In general, negligence is any conduct below the legally established standard for the protection of others against unreasonable risk of harm. Basically there are two types of negligence:

1. An act which a person of ordinary prudence or judgment would realize involves unreasonable risk to others
2. Failure to act for the protection of another

Thus, negligence can be acts of commission or omission. The specific details of each case determine whether there has been negligent behavior. Harper has outlined the types of negligent behavior very well. According to him an act may be negligent in any of the following circumstances.

1. It is not properly done; appropriate care is not employed by the actor.
2. The circumstances under which it is done create risks, although it is done with due care and precaution.
3. The actor is indulging in acts which involve an unreasonable risk of direct and immediate harm to others.
4. The actor sets in motion a force, the continuous operation of which may be unreasonably hazardous to others.
5. He creates a situation which is unreasonably dangerous to others because of the likelihood of the action of third persons of inanimate forces.
6. He entrusts dangerous devices or instrumentalities to persons who are incompetent to use or care for such instruments properly.
7. He neglects a duty of control over third persons who, by reason of some incapacity or abnormality, he knows to be likely to inflict intended harm upon others.
8. He fails to employ due care to give adequate warning.
9. He fails to exercise the proper care in looking out for persons whom he has reason to believe may be in the danger zone.
10. He fails to employ appropriate skill to perform acts undertaken.

11. He fails to make adequate preparation to avoid harm to others before entering upon certain conduct where such preparation is reasonably necessary.
12. He fails to inspect and repair instrumentalities or mechanical devices used by others.
13. His conduct prevents a third person from assisting persons imperiled through no fault of his own.*

Liability for negligent conduct is affected by the nature of both the act and its results. Carelessness is a relative term. In general a person is considered to be careless or negligent when actions are not those of a person of ordinary prudence. If a pupil is injured because a teacher's actions were not those of a prudent person or the teacher failed to act, a lawsuit may be instituted by the parents and the teacher held liable. Each teacher is responsible for her negligence which results in physical harm to others. A teacher's administrative superior may be held liable only when he directs the teacher to do some act which is dangerous and results in injury to a pupil.

A school board is usually not liable for its own negligent acts since it is a government entity and thus is immune to lawsuit unless the board consents to a suit. Washington has a permissive law which is effective in permitting suits against school boards. California, New York, New Jersey, and Connecticut have annulled this common law immunity, but these annulments are exceptions to the basic philosophy. However, at present there is a slight trend toward abolishing the theory of nonliability for school boards. Many legal authorities question the justice of common law nonliability, contending the theory survives entirely by virtue of its antiquity. They further contend that it is harsh and unjust to require the teacher alone to suffer. However, so long as nonliability for school boards exists, the teacher must proceed with the knowledge that he or she alone may be held liable for any pupil injury. In Connecticut, New Jersey, and New York, judgments against teachers may be paid out of school funds.

Teachers are not often defendants in lawsuits that allege negligence has resulted in injury to a pupil. Teachers tend to be conservative, and their conduct usually is prudent. Courts recognize the problem of close supervision of thirty-five or forty children at a given moment, and only when the teacher has displayed deplorably poor judgment does the court tend to hold her liable. The low premiums for liability insurance for teachers attest to the small likelihood that a teacher will be a defendant in a lawsuit resulting from injury to a pupil.

The best safeguard against such a lawsuit is a well-planned functioning program for the prevention of accidents to pupils. Such a program will also be assurance to the parents that the school has taken definite steps to reduce student injuries to a minimum. The safety of the students

*From Harper, F. V.: A treatise on the law of torts, Indianapolis, Ind., 1938, Bobbs-Merrill Co., pp. 171-176.

is the first consideration, but here, as usual, student and faculty interests are one.

Prevention of accidents in school. Not all accidents can be anticipated nor can one foresee all situations which cause accidents. Yet, most hazardous conditions can be recognized and unsafe practices detected if the school has a well-organized safety program. Safety programs, financially speaking, are not costly. What they demand is vision, organization, leadership, and cooperation. They should be programs which are in action, not programs on paper. A well-planned program evaluates the conditions and practices in the school in terms of safety and then undertakes to modify those which are not adequate.

A necessary first step in the prevention of school accidents is to make a survey to detect all potentially hazardous conditions. It should be a *positive* survey in which all *Yes* answers denote acceptance and all *No* answers denote need for correction. The following survey form is one which from experience has proved highly satisfactory and which any school can adapt to its use.

SURVEY OF CONDITIONS AND PRACTICES AFFECTING SAFETY IN THE SCHOOL ENVIRONMENT

Reporting of accidents

1. Are accident report cards or forms available?
2. Is a complete written report on file for every accident which results in an injury?
3. Is a special study made of the causes of each accident?
4. Is an adequate constructive follow-up made after each accident analysis to prevent recurrence of the accident?
5. Is a rapid inspection made of the building each morning and a thorough inspection once each month?
6. Are adequate first-aid equipment and personnel available?

Fire protection

1. Are vacant rooms, basements, and attics free from inflammable material?
2. Is there proper insulation between heating equipment and inflammable material?
3. Are there two or more exits from every floor with doors swinging outward?
4. Are there adequate fire escapes on buildings of two or more stories?
5. Are fire extinguishers of an approved type provided for every 2000 square feet of floor space?
6. Do the older pupils know how to use the fire extinguishers?
7. Are fire alarms centrally located?
8. Are fire drills so proficient that the building can be emptied in an orderly manner in less than three minutes?
9. Are student organization and lines of exit well established?

Gymnasium, pool, and locker rooms

1. Is equipment in good condition?
2. Are all exposed projections covered?
3. Is the floor treated to prevent its being too slippery?
4. Are doors of a safe type?
5. Are fountains in a safe location?

6. Are definite rules for the use of the gymnasium and pool posted and practiced?
7. Are students properly dressed for gymnasium activities?
8. Is horseplay prohibited?
9. Is unsupervised use of the gymnasium and pool prohibited?
10. Are pool users classified according to skill?

Halls and stairs

1. Are all obstructions removed?
2. Are the floors and stairs treated to prevent them from being slippery?
3. Are worn or broken stairs replaced?
4. Are railings provided so that every person using the stairs can hold a railing?
5. Is undue congestion of hall traffic prevented by changing routes, practices, and schedules?
6. Are horseplay and running in the halls prohibited?
7. Are stairs taken one step at a time?

Shops, laboratories, and home economic rooms

1. Is all equipment in good repair and inspected daily?
2. Are all possible safety devices and attachments available and used?
3. Are good housekeeping practices followed?
4. Are lighting and space adequate?
5. Are machines stopped for oiling and adjustment?
6. Are safety rules posted and practiced?
7. Are students properly instructed in the use of equipment?
8. Are horseplay and running prohibited?
9. Is the unsupervised use of the shop, laboratory, or home economics rooms prohibited?
10. Are first-aid supplies immediately available?

Classrooms and auditoriums

1. Are all obstructions removed?
2. Are exposed projections covered?
3. Are sharp objects placed in protected places?
4. Are radiators and electric fixtures properly protected?
5. Are dropped objects picked up immediately?
6. Is an orderly routine followed, with running and pushing prohibited?

Playground

1. Is the playground space allocated in terms of safety?
2. Is apparatus in safe condition and checked regularly?
3. Are children taught the proper use of each piece of apparatus?
4. Is supervision always provided when the playground is used?
5. Do beginners receive special instructions and supervision?
6. Are horseplay and stunting prohibited?
7. Are caution and courtesy stressed at all times?
8. Do the children assume cooperative responsibility for playground safety?

Athletics

1. Is the playing area constructed in terms of safety?
2. Are all hazardous obstructions removed?
3. Is approved equipment used?
4. Has every participant received medical approval?
5. Is competent supervision always provided?
6. Are the participants properly trained and sufficiently skilled?
7. Is parental approval required for participation in vigorous athletic events?

8. Is parental approval required if students are to be transported for athletic contests?
9. Are adequate first-aid and medical services available?

Going to and from school

1. Are intensive studies made of hazards children may encounter going to or from school?
2. Are specific routes outlined for students?
3. Are the roads direct, requiring a minimum use of roadways and busy intersections?
4. Are stop and go signals, stop signs, school signs, police supervision, and one way streets used to the greatest advantage?
5. Are ice, glass, and other hazardous obstructions removed from walks?
6. Do children stay on the walks and in crosswalk lanes and do they obey rules, signs, and traffic directors?
7. If school traffic patrols are organized, are the patrols under proper adult supervision?
8. Is maximum use made of traffic enforcement officers and facilities?
9. Are the parents enlisted in the safety program to and from home?

School safety organizations. School life becomes increasingly organized as school functions expand, but organization is necessary for effective action. Various plans for the promotion of safety are in operation, but three plans are in most general use. The first has a general *School Patrol* unit with subdivisions such as traffic patrol, fire patrol, and building and grounds patrol. The second plan recognizes three independent but correlated patrols—the traffic patrol, the fire patrol, and the building and grounds patrol. The third plan provides merely for a school safety patrol which directs and controls student pedestrian traffic near the school.

A *school safety patrol* is perhaps most valuable as a safety education measure, but its value in accident prevention should not be minimized. Careful planning and supervision are necessary. Standard rules governing the operation of safety patrols have been adopted by states and on a national level by representatives of the National Safety Council, National Congress of Parents and Teachers, National Education Association, American Automobile Association, National Association of Chiefs of Police, and the United States Office of Education. Standard rules have been published by the National Safety Council. A condensation of the rules will indicate the essential requirements of a safety patrol.

Standard rules for operation of school safety patrols. Experience has led to the development of standards and procedures that provide an optimum basis for the operation of a school safety patrol. These proposed rules are universally applicable and provide for the full effectiveness of the safety patrol.

FUNCTION. The functions of the school safety patrol are (1) to instruct, direct, and control the members of the student body in crossing the streets and highways at or near schools, and (2) to assist teachers and parents in the instruction of school children in safe practices in the use of streets and highways at all times and places.

Patrols should not be charged with the responsibility of directing ve-

hicular traffic, nor should they be allowed to direct it. They should not function as police.

ADMINISTRATIVE SUPPORT. The approval, support, and encouragement of all school authorities are essential if the safety patrol is to function effectively.

SELECTION. Patrol members, either boys or girls, ordinarily should be appointed by the principal or faculty sponsor. They should be selected from the upper grade levels. Patrol service should be voluntary and only when the student has written approval of the parent or guardian.

SIZE AND OFFICERS. The number of members on a school patrol should be determined by local factors, such as street and highway conditions, number of intersections, volume of vehicular traffic, school enrollment, and number of school dismissal times.

Every patrol should have a captain and one or more lieutenants. Other officers may be appointed as required. Officers should serve for at least one school term; other members may be changed periodically.

INSTRUCTION, TRAINING, AND SUPERVISION. Safety patrols are a means to extend traffic safety education beyond the classroom. Therefore careful and thorough instruction, training, and supervision of patrol members are essential if the patrol is to be efficient and continuous. School officials are responsible for the operation of school safety patrols.

INSIGNIA. The standard insignia for patrol members is the white Sam Browne belt made of 2-inch wide material. It must be worn in plain view at all times while the patrol member is on duty. If the visibility of patrol belts must be increased when worn over white or very light clothing, either a narrow dark stripe at or close to each edge of the belt or a Federal yellow-colored belt may be used.

INCREASED VISIBILITY OF PATROL MEMBERS IF NEEDED. If the patrol member cannot be seen at least as far away as the safe stopping distance for the legal speed at that location, one of these procedures should be followed:

1. Select another location for the patrol-protected crossing.
2. If the selection of another crossing is not practical, station an auxiliary patrol at the approach to the crossing so that he can be seen in time for a driver to make a safe stop or other driving adjustment.
3. If it is not practical to select another crossing or to use an auxiliary patrol member, place an effective flashing or other signal or sign to warn of a school crossing ahead.

WARNING FLAGS. Warning flags are used only as auxiliary equipment and *only* where necessary to increase the distance at which patrol members may be seen and recognized.

All warning flags shall be approximately 24 inches square and shall be made of colorfast, Federal yellow-colored material. Such flag shall be fastened along one edge to a rod approximately 4 feet long. The flag may bear the word *School* or the words *School Crossing.* The flagstick shall be held upward and outward at an angle of about 45 degrees.

POSITION AND PROCEDURE. The patrol member must stand on the curb, not in the street, and restrain the children until he sees a gap in traffic. When a gap occurs, he steps aside and motions for the children to cross the street in a group.

RELATION TO TRAFFIC SIGNALS AND POLICE OFFICERS. At intersections without any traffic control, the traffic may be sufficiently heavy to require the assignment of a police officer at those times when children are going to and from school.

At intersections where traffic is controlled by a police officer or a traffic signal or both, the safety patrol member will assist by directing children across the street in conformance with the directions of the signal or the police officer.

HOURS ON DUTY. It is essential that patrol members be on duty at all times when children are crossing streets or highways in going to and from school. The patrol members should reach their posts at least 10 to 15 minutes before the opening of school in the morning and at noon and should remain on duty until the tardy bell. At dismissals they should leave their classes 2 or 3 minutes before the dismissal bell and should remain on duty until all pupils who are not stragglers have passed their posts.

BUS DUTY. If pupils are transported to and from school by bus, patrol members should be assigned to bus duty. The function of the bus patrol is purely that of assisting the bus driver. School authorities should instruct children to obey both the bus driver and any patrol member assigned to bus duty.

Any school planning to have a safety patrol should obtain a copy of the complete rules from the National Safety Council. If standard rules for safety patrols have been developed on a state level, these should guide the schools within that state.

Fire patrol. A fire patrol inspects buildings for fire hazards, periodically checks emergency exits and fire escapes, is familiar with the use of school fire fighting equipment, and directs regular fire drills. Officers of the fire patrol are elected by the pupils, and their duties include the following:

Fire chief
1. To consult with the principal about planning drills, mapping exits, and assigning duties to the fire squad
2. To assist the principal in calling, supervising, and reporting drills
3. To promote education on fire drills and fire prevention in the school through such means as assembly programs, personal appearances in rooms, organizing committees, and contacting the local fire department
4. To instruct fire squad members in their duties and to check on their performance at the time of each drill
5. To plan the meetings of the fire squad and act as presiding officer

Assistant fire chief
1. To assist the chief as directed and to take his place when he is absent

Captains

1. To supervise drills in different parts of the buildings
2. To check the completion of drills and notify the chief as soon as the section is free of occupants
3. To instruct and supervise room marshals and inspectors in performance of duties

Room marshals (two for each room)

No. 1 marshal

1. To lead the class in formation to point of safety outside of building
2. To set the pace for the room along the route of exit
3. To assist No. 2 Marshal and the teacher in taking roll and accounting for all pupils
4. To report to the captain on the completion of the drill

No. 2 marshal

1. To close windows, turn off lights, see that everyone is out of the room, and close the door.
2. To follow the class, keep the formation compact, and prevent anyone from going back
3. To become the leader of the drill in case an exit is blocked and necessitates a reverse in direction (Marshals must be familiar with all alternate exits.)
4. To assist the teacher in supervising the pupils in the maintenance of strict fire drill discipline

Inspectors

1. To inspect all special rooms (close windows, turn off lights, see that room is clear of occupants, and close the door)
2. To report to captain upon completion of duties (Every conceivable place in the building where there might be persons not under direction of a teacher should be inspected. These stations would include offices, nurse's room, lavatories, gymnasium, and dressing rooms. Not more than two or three simple inspections should be assigned to one inspector.)
3. To leave the building promptly and report to their proper groups

Pupils who are members of the fire squad should be selected and trained in their duties so that a drill can be held during the first week of school. The first drill should be announced to the teachers in advance and should be staged as a slow-motion rehearsal. Special training should be given to pupils of the kindergarten and the beginning first grade. A meeting of the fire squad should follow each of the first drills so that imperfections can be corrected. Numerous suggestions for the improvement of future drills will be forthcoming from the pupils.

Building and grounds patrol. A building and grounds patrol is appointed to prevent disorders and accidents on the school premises. Patrol members assist teachers in preventing dangerous play practices on the playground and in preventing horseplay in the building. In addition the patrol helps to keep the grounds in order by inspections for broken glass, refuse, uneven surfaces, holes, defective playground equipment, loose boards and railings, slippery floors and stairs, and other hazards. Patrol members also help crippled pupils and greet and guide visitors.

School safety council. A school safety council is organized in some buildings and, under effective faculty supervision, can be valuable in both accident prevention and social experience. However, to avoid overorganization in the school, many administrators prefer to have patrols operate as self-contained units or under the general surveillance of the student council.

Evaluation. A school safety program can be evaluated entirely in terms of student safety knowledge, practices, and attitudes since the program encompasses safety education. Yet, a school safety program must also be appraised in terms of the degree to which it reduces the incidence and severity of injuries to pupils. Repeated surveys must be made to determine the extent to which the program actually deals with the particular safety needs of the students. Records on accidents to students must be studied by month, time of day, place, age of pupil, nature of accident, nature of injury, and all other pertinent factors. In some schools an analysis of the activities of the pupils is the principal instrument used in evaluating the school safety program. That student practices in terms of established safety measures have improved is laudable, but practices are but a means to an end—accident prevention.

A new program may not yield immediate tangible results, nor will the most effective program yield spectacular changes, but an effective school safety program will produce a measurable reduction in the number and severity of injuries.

Emergency care

In any situation in which relatively large numbers of children are assembled, emergencies occur despite the best laid plans and thoughtful precautions. Wisdom would dictate preparation for such emergencies. Experience indicates that such preparation need not be elaborate, but that it be organized.

Planned program. One could not possibly foresee every emergency which might occur in the school, nor is such foresight necessary. Emergency situations fall into patterns, and a school plan to take care of major illness, minor illness, and emergencies due to accidents would take care of a school's needs. The program could be so completely planned that modifications would rarely be required and, if necessary, could be made quite readily.

Facilities for emergency care
1. Emergency rest rooms (one for girls and one for boys) each with at least two cots, adequate blankets, washbasin, soap, towels, chairs, and table
2. Splints, slings, gauze, rubber tubing
3. Emetic (e.g., mustard to produce vomiting)
4. Phone numbers posted at all phones
   (a) Physicians
   (b) Ambulance
   (c) Hospital
   (d) Clinic
   (e) Fire department

5. Phone numbers filed
   (a) Home of each child
   (b) Child's family physician

Personnel assignments for emergency care

1. Person first in command and duties
2. Person second in command
3. Person third in command
4. Person to phone
   (a) Physician
   (b) Ambulance
   (c) Hospital
   (d) Home
   (e) Fire department

With an organized program such as this the school is well prepared to meet its responsibility during emergencies. If the school emergency program is part of the community civilian defense program, the school should rehearse its procedures as part of the community rehearsal. Otherwise, on its own initiative the school should go through simulated emergencies.

Major illness. Occasionally a child in school may become seriously ill with high fever, severe pain, general distress, gastrointestinal upset, and even some indication of prostration. The condition should be considered serious, but not critical. It is not likely to be a matter of seconds; yet the teacher should handle the situation as if it were extremely important. A systematic procedure will apply to any situation.

1. Have the child rest on a cot in a moderately darkened room.
2. Keep the child warm.
3. Contact the child's home by telephone or other means.
4. Carry out the parent's instructions.
5. If the parents cannot be contacted within an hour, call the child's family physician.
6. If the child's family physician is not available, call some other physician.
7. State the condition of the child.
8. Carry out the physician's instructions.

It is apparent that in most occurrences of major illness the school will have met its obligation when it has carried out the parents' instructions.

Minor illness. A child in school may become mildly upset or ill. Perhaps a mild headache, slight distress, the aftereffects of overexertion, or a general malaise has developed. At least at the outset it may not be necessary to contact the home since there is a good probability that after rest the child will be able to return to class and resume work.

1. Have the child rest on a cot in a moderately darkened room.
2. Keep the child warm.
3. Have someone in attendance or responsible for visiting the child at intervals.
4. Use no drugs.
5. If the illness appears to become more severe, follow the procedures for major illness.

Emergency due to accident. Specific first steps are necessary in virtually all accident emergencies although not every measure will apply to all cases. The order in which measures are carried out is determined by the particular situation.

1. Note whether the subject is breathing.
2. Note whether air passages are obstructed and remove any foreign bodies in the mouth.
3. Note any profuse hemorrhaging.
4. Note whether the subject is in a state of shock.
5. Have him lie on his back with his head raised if his face is flushed, or lower him if his face is pale.
6. If he is vomiting, turn his head to the side.
7. Loosen his clothing, particularly if breathing is hindered.
8. Place blankets or wraps under and over him and keep him warm. Injury usually produces a drop in body temperature.
9. Do not move the subject unless absolutely necessary until a physician or an ambulance arrives.
10. If it is necessary to move the child, apply a splint to the injured parts and handle the injured parts with extreme care.
11. Give no liquids or solid foods.
12. Comfort and reassure the child. Perhaps it is advisable not to allow the child to see his injury.
13. Remain with the victim until a physician or ambulance has arrived.

In case of really serious injury, as soon as the nature of the child's condition has been determined, the family physician should be called. The call should report the general condition of the child including the pulse rate and whether the breathing is faint or heavy and the child warm and perspiring or cold and clammy, conscious or unconscious, and in pain. The physician also should be told of the nature and extent of injury, the nature of any bleeding, and possible fractures or dislocations.

Transporting the injured child by ambulance is the most satisfactory means of conveyance, but, if an ambulance cannot be obtained, care should be exercised in selecting a vehicle. A vehicle which will be most comfortable for the patient, not the one easiest to recruit, should be selected.

When the injury does not appear to be serious, one may notify the home first. Whenever the parents are informed of an accident to their child, calmness, and assurance are in order. Perhaps going to the home, rather than phoning, might be advisable. Report the kind of accident, the nature of the injury, and the condition of the child. If the child is being taken directly to a hospital or a physician's office, report the name of the hospital or physician. If the school and parents agree that the child should be taken home, suggest that immediate preparations be made for the arrival of the child.

First aid at school

As the term implies, first aid is the assistance first given to the injured person and is aimed at the prevention of further harm. It is the tempo-

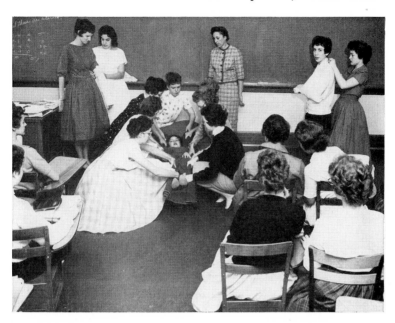

Fig. 31. First-aid practice. A high school unit on first aid properly includes demonstrations of knowledge and skill.

rary treatment given at the site of the emergency. It is the aid given by a skilled lay person before the subject is in charge of a physician. At this point the first-aid phase terminates, and the layman's first-aid duty is done unless he is directed by the physician to perform additional tasks. The correct first-aid measures can reduce suffering, be instrumental in speeding up subsequent recovery, prevent permanent disability, and even save life.

Basic philosophy. Every accident is tragic because it might have been prevented. Yet in an imperfect world of imperfect people accidents will occur and emergencies which require people skilled in first aid will arise. There is nothing mystical about first aid. It simply involves acknowledged procedures for giving immediate help to an individual who has been injured. Yet simple though it may be, first aid can be of greater importance than the subsequent aid of a physician. Whether a major or a minor emergency exists, know-how is the important ingredient for resolving the situation and every teacher should be trained in first aid.

Most first-aid situations in the school are minor and subsequently are not brought to the attention of a physician. Even the most incidental injury should command the teacher's attention and care. Dealing with human health and life is a challenge to the teacher's best efforts. Parents should be informed of the first-aid measures which were taken when their child has been injured or otherwise incapacitated.

Even in the best administered schools with well-organized and wellfunctioning safety programs, serious accidents occur. The poise and skill which enable school personnel to face the most serious situation, sufficient for whatever may be required, are usually the result of following recognized procedures and assuming adequate self-reliance in many specific, though minor, emergencies over the span of time. Each teacher should be prepared in first-aid procedures so that when the emergency arises she will be equal to the occasion and confident in her ability to deal with the situation. First-aid procedures are definite and specific, but not involved. Time given to a standard first-aid course is well invested. In the absence of an opportunity to take a standard course a study of first-aid measures for typical emergencies of school life can be highly profitable to the teacher who applies herself conscientiously.

Guiding principles. A few basic principles or rules can guide the teacher in any first-aid situation.

1. Be sure there is need for haste before you hurry. Many people needlessly rush blindly in emergency situations. Few emergencies require haste. If breathing is obstructed or profuse bleeding occurs, haste is necessary, but it is difficult to envision any other emergency in a school which would require extreme haste.

2. Do the common sense thing which is indicated. Often the correct thing may appear to be ridiculously simple; most first-aid procedures are simple and obvious.

3. If in doubt, assume that the worst possible condition exists. If a child has a head injury of unknown extent and the teacher proceeds on the assumption that intracranial hemorrhage is present, the procedure will be more than adequate if the injury is of a lesser nature.

4. Even though your first-aid procedure may not be beneficial, at least make sure that it is not injurious. Many well-meaning individuals, in their efforts to do something for an injured person, actually harm the victim. There are many things worse for the victim than to lie quietly on the ground while waiting for a physician and an ambulance. If the victim is moved improperly, it may cause greater damage than the original injury.

Whenever a question of liability arises in the administration of first aid, the whole issue is based upon the question of whether what was done was reasonable. Subsequent events may indicate that what was done was not the best that could have been done; yet in view of the circumstances it was sensible and perhaps what a person of ordinary prudence would have done.

General conditions and injuries

Certain conditions and injuries involve the entire body. Aid in these conditions involves procedures different from those in which the injury is localized. In the school five types of emergencies involving the entire body may occur—asphyxiation, shock, epileptic convulsions, fainting, and possible poisoning.

Asphyxiation. Any interference with aeration of the blood can be termed asphyxiation. There may be only a mild interference with aeration, such as a small obstruction to breathing or mild carbon monoxide poisoning. Or the interference may be so great as to stop the breathing completely. When the oxygen concentration of the blood drops appreciably, the vital respiratory and cardiac centers in the brain are affected and may not carry on their normal functions.

In the school asphyxiation by the inhalation of gas is a rare occurrence. Asphyxiation usually occurs as a result of mechanical obstruction of breathing. This includes foreign bodies in the throat, larynx, or trachea, submersion in water, and strangulation.

First-aid treatment for asphyxia consists first of removing the cause and second providing air to the subject. If the subject does not breath, artificial respiration must be performed. Delay may cost the subject his life. Few persons can go without breathing for more than five minutes; therefore, action to restore breathing should begin at once. Whether or not artificial respiration is necessary, certain other measures are helpful in producing recovery.

1. Loosen all clothing, which interferes with breathing or circulation.
2. Keep the subject warm. Shock usually is present.
3. Provide ample fresh air.
4. Keep the subject quiet and at rest.
5. Summon a physician immediately even though the subject appears to be recovering fully. The recovery may only be temporary.

Resuscitation is the revival of a person who is almost dead. In artificial respiration, breathing is produced by some agency outside of the subject's own body. If a pulmonary ventilator (pulmotor) and a competent operator are available, these should be used. In the absence of these mechanical means manual artificial respiration should be used. At least one teacher in every school building should be trained in artificial respiration. Such training should be obtained from a skilled operator, which will provide ample opportunity for supervised practice. It is a skill which is mastered by explanation, demonstration, and supervised practice.

Mouth-to-mouth or mouth-to-nose artificial respiration, properly done, is the most effective method of rescue breathing other than the use of mechanical devices. It is not a difficult procedure and can be mastered effectively by any normal adult who can follow the prescribed directions.

1. Place the subject on his back at once right where he is; no need to loosen clothing or drain water from the subject.
2. Clear the mouth and throat of all obstruction.
3. Tilt the head far back in a "chin-up" position and the neck stretched.
4. Draw the lower jaw far forward, being careful not to depress the tongue. It is important that the jaw be held far forward to open the passageway of the throat.
5. Pinch the nose with the thumb and forefinger of the other hand.

Fig. 32. Mouth-to-mouth resuscitation. Note the head tilted far back and the neck stretched. The jaw is held forward to open the breathing passageway. (Courtesy Oregon State Board of Health.)

6. Take a deep breath and, with your mouth wide and over the subject's open mouth, blow forcefully into the subject's breathing passageway until you see the chest rise.
7. Quickly remove your mouth when the chest rises and listen for exhalation. If the subject makes gurgling or snoring sounds, lift the jaw higher.
8. Repeat the process at the rate of 16 to 20 per minute for a school-age youngster until the subject begins to breathe normally.

While artificial resuscitation is being administered, a physician should be called. Once the physician arrives, he is in complete charge of the situation.

Shock. Shock is a depressed level of body function. It results from emotional upsets and from injuries of various kinds that involve a general blow to the body or localized injuries. Some degree of shock follows most injuries. Shock may occur at once or its onset may be delayed, even for two or three hours.

Symptoms of shock vary in degree, but the pattern is quite standard; usually the subject is conscious.

1. Cold clammy pale skin
2. Anxiety and fear characterize facial expression

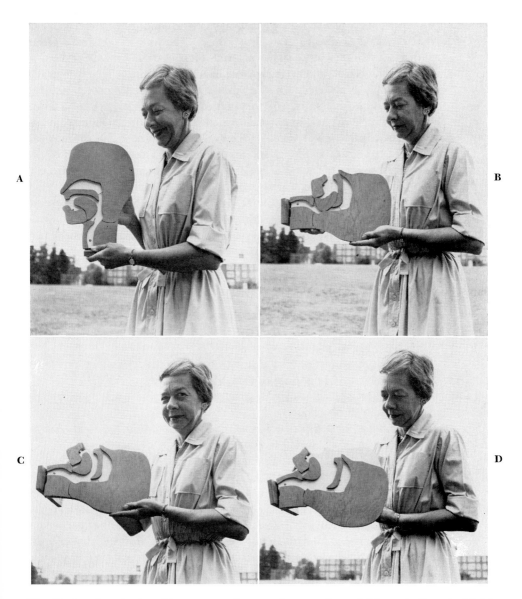

Fig. 33. Opening the breathing passages for mouth-to-mouth artificial respiration. **A,** Model showing normal respiratory passages in relation to associated structures. **B,** Model showing obstruction of the breathing passages when the tongue is retracted while the subject is in a lying position. **C,** Thrusting the jaw forward helps to widen the breathing passageway. **D,** Tilting the head far back and stretching the neck aids further in assuring a wide air passageway.

3. Bluish lips and fingernails
4. Irregular breathing
5. Rapid weak pulse
6. Chills often occur
7. Limp relaxed muscles

A knowledge of the physiology of shock is helpful in providing the proper emergency care for a person in a shock condition. If death results from shock, it is due to circulatory failure. Normally the heart pumps against a moderate amount of arterial pressure, which is necessary for normal contraction and output of the heart. Blood pressure is due to constriction of the arteries and the viscosity of the blood proteins. These proteins cannot normally pass through capillary membranes. The injury or blow which causes shock produces dilation of the arteries and also makes the capillaries permeable to blood proteins, and the proteins diffuse out of the capillaries. This relaxation of the arteries and loss of proteins by the blood causes a decline in blood pressure which in turn causes poorer heart action, which produces a further drop in blood pressure. The downward spiral of blood pressure continues unless something reverses the course. Transfusion of blood plasma to the subject adds blood proteins which will increase the blood pressure and thus start the recovery process. However, this is a procedure for a physician and hospital personnel. Teachers must concern themselves with first-aid measures.

First-aid treatment for shock is simple, but highly important.

1. Keep the patient warm. Blankets, coats, and similar materials underneath and covering the subject help to prevent loss of body heat. Massage is not recommended.
2. Lay the subject on his back with his head low. A pillow should not be used, and he should not sit up.
3. Do not give the subject a stimulant or water unless instructed to do so by a physician.
4. If the subject must be moved, a stretcher should be used. An ambulance is best suited to convey a person in shock.

Epileptic convulsions. The United States has about 820,000 persons with epilepsy, which means about one in every 220 persons. Although the incidence is lower in the school population than in the general population, a teacher may be confronted with the problem of emergency care of an epileptic child during a seizure. With understanding the teacher can approach the task confident in her ability to handle the situation. For the prepared teacher a child in an epileptic seizure is not a frightening sight, but a signal for action which will be helpful to the child.

Minor (petit mal) epilepsy is characterized by a transitory loss of consciousness, with or without muscle tremors, and no other symptoms. If the child is standing, he remains in that position. He may recognize that he has lost consciousness for three or four seconds, but will experience no particular ill effects. These children are not a problem in the school unless they should develop the **major form**.

Major (grand mal) epilepsy is characterized by extreme convulsive thrashing about, followed by prolonged stupor.

First-aid care of epileptic persons is rather simple.

1. Do not resist the seizure. Resistance would not shorten the time of the seizure nor reduce its intensity.
2. Get the person in the clear so that he will not injury himself by striking something hot, sharp, or hard. If the child has a seizure while sitting in his seat, the first procedure indicated is to carry him to the free area in front of the room.
3. Open his collar if it is tight.
4. If the subject is swallowing his tongue, there will be an audible gurgling in the throat. The tongue has retracted and needs to be drawn forward. To do this place a stick between the subject's molars. With the fingers, draw the tongue forward. It may be necessary to hold the tongue forward for several minutes. If a wooden stick is not available, something else, such as rubber, may be used to hold the month open. Hard materials which may chip the teeth should not be used, but under no circumstances should the operator put his fingers in the victim's mouth without some such guard.
5. After the convulsion place the subject on a cot and let him sleep.
6. Call the parents. Usually parents indicate at the opening of the school year that their child is subject to convulsions and will instruct the school on what procedures they wish to have followed.

Children will accept a child who has an occasional seizure, but, if a child has seizures so often that the routine of the room is disrupted frequently, he should not attend school. The family physician should make the decision on whether the child's condition warrants discontinuance of school.

Fainting. The technical term for fainting is syncope. It may be induced by a psychological experience such as fright or a physiological factor such as fatigue. During fainting the physiological change which takes place is dilatation of the large arteries in the abdominal cavity. This results in a shifting of the blood mass so that a disproportionately large share is in these vessels and a diminished amount is in the brain and surface areas. The reduced blood supply in the brain area is inadequate for consciousness. Paleness, or blanching of the skin occurs and is the distinguishing symptom.

First-aid care must based on the recognition that the blood supply to the brain must be increased.

1. Place the person in a horizontal position or with the head slightly lowered. Raise the legs to help hasten blood flow to the brain. Do not throw water on the person.
2. Following recovery of consciousness the person should not return to a standing position too soon. After lying flat for perhaps five minutes, he should sit up for another five minutes before standing again.

3. If the child is sitting when he faints or appears likely to faint, the teacher, with her hand on the back of the child's neck, should lower the child's head between the knees.
4. After the child gains consciousness, a cold wet cloth placed over the forehead will produce a feeling of comfort and freshness.
5. If fainting is prolonged or recurrent, treat for shock and call a physician.

Possible poisoning. Occasionally a child at school may ingest poison such as toalstools, wild berries, roots, and some types of leaves. Symptoms of ingested poisoning include discomfort in the upper abdominal region, cramps, pain, nausea, and vomiting. Some degree of prostration quickly sets in.

First-aid care should start by making certain that the child actually has swallowed the substance suspected of being poison.

1. Evacuate the stomach with an emetic such as mustard water, soapsuds, salt water, or lukewarm water.
2. Call a physician or take the child directly to a hospital or clinic.
3. Keep the subject warm.

Localized conditions and injuries

Perhaps it is oversimplification to classify conditions as purely localized, because an injury in one location of the body can affect the entire constitution. Yet most of those conditions and injuries listed as localized are more important in terms of their localized effect and affect the general body but slightly.

Wounds. An injury caused by violence is called a wound. Many classifications of wounds are possible, but purely descriptive terms are most meaningful and will be applied here.

Abrasions occur when the superficial layers of the skin are scraped off, such as a brush burn or rope burn.

Contusions are bruises in which some of the tissues are ruptured, but surface continuity remains.

Incised wounds are those made by a sharp cutting edge.

Lacerated wounds are those with uneven or torn edges.

Punctured wounds are deep and narrow, such as a pointed tool would cause.

Penetrating wounds are those which penetrate internal organs.

First-aid care should be concerned with two factors—to stop bleeding and to prevent foreign materials from getting into the wound. Procedures must be adapted to the severity and nature of the wound, but certain steps apply to all wounds.

1. Elevate the part to stop bleeding. Over 90% of all wounds will stop bleeding simply if the affected hand is raised or the person lies on the floor with the injured foot on a chair. By reducing pressure this simple device provides a situation favorable for a clot to form.

2. If a clotting does not occur, pack gauze into the wound.
3. As a third resort put pressure on the severed vessel. If the wound is not deep and blood oozes out somewhat, a vein has been cut. Since veins carry blood *toward* the heart, the pressure point should be farther from the heart than is the wound. In deep wounds with gushing hemorrhage, an artery carrying blood *away* from the heart likely is involved. Then the pressure point should be between the heart and the wound.
4. A tourniquet of soft rubber can be used in place of manual pressure, but one must be certain a tourniquet is needed and properly applied. More than half of the instances in which a tourniquet is used it is unnecessary and frequently applied improperly.
5. If the wound is clean, small, and rather inconsequential, place a sterile gauze pad (e.g., Band-Aid) over the wound and notify the parents of what has been done. Make the dressing snug, but not tight. Do not put a disinfectant on the wound. It is recognized that in school the teacher acts in the place of the parent (*in loco parentis*) in the control of health, and doubtless the parent would apply a disinfectant to the wound. Yet practice indicates that the teacher's role here is limited to first aid, and medication is not a first-aid measure.
6. If the wound is serious or contains foreign materials, call the home. After stopping the hemorrhage, carry out the instructions of the parents. If the parents cannot be reached, contact the family physician.

Whenever indicated, place the injured part at rest by elevating it, splinting it, or placing it in a sling.

Nosebleed. Most nosebleeds are caused by a blow, but a sudden rise in blood pressure, violent activity, atmospheric change, and some local disorders may also cause the nose to bleed. Usually bleeding is confined to one nostril in what is known as Little's area. Along the nasal septum about 1¼ inches up from the opening, the mucous tissue is exceedingly thin and delicate. In this area the blood vessels are near the surface and can be ruptured quite easily.

First-aid treatment is not always necessary because the bleeding often subsides spontaneously. If bleeding is profuse or persists, a series of measures should be followed until the first aid is effective in checking the flow.

1. Have the child sit erect with the head tilted back slightly, but not so much that the flow will be back into the throat.
2. Apply pressure to the sides of the nose by grasping it with the thumb and forefinger.
3. Place cold packs on the nose.
4. Irrigate the nose with spray, drops, or inhalant, using salt water or vinegar water (half water, half vinegar).

5. Pack the nostril with a long (2 inches or more) gauze roll about ¼ inch in diameter. Be sure that sufficient length protrudes for grasping when the pack is removed. Be careful there is no blood flow back into the throat. Let a physician remove the gauze roll.
6. Call a physician immediately or take the child to a physician if the flow appears to be profuse.

Ear injuries. Bleeding from the ear canal may be caused by scratching and by probing the canal with a pointed article, as well as by a direct blow. In itself, the bleeding may not be serious, but serious complications may develop. To arrest bleeding, have the child sit erect and still and apply a cold pack to the ear. Some bleeding may be desirable.

Foreign bodies in the ear usually can be removed quite easily. It may be sufficient simply to tilt the head. If the object will not swell in water, a syringe of moderately warm water may flush it out. If neither of these methods is successful, a physician should be consulted.

Eye injuries. Bleeding from an injury in the region of the eyes rarely is profuse. However, the bleeding should be checked by having the child sit erect and placing a cold pack and light bandage over the area. There should be a minimum of pressure on the eyeball itself.

If any object penetrates the eyeball, no attempt should be made to remove the object. A cold pack to close the lids will serve until the child gets to a physician.

Most objects which get into the eye lodge in the mucous lining of the lid or on the eyeball. Embedded objects such as metal chips should be removed by a physican. Small objects such as dust particles can be washed out with warm water gently applied with a dropper. Other objects can be removed by everting the lid and cautiously picking them out with the flat tip of a toothpick or an applicator. A most effective procedure is to approach the child from the rear and rest the fingers on the face and forehead, which prevents one from jabbing the child. With this technique, if the child should move, the operator's fingers and the applicator will move with the child's head.

Chemicals in the eye should be flushed out immediately with water. The eye lids should then be covered with a wet gauze pad while the child is enroute to a physician.

Burns. A burn is an injury caused by dry heat; a scald is caused by moist heat, including that of hot fats. Burns are classified according to intensity:

1. First degree—redness of the skin
2. Second degree—blistered skin
3. Third degree—destruction of the outer layer of the skin
4. Fourth degree—destruction of all of the layers of the skin

A child reacts physiologically more violently to a burn than an adult, and shock is always a threat when a child suffers a burn.

First-aid measures depend upon the extent of the burn. If the area is extensive or the burn is penetrating, the child should be referred to a physician as soon as possible. Until the physician takes charge, all measures should be directed toward the prevention and treatment of shock. Put nothing on the burned area. If the burn is very minor, leave the area exposed to the air. Neither medication nor a bandage should be placed over the burn. The child could remain in school for the full day, and a note or phone call to the parents can explain the nature of the injury. If the burn is moderate, parents should be called and their instructions followed. The teacher should put nothing on the burn.

Sprains. A sprain is an injury to the soft tissues about a joint in which the ligaments, tendons, and even muscles are stretched or torn.

First-aid care must be directed toward the prevention of swelling and further damage. Since it is the most common, care of an ankle sprain will illustrate the procedures.

1. Elevate the injured joint immediately. If the child is lying on the floor, he can put his foot up on a chair.
2. Wrap a gauze pressure bandage about the joint. The bandage should be quite snug, but if it appears to be too tight a few clips with a scissors will allow adequate circulation.
3. Apply cold packs such as wet towels or ice bags.
4. Do not allow the child to bear weight on the joint.
5. Call the child's parents and carry out their instructions. Advise medical service because many sprains also involve fractures. In addition proper care will assure complete recovery. Proper first aid adds measurably to an early and complete recovery.

Dislocations. A dislocation is a displacement of a bone from its normal position at a joint. In a dislocation soft tissues are under extreme tension, and improper handling of the injury may cause further permanent damage. A dislocated finger joint gives the finger a marked crooked appearance. A dislocated shoulder produces a drooped appearance, and the head of the humerus produces a prominence in the armpit.

First-aid care must be directed to the prevention of further damage. If a finger joint is dislocated, it can be replaced by grasping the part of the finger beyond the dislocation and pulling steadily and strongly. Do not jerk. When the muscles fatigue as a result of the pull, they relax and the joint slips easily back into place. Wrap a splint (e.g., a tongue blade) along the finger which is extended at rest.

A shoulder dislocation should be reduced by a physician. The principal first-aid measure is to support the arm comfortably in a sling until a physician is available. Older boys and girls may prefer to hold the injured arm in their other arm. This practice can be acceptable though the sling has advantages during vehicular travel. Other dislocations, e.g., the elbow, should be given this same type of first-aid care until a physician takes charge.

Fractures. Any break in a bone is called a fracture. Some fractures are readily recognized from the resulting deformity, but many fractures involve no visible anatomical change. Marked pain is sufficient to suspect a possible fracture.

First-aid measures should be based on the assumption that the fracture is serious and soft tissues are in danger. Further, the likelihood of shock is considerable. Several procedures should be followed.

1. Prevent further damage by gentle handling in order not to damage soft tissue.
2. Keep the patient comfortable.
3. Place full support under and completely across the possible fracture. The subject should not be transported unless an adequate splint supports the injured limb.
4. Keep the child warm to prevent shock or to counteract shock if it does develop.
5. Do not attempt to set the bone. If a bone fragment projects through the skin (compound fracture), do not attempt to put the bone back. Check any profuse bleeding by packing the wound with sterile gauze pads.

Head injuries. A blow to the head is often more serious than the teacher realizes. A child may receive a hard blow to the head and still not fall to the ground. Or if he does fall, he may get up immediately. Yet in either case the child may have suffered serious injury. All blows to the head should be regarded as serious.

A skull fracture with or without intracranial hemorrhage may result from a blow. The child does not have to be unconscious for the condition to be serious. If it is assumed that there is a possible skull fracture and first aid is administered accordingly, proper care will also have been given should the condition be a lesser one, such as concussion. In brain concussion, dizziness, nausea, slow respiration, weak pulse, and even unconsciousness indicate that it, too, is a serious condition.

First-aid measures should emphasize a minimum of handling.

1. Place the child in a prone position with the head raised slightly if the face is of normal color. If the face is pale, keep the head level.
2. If no abrasions are present, apply cold towels or ice bags to the head.
3. Do not move the subject any more than necessary, and while enroute to medical aid use a stretcher.
4. Keep the child warm.

Neck and back injuries. Pain in the neck or back caused by a violent accident is sufficient cause to assume a fracture of the vertebral column. Such fractures are more frequent than is commonly realized. The injury may be a slight chip, a complete fracture, or a displaced vertebra—all are serious. Incorrect handling can cause permanent injury and even death. In all such cases, it is wise to assume the worst and proceed accordingly.

First-aid care should emphasize a minimum of handling.

1. Call for an ambulance. If the subject is comfortable, do not move him until the ambulance attendants arrive.

2. Do not let the child sit up or even raise his head.
3. If no ambulance is available and the subject must be moved, obtain a door, a wide board, or other flat wide surface.
4. Place the door beside the child so that it extends beyond the head and feet. Raise the child's near arm above his head. Three people should kneel alongside the board, reach over the subject, grasp his clothing on the far side, and gently roll the child slowly toward themselves so that he will be lying face down on the board. Another person at the head and one at the feet guide the head and feet as the child is rolled.
5. Keep the child warm. Shock usually accompanies fractures of the vertebral column.

First-aid supplies

Every school building should have at least one fully stocked, conveniently located, first-aid cabinet. In the elementary school the cabinet should be placed in the health services room if there is one. Otherwise the emergency rest room or principal's office are acceptable locations. In addition to at least one complete cabinet in the building, each classroom might have a first-aid kit. This kit should be regarded primarily as a health education aid and secondarily as a device for first aid.

A junior high school might profitably have a cabinet convenient to the physical education staff as well as an additional cabinet in the health services room or principal's office. If the school has a director of school health who assumes primary responsibility in emergency situations, one of the cabinets should be convenient for his use.

A senior high school will need a cabinet in the physical education offices as well as one in the health services room or principal's office. Two or three cabinets should be adequate for the typical high school, and one may be sufficient. Note that no antiseptics are included in the following list.

INVENTORY FOR FIRST-AID CABINET

Suggested supplies	Purpose
Glass jars (2)	For applicators and blades
Blades, wood (500)	Splints, depressors
Wooden applicators (1000)	Swabs, remove particles
Toothpicks (750)	Remove particles
Tincture of green soap	Wash injured parts
Absorbent cotton roll	Large pads or dressings
Sterile gauze, 4 in. roll	Dressings
Sterile gauze, 3 in. × 3 in. squares (100)	Protect injuries
Sterile gauze, 2 in. × 2 in. squares (100)	Protect injuries
Compress on adhesive band, 1 in. (100)	Protect injuries
Roller bandage, 1 in. (12 rolls)	Dressings
Roller bandage, 2 in. (12 rolls)	Dressings
Roller bandage, 4 in. (12 rolls)	Dressings
Triangle bandage (4)	Sling, area coverings
Adhesive tape, roll (widths ½ to 2 in.)	Fasten splints and dressings

INVENTORY FOR FIRST-AID CABINET—cont'd

Suggested supplies	Purpose
Scissors (blunt or bandage)	Cut dressings
Forceps (3 in. pincer or tweezer type)	Grasp small objects
Eye droppers (6)	Apply oil
Safety pins (24)	For triangular bandage
Tourniquet (3 feet ¼ in. rubber tube)	Check excessive bleeding
Splints (metal or yucca) (10)	Support
Ice bag (2)	Relief of swelling
Hot-water bottle (with cover) (2)	Local relief of pain
Mineral oil or petroleum jelly (nonmedicated)	Relieve irritation
Aromatic spirits of ammonia	Stimulant
Paper cups (100)	Receptacle

INVENTORY FOR FIRST-AID KIT

Suggested supplies

Compress on adhesive band, 1 in. (20)	Adhesive tape, roll ½ and 1 in.
Sterile gauze, 2 × 2 in. squares (10)	Scissors
Roller bandage, 1 in. (1 roll)	Forceps
Roller bandage, 2 in. (1 roll)	Paper cups (10)

A responsible person should be in charge of first-aid cabinets, kits, and supplies, and adequate supplies should be on hand at all times.

Selected readings

Aaron, J. E.: Are you a safety educator? Safety Education **39**: March, 1960.

American National Red Cross: First aid textbook, Philadelphia, The Blakiston Co., current issue.

Dolce, J. A.: Until the doctor comes, Washington, D. C., United States Public Health Service.

Dzenowagis, J. G.: What they believe, Safety Education **41**: Dec., 1961.

Eliason, E. L.: First aid in emergencies, Philadelphia, 1942, J. B. Lippincott Co.

Florio, A. E., and Stafford, G. T.: Safety education, ed. 2, New York, 1962, McGraw-Hill Book Co., Inc.

National Committee on Safety Education: Safety in physical education for the classroom teacher, Washington, D. C., 1952, National Education Association.

National Education Association: How experienced teachers develop good traffic citizens, Washington, D. C., 1958, The Association.

National Education Association: Safety education, eighteenth yearbook of the American Association of School Administrators, Washington, D. C., 1938, The Association.

National Safety Council: Safety in physical education and recreation, Chicago, 1941, The Council.

Olson, Lyla M.: Prevention, first aid, and emergencies, Philadelphia, 1946, W. B. Saunders Co.

O'Neill, Florence Connor: Safety education including first aid, Albany, N. Y., 1946, New York State Department of Education.

Rosenfield, H. N.: Liability for school accidents, New York, 1940, Harper & Brothers.

Stack, H. J., and Elkow, J. D.: Education for safe living, ed. 3, New York, 1957, Prentice-Hall, Inc.

Steward, R.: Living safety, Minneapolis, 1957, Burgess Publishing Co.

Warwick, F. J., and Tunstall, A. C.: First aid to the injured and sick, ed. 19, Baltimore, 1952, Williams & Wilkins Co.

Weeden, Vivian: Beware the ides of April, Safety Education **40**: April, 1961.

Healing is a matter of time,
but it also is a matter of opportunity.

—Hippocrites

Chapter 10

Remedial aspects of health services

Often a neglected area of school health services, the remedial aspects of the program are an index of the vision, completeness, and thoroughness of the health services of a school. Further, they reflect the concern of the professional staff for the long-range effect of the school's health program on the health of the children who have defects or disabilities. To give special attention to children with defects does not conflict with the basic philosophy that the school health program is concerned primarily with the normal child. This philosophy also acknowledges that each child should be served in terms of his needs in order to attain the highest level of health possible with his basic endowment.

Importance of follow-up programs

An essential first step in health service is to identify defects, but this becomes valuable only if action to remedy or correct the situation results. The school deals in futures, and, however small may be the defect, it can be important when considered in terms of the 60 or 70 years of life the child faces. Because of many unrecognized health obstacles, none of us attains 100% of our potential in effective and enjoyable living. Thus it is imperative that any recognized defect, harmful to health, be corrected as soon as possible. It may not be a defect which threatens life. Yet, if it reduces the child's effectiveness and enjoyment in living, it merits correction. In some instances complete recovery of function may not be possible, but the child has the right to the recovery of whatever function can be attained.

In the correction of physical disorders the mental health component is often overlooked. Frequently a child with a disability develops an unwholesome self-identification. He considers himself different and perhaps even senses an aura of stigma about his identity in the school situation. Each child wants to be distinctive but not different.

An organic defect may lead to feelings of inadequacy and even to extremely deep-seated feelings of inferiority. This occurs even in children with a minor defect. The child may develop aggressive, even belligerent, attitudes as compensation for his feelings of inadequacy. Sympathy is resented and leads only to further belligerence.

Fear of ridicule may cause the child to conceal the defect or even deny its existence. Equally unfortunate is the tendency of some physically handicapped children to segregate themselves from their normal group. They may seek companionship with someone outside of the normal age or peer group. Children of their own age group are willing to accept a handicapped child, but find their efforts frustrated by lack of response on the part of the child with the defect.

A physical disability, such as a defect of vision, may hinder immediate educational progress, which aggravates the total problem. A combination of defective physical health, emotional maladjustment, and educational retardation more than triples the problem of correction and adaptation. Yet, in the social evaluation of child defects these factors may exist in varying degrees. Even partial correction of a physical disorder may be sufficient to reverse the downward trend of maladjustment. To understand that some corrective devices are accepted may aid the child in his adjustment. He can be helped to regard himself as a regular accepted member of his peer group. Correction of a defect may be only a starting point which sets off a chain reaction of total readjustment, but the direction of the reaction requires guidance.

Role of the school. A school has no recognized legal responsibility in the correction of children's defects; however, school personnel universally recognize a professional obligation to do everything reasonable to assure that every child with a remediable defect receives the necessary medical treatment. Inherent in teacher ethics is the acceptance of a personal obligation to supplement the medical service with such other supporting services as the school is in a position to give. The following four objectives will enable the school to fulfill its role in the follow-up program: (1) promote corrective measures, (2) perform corrective functions, (3) assist in adaptation to noncorrectible defects, and (4) rehabilitate after corrective work is done.

Promote corrective measures. The most important and frequent function of the school in the follow-up program is the promotion of corrective measures. Although most parents take immediate steps to have their children's defects corrected, some parents will delay action. Lack of concern, lack of finances, lack of appreciation of the necessity for prompt action, wishful hope that some miracle may happen, and even gross neglect are typical causes of delay. None of these is a justifiable reason. In this day of medical insurance there should be no instances of total inability to pay for medical services, but such cases do occur. Yet even with the greatest financial hardship a solution to the problem can be worked out. Every child in need of medical care is entitled to that medical care, and means should be devised to give it to him.

When parents have knowledge of their child's disability and the need for correction but neglect to arrange for the necessary medical care, the school can be the catalyst. Diplomacy and persistence may be required, but the goal is worth the effort. A considered methodical plan should be worked out.

The first step in such a plan is to learn whether the family has a definite plan. This information can probably be obtained from the child, an older sibling, the parents, or the family physician or pastor. If the parents have no plan, the school should consider what it might do in behalf of the child. First there should be a conference of interested school personnel who may have something to contribute. Together this group could plan a course of action. Perhaps they will decide to have the school nurse visit and confer with the parents. In the absence of a nurse perhaps the school health director, the principal, or the child's classroom teacher will be designated to make the visit. On these assignments the teacher may have to be a combined salesman-promoter-middleman because the problem is to ensure medical treatment for the child.

When the school representative is not able to convince the parents of the necessity for corrective work, an indirect approach might then be tried by enlisting the assistance of others. Ministers have been successful in these missions. Employers of fathers may be influential. Union officials, lodge members, club members, even relatives of the parents in certain instances have been successful in this role. If the family has a family doctor, the logical approach is through him. Unfortunately children who need a physician often have the kind of parents who lack the foresight to see the need for a family physician.

When the basic problem is financial, the school can be helpful. However, the school representative should confer with the parents who should designate the physician of their choice. They may ask for advice as to which physician to engage. Neither the teacher nor the nurse should designate a particular physician. It is proper, however, to suggest the names of the various qualified physicians. If the parents cannot make a decision, it is in order to suggest people with whom they might confer on the choice of a physician. If the parents are totally without funds, an outside source or sources must be found. Several could be considered.

1. Official funds, e.g., Crippled Children's Fund
2. Voluntary health agency funds, e.g., The National Foundation
3. Shriners' Hospital
4. Service organizations, e.g., Rotary, Lions, Kiwanis
5. Parent-Teacher Association
6. Labor union
7. Church group
8. Private individuals

However, before any of these sources are contacted, the school representative, together with the parents, should confer with the designated physician and inform him of the willingness of the school to be of assistance. Often, when the physician knows of the financial difficulties of the family, he makes no charge for his services. No child will go without needed medical service just because his parents have no financial means. The medical profession will make provision for any worthy case. This does not mean that persons with funds for everything except medical service will be permitted to impose upon the medical profession, but physicians will always see that worthy persons, especially children, receive the necessary medical care.

When all arrangements between the family and physician have been made and the fee and hospital costs determined, the teacher, the nurse, and other associates can proceed to find the necessary funds. Wisely some schools have stand-by arrangements with organizations and individuals in the event that such funds are needed. Whatever the approach, ingenuity and promotion are essential, but dedication to a worthwhile cause is the indispensable element for success. This dedication projects itself to others and enlists the necessary support.

Many examples are recorded in which teachers, individually or collectively, paid the cost of correction for a child. In some instances the student body has contributed the funds. Perhaps under certain circumstances these measures are acceptable, even commendable, but they would not serve the purpose of an established workable program and may invite some difficulties and even unpleasantries.

It is often a frustrating task to assist a child and his family to obtain these specialized services, but most of life's worthy tasks are difficult. The challenge and the gratification of achievement will repay the teacher fully for all of the difficulties and sacrifices involved. Every avenue of assistance should be exhausted before the school gives up the attempt to aid a child who is in need of medical care.

Perform corrective functions. Corrective work which no one else seems concerned about and which the school staff is qualified to do offers numerous opportunities for service to the pupils. Many deviations from the normal would go unnoticed, unheeded, and unaided except for the assistance the school staff gives. Most of these conditions are minor but important. A physician is never consulted, and often physicians have little interest or time for these conditions.

Members of the school staff may be competent to aid children with poor posture, poor body mechanics, foot difficulties, malnutrition, and low vitality. In addition, through a modified program for the handicapped, the school plays a secondary role in aiding the correction of defects.

Assist in adaptation to noncorrectible defects. It has been the plea of parents and the admonition of physicians that the school help children adapt to noncorrectible defects. It is an assignment the teacher accepts with the knowledge that perhaps no one is in a better position to do the job than the school personnel.

First, the school should accept the task only if it is capable of the assignment and no extreme demands are made of either the staff or other pupils. Second, the school should require a written statement from the supervising physician which indicates the nature of the child's condition and the role of the school in helping the child to adapt. This should be an established and publicly known policy. Third, whenever there are indications that the program is not working out as it originally was planned, the physician and parents should be asked to reappraise the original plan. These are steps to protect the teaching staff in the event of serious mishap. Though tragedies or even near tragedies rarely occur, instances of chronic cardiac patients who die on the school premises are solemn reminders that the school needs to anticipate such mishaps and protect itself accordingly.

Usually the major concern for a school-age child with an uncorrected disability is not survival. The problem is to get the child to assume a normal role in the life of the school. If he cannot attain normal status, then the goal should be as nearly normal as is practical.

Adjustment physically, emotionally, socially, and academically must be fostered. These are not separate entities, but are integrated in the whole child. Adjustment involves many things, but all aspects of adjustment are dependent upon the child's attaining status in school. When he gains satisfaction from his Self status, the door to adjustment is open.

Nothing is gained by pretending before the child that he does not have a disability. He knows that he has it. It is important that he have an acceptable understanding of his disability. All of us have shortcomings. Ours are different from his. He has to learn to adjust to his problem, just as all of us must adjust to ours. An understanding insight on his part is important. To see himself fully he must also be helped to appreciate his assets, his capabilities, his outstanding qualities. He should strike a balance between emphasizing his assets and understanding his disability. This approach was indirectly expressed when a high school sophomore remarked, "But I am lame in my left leg," to which his instructor replied, "Yes, but not lame in the head like a lot of people in this world." A single incident rarely has the effect on a person's life that this timely remark had upon that boy who rose to outstanding academic heights.

Often ingenuity is required to satisfy a child that he is one of the normal members of the group. The old ruse of having him keep score does not fool nor please him either. To find some spark of interest and ignite it challenges the best of teachers. Perhaps the child may get personal gratification from being outstanding in some activity or enterprise that others are less skilled in. The crippled boy whose model airplanes were the admiration of all his associates was accepted and held in special esteem. The girl with the cardiac disorder whose skill on the piano made her of special importance in her class was well adjusted and thoroughly enjoyed her role in the school. The school may find it necessary to provide extraschool aid for the child's benefit. Arranging for piano lessons from a private teacher may be the cardinal factor in adjustment and provide the self-gratifying skill which will enable the child to attain the Self status for which the school is striving.

While one member of the school staff establishes rapport with the child and serves as counselor, several members of the teaching staff may contribute to his adjustment. If the aid of selected classmates is enlisted, the school may be able to carry out certain desirable measures and activities which otherwise would not be possible. All that can contribute constructively to the adjustment of a disabled child, including the services of classmates, school personnel, and teaching staff, should be incorporated into the school's plans for the child.

Some schools err in trying to do too much for a child who can and wants to do things for himself. If his self-propelled activities do not transcend the acknowledged bounds of his capacities, he should be encouraged in the wholesome interests he manifests.

Rehabilitate after corrective work. Rehabilitation of a child who has undergone correction for a defect really consists of effective counseling. First there should be a thorough study and understanding of the child as he is when he re-enters school. The child's physical, emotional, intellectual, and academic states should be understood well. Parents and the family physician are the most fruitful sources of information. A school rightfully should expect the physician and parents to provide a comprehensive appraisal of the child. Second there should be a well-defined course of action which is based on the appraisal and which is the result of a conference of the physician, the parents, and the school. If the physician is not available for such a conference, he should either send his recommendations to the school or give his approval to the plan agreed upon by the parents and the school.

Selection of a counselor is imperative. The child will need guidance, which will be considerable at first, but can be reduced as the child is able to assume self-direction. While the greatest attention must be given to the child's major handicap, rehabilitation includes readjustment of the whole child. Usually the child re-entering school has been absent from school because of the correction of a major disability. Adjusting to his physical condition is a major consideration, but rehabilitation will also mean being restored to his entire former status.

Rehabilitation can be rapid and uneventful, but usually some difficulties are encountered. The path may be punctuated with setbacks, and progress may be disappointing. A child who has been out of school for months may feel like an outsider and, because of the associated timidity, may not respond to the friendliness of his classmates. Some children would never become fully rehabilitated if left to their own resources. More effort is needed for rehabilitation than for typical readjustment. The teacher must use ingenuity to create situations which literally push the child into the normal channels of life. Usually he is better able to do things than he thinks he is. Suggestions and expressions of confidence by the teacher can give the encouragement necessary for satisfactory progress. If a child understands his progress, he will be stimulated to further attainment.

Some plans for rehabilitation will prove to be inadequate and a reappraisal is in order. The reason for the failure of the program may well provide the key to what needs to be done. Change that will yield results rather than change for the sake of it must be the guide. A modification of the first plan or a new plan which will be more effective may be devised. Or the conferees may be unable to devise a satisfactory plan of action. Before deciding that an agency other than the school must effect the rehabilitation, the teaching staff must be agreed that the school has exhausted its means. Occasionally the school is unable to rehabilitate a child who has suffered a disability.

Defects which are the province of the physician or orthodontist

Every human being is imperfect, but most school children have imperfections which are negligible in terms of effective enjoyable living. However, a small percentage will have deviations of consequence which a skilled physician or orthodontist can correct or relieve. If the teaching staff is familiar with the types of defects of children which physicians and dentists treat, the role of the school in instigating medical treatment and helping in readjustment will be fulfilled more enthusiastically and effectively. Understanding both the possibilities and the limitations of professional skill, the school will be in a position to make its service more realistic and effective.

Orthopedic defects. Literally the term orthopedic means straight child (Gr. *ortho,* straight; *paidos,* child), but in its generally accepted sense it refers to conditions of the bones and joints. In his work the orthopedic surgeon is obliged to deal also with muscles, tendons, and ligaments in giving the patient functional joints, proper use of limbs, and a proper skeletal alignment. Although surgery is frequently the method used in correcting orthopedic defects, muscle training as well as mechanical appliances which provide for calculated stresses and strains may be utilized. The orthopedist must implement his scientific background and surgical skill with ingenuity to solve the particular orthopedic problem of each patient.

Fundamentally the objective of the orthopedist is to restore function to a part compatible with the importance of the need and the risk involved. At times parents and teachers are disappointed that a child did not benefit more from surgery. Even the finest orthopedic surgeons are not miracle men. They strive to make the most of what the condition has to offer. If a 20% increase in the use of a joint or a limb is considered in terms of 60 years of usefulness, the true value of the surgery can be appreciated.

About 400,000 school-age children are handicapped by orthopedic impairments. Some are congenital defects which occurred as a result of conditions of the environment before or at the time of birth. An unrecognized and uncontrollable condition present in the body of the mother or an injury at birth accounts for these defects. Congenital defects include clubbed feet (talipes), clubbed hands, and dislocations such as dislocation of the hip. Some disorders may be due to incomplete development, the cause of which is not known. Among the more common developmental defects are harelip, cleft palate, failure of the vertebrae to fuse (spina bifida), and displacement of internal organs. Most of these prenatal (congenital and developmental) defects are amenable to treatment and usually have been corrected before the child enters school.

The school should assume some responsibility for the early detection of crippling conditions and see that the child is directed to the proper source for thorough examination. Some of the signs (stigmata) of orthopedic defects the teacher can quite readily recognize are as follows:

Tilted head	Backache
Wryneck	Bowed legs
Elevated shoulder	Knock-knees
Hollow chest	Limp
Narrow chest	Unusual gait
Round shoulders	Walking on heels or toes
Limp arm	Weak angles
Deformed fingers	Toes pointed in or out
Humped back (kyphosis)	Pain in the legs or feet
Sway back (lordosis)	Calluses, corns, and other growths

It is not the task of the teacher to determine why a child's shoulder is elevated or why a child limps. The function of the school is to identify those children who appear to deviate from the normal. By the early discovery of an incipient defect the teacher and the school can help to prevent increased deformity.

Poliomyelitis accounts for about one fifth of the orthopedic defects in school-age children. For practical purposes a child with less than a 20% functional loss in a single muscle or even a muscle group has no limiting handicap. He likely performs within the normal range of physical activity and skill though he may not be near the top of his group. Children with considerably more functional loss will be somewhat handicapped, but compensations can be developed. The child with extreme loss of function in one or more limbs may have to adapt to his physical limitations because the surgeon is not likely to have too much to offer. Appliances, muscle training, and even muscle transplants will be of some help in selected cases, but even here an improvement, not a correction, is the best that can be expected.

Cerebral palsy, paralysis due to injury of the brain, accounts for about one tenth of the orthopedic disorders in children of school age. It is characterized by irregular gait, awkward movements, lack of balance, and guttural speech. Loss or impairment of control may be in the arms, legs, speech mechanism, or eye movements. There may also be a disturbance of vision, hearing, or other sensory perception and of the intellect. The condition may be caused by injury to the brain before, during, or after birth. Prematurity and congenital malformation of the brain may be factors. Head injuries and diseases such as diphtheria, encephalitis, German measles, scarlet fever, and whooping cough can be postnatal causes. If the damage to the brain is small and does not affect important motor action, the child not only can attend school, but also can be aided by his school activities.

Since muscle training will improve the efficiency of the neuromuscular patterns a child possesses, the school can be highly valuable in the program of muscle training. By supplementing and compensating for his lack of normal action, the child can improve his coordination measurably. Here the stimulation and challenge of the school situation are ideal for the development of such motor potential as he may have. The school can do more therapeutically for some of these children than can the surgeon.

Muscular dystrophy is a biochemical disease characterized by a progressive weakness and wasting away of the muscles. In the United States about 50% of the 200,000 persons with muscular dystrophy are between the ages of 3 and 13 years. The cause is a biochemical irregularity of unknown nature. No pain exists, but certain indications, such as frequent falls, waddling gait, and difficulty in climbing stairs and in assuming a standing position, are usually apparent. The pseudohypertrophic type is most common. It begins between the ages of 3 and 10 years, progresses rapidly, and occurs three times more often in males than in females. The onset of the juvenile type may occur during late childhood or even youth. It progresses more slowly, and the incidence for both sexes is about the same. A child with muscular dystrophy can attend school and be happy in the school situation. He may need considerable help in moving about. Classmates are usually pleased to be of assistance. The child may pass successively from difficulty in walking, to the use of a wheelchair, and finally to confinement in bed. Muscular dystrophy in itself is not fatal, but death may be due to related disturbances such as weak chest muscles which affect breathing.

Accidental injury (trauma) is the cause of about one tenth of the orthopedic impairments present in the school population. Immobile joints, deformed limbs, and amputations usually cause the child's classmates to call him "cripple." It is the difficult task of the school to see that all the children accept the crippled child as a normal member of the group. Most children are solicitous of the one who is handicapped, but a small group will delight in treating the defective with derision. This can best be handled by conferring with the gang and appealing to their sense of fair play. That the teacher expects them to show the way in accepting responsibility for the welfare of the handicapped classmate will appeal to their feeling of importance and social status. Besides aiding the handicapped child, the teacher will be guiding the gang in wholesome development.

Osteomyelitis is an infection of bone usually caused by the staphylococcus organism. It frequently occurs before the age of 10 years and may either develop from an injury or without any known injury. The large bone (tibia) of the lower leg is frequently involved. Early symptoms are pain and inflammation at the site of infection. Early diagnosis and medical care are highly important because in the early stages antibiotics and sulfonamides can be highly effective in eradicating the infection. Later the condition may be intractable and persist as a recurring infection for years.

A child's physician may recommend that the child return to school even though the infection is not eradicated. The condition is not communicable, and experience indicates that the child may be able to carry on the normal activities of childhood. Indeed, athletes with chronic osteomyelitis have successfully pursued professional careers. An afflicted child will likely give little attention to the infection; therefore the teacher may be helpful in guiding the child in the regimen prescribed by his physician. When the child limps or otherwise favors the diseased member, the matter should be called to the attention of the parents. Renewal or change in treatment may be necessary, and the family physician should be consulted.

Torticollis (wryneck) may be of either prenatal or postnatal origin and is caused by contracted cervical muscles, injury to a neck muscle (sternocleidomastoid), hematoma, or muscle inflammation. Some wryneck conditions are somewhat minor and temporary and can be corrected by heat and stretching exercises. Others will respond only to surgery. Yet physicians frequently advise against surgery because the wryneck condition has no appreciable effect on general health. If the teacher knows that a child with wryneck has had the benefit of medical counsel, she should assume that the condition does not warrant surgery, and he should be treated as a normal member of the group. When the child has not been examined by a physician, the teacher may be of assistance in obtaining a physician's opinion of the condition.

Other orthopedic disorders of school children also occur. It is important that the school have a medical history as well as the physician's instructions to the school. The school should report to the parents any observable change in the child's condition. Surprisingly often a child with an orthopedic defect develops an abnormal gait or posture. Early recognition by the school of this tendency may enable a physician to correct the abnormality.

Cardiovascular conditions. Correction of heart disorders is definitely limited. Using surgery a physician may correct a cardiac valvular stricture. Because constricture of the valvular orifice is gradual, this disorder occurs most often in adults. Occasionally surgery is necessary if a child is to survive. Some heart irregularities can be aided by medication, but the supervising physician is obliged to check the patient closely.

Although correction of cardiac disorders is infrequent, successful treatment is possible for most patients. Basic to the program of treatment is a daily routine in keeping with the child's capacity. The former concept that a person with a cardiac condition should remain totally inactive has been displaced by a newer belief that these persons should engage in definite but limited activity. With old people the task is to get a person with cardiac disease to be active enough, but with children the task is to prevent the child from becoming too active. The school should have on file a set of instructions from the supervising physician for all children with cardiac disorders. The school would be wise to err on the side of conservatism in order to safeguard against overexertion. Yet the child should have opportunities for normal participation in school pursuits.

Teachers are often surprised when physicians tell them that a child has a murmur but not a defective heart and is not restricted in his activities. On the other hand an organic murmur acquired as a result of infection does limit the cardiac capacity of the child and calls for a restricted regimen. The school can carry out the physician's instruction without isolating the child or causing him to feel subnormal.

High blood pressure (hypertension) is usually caused by overstimulation of the constrictor nerves to the arteries. The resulting constriction of the arteries forces the pressure upward. Hypertension is rare in children, but occurs occasionally in high school students, usually in boys. Physicians may prescribe ordinary activities for hypertensive students, but exclude vigorous athletics. Some of these students are permitted to participate in athletics. Whatever the decision of the physician, the school is obligated to carry out his written instructions.

Defects of vision. Almost all defects of vision in a school population are amenable to correction. Errors of refraction can be corrected by proper prescriptions for glasses. Thus myopia, hyperopia, and even astigmatism can be corrected. In this instance a mechanical device is the correcting factor. Only a licensed practitioner should prescribe lenses for a child. Occasionally total correction cannot be prescribed. For these children the practitioner prescribes lenses which give the optimum benefit for their most frequent and important needs. Since the condition in a child is not caused by a rigid crystalline lens as it is in late adulthood, bifocal and trifocal (continuous vision) lenses are of no particular value. Contact lenses can be especially valuable in the treatment of astigmatism.

Although prescription of lenses is in the province of the ophthalmologist, the school can serve in four capacities in the program for correction of defects in vision. First the teacher can refer new students she has reason to believe should have a thorough vision examination. Second the teacher can assist in obtaining professional service and glasses if they are needed. Third the teacher can see to it that a child wears his glasses. Fourth the teacher can observe a child who wears glasses and continues to have difficulty in seeing and who should be rechecked by the person who prescribed his glasses. Occasionally a child may need a new prescription in less than a year's time.

While surgery can correct many eye abnormalities, not all are correctible. Sometimes, if strabismus (squint or cross-eye) is not corrected early, it is not easily remedied after the child has entered late childhood. Eye exercises under the supervision of a specialist in eye alignment (orthoptics) can be helpful. If the dominant eye is covered, the child may be able to focus the squint eye normally. In convergent strabismus (estropia) or true cross-eye, the short inferior oblique muscle may be lengthened by surgical means, but not all strabismus disorders are operable, even by the most skilled surgeon.

Whenever the school has any doubt about the visual capacity of a child, the parents should be notified and be urged to have the child's vision checked by a licensed practitioner. The school should follow up the referral and request a report of the practitioner's recommendations. Once the teacher fully understands the vision range of a child, she can accomplish more effective guidance and include him in the normal routine of school life.

Hearing impairment. To persuade a child that wearing a hearing aid is not a disgrace requires the ingenuity of the best of counselors. Yet it is the key to the remedial program for hearing impairments. When the hearing screening conducted by the teacher or school audiometrist indicates that a child has an appreciable hearing loss, his resistance to an examination by a physician is based on apprehension of a hearing aid and of possible ridicule. Once this resistance has been overcome and the otologist has prescribed a hearing aid, it may be necessary to reinforce the original counseling. Since most childhood hearing loss is due to rigidity of the conducting apparatus (conduction deafness), a hearing aid is the means of correction. A person is fortunate if his only defect is one for which a mechanical device can compensate.

Some hearing disorders can be aided by surgery, some even by medication. Obstructions or partial obstructions may be removed, with improvement in hearing. Children who are under continuing treatment for chronic infection of the middle ear or have a chronic discharge of the ear can attend school without jeopardizing others or themselves. Their physician may instruct the child and the school to avoid certain hazards. These hazards may include showers, swimming pools, chalk dust, vigorous contact play, and exposure to drafts.

Some children with hearing loss may fatigue easily. Both the physical and mental strain imposed by the hearing difficulty will predispose the child to fatigue. As a reuslt, a routine classroom schedule may be sufficiently fatiguing to the child to warrent a special rest period. All factors must be considered in deciding the course of action for the hard-of-hearing child who is unduly fatigued by the day's activities.

Dental defects. It is readily recognized that dental cavities should be corrected by the dentist. Less commonly acknowledged is the urgent need for dental services for the treatment of malocclusion. A child with improper alignment of the dental arches should be treated by an orthodontist before the tooth-bone relationship is permanently established. To wait until a person is 20 years of age may be too late. To shift the teeth at that age may so disturb the alveolar (spongy) bone of the jaw that the teeth will never be well imbedded, and both the teeth and bone are exposed to serious disturbance.

All gum inflammations should be treated by a dentist. Whether the condition is due to a vitamin C deficiency, to accumulation of tartar, or to infection, the dentist is best qualified to give the child the needed care. Perhaps the school can be most helpful by re-emphasizing preventive measures through health instruction.

Neurological disorders. A child with a serious organic nervous disorder is not likely to be attending school.

St. Vitus' Dance (Syndenham's chorea) appears to be due to toxin which affects centers in the brain. The condition may be associated with rheumatic fever. Chorea is characterized by involuntary, irregular jerky movements, facial grimacing, irritability, and depression. Although the child may be normal in most respects, other children are distracted by his actions. More important, the child needs and should have the service of a physician who can do much to relieve the condition.

A *highly nervous child* is not normal and doubtless has a remediable condition. Merely to accept the condition as being but characteristic of the child is to take a neutral course. The highly nervous child is that way for a reason. Likely the cause can be diagnosed and successful treatment instituted by a physician. If the condition is functional, the school, under the physician's direction, may be especially valuable in helping the child to dispel tenseness and attain a normal level of ease and relaxation.

Tic is the designation given to spasmodic movements or twitchings of the face, the head, the neck, the shoulder, or other limited area. These spasmodic peculiar twitchings attract the attention of others, but an afflicted child may be unaware of his peculiarity. A tic usually develops early in life and occurs among school populations. Some tics are psychologically conditioned responses; others have a true neurological basis. Some have no associated emotional complement; others are fundamentally a psychoneurosis. Whatever the cause or nature of the disturbance, a condition exists which demands the best of medical competence.

Corrective work of the school

Ideally all children with remediable defects should have the benefit of medical advice and care. We live in a realistic world in which the ideal serves as a guide very much as a star serves the mariner for navigation purposes. For various reasons children with defects or disorders do not always receive medical care. In some instances medical services are not available. In others the available physician does not consider such conditions as mild malnutrition, faulty posture, or sore feet of any great consequence. Or he may consider the condition beneath his professional dignity. In other instances the physician may brief the family on what might be done, but they, because of indifference or ignorance, do nothing.

When a child with these apparently minor disorders obviously will receive no help elsewhere, the easiest course for the school is to disclaim any responsibility. Yet the teacher who accepts the fundamental ethics of the profession will do everything possible to promote the best development of the child. Many teachers in this situation, eager to be of some help, have been frustrated by a lack of understanding of what can be done. A working knowledge of some of the more common conditions and of the relatively simple measures which can be so highly helpful is all teachers need for the confidence and self-assurance to help the child to help himself.

Examples of schools which have undertaken to help children with malnutrition, low vitality, poor posture, and foot conditions are many. In no instances were the results spectacular. In some cases the improvement was relatively small, but nonetheless valuable. In many instances the improvement was considerable. In terms of the long-range effects even a small health improvement during childhood will assume value of immense proportions when it is considered in terms of benefit projected over many years.

Malnutrition. Gross malnutrition is rare in America's school population. Mild and even moderate nutritional deficiency exists in greater numbers than is commonly supposed. From a practical standpoint the school is concerned with two basic nutritional problems—obesity and a deficiency of protein and vitamins B_1 and C. Occasionally there will be a child with an apparent deficiency in caloric intake, but usually he is deficient in proteins and vitamins, also. An increase in calories can be incorporated into a diet to increase the intake of vitamins and proteins.

In *obesity* the basic problem is to decrease the intake of calories or increase the number of calories the body uses in a day. Vigorous prolonged exercise is required to increase the amount of fuel the body burns, a discouraging task for the child. In addition his physical condition may preclude vigorous prolonged activity. A less difficult, but not easy, way to reduce weight is to reduce the daily caloric intake. The assistance the school gives to the child may mean the difference between success and failure. The school merely assists the child. Responsibility rests with the home, and the parents should be urged to seek the services of a physician.

The obese child must be motivated to want to lose weight if he is to overcome the many trials and difficulties of weight reduction. An appeal to his pride in terms of appearance, performance, and self-mastery is important. The reasons for his overeating must be analyzed. Many factors or combinations of factors may contribute to the overeating: (1) a family custom of overeating, (2) a release from tension, (3) a low blood sugar level which produces constant hunger, and (4) a poorly balanced high caloric diet. Next the daily caloric intake must be calculated. From these data the program of action can be formulated.

Obviously the child must understand the plan fully and be impressed with the necessity for adhering to it closely. The basic principle of the plan is to reduce the daily intake by at least 600 calories. Since 4000 calories represent approximately a pound of body weight, the child will average a loss of a pound per week. Several measures can be helpful to the child: (1) The number of meals per day remain the same, the change being a reduction in the amount of food for each meal. (2) So far as possible the fat intake is reduced; otherwise the customary items in the meal are retained. (3) Proteins are substituted for carbohydrates. (4) The water intake at mealtime is reduced. (5) Low calorie wafers, raisins, water, or unsweetened grapefruit halves are used to relieve between-meal hunger. Always remember that there is no easy, safe way to lose weight.

A sample high protein-low calorie diet indicates that a reducing diet can be reasonably balanced in vitamins and minerals. Sugar, salt, and fats should be omitted. While this appears to be a Spartan diet, it can satisfy hunger. Two weeks on this diet should be sufficient. At that time the child can shift to a diet which is more varied, but has low calorie value.

> *Breakfast*
> Grapefruit (no sugar), 2 eggs (not fried), dry toast, skim milk
> *Lunch*
> 2 eggs (not fried) tomatoes, green vegetable, dry toast, skim milk
> *Dinner*
> Steak (not fried), celery, tomatoes, toast, skim milk
> *Alternate lunches*
> Fruit salad, toast, skim milk
> Combination salad, toast, skim milk, grapefruit
> Cold chicken, vegetable salad, toast, skim milk
> *Alternate dinners*
> Fish, salad, toast, skim milk, grapefruit
> Chicken (not fried), beans, tomatoes, celery, skim milk
> Lamb chops (broiled), cabbage, carrots, toast, skim milk

The general condition of the student should be followed. Some uneasiness may occur, and the child will experience a feeling different from normal. Because of a tendency for some bodies to displace burned fat with water, which is heavier, there may actually be an increase in weight at the third day. A new water balance is soon attained, and a sudden drop in weight occurs.

Usually school children do not display pronounced symptoms of *deficiency disease*. General weakness, chronic fatigue, lack of normal endurance, poor muscle tone, protruding abdomen, sagging posture, strained facial expression, listlessness, irritability, and lack of appetite may indicate inadequate nutrition. These characteristics may be due to other causes, but in the absence of knowledge of any other cause the need for an improved diet is indicated. When no physician has been engaged and all efforts have failed to have the parents obtain medical counsel for the child, the school, through counseling and the school lunch, should make an effort to help.

First a study of the family's day-to-day menus may be revealing. If the child's diet is deficient, it will likely be inadequate in protein and vitamins B_1 and C. A starting point is to encourage the home to provide foods high in these constituents. Through the parent-teacher association or other source, it may be possible to provide a supplementary lunch program at school. A special midmorning, noon, and midafternoon lunch, high in proteins and vitamins B_1 and C, will likely provide adequate amounts of all nutritional elements.

Sources of protein include eggs, cheese, milk, meat, fish, poultry, nuts, peanut butter, dried beans and peas, bread, and cereals. Sources of vitamin B_1 include liver, lean meat (especially pork), milk, eggs, wholegrain and enriched bread and cereals, wheat germ, nuts, beans, and peas. Sources of vitamin C include citrus fruits, tomatoes, raw cabbage, raw apples, potatoes, and other raw vegetables. Patent vitamin preparations should not be taken except upon a physician's prescription.

Child with low vitality. Some children who have no organic defects of any kind seem to lack the vitality necessary for the normal activities of school. They have no outstanding symptoms, but display such general characteristics as listlessness, irritability, short attention span, nervousness, tenseness, frequent illness, frequent absence from school, fatigability, digestive difficulties, and frequent headaches. One or two or several of these factors may be present. Life seems to be a trial, and these youngsters do not seem to be able to function at a maximum rate. Several factors or combinations of factors may account for the sluggishness. Habit, lack of rest, poor nutrition, lack of interest in school life or life in general, natively slow reactions, general depression, constitutionally sluggish response to fatigue conditions, imitation of members of the family or others as an attention-getting device, or even an escape mechanism, all may be involved. It is almost impossible to single out one factor as *the* factor. To reduce the cause to two or three factors would be excellent progress. So far as possible the best approach is to remove or modify these factors. A duty-obsessed teacher may make the child's school life unbearable. To drive this type of youngster is rarely successful. Situations which will modify his deficiencies, through a gradual process, can produce tangible results. Stimulation, encouragement, patience, and appreciation of his success will be helpful. Vitality is a psychophysiological pattern, and both the psychological and physiological aspects must be considered. It may be helpful to reschedule the daily routine, including shorter sessions with television, a new sleep cycle (perhaps with a noon-hour rest), and new diet and meal habits (with midmorning and midafternoon snacks). A physical activity such as table tennis could be helpful. Participation in school activities such as dramatics may challenge the child. Setting realistic deadlines may speed up the work pace. He may never attain a satisfactory level of vitality, but an acceptable level can be attained with diligence and persistence.

Posture defects. A defect of posture due to a structural disorder certainly is a problem for the orthopedic surgeon. If the bony architecture is out of alignment or a skeletal malformation exists, immediate referral to the parents and then to the surgeon is in order. However, most poor posture observed in school children is not due to skeletal disorders.

Slovenly habits in standing and sitting can be responsible for poor posture. An appeal to pride in personal appearance and a plan for improvement can be initiated through counseling. If the whole class develops a consciousness of posture, it will lend support to a child who needs especially to improve his posture. The group effect is motivating to all. It sincerely is hoped that there will be no best posture contests.

Poor muscle tone due to the effects of illness, malnutrition, focal infection, or inadequate rest will cause poor posture. The first step must be to correct the basic cause. Muscle tone can be built up gradually through planned activity.

Round shoulders is the most common posture defect among school children and is particularly prevalent among junior and senior high

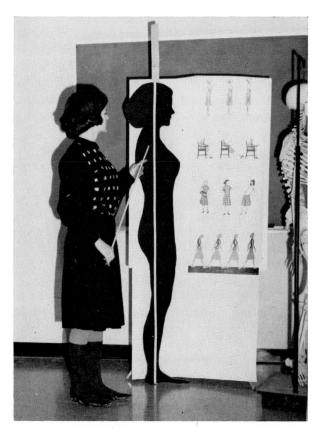

Fig. 34. Use of models. Posture model to make the study of posture more meaningful and thus more effective. Junior high school students, particularly girls, have a special need to concern themselves with posture. (Courtesy Salem Public Schools, Salem, Ore.)

school students. The condition results from continuous activities in which the arms are held in front of the body. Most normal activities require the arms to be in front of one. The shoulders and arms are held forward by the continuous contraction of the muscles (pectoralis) of the chest. As a result the relatively powerful pectoral muscles gradually shorten, increase in strength and bulk, and develop a tonus out of all proportion to the light muscles which draw the shoulder blades back. The strong muscles of the chest thus keep the shoulders drawn forward. The pectoral muscles must be stretched in order for the condition to be corrected.

The *gravity method* for the correction of round shoulders aims primarily, by an easy and simple process, to stretch the chest muscles and thus permit the architecture of the shoulder to assume its normal form. This is done by applying the force of gravity in such a way that the body weight produces the muscle strain.

First the teacher measures the distance between the inner borders of the child's shoulder blades when they are drawn back moderately. Then a wooden block, three inches wide, is cut to a length one half inch greater than the distance measured between the borders of the shoulder blades. The *thickness* of the block will depend upon the size of the child and the severity of the condition. The block should be somewhat thinner than normal for a severe condition and somewhat thicker for a mild condition.

Senior high school age	1¾ inches
Junior high school age	1½ inches
Intermediate school age	1¼ inches

The block is placed flat on the floor, and the subject lies so that the inner borders of the shoulder blades rest on the ends of the block, the block overlapping about one fourth inch on each shoulder blade. If the head rests on the floor and the arms are bent slightly and raised above the head, the pectoral muscles will be stretched. The subject should feel a decided pull on the chest muscles. In the first trial the child should not remain in position for more than three minutes because a soreness will develop in the chest area. Each day the time is increased about one minute until the period reaches about ten minutes.

If no pull is felt on the pectorals, the block is too thin or too long. As the round shoulder condition improves, the block must be made thicker by the addition of a quarter-inch piece to the bottom of the block. In some cases it is necessary to cut the block shorter as the condition improves.

Experience has demonstrated that morning, immediately after one arises, is the most convenient for lying on the block. More than ten minutes on the block at a time is neither advisable nor necessary. The merit of the gravity method lies in its simplicity; yet it yields a maximum result, with a minimum of time and effort.

Foot conditions. Gross foot deformities require orthopedic care, and through one of the many channels available an affected child should receive orthopedic treatment. Gross abnormalities of the foot are usually

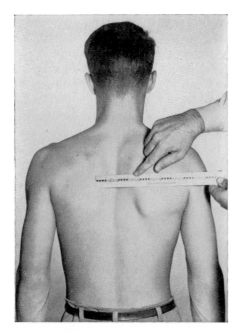

Fig. 35. Measuring the distance between the shoulder blades. The shoulders are drawn back slightly, and the distance is measured between the inner borders of the scapulae. (From Langton, C. V., and Anderson, C. L.: Health principles and practice, St. Louis, 1953, The C. V. Mosby Co.)

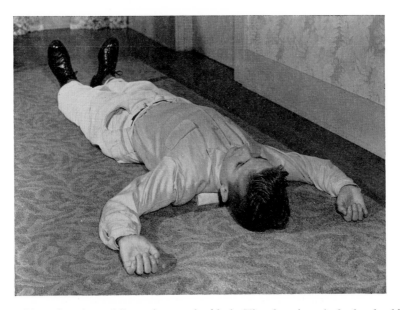

Fig. 36. Position of student while resting on the block. The chest is arched, the shoulders do not touch the floor, and the weight of the arms stretched above the head exerts a pull on the chest muscles. (From Langton, C. V., and Anderson, C. L.: Health principles and practice, St. Louis, 1953, The C. V. Mosby Co.)

corrected. It is the so-called nuisance types of foot conditions which never receive professional attention. Most physicians have very little interest in corns, calluses, perspiring feet, tender feet, or low arches. Podiatrists are professionally prepared to care for foot disabilities, but their services are available in few communities outside of metropolitan areas. In consequence both adults and children frequently suffer from foot difficulties which would readily respond to treatment, but no service is available.

It is surely not the function of the school to treat foot disorders. Yet the school can be of service to children with foot difficulties by helping them obtain professional treatment by a physician or a podiatrist. Examination by a physician first is logical. If the condition is one for treatment by a podiatrist, the physician will recommend that course of action. If it is not, he will recommend treatment which is in the best interests of the child.

A teacher with a working knowledge of common foot disabilities will have a better appreciation of the problems involved and the essential action which should be undertaken. A painful condition of the feet markedly reduces effective and enjoyable living, causes general bodily fatigue, and contributes to premature aging. An informed teacher may help a child to better health by helping him solve his foot troubles.

Foot strain involves the muscles, tendons, and ligaments essentially. The foot may appear to be normal, but be tender and painful on walking. Or there may be acute marked swelling, pain, tenderness, and spasm (cramp). If the condition is to be relieved, improper weight-bearing, faulty posture, improper shoes, or other causes must be eliminated. If the cause is improper weight-bearing, a person should walk as little as possible and keep the feet elevated as much as is practical. Severe strain may mean that one must remain in bed until the swelling and pain have disappeared. Contrast baths (30 seconds hot alternated with 30 seconds cold) or whirlpool baths are helpful. All exercise should be at a minimum during the painful period.

Morton's painful foot is characterized by cramps or sharp pains at the ball of the foot because of a fallen metatarsal arch. Any condition which throws the weight forward on the transverse arch may cause it to become concave and thus pinch nerves. As a first measure it is necessary to correct the cause of the forward weight-bearing. Artificial support for the fallen arch relieves the pain. Piano felt pads or commercial pads serve. Any child with a fallen metatarsal arch needs immediate care. Because of the flexibility of youthful structures, corrective measures can be highly effective. If it is permitted to persist, a fallen arch can mean lifelong foot trouble.

Plantar callus may form under the metatarsal arch as a result of constant rubbing caused by ill-fitting shoes or foot imbalance. In its early stage the callus is a symptom of an abnormal condition and a warning of trouble ahead. To remove the callus by medicated applications is advisable, but to correct the cause of the callus is the important thing.

A *plantar wart* is a wart on the sole of the foot. If the wart is on a weight-bearing area of the foot, a child may suffer intense pain. Since a wart can persist for years, immediate means should be taken to remove it. If a podiatrist is not available, the application of salicylic acid in collodion twice daily will destroy the wart in about two weeks. If the wart is embedded in a heavy callus, three weeks or more may be required to remove it. A sterile gauze-adhesive pad over the wart will help to prevent infection. Constant vigilance should be exercised to prevent infection, and immediate attention is imperative if it appears.

Pes planus is a condition in which the arch is low, but the foot is normal. Contrary to popular belief, a low arch can be an excellent arch.

Pes cavus is a condition in which the arch is high and the foot is normal. The arch is excellent in this condition, also.

Weak arches tire because of weak musculature. Exercises which flex the arches are helpful. An excellent exercise is to roll the arch over a 4-inch roller and attempt to grasp the roller with the arch and toes. An equally good exercise is to attempt to pick up a marble or a pencil with the toes. Wrapping the arch with a stirrup bandage could be a temporary measure. The integrity of the foot should be attained as soon as possible.

Tender feet can be relieved by contrast baths followed by covering the foot with tincture of benzoin compound. This is a sticky fluid which should be covered with clean white cotton socks and is highly effective in toughening the skin.

A *corn* is an accumulation of dead cells piled on one another. It results from friction and pressure which irritates the skin and causes an increase in the rate of cell division. Pressure on the sensitive nerves beneath the corn gives rise to the pain. Corns themselves have neither nerves nor roots. Most corns are on top of the toes, but soft corns form between the toes and seed corns form on the sole.

Corns are important as an index of foot imbalance, improperly fitting shoes, or other condition which calls for correction. A corn should never be cut with a knife or other instrument. Danger of infection is too great. Common medicaments are acceptable, but, after the corn has been lifted, until firm tissue forms at the site of where the corn was lodged, a gauze pad should be applied to prevent infection. Podiatrists remove corns easily and safely.

Achilles bursitis is an inflammation of a fluid-filled sac along the tendon of Achilles. It results from overexertion and the resulting strain or from trauma. The condition is usually temporary and can be readily corrected if the foot is rested as much as possible, preferably in an elevated position.

Speech defects. Various studies reveal that about 1,000,000 children in American schools have speech defects. Generally speech is considered to be defective when it deviates sufficiently to attract the attention of others or causes some difficulty in communication. Many persons have speech defects which are so minor as to be negligible. Yet, if correction of the defect is possible, the individual should have the benefit of the correction. However, many youngsters have serious speech impediments, and, because speaking is so important in academic, social, and other relationships, the school should lend every effort to assist in correcting these impediments. If the school does not help, in most cases there is no other recourse.

The mental health rather than the physical health of the child is of concern here. Of itself, a speech impediment can be an obstacle to normal mental health. Combined with one or more other factors it can be an insurmountable handicap to wholesome adjustment.

Speech examination for every school child by a qualified examiner is the ideal. Except for metropolitan areas few schools have such a service. As a consequence classroom teachers must recognize speech difficulties. It is fortunate if as a part of her professional training a teacher has had work in the recognition of speech disorders. After the teacher recognizes that a child has a speech difficulty, an examination by a speech clinician or speech correctionist should follow. A correctionist or teacher with special training should carry out the recommendations of the examinations. This is a task for a specialist, not for an unqualified person.

If a speech clinic or speech correction specialist is available, even at some distance, a diagnosis and suggested training program can be extremely valuable because the parents and teacher can carry out the necessary training under the supervision of the specialist. An effective program can be devised for almost every child with a speech impediment if the school is resolved that something shall be done for him.

Modified program for the handicapped

Many states have a crippled children's commission and have established schools to give the special training many handicapped children require. Though nobly conceived, these schools do not solve the problem even in the most populous states. Many parents will not permit handicapped children to leave home to be domiciled at these schools, which are usually located in a central section of the state.

In large school systems special programs and even special schools, staffed with qualified experts, have been established for the handicapped. Small systems and even those of moderate size do not feel financially able to support such a program. Yet every school can do something for handicapped children. Many possibilities are open. Many states subsidize the program for the handicapped of local school districts. This subsidy usually applies to any standard local program of special classes, home instruction, or modification of the regular classroom program.

Special classes, particularly on the elementary school level, have been effective. Specialists in various phases of education, including occupational therapists, have been engaged for these classes. In some situations a single teacher is used to fulfill the requirements of the children. This is exceptional since a teacher-student ratio of about 10 to 1 is usual. Ramps, wheel chairs, cots, and other special provisions may have to be supplied. Special lighting may be necessary. The needs of certain handicapped children can best be met by these special classes, but some handicapped children, such as those with a heart condition or hearing impairment, may resent the class. From the mental health aspect the special class could be a liability for certain children. Selection of students for the special class must be a carefully considered process.

Home instruction can be made effective for many handicapped youngsters. Capable visiting teachers and a good home situation can provide an adequate education. However, home instruction is not always satisfactory. Poor light, distractions, inadequate ventilation, and lack of sanitation are not conducive to effective learning. In addition the child dwells there twenty-four hours of the day, which tends to produce a monotonous stultifying atmosphere that outside diversion alone could pierce.

It is apparent that with modifications most handicapped children can be fitted into the regular school organization. What should these modifications be and how are they to be determined? An effective plan can be based upon individualization of instruction. A counseling team sets the basic policies. Using these policies, the team with the assistance of other teachers makes a thorough study of each case which involves a handicapped child. The collective judgment of this group produces a proposed program for the child in question. The teacher or teachers who will be in day-to-day contact with the child should be given a complete picture of the counselors' recommendations. After this review the final program is put into operation, with reappraisals as necessary from time to time.

So far as possible the handicapped child should be accepted as a normal member of the group and live a normal school life. Adjustments should be made in accordance with his assets and liabilities. Goals and standards should be realistic. The child must have reasonable insight into his abilities and limitations; otherwise he may be too ambitious, with resulting disillusionment. Or he may lack incentive to reach the standards of which he is capable.

The situation requires a teacher who is adept at adjustment and improvision and who is skillful in dealing with problem situations. A confidential relationship with the child is especially important. To make necessary adaptations in terms of the child's capacities while retaining the child's feeling of being a normal member of the group challenges the most ingenious of teachers.

Modification of any one phase or all phases of the program for the benefit of a handicapped child should not be made at the expense of all other children. This is both unnecessary and unjustified. When a handicapped child upsets or seriously affects the normal program, a thorough reappraisal is necessary. There may be agencies other than the school or persons other than the teachers who have more to offer a particular handicapped child than does the school and the teacher. When the child is a constant disrupting element in the classroom, in justice to the thirty or more other children, outside agencies or persons should be importuned to assume the guidance of the handicapped child. This action should be taken only after the school has exhausted all of its resources.

Selected readings

American Medical Association, Department of Health Education: Physicians and schools, report of the Eighth National Conference on Physicians and Schools, Chicago, 1961, The Association.

Bowen, Carolyn: Posture training for adolescents, Physical Therapy Review **28**:60, 1948.

Daniels, A. S.: Adapted physical education, principles and practices for exceptional students, New York, 1954, Harper & Brothers.

Eilola, R.: Adjusting the school program to the allergic child, Journal of Exceptional Children **12**:162, 1946.

Fiedler, M. F.: Teachers' problems with hard of hearing children, Journal of Educational Research **46**:618, 1949.

Gates, A. I.: Learning to use hearing aids, New York, 1946, Columbia University Press.

Geyer, M. A.: Counseling for physically impaired students in high school, Personnel and Guidance Journal **32**:214, 1953.

Gratke, Juliette: Help them help themselves, Dallas, Texas, 1947, Society for Crippled Children.

Irwin, R. B.: Adolescents with speech disorders, National Association of Secondary School Principals Bulletin **39**:112, 1955.

Leavitt, J., and Taran, L. M.: Some of the problems in the education of rheumatic children, Journal of Pediatrics **32**:553, 1948.

Licht, S. H. (editor): Therapeutic exercise, ed. 2, New Haven, Conn., 1961, Physical Medicine Library.

Mackie, Romaine P.: Crippled children in school, Washington, D. C., 1948, United States Government Printing Office.

Oberteuffer, D.: School health education, ed. 3, New York, 1960, Harper & Brothers.

Rathbone, Josephine L.: Corrective physical education, ed. 6, Philadelphia, 1959, W. B. Saunders Co.

Stafford, G. T.: Preventive and corrective physical education, ed. 3, New York, 1958, A. S. Barnes & Co.

Stafford, G. T.: Sports for the handicapped, ed. 2, New York, 1947, Prentice-Hall, Inc.

Turner, C. E., Sellery, C. M., and Smith, Sarah L.: School health and health education, ed. 4, St. Louis, 1960, The C. V. Mosby Co.

Wallin, J. E. W.: Education of mentally handicapped children, New York, 1955, Harper & Brothers.

Yahraes, H.: Games for handicapped children, New York, 1954, Public Affairs Committee.

Part 4

Health instruction

*Let the main object of this, our didactic, be as follows: To seek
and to find a method of instruction, by which teachers may
teach less, but learners may learn more.*

—The Great Didactic of Comenius (1628-1632)

Chapter 11

Foundations of instruction

One central theme runs through all phases of the school health program:
the preparation of every child to make the necessary decisions relating to
his health. Education implies self-growth for the adventure of life. It is
an expression of a person's knowledge and his ability to utilize it and
apply meaning and value to it. Education is growth in the ability to distinguish, to discriminate, to appraise, to interpret, and to evaluate. Applied to health, education is self-growth in one's understanding of health
and the capacity to apply the fundamental principles of health to specific
life situations.

During his school years a child has a multitude of varied experiences,
both in and out of school, which contribute to his health education.
School experiences such as the health examination, activities for control
of communicable disease, vision and hearing screening, sanitation activities, emergency measures, supplementary reading, counseling, and informal discussions contribute tangibly to health education. Out-of-school
activities which contribute to a student's health education include dental examinations, visits to medical clinics, observation of public health
personnel in action, community health measures, family health problems, family health discussions, the reading of newspaper and magazine
articles which deal with health, and viewing and listening to television
and radio programs on health subjects. Health education obtained from
these experiences can be highly valuable, but, of and by themselves, these
incidental or somewhat isolated measures are inadequate. In addition to
the inevitable omission of many areas of health function, a lack of integration diminishes the true educational value of these experiences. For
the purposes of life an integrated core of learning experience is necessary
if persons are to be well informed on health measures and be able to utilize and apply meaning and value to health knowledge. The logical medium to complete the job of filling out, putting together, and finishing up

the structure we call health education is systematic coordinated health instruction.

Health instruction

In its true meaning *instruction* is the methodical imparting of information and knowledge. It includes the formal planned classwork as well as the special assignments, the projects, and the incidental learning experiences which the teacher utilizes to impart further understanding. Instruction may be rigidly formal or casually informal. *Training* may be regarded as a phase of instruction since it involves the systematic development of one's skills or abilities by practice and drill. Teaching is the process of making the student aware through subject matter and experience. Fundamentally teaching is a process of helping another person to learn.

Health instruction can be academic, vocational, cultural, and practical. Too many teachers make health instruction purely an academic subject. Perhaps it is personally gratifying to a student to know the chemical formulas of the various vitamins or to know the names of all of the bones of the human skeleton. Maybe the elementary school teacher is elated that her pupils know the dietary customs of natives of the South Sea Islands. Sheer isolated academic instruction of this type is indefensible. Some health knowledge which is largely academic may be defensible, but it should be incidental and serve other than an academic purpose. Health instruction in public schools is not intended primarily for vocational education, but students can be motivated by the preparation of health materials related to the hazards of their various occupational interests. Health instruction may motivate a student to go into one of the health professions and thus serve a laudable purpose. There may be vocational outcomes, but health instruction in schools should not be deliberately directed to vocational objectives. It should be directed primarily to *practical* needs and secondarily to *cultural* needs.

In a society in which the adult citizen is responsible for the promotion of his own health, it is only logical that the school health instruction should give major emphasis to practical personal health needs. A clear concept of what constitutes sound health is a practical matter. Knowledge of measures for the maintenance and promotion of health is of practical value. Prevention of disease and the correction of defects are realistic concerns. The understanding of normal mental health is of daily value. Procedures for the extension of the prime of life and life expectation have a down-to-earth interest and value for all citizens.

Properly cultural needs are incorporated into health instruction. Perhaps grooming and some other health practices affect the physical health but little; yet they have value in the promotion of mental health. Emphasis on personal care promotes an interest in one's general well-being, which yields a high return in terms of native endowment. High self-esteem not only promotes physical health, but also is indispensable for a high level of mental health.

That health instruction has failed which has not created in the student a personal association with the knowledge under consideration. With effective health instruction the student always thinks in terms of "This means me; this is what I need; this is what I am; this is what I am going to do; this is what I am going to be; I must use this in every way." This type of thinking is true identification with the subject at hand and is motivation in terms of self-growth, self-promotion, and self-improvement. Too often health instruction creates in the student's mind the idea that all of this is for somebody else. Or the whole subject becomes an academic matter to be learned for test purposes. The ultimate goal can be attained most effectively by following two guideposts—practical needs and cultural values. Health instruction must be personally meaningful to the youngsters.

Curriculum procedures

Change is constant in the aim and purpose of curriculum procedures. The emphasis is no longer on mastery of an abstract classical curriculum but upon development of an individual's abilities. The aim is not to prepare a few to be leaders and the rest to be followers in a formalized static social routine, but to prepare each individual in terms of his abilities to adapt to a dynamic democracy in which new problems to solve arise constantly. Today education is in the process of changing from classical traditional subject matter to functional experiences and materials with which to meet existing problems. In consequence material becomes stimulating and realistically meaningful. Dealing with existing problems promotes desirable work practices.

On the elementary school level traditional organization of subject matter is giving way to functional or experience-centered studies, centers of interest, and projects. On the secondary level subjects are being reorganized in the light of present-day interests and needs. A correlated curriculum based on a functional core subject is emerging. New subjects and areas of experience are appearing.

Health instruction can be effective in any type of curriculum if the health instructor has a tangible philosophy of health education, formulates (perhaps with the pupils) realistic objectives, has command of various instructional methods, has the ingenuity to adapt to situations, and is imbued with the professional desire to contribute to the development and well-being of each child. Four types of curriculum are recognized.

1. *Separate subjects.* Even in this organization the subjects are not isolated islands. Bridges are built between the islands of subject matter, but integration of learning is left too much to the student's mind.

2. *Correlated subjects.* The use of a core subject about which all learning evolves has merit, particularly where all concerned work as a team and have a concept of the coordination required.

3. *Broad fields of learning.* The integration of knowledge through the incorporation of subjects into broad areas has merit, also. The broad area of language arts includes reading, writing, spelling, grammar, punctuation, speech, and listening. Social studies encompasses history, geography, civics, and the modern way of life. The arithmetic-science field integrates the physical and biological sciences into what sometimes is designated as natural science. Health properly can be regarded as a broad area including personal health, community health, safety, emergency care, socio-economic problems, and the related problems of the family and individual. Health also can be conceived as a phase of a broader area or an integrated aspect of a core subject.

4. *Developmental activities.* A curriculum which provides effective learning experiences that are based on interests, circumstances, and personal discoveries and that are outgrowths of other activities requires ingenuity and teaching skill. Yet this type of curriculum has the greatest potential in terms of functional instruction.

Regardless of its organization there are seven criteria which the curriculum must satisfy:

1. Help to coordinate the efforts of teachers
2. Provide a well-balanced day of living for students
3. Orient the student to life about him
4. Provide for participation of pupils in planning
5. Provide for unified learning
6. Provide for continuity of learning experiences
7. Provide for development of fundamental skills

In actual practice few schools have a single curriculum pattern at present. Rather typical is a combination of two or more since types of curriculums overlap considerably. Schools with a separate subjects curriculum utilize developmental activities as a vehicle within the subject field. With experience teachers extend the activities and learning by purposing. Perhaps teaching by means of projects or experiences is primarily a matter of professional growth. It is a form of development a teacher acquires only through participation.

Health factors modified by instruction

Both the maximum possibilities and the practical limitations of health instruction must be appraised if there is to be a proper perspective of the school health instruction program. This appraisal must be a realistic assessment of the specific health factors which can actually be tangibly modified by instruction.

An objective appraisal does not support the view of the extremists who maintain that instruction is the only approach to health and the solution to all health problems. This group would devote all its energies to health instruction in the belief that instruction can change everything. No one familiar with the school health program would deny that instruction has had some influence on all phases of the complete health program.

The health examination grows out of the instruction which the physician received; good lighting has been made possible because of the instruction certain illuminating engineers received. However, we deal here with direct instruction for specific problems, and instruction cannot deal directly with all existing health problems nor modify all factors affecting health. School health services and healthful school living must be strong legs to complete the school health tripod.

At the other pole are those individuals who question the value of health instruction in actual health terms. This group contends that health can and must be bought. To them a physician is a technically trained expert in the human problems of life and death, and his services are available at a price. What these people are talking about is the treatment or control of disease. Even here health instruction is valuable in the choice and use of health services and products. When a person has had the benefit of competent health instruction, he will know when to seek the services of a physician or dentist. Further he will understand how to go about selecting the right practitioner. However, proper choice and use of health services and products are but small segments of the true value of health instruction.

The real worth of health instruction is its preparation of a person to promote his own health and make the decisions necessary to protect and maintain his health. In attainment of this state it is possible to modify specific health factors. By recognizing that these factors can be modified by instruction, the teacher can make the end results of health instruction more effective and valuable.

Health attitudes

1. Acceptance of personal responsibility for health promotion
2. Application of reason to health problems
3. Ideal of a vigorous high level of health
4. Dissatisfaction with low vitality
5. Confidence in scientific health principles
6. Awareness that prevention is preferable to treatment or cure
7. Conviction that any deviation from normal commands immediate medical service
8. Reliance upon scientific medicine
9. Rejection of fads, nostrums, and quackery
10. Regard for high standards of personal care
11. Appreciation of mental health needs and standards
12. Predisposition to anticipate hazards to health
13. Respect for the health of others
14. Willingness to suffer inconvenience for the protection of the health of others
15. Eugenic concept of responsibility for coming generations

Health knowledge

1. Understanding of health promotion
2. Understanding of prevention and control of disease
3. Recognition and understanding of special health problems
4. Determining and using reliable health and medical services and products

5. Principles of mental health
6. Health problems peculiar to different age levels
7. Safety promotion
8. First-aid procedures
9. Sanitary standards and measures
10. Community health responsibility and promotion

Health practices
1. Healthful personal practices
2. Nutrition
3. Rest and sleep
4. Activity in keeping with needs and capacity
5. Cleanliness
6. Conservation of vision
7. Safe conduct
8. Periodic health examinations
9. Dental examinations
10. Immediate correction of all remediable disorders
11. Immunization
12. Isolation
13. Emotional and social behavior

Conditions
1. Adequate housing
2. Safe water supplies
3. Protected milk supplies
4. Sanitary sewage disposal
5. Adequate protection of food supplies
6. Adequate recreation facilities
7. Adequate health services
8. Safe community, industrial, school, and home conditions
9. Attractive community appearance
10. Hygienic mental environment

Health instruction is the base of the school health pyramid. Its breadth and soundness determine the strength of the entire program and the height to which the pyramid can rise.

Triad of objectives of health instruction

To ensure healthful living now and in the years to come, health instruction must be directed to three basic purposes.
1. Establishment of *practices* essential to health
2. Acquisition of *knowledge* necessary for health promotion
3. Development of *attitudes* and *ideals* which will motivate each individual to attain the highest possible level of well-being

These basic objectives are not independent, but are mutually interrelated and reciprocal. One serves as a vehicle for the others. The development of one indirectly promotes the development of the others. Yet all three basic objectives should command the attention of the health instructor. To direct all attention to health knowledge will to some extent develop desirable health attitudes and initiate certain health practices. Yet such an approach is inadequate. Attention must be directed to attitudes and practices as well as to knowledge. Evidence is ample that without the proper attitudes little use is made of health knowledge. Further unless a person puts his knowledge into practice, he experiences little if any benefit from it.

Emphasis at different levels. The relative emphasis placed upon the development of attitudes, knowledge, and practices varies at different school levels. Studies of psychologists and educators make it clear that at certain stages of development in children they are more ready to establish practices, at other stages they are more ready to develop attitudes and ideals, and at still other stages to acquire knowledge.

The best results will be attained by giving primary emphasis to health practices during the early years of school life. Health attitudes will develop as by-products. Such knowledge as the child acquires, incidental to the practices, will not be extensive, but health knowledge at this stage is not an important factor.

In grades five and six the order of emphasis in terms of readiness is attitudes, practices, and knowledge. This is the age at which a child is highly impressionable and attitudes are readily acquired. Thus it is important that he acquire desirable health attitudes and that he not be denied the opportunity for developing health attitudes. Practices already formed should be further established and fortified. Knowledge to sustain the attitudes and support the practice will be necessary.

In junior high school the relative emphasis is upon attitudes, knowledge, and practices. By this time health practices should be well established. The idealism of this age lends itself admirably to the acceptance of recognized ideals of health and the development of additional attitudes toward health. Knowledge becomes more important with the near-mature concept of the significance of health knowledge.

In senior high school the health practices and attitudes which have been formed previously should be reinforced as rapidly as possible by accurate scientific knowledge. At this stage to know not only the *what,* but also the *how* and *why,* is important. Conviction that his health practices, ideals, and attitudes are sound scientifically will cement the health instruction of a student and assure him of adequate preparation to make the necessary health decisions.

For clarity a graphic representation best pictures the relative emphasis

Table 17. *Relative emphasis on basic health instruction objectives at various levels*

Level	Practices	Attitudes	Knowledge
Kindergarten Grades 1, 2, 3, 4	Primary	Secondary	Tertiary
Grades 5, 6	Secondary	Primary	Tertiary
Junior high school	Tertiary	Primary	Secondary
Senior high school	Tertiary	Secondary	Primary

placed upon the basic instructional objectives at the various school levels (Table 17). The three categories of emphasis do not express uniform gradations nor precise qualitative differences. Rather they present the order of teaching importance in terms of the readiness and receptiveness of students at the different school levels.

The health practices, attitudes and ideals, and knowledge an individual possesses are the expression of his level of health education, i.e., his equipment to promote health.

Basic principles of health instruction

Certain basic principles have been recognized as fundamental to sound, effective health instruction. These principles have been developed as the result of research, the contributions of the field of psychology, the fundamental needs of the child, and the experience of education through the years.

1. Emphasis is on the positive, not the negative, aspect of health; i.e., the aim is to build up and maintain as high a level of health as possible in each child.
2. Health is an end to be gained, not an academic subject.
3. Instruction is directed to the well or normal child. Children temporarily below par will benefit from the health practices acquired by the whole class.
4. Throughout school life health promotion should be one of the objectives of the whole school program.
5. Learning experiences must be adapted to the physiological, psychological, and social development of the children.
6. Instruction must be based on the interests, needs, abilities, and background of the child.
7. Learning results from experience, and opportunities must be provided for experience through participation, doing things, and reacting to situations.
8. Problem-solving provides the most effective learning situation, but only when the problems are real and meaningful to the learner.
9. The objectives of any activity must be specified in terms of outcomes for the learner and must be recognized as personal goals by the child if learning is to be effective.
10. Instructional activities must always be related to the actual experiences of the learners.
11. Learning experiences are most effective when the child sees the relationship of one experience to the whole of experience.
12. Learners should be helped in making generalizations and in applying these generalizations to various new experiences.
13. Integrated learning is most effective, and only as it becomes unified will learning be lasting. Both fragments of learning and isolated facts are ineffective and soon forgotten.

14. Repetition or drill is justified when the learning must be precise and is useful as a tool or skill.
15. Each child is unique and learns at his own rate and in his own way; thus a variety of activities and materials is essential.
16. Accompanying incidental learning always takes place, and teachers should be alert for opportunities to make each learning experience yield greater returns.
17. Health work in the school cannot be fully effective unless it is integrated with the life of the home and the community and the forces in both which can contribute to the child's education.

Practices avoided in health instruction

Certain practices that are outwardly appealing have been found to be more injurious than beneficial and have been renounced as taboo by recognized school health authorities. Often these activities grow out of certain outside pressures, but occasionally they are the creation of the teacher responsible for health instruction. In the search for motivating devices the teacher may be tempted to use questionable activities and materials. By accepting and using only recognized approaches and materials and by insisting that the whole school follow accepted and recognized health practices, the health instructor will have an effective gratifying program on a high professional plane. Practices to be avoided:

1. Healthiest child contests
2. Competition between students (e.g., height, weight, poster, essay, speech, etc.)
3. Artificial rewards (e.g., stars, banners, movies, etc.)
4. Unrealistic or impossible standards
5. Technical material from medical schools
6. Prejudice and hearsay
7. Use of dogmatism
8. Use of morbid, abnormal, or fearful subject matter
9. Using a child in the class or school as an example of a defect
10. Causing a child to be conspicuous or to feel humiliated
11. Teaching in abstractions
12. Infantile attitudes
13. Use of parodies on nursery rhymes or songs
14. Information on venereal diseases as sex instruction
15. Herding large groups into a gymnasium or auditorium for health instruction
16. Health instruction as a fill-in for physical education
17. Poor health practices by the teacher

There are many wholesome opportunities, activities, methods, materials, and techniques for effective health instruction without tainting the program with discredited means and measures. The very importance of health is ample evidence of its nobility and the respect it should command in the school program.

Selection of materials for health instruction

Because of the vast store of existing health instruction materials and the limitless possibilities for creating new materials, any attempt to establish criteria must be confined to fundamental concepts. Further these criteria must be in positive terms to be in harmony with the present-day philosophy of health education and should express the standards of accceptable materials. They can be expressed precisely and concisely.

1. Do the materials truly relate to the experiences of the children?
2. Are the materials adapted to the maturity of the children?
3. Do the materials harmonize with the needs and interests of the group?
4. Do the materials provide for individual differences and needs?
5. Are the materials accurate and scientifically sound?
6. Are the materials interesting?
7. Do the materials provide for progress and growth?
8. Do the materials have broad educational value?

Development of health practices

So much emphasis has been placed on health habits that a few moments may profitably be invested in a consideration of the difference between the terms *practice* and *habit*. *Practice* is the customary action which one pursues with reference to some phase of life. It encompasses the term *habit* since habit is also an action but a more limited tendency or disposition to action. *Habit* is a relatively more simple psychoneurological pattern which has been repeated sufficiently so that function is totally without conscious initiation or with a minor awareness. Habits are established generally at the second neurological level and not the higher cerebral cortex level of consciousness. Practices of a higher form arise from an awareness associated with values or desire. Most health actions called habits are not actually habits. The broader term *practice* is more appropriate. A periodic health examination is a practice, but not a habit. Washing the hands is a practice. Even brushing the teeth is not a habit, but a practice as it applies to virtually all persons. Perhaps a few people have a habit of brushing their teeth as they have a habit of crossing their legs when they sit down.

Although some health actions might be termed habits, from the standpoint of effective health instruction the wise course is to deal in terms of practices. If a general health practice does acquire the status of a habit, there is no loss in the value of the instruction. Good health depends upon good health practices which are initiated by an understanding of the need for the action and propelled by an appreciation of the inherent values.

The formation of a practice follows a fairly well-established sequence of events. In this sequence certain concomitant factors serve as catalysts to continue the chain reaction.

1. *Understanding* of the *nature* of the health factor being considered and the *action* necessary to implementation must be established.

2. *Appreciation* of the *worth* or *value* of the practice in terms of personal health benefits must be a by-product of understanding. The child must realize and appreciate fully that the practice may contribute to self-esteem, appearance, general well-being, and enjoyment in life.

3. *Interest* must be supplied in the kind and amount necessary to arouse *desire* and *will*. Once the learner associates the practice with his own self-welfare, he has the energizing motive to give force and direction to his action. It now becomes something which emerges from within, not something imposed upon the child.

4. The *act* must be *performed* under favorable conditions and have a pleasant emotional result. The encouragement, recognition, and appreciation of the teacher as well as of classmates and parents can lend force and strength to the establishment of the practice.

5. The *act* must be *repeated* as often as necessary to become well established.

6. The *practice* must be *reappraised* and re-evaluated in terms of past, present, and future benefits. The emotional exhilaration which vitalized the practice at the outset is gradually replaced by reason as the logic and value of the practice becomes established.

Modification of health practices to fit particular circumstances and personal needs is entirely within the framework of the present-day philosophy of school health, which emphasizes the individualized nature of health and health promotion.

Development of health attitudes

In the final analysis the effectiveness of health instruction should be measured in terms of its actual effect upon the health of a person. Since this is difficult to do, especially over a brief span of time, an alternative is to determine the extent to which an individual actually applies the health instruction he received during his school years.

A study of adults to determine the effectiveness of their school health experiences is quite revealing. One finds that many adults who went through a planned extensive program of health instruction during their school years fail to apply the health knowledge they acquired. Apparently the health instruction in their formative years was confined to academic knowledge put into a small compartment for examination time. Omitted from his health education was the establishment of attitudes which would enable him to respond to life's situations and demands and make health knowledge functional.

Health attitudes, knowledge, and practices are reciprocal and interrelated. Health attitudes grow out of knowledge and practices. Likewise to assure that a health practice is to be most effective and lasting, it must be cemented by well-established attitudes; if health knowledge is to be most effective, it must be applied through proper health attitudes. Attitudes, being part of one's psychoneural organization, are the directors of life. They are developed out of and associated with the gratification of the Self in the biosocial motivation of a person. They are the stick which controls the rudders of knowledge and practice.

In attempting to develop certain attitudes in children, a teacher must interpret the attitudes which are required by life in this social order. In the development of specific attitudes in children, a considerable amount of indoctrination doubtless occurs. In teaching it is difficult to avoid a certain amount of indoctrination because the teaching situation itself involves the influence of one personality upon another. Perhaps benevolent (as it is usually professed to be) indoctrination is an unavoidable and inherent corollary of teaching.

Concept of attitudes. An attitude may be thought of as a tendency to react in a certain way in a given situation. Two general schools of interpretation may be recognized.

The first school holds attitudes to be emotional sterotypes, or as Thurstone† puts it, "a generalized reaction for or against a specific psychological object." This view assumes that a person is conscious of the object toward which he is reacting. Thus one could study an individual's attitudes toward the health examination by asking direct questions on the health examination.

The second school holds attitudes to be patterns of behavior, or as Allport defines it, "An attitude is a mental and neural state of readiness organized through experience, exerting directive or dynamic influence upon the individual's response to all objects and situations with which it is related."‡ Thus one might investigate a person's attitudes toward the health examination by finding out how he behaves in situations which involve practices and ideals which relate to the health examination.

Health attitudes have a well-defined value or object. Those related to an object are specific, but those related to values (the vast majority in the health area) tend to be general although not of such a generalized nature as to be classed as traits. Frequently in the development of health attitudes, several specific attitudes may be integrated with or even be incorporated into a more general attitude. Thus the development of attitudes toward the health examination, self-appraisal, self-evaluation, self-protection, and responsibility to others may result in a more generalized attitude or even farsightedness or prevention in regard to the protection of one's own well-being. However, the teacher must recognize that the predisposition to respond in one given situation does not necessarily mean that there is a transfer of that same predisposition to

---

*From Anderson, C. L.: The development of health attitudes, Elementary School Journal 50:6, 327, 1951.

†Thrustone, L. L., and Chave, E. H.: The measurement of attitude, Chicago, 1929, University of Chicago Press.

‡From Allport, G. W.: Attitudes. In Murchison, C. (editor): Handbook of social psychology, Worcester, Mass., 1935, Clark University Press.

another situation. For the most part attitudes must be developed for specific or closely related situations.

Attitudes are basically emotional, but do not necessarily involve pronounced likes or dislikes. However, in the development of health attitudes a tangible degree of favorable acceptance, of satisfaction, and of self-gratification is essential. The Self is the most important element in any person's conduct. It may be gratified by satisfying physiological patterns of physical well-being or by social attainments such as achievement, attention, praise, acceptance in a social group, or recognition as a leader of the group by measuring up to its ideals and practices.

Developing health attitudes. The problem for the teacher then is this: To determine the various kinds of situations children must encounter in order for them to develop desirable health attitudes.

Health attitudes cannot be built by any artificial process of manufacture as one may build practices or develop knowledge. They develop as by-products of experience, and the task of the teacher is to prepare situations which will arouse the desired attitudes. Immediately the teacher says, "I have forty youngsters in my classroom; each one is unique, different from all the others; that means I must prepare forty different situations, obviously an impossibility." Children *are* all different, but not so greatly different. A given situation will not bring forth exactly the same response in all of them, but in most cases the responses will not differ greatly. The pronounced deviates can be given the individualized attention which is indicated.

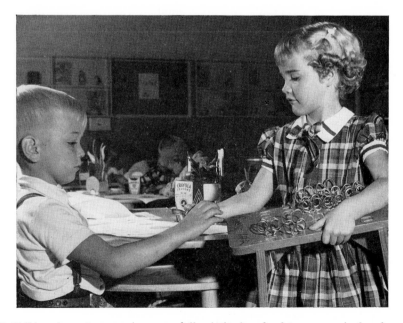

Fig. 37. Children learn to pass scissors carefully. Attitudes of safety are acquired as by-products of meaningful experiences. (Courtesy Portland Public Schools, Portland, Ore.)

The teacher can follow the procedures that an expert grower of gladoli uses. He learns all he can about his field, and he treats bulbs as well as he can with the scientific knowledge at his command. He does not profess to know all that might be known about the bulbs, but he uses the knowledge he has. He then prepares the soil as skillfully and thoroughly as his available knowledge and ability permit. Again the soil is not perfectly prepared because no one particular plantar knows all there is to know about soils. He plants forty bulbs, each bulb unique; yet the soil is prepared and conditions are right so that each bulb can grow in its own way. As the stalks begin to grow, most of the plants will do very well. However, a few will not do so well as the others. To these the grower gives the special attention indicated and at the same time maintains conditions generally which will best enable each bulb to develop into the finest quality of flower possible. Individualization of instruction is analagous. Differences in the final quality of the various blooms will be apparent, but each has attained a high, not perfect, level of development in the situation prepared by the grower, limited though his knowledge admittedly is.

The course or procedure which a teacher might follow in developing health attitudes suggests itself.

1. *Survey* or inventory of health attitudes and the health purposes which the children already have and the situations or stimuli to which they are likely to respond. Existing health attitudes tests are not too satisfactory for the purposes of elementary school teachers. To begin with, these do not test health attitudes as such, but largely test the student's knowledge of acceptable and unacceptable health practice, the inference being that the child has the desired attitudes if he has the requisite knowledge. The emotional pattern is not necessarily revealed, either qualitatively or quantitatively. If the classroom teacher wishes to know something of the attitudes of the children toward exclusion from school, a group discussion on the question will perhaps provide her with greater knowledge than would the standard health attitude tests. It must be conceded that her approach may not be the most scientific, but from the practical standpoint it is perhaps her best means for obtaining some degree of understanding of the children's attitudes. She needs to study the emotional responses of the children in order to obtain some grasp of the qualitative aspects of their responses.

In her survey the elementary school teacher must analyze the attitudes of the children which relate to such areas as the daily health review, health examinations, dental examinations and visits to the dentist, vision tests, hearing tests, cleanliness inspection and keeping clean, weighing and measuring, exclusion from school, health ideals and standards, health training and instruction, dietary practices, exercise and play, sleep and rest, dress, prevention and control of disease, accident prevention, community living, and social adjustment.

2. *Implement* instruction by providing situations in which the children will be able to *express* the attitudes and purposes they have already developed.

3. *Supplement* instruction by providing additional situations which will develop *further* attitudes. The experiences must arouse pleasant emotions in the children which are results of achievement, recognition, or success in some form. The first emotional responses are spontaneous as the Self is gratified by the performance or fufillment of some desirable action, by being one of the group, or by comprehension of ideals as applied to the Self. Ingenuity is required of the teacher in creating situations which will arouse the desired responses. If health knowledge is used as a vehicle, desirable attitudes are often developed as by-products, but too often the development of attitudes is completely forgotten and knowledge becomes the end product.

4. *Project* the attitudes to wider areas or experiences. Thus attitudes toward exclusion from school can be extended to include quarantine and isolation, personal inconvenience for the betterment of others, one's responsibility to his neighbor, and general community citizenship service and pride. Again let it be emphasized that desirable attitudes in the area of community responses in matters of quarantine and isolation are not as such automatically transferred to community responsibility in other areas.

5. *Intensify* by interpreting the pertinent experiences and comments of the teacher as well as the experiences of others.

6. *Evaluate* and *indoctrinate* by appraising the standards and ideals established and achieved and by helping the child to realize that he now has something fine (a self-achieved standard) to live up to in the future. The teacher must strive to integrate those attitudes which she holds to be desirable and at the same time to be sure that the child understands why certain other attitudes are considered inadequate or even undesirable.

Most educators will agree that the greatest challenge to teaching is the development of desirable attitudes. The comprehension, analysis, and skill demanded are the most exacting made of the teacher. Greater attention to the development of health attitudes is inescapable if instruction in health is to ensure effective healthful living now and in future years by developing children who will utilize health knowledge and experience to the fullest extent in achieving the highest possible level of well-being.

Acquisition of health knowledge

Too many teachers in too many health classes are teaching too many things that children care nothing about. It is little wonder that students complain that health is a dull subject. No health instruction will be fully effective if the substance is of no value or interest to the members of the group. Only when the knowledge is meaningful in terms of personal needs and interests will the children truly acquire the knowledge which is available to them.

Using all possible means, the teacher must discover the health needs and interests of both the children and the community. Every child must have some interests in a field as personal as health. These interests must be implemented by knowledge which is stimulating and meaningful. The need is not for parroted information, but for knowledge in terms of basic principles, practical applications, and vitalizing interpretations.

The usefulness of knowledge is determined by the manner in which it was learned. Since teaching sheer factual information may demand little imagination or creativeness of the teacher and testing of memorized material is not difficult, it becomes extremely easy for a busy teacher to slip into a pattern of teaching which is frequently referred to as factual regurgitation. Studies have demonstrated that learning which involves unrelated facts and unorganized information is comparatively temporary or even transient. That learning is most permanent which involves the integration of knowledge, old and new, into purposeful, meaningful, organized behavior and problem-solving mental processes.

The permanence of this form of learning has been tested in various studies. To a group of eighty-two students in a beginning course in zoology, Tyler[*] administered a test which measured five basic objectives. The test was given at the beginning and end of the course to determine the students' gain during the course. Again fifteen months later the students were given the same test. The percentage of gain or loss on the five phases of the test during the fifteen-month interval was computed on the basis of what the students had gained during the course. The results are significant.

1. Names of organs identified from pictures—22% loss
2. Recognition of technical terms—72% loss
3. Recall of facts—80% loss
4. Application of principles to new situations—no loss or gain
5. Interpretation of new experimental data—126% gain

Another study was conducted subsequently by Wert[†] who measured the percentage of gain or loss over an interval of three years as related to the amount gained by the students in the course.

1. Application of principles to new situations—60% gain
2. Interpretation of new experiments—20% gain
3. Associating names with structures—80% loss
4. Terminology and function of structures—50% loss

For the teacher responsible for health instruction the implications are clear: teach health in terms of real problems and experiences which children need to solve and are interested in solving, not as an academic subject.

---

[*]Tyler, R. W.: Permanency of learning, J. Higher Education 4:203, 1933.
[†]Wert, J. E.: Twin examination assumptions, J. Higher Education 8:136, 1937.

The process. Anyone familiar with the development of children knows that there is no such thing as the *only* process of learning. No royal magic formula applies. Yet there are patterns of learning which experience has proved to be effective. One such pattern will be developed as a suggested approach. No situation will necessarily incorporate or involve all of the elements presented. Modifications are inevitable in its use, but the principles on which the program is based apply to the myriad of situations which evolve in school and the vast variations among children.

A *favorable situation* is a first essential in view of the conditioning or association which exists between the experience and the environment. A pleasant orderly spacious classroom, properly lighted and adequately furnished, could be important in creating a favorable learning situation. Yet it must be remembered that some very effective learning has taken place in old buildings, not too well furnished nor too spacious. Most important in the learning situation is that intangible thing commonly called atmosphere.

Atmosphere is created and then matured. It requires an awareness of unity, of worth, and of common purpose. A pleasant emotional climate is one in which children have a high level of self-esteem and are secure in their feelings of being accepted. For the learning adventure immediately ahead they should receive a briefing which will whet their appetites, elicit questions, and provide them with an opportunity to contribute to the preparation. The overview may be a preliminary exploration of the problem, of a movie, or of posed questions which a subsequent unit will develop, or it may be a comprehensive look at a goal to be attained. To know what the goal is gives direction to the efforts of the students, especially when they are interested in it as their own goal.

Readiness is related to timeliness and to past experience. Personal identification with the project motivates the desire to experience—to learn. Each child should know what is required, and the requirement should have value and be meaningful to him. It is necessary that he be aware of the procedures to be followed if his efforts are to be effectively productive rather than needlessly wasteful.

Motivation gives force and direction to a child's responses. Interest grows out of personal identification with the project. A teacher can do much to stimulate learning by helping a child to understand his progress. It makes goals realistic and encourages repetition. The closer the youngster gets to the goal, the greater the effort he will exert. Success as a motivational force is universal. Praise for progress as well as justified reproof can motivate. Emulation and self-rivalry may be the catalytic agents which enable some children to reach their near-maximum level of performance. Cooperation, working with others, and serving a special purpose in the group can stimulate learning.

The *acquisition of knowledge* is a psychophysiological entity which is developed by various means. By a process of contiguity a conditioning occurs which enables a child to associate a new concept with previous experience. Related facts or concepts become more permanent than do isolated facts and concepts. Insight and understanding, particularly of relationships, are essential for acquiring the broad more complex knowledge of health. Through use of meaningful material the whole picture must be made available to the child so that he sees the concept in its totality. Once he understands the whole, he can grasp the significance of the parts and organize them into an intelligent whole. Thus once he understands the whole problem of nutritional needs, he can appreciate the significance of his specific needs and how to meet them. In all learning the child learns best by participation, by doing. A child retains what he uses and does. This suggests the importance of small groups in learning experiences.

Progress can be obtained by distributed effort. If learning experiences are spaced out, time is conserved and the effectiveness of the learning is increased. It is psychologically sound teaching to space learning over several days. Interest will be fostered and repetition will not tend to stagnate. If a child has overlearned beyond the original learning, he usually retains it much better. Drill and practice should be as stimulating as possible. Guidance in the learning process should be available, particularly when the child's efforts are diverted, frustrated, or ineffective. If children are guided in a review of their experiences, further exploration as a result of their growth and concomitant interest may well develop. Learning is a continuing process.

Planning for health instruction

Any plan must be preceded by definite steps which identify and define the situation in which the planning is to develop and the problem with which the planning is to be concerned. Surveys, observations, conferences, reports, and records are fruitful sources of information. It is not always possible nor even practical to gather all the information one might wish to have. However, when sufficient background material to construct a framework of the problem is available, planning for the instructional purposes should begin. Planning is a continuous process. Modification of the original plan is evidence that there are flexibility and growth.

Within the school. Health is one phase of the larger school program. As such any planning in health instruction must be an integrated part of the total school program planning. The scope and plan of health instruction in the school or in the system should not be the exclusive province of the health instructor, nor should they be the prerogative of the administrator. The objectives, scope, and nature of health instruction in the school should be adapted to the over-all curriculum planning.

General planning and development of the curriculum are the province of the entire faculty. The composite background and wisdom of all of the faculty not only produces a better curriculum, but also gives each faculty member a better concept of the total program and his role in it. Most important is the wholesome effect on morale of the teachers.

The *staff meeting* is the integrating or unifying agency in the development of a curriculum. In terms of the requirements prescribed by the state and local boards the basic curriculum plan is developed in the staff meeting. From this basic plan committees or groups develop the various areas for consideration by the whole staff. The health area of the curriculum is in a unique position since it can and should call upon the services of many individuals not on the school staff.

Nurse-teacher conferences are extremely meaningful in terms of the actual home and individual needs which health instruction should reach. The public health nurse especially has her finger on the health pulse of the community. This is one source of assistance in determining the form and content of the school health curriculum.

Public health staff-teacher conferences can serve to guide the health instruction program into the proper areas. From its records, observations and special surveys the public health staff can provide meaningful data to guide the development of health instruction in the school. Voluntary health agencies can add to this information.

The *school-community health council* is a coordinating body which can reflect the health instruction and other health needs of the community which the school system or school should meet. This council may be composed of representatives from the local health agencies, the medical society, the dental society, the parent-teacher association, the student council, the school administration, the school nurse, and instructors in home economics, biological science, physical education, and health education. The director of food service and the chief custodian may be included.

The council can serve as a guide and support for the total school health program, but its greatest value can be that of assisting in the development of the curriculum. To date, the school-community health council has not received general acceptance. Many difficulties are encountered in the functioning of such an organization.

The *faculty correlated committee* is composed of staff members whose subject field encompasses health interests and objectives. Together this group of teachers can develop a proposed health curriculum to present to the entire teaching staff. If such a committee serves the entire school system, both elementary school and high school teachers should be on the committee. If the committee is to serve the high school only, the instructors in home economics, social studies, biological science, physical education, and health should be included. Student representatives may be valuable. An elementary school health curriculum committee should include at least one person from each grade level.

Committee meetings, conferences, seminars, and workshops are used for curriculum development purposes. Today many schools have a central curriculum committee which functions the year around, with subcommittees serving special functions. Large school systems have a curriculum laboratory and a curriculum director.

Procedures for the development of a health curriculum, whichever group is engaged in the task, must be as follows:

1. Determining the health needs to be met
2. Establishing basic objectives
3. Determining responsibility for instruction
4. Establishing areas of major emphasis
5. Plans for core instruction
6. Plans for correlated instruction
7. Integration

Leadership must come from the health director in the development of health curriculums for both the elementary school and the high school. In the absence of a health director the health instructor in the high school should provide leadership. For the elementary school a classroom teacher with a good background and interest in health can lead the way. Coordinating the health curriculum from kindergarten to graduation ensures an effective functional program in health instruction.

Within the classroom. The health curriculum for the elementary classroom or the high school health class must be planned and designed in terms of the requirements of the state department of instruction and the framework of the over-all system and school curriculum. Usually the state requirements and the school curriculum recognize the general health needs and interests of children. Yet within the health instruction plan for the classroom, provisions must be made for the special needs and interests of the children in a particular room.

When state or local health instruction guides are available, the teacher can rely upon the guide as a general framework. Yet the teacher should seek to supplement and expand the provisions of the guide. Analysis and originality are needed to adapt the guide to the specific needs of a particular group. Students can be helpful in developing various aspects of established topics and areas, but their greatest contribution can come in suggesting and implementing new health interests.

When the classroom teacher herself develops the course of study, she must appraise the total situation. Several questions are evident.

1. What has been the health background of the pupils?
2. What will follow in subsequent years?
3. What are the real health interests and needs of the youngsters?
4. What devices should be used for determining these interests and needs?
5. What home and community factors are significant?
6. What is the relationship of health instruction to the total school program?
7. What possible correlation among subjects exists?
8. What resources are available?
9. What outcomes should result?
10. How will the program be evaluated?

A minimum program of instruction for the entire year should be developed. Although the original plan must be reasonably definite, it must be flexible enough to permit adaptation to specific situations which will inevitably arise during the year. A minimum plan permits desirable expansion without eliminating those things originally deemed to be important. The all-year program gives the teacher a chart of the health course for the year. Pupils obviously should contribute to the final plans. The pupils receive real value, not from verbalization, but from tangible active participation. Later if this original participation in the planning is transferred into solving the problems inherent in the plan, it will represent real self-growth for the youngsters. From such experience comes true and lasting education.

Various patterns for health instruction planning are in use. A straight textbook or a rigid outline approach require little planning and less originality. Teaching by purposing, in which the recognized expressed health problems of the students are directly channeled into activities which the students pursue, requires an extensive teaching background, broad health knowledge, and acumen in directing group action. Because such teaching is highly effective, many teachers use this approach in modified form. In health instruction the development of units has been found to be an excellent vehicle from which to carry forward various methods and procedures. Unit planning lends itself to effective health instruction.

Unit types. Interest in units can be traced to the work of Morrison[*] who conceived of "the-thing-to-be-learned" as a learning unit. It may be aspects of the environment, an organized science, an art, or a conduct. Thus a unit may be regarded as a coordinated series of learning experiences directed toward a recognized goal or goals. The goal may be set by the teacher or the children or by the cooperative efforts of both. Always, however, the student should understand the goal and accept it as worthwhile.

A unit is more than a convenient subdivision of subject matter. It is an integrated unified whole experience. It may cut across many interrelated fields or areas. It provides opportunities for a variety of activities and thus satisfies fundamental interests and drives. Learning situations are inherent in a unit, and there are opportunities to use fundamental academic and social skills. Three basic types of units are recognized.

1. *Subject matter units* harmonize with a subject matter curriculum. They are organized and developed in terms of sequence and emphasis of subject matter. They stress facts and skills, particularly in handling facts. These units may be well organized in precise outline form because the

---

[*]Morrison, H. C.: The practice of teaching in the secondary school, Chicago, 1931, University of Chicago Press.

subject matter itself is of a rigid pattern. Subject matter units may be survey units, problem units, topical units, or generalized units. Subject matter units frequently lack flexibility. However, some teachers who use this type of unit provide for activities and experiences which contribute effectively to growth in terms of adaptation to the situations of life. In this respect the unit offers both experience and problem-solving aspects.

2. *Experience units* may be called *center-of-interest units* and are what the youngsters actually experience in classrooms. This unit is characterized by planning what to teach and planning as an outgrowth of children's needs, interests, motives, and abilities. Opportunities are provided for student leadership and cooperation in group enterprises. The experience unit approximates normal life outlets and provides for integrated purposive stimulating growth in adaptation. Many teachers prefer to call these adaptation units, project units, problem units, or activity units. Actually subject matter and resource units may use projects, problems, and activities.

3. *Resource units* are devised to present a variety of topics, objectives, facts, general content, activities, motivating devices, interest-stimulating measures, teaching procedures, resources, evaluation instruments, and integrating experiences from which selection can be made by the teacher. Usually the unit has far more material than the teacher will cover. Resource units are built by a committee of teachers, a curriculum workshop, a curriculum laboratory, special-area team, supervisor, or a teacher.

Resource units in health should be designed in terms of health promotion in keeping with the interests of the children for whom the experience is intended. They should be directed to outcomes which are meaningful and important in terms of health promotion and the growth in ability to make decisions relating to health.

Resource units can incorporate the elements of experience, adaptation, projects, problems, activities, and even of subject matter units. They allow for flexibility and variation. They permit the use of the particular talents of each teacher and allow for a variety of procedures and techniques. Resource units provide for planning, implementation, and evaluation. They allow for exploration into other areas and for further investigations in the central area. They meet the various needs, interests, and abilities of the different students in a typical classroom.

Unit format. Various patterns of unit construction are in use. Perhaps no one format serves all purposes. Of the several patterns in use, two lend themselves especially to the needs of most health teaching.

Unit Format A

I. Title	IV. Objectives
II. Overview of area	V. Content and activities
III. Resources	VI. Evaluation

Unit Format B

I. Title
II. General objectives
III. Specific objectives
  1. Knowledge
  2. Practices
  3. Attitudes
  4. Direct health benefits
IV. Study—outline guide
V. Activities
  1. Group discussion
  2. Dramatization
  3. Panel
  4. Symposium
  5. Field trip
  6. Practice and demonstration
  7. Construction
VI. Evaluation
  1. Knowledge tests
  2. Practices surveys
  3. Health improvement indices
VII. Resources
  1. Books
  2. Pamphlets
  3. Bulletins
  4. Journals
  5. Films, slides, and filmstrips
  6. Agencies

Teaching methods or procedures

Method is a systematic plan for presenting instructional material. It is a definite system of procedure. Thus we speak of the lecture method, the problem method, the project method, individualized instruction method, and a number of others. Actually the prevailing concept of what constitutes method in teaching changes from year to year.

Procedure is a mode of conducting a course of action. In education if procedure differs from method, it is a difference in form rather than a pronounced one. Perhaps most educators conceive method as being a broad type of systematic procedure. At the other pole a limited mode of action would be termed a procedure. Between the two poles a selection of one of the terms would be difficult at best. It is of minor consequence whether a systematic mode of instructional action is called method or procedure. The important consideration is that the mode of action provide an effective avenue of instruction.

Technique refers to the specific manner or means an individual uses in executing or accomplishing something. It is a personalized way of doing a task. One teacher uses one particular technique for bringing out the importance of some factor, and another teacher uses a vastly different means for attaining the same result.

Educators long ago ceased to look for the one best method. A procedure which is particularly adapted to one teaching situation may be totally inadequate or unsatisfactory for another purpose. Individual teachers find that they teach most effectively by using certain methods and become partial to certain procedures. A teacher may be pleasantly surprised by their effectiveness once other means of teaching have been explored. Experimentation and variety make teaching more stimulating and indicate professional vitality.

Types for health instruction. Perhaps a skillful teacher can apply all the known teaching methods to health instruction. However, certain methods or procedures have proved to be especially applicable to situations in the health instruction program. In the discussion of these procedures no attempt at elaborate evaluation will be made. Instructors can best evaluate the procedure in actual practice. An alphabetical sequence is helpful for reference.

Anecdote is the use of a biographical sketch of an outstanding health figure or the account of some event such as the building of the Panama Canal. It can be particularly effective in creating an interest in health study.

Audiovisual aids have been developed because the importance of both visual and auditory stimuli is recognized. Audiovisual aids make abstractions tangible and replace verbalization with concrete experience. These aids include the use of models, charts, graphs, pictures, exhibits, samples, recordings, slides, film strips, films, radio, television, and printed material. Visual aids are preceded and followed by discussion.

Random use of visual aids is too common. Although of value, indiscriminate use of audiovisual aids fall far short of their potential. These aids should be selected for their contributions to the recognized objec-

Fig. 38. Motivation in health practices. Even little people can benefit healthwise from a simple poster designed to bring to their attention constantly the need to follow certain health practices.

tives of the health program. They should be meaningful, accurate, appealing, adapted to the particular grade level, and justify the time, effort, and expense involved. Rather than itemize distinctive audiovisual aids, an integrated presentation of such source materials by subject areas is included in Appendix A.

Chalkboard exercise in which several students at the chalkboard diagram the manner in which disease is spread or answer questions raised by the class or teacher may be a stimulus to originality. Sharing can be real.

A *buzz session* is a modified type of conference and is also referred to as a cloister discussion. It is a device for dividing a large group into small groups. It can be used to deal with a difficult question which requires judgment, setting of values, or a clash of interest. The class is divided into groups of five or six members. Each group is seated in a small circle, and members of the group exchange ideas. All groups may have the same question to consider, or each group may have a different question. A buzz session lasts about ten minutes. By that time each group has crystallized its thinking, and a spokesman for each group submits a report to the class. Thus in a very short time a buzz session can solve difficult problems, answer complex questions, evaluate action, and, above all, get everyone into the activity.

Competition in the classroom can be wholesome, but too frequently the negative aspects outweigh the positive factors. Competition with oneself or with a standard can be wholesome and effective teaching. Whenever competition or rivalry between students develops in a classroom, it is advisable to guide and channel interest into cooperative enterprises.

Conference of students in learning is especially valuable in stimulating student initiative and cooperative action. Committees of five or six students working on phases of a special problem can explore the different aspects of their task, through research collect data, analyze the data, draw a conclusion, and report their experiences and recommendations to the rest of the class. Perhaps several days will be required for the task.

Counseling provides very effective health teaching through the individualization of instruction, especially in connection with personal health problems of the deepest personal concern. This procedure is valuable in helping a student to see his personal health problem and the course of action necessary for a solution.

Construction, such as a replica or model of a dairy farm or a simple microscope, employs many phases of learning. Most important is the motivation which comes from such participation or learning by doing.

Demonstration by exhibiting and describing a process or operation must be handled skillfully if it is to be an effective learning experience for the group and not assume the role of entertainment. When the demonstration is well done by a student or students, this method is doubly valuable. A review and even a spot test could reveal the effectiveness of the demonstration.

Fig. 39. Demonstration of body mechanics. Novelties that provide opportunities for building or making something constructive can add to pupil interest and provide increased effectiveness in learning. (Courtesy Corvallis Public Schools, Corvallis, Ore.)

Fig. 40. Dramatization complementing construction. Several teaching procedures can be combined to produce more effective learning.

Division of the class is rarely thought of as a teaching device, but practical considerations at times make it necessary to divide for effective learning. In dividing a class care must be exercised so that the two groups do not disturb each other. The sharing of experiences and accomplishments has a value worth exploiting.

Dramatization through class performance or the performance of others can be a valuable experience in health education. The use of class-made puppets in health dramas serves several purposes. Published health plays or health skits created by the children can have health education possibilities, but method should not distract from the core purpose—health education. In the elementary school, health plays which require parts for all the members of the class are recommended.

Drill or intensive repetition sometimes may be necessary to learning, but it need not be monotonously boring. The law of diminishing returns soon sets in. Interest is kept alive by spacing the drills and interspersing them with games or tricks.

Examinations can be more than measures of achievement. They can measure progress and can be a valuable learning experience, especially if they introduce opportunities for applying the new-found knowledge to new situations. In addition a first test can determine the level of progress. If the teaching which follows takes into account the needs of the children as revealed by the test, repeating the test or giving a comparable test will indicate how effective the teaching was.

Excursions or group trips usually serve several educational objectives, often to exclusion of health education which frequently can be incorporated into the learning experiences associated with the journey. Health practices, safety measures, environmental conditions including food services, regulations designed to safeguard the citizen, as well as other factors can be opportunities for functional health education. Advance planning, including class discussion, can prepare the youngsters to be alert for health factors as well as other factors they observe. Discussions during the excursion and a review after returning to the classroom contribute to the fullest utilization of the experience.

Exhibits and even exhibitions are frequently questioned as being of value in health instruction. If the display is only an isolated island for sheer promotion purposes, it is unjustified. Yet if the display grows out of interests and experiences, it can have instructional value.

Experiments, both laboratory and field studies, motivate the students and can provide lasting learning. Nutrition experiments with animals have become rather passé, but studies using the students as subjects will identify the health factor with the student himself. Surveys of health factors in and about the school, the neighborhood, and the entire community can be fascinating to these future community leaders. Some of the teaching units presented in subsequent chapters will contain suggested studies.

Field trips such as visits to health departments, food processing plants, dairies, water treatment plants, and other points of health interest will have the most value if they are preceded and followed by a group discussion.

Forum or an assembly to discuss a health matter of general or public concern can be highly effective in arousing interest in a health question of general consequence. "What should be this school's policy on matters of student safety?" "What are the responsibilities of each student in safeguarding the health of all other students?" These and similar broad, yet specific, questions discussed in an open forum present opportunities for more than just direct instruction in health. Two or more classes can meet jointly, or a single class can conduct its own student-directed forum.

Group analysis in which sheer reasoning is used can be a challenging experience for children. Analyzation of the rights of human beings as they share in the advances of health science can be provocative in nature and meaningful in terms of experience in analysis.

Group discussion in the form of free general discussion by the class members and the teacher permits participation by most, if not all, members of the group. Skill in bringing out responses from reticent class members is especially valuable. Student leaders should be used whenever feasible.

Guest participants are highly recommended for instruction in health procedure. Participation of a member of the health department staff, a physician, or a medical technician interested in a particular health matter can bring vitality to the class. Any guest appearance merits special preparation and follow-up.

Homogeneous grouping, as a purely temporary measure, on a basis of ability may be justified, especially if each group has something to contribute to the other groups as a result of its unique experience.

Independent study, such as permitting outstanding students or groups to carry on self-propelled study, is commendable. By thus enriching the curriculum for the superior student, the teacher may replace a stultifying situation with a challenging one. Teacher guidance is desirable. As a result of his explorations the superior student should have something to contribute to his classmates in the form of a report or demonstration.

Individualization of teaching is the ideal. It is not feasible to individualize instruction completely in most public school situations, but a certain degree of individualized instruction is both possible and desirable. A child with special difficulties can be well on his way again with just a small amount of assistance. Theoretically complete individualized learning is ideal if self-growth is the mode of education. Practically, spot individualized instruction is effective.

Laboratory situations lend themselves to effective learning. Even the fumbling, wasted motion, and trials and errors of the laboratory have value, provided the laboratory session is not just a matter of mechanically following a set of instructions. Laboratory should mean opportunities to explore and think and to experience the joy of discovery. The emphasis should be on labor, not oratory.

Lecture, the traditional didactic method, in many instances represents passivity on the part of the student. When it is challenging and stimulating and if it is supplemented by other procedures, the lecture has value.

Lecturette is a short informal explanatory lecture at the beginning of a session. It can be an effective way to initiate class activity. The teacher will lead up to the main issue or question and at that point leave the matter with the class. It is apparent that the lecturette is followed by some other procedure.

Oral presentation should be used frequently. The experience of presenting an oral report to the group is a real opportunity to develop a highly valuable skill. It is particularly important that a student be well prepared and that he be given proper encouragement and praise.

Panel discussion in the form of a planned conversational exchange of ideas on a subject gives the participants a valuable experience in which the class shares in the thinking brought out by the active participants. Some panels take on too authoritative an air and thus diminish their contribution to all concerned.

Problem-solving is a realistic life-type approach. A realistic health problem can be a challenging learning situation. Since life involves the

Fig. 41. Safety in the community—safest routes and location of through streets and traffic lights and signs. The importance of safety knowledge, skills, and attitudes warrants the development of extensive and ingenious teaching procedures and devices. (Courtesy Portland Public Schools, Portland, Ore.)

need for repeated problem-solving, this method is surely in keeping with the school's professed goal of preparing the youngster for the life he will live. Problem-solving includes the following:

1. Discriminating observation
2. Identifying the problem
3. Proposing a hypothesis or possible solution
4. Designing a study or means for testing the hypothesis or solving the problem
5. Obtaining accurate extensive data
6. Analyzing and interpreting the data
7. Drawing a tentative but definite conclusion
8. Applying the conclusion to the immediate situation
9. Appraising the results
10. Projecting the conclusion into further possibilities

Programmed instruction perhaps should be considered a teaching technique rather than a procedure. This holds true particularly with intrinsic programming, but it is true also in linear programming. Either form of programming is basically an application of sequential learning, whether a textbook approach is used, an opaque projector is used, or machine teaching is utilized.

Intrinsic programming is based on the fact that a student's choice of an answer to a multiple-choice question can be used to direct him to new material. In a Tutor Test (TM) format the student is given a brief discussion of what is to be learned, followed by a multiple-choice question. Each answer has a page number next to it. The student chooses his answer and turns to the indicated page number. If his answer has been the correct one, the page to which he has been referred will contain the next unit of material and the next question. When he chooses the incorrect answer, the page to which he is referred will have an explanation of why this answer is incorrect and will instruct the student to return to the original page to try another answer. He will not get to the next unit until he has selected the right answer.

In the linear technique the student is given a short presentation of new material and is required to make an immediate response, perhaps by writing a word, a phrase, or a sentence. By turning to the next page he then compares his response with the correct response and is rewarded by finding he has answered correctly. Materials generally are presented in a way which, in all likelihood, the correct answer will be elicited. Errors are few in a well-developed program and thus are disregarded.

Rather than textbooks or other constructed formats, opaque projectors can be used. Discussion material is thrown on the wall for all students to read. Test questions are then thrown on the screen, and each student makes his choice. Then follows the correct response. Perhaps a brief explanatory confirmation is included. Teaching machines are used to facilitate the process of programmed instruction and can contribute to this technique.

Science and mathematics have used programmed instruction with some degree of success. Health teaching may be done effectively through this medium, and experimentation with programming should be done. Any decision on the merits of this medium for health teaching should await a fair and extensive test of its possibilities. Individual classroom teachers may be too busy to develop the necessary materials, but publishers are interested in turning out the necessary books or other materials for programmed instruction. This may be a fertile field that health educators should begin to till.

Project method offers originality and self-direction. To recognize and define a health problem or enterprise which merits study are the first requirements in a project, By agreement with the teacher, the student or the special group undertakes to make a complete study of the various aspects of the problem. Surveys, studies, discussions, and other experiences are brought to bear upon the task.

Recitation or class quiz is the traditional practice of batting the ball back and forth between teacher and students in sort of an academic ping-pong game. The quiz can be made vital if it is used as a device for review. Too often it is used as a pressure scheme to force students to study.

Report of specially prepared written material on a subject after exhaustive study is a truly valuable learning procedure.

Fig. 42. Promotion of special programs. Bulletin board in the main hallway to stimulate special interest. This bulletin board is used as a focus for all special programs in the building. (Courtesy Corvallis Public Schools, Corvallis, Ore.)

Research is an especially worthwhile experience for superior students. Health lends itself to elementary research. Surveys, statistical studies, and laboratory experiments can be designed.

Review is an essential in most teaching situations. The value of review lies principally in its integrating possibilities. In addition it helps self-appraisal by the students.

Social participation, such as to serve as a member of the health department, to operate the water treatment plant, to work in a dairy plant, or to assist in the chest x-ray program, is a vital learning experience.

Sociodrama is more than a vicarious substitute for reality. A true example of the use of the sociodrama in teaching is to conduct a courtroom trial in the classroom to consider whether a certain condition is a health hazard and should be declared a health nuisance. The situation must be realistic and have a definite learning goal or goals to be effective.

Student conduct of the class is a maturing experience. Entire preparation for the conduct of the class can be left to the students at various times. Opportunities for growth of the students are inherent in any procedure which places responsibility on them.

Study guide, outline, special forms or lists, and syllabus can be of value as a replacement for lectures. Students may become conditioned to rely too much on such devices. The student needs to learn to organize, plan, and assemble his own procedures and materials.

Symposium consists of several persons each of whom gives a report, explanation, or viewpoint on one particular phase of a topic and tends to make the treatment of the topic more complete than does the panel discussion. A symposium-panel incorporates the features of both by providing a free exchange discussion after the symposium.

Team teaching is a method in which two or more instructors or resource people conduct a class. Since all are specialists, team teachers can both supplement and complement the abilities of each other. Team teaching involves added instructional cost, but for selective purposes, the added cost can be amply justified by the expansion of student learning that this procedure affords.

Television perhaps properly should be considered as one use of audio-visual aids. Yet in a sense teaching through television has aspects that identify it as a procedure as contrasted with radio teaching which has either been the use of the lecture or of dramatization.

Where the schools have available television stations, the school system can develop a complete televised health course. This has been done satisfactorily on the college level. Where such sending facilities are not available, schools can watch for programs in the health field which are to originate from commercial stations.

Health knowledge coming from the rather novel medium of television can have a special appeal and be highly stimulating and extremely effective. In addition to the motivation which television can provide, it can supplement traditional classroom teaching, particularly when experiments are shown and health authorities participate in the television program.

There is one important opportunity for effective lasting health education which commercial television and radio provide which teachers should utilize to the fullest extent. This is the opportunity to develop youngsters into critical listeners and viewers and by this means prepare future adults who will be critical of health claims on radio and television. Group discussions of radio and television commercials having health significance can develop the practice of applying reasoning to what is presented rather than be misled by the half-truths, exaggerations, distortions, and even deception sometimes used by radio and television advertisers. This would be health education of the highest order.

The possibilities of combining various instructional procedures are almost limitless. Modifications are also possible. By giving thought to the area to be considered and the desirable objectives to be gained, the health instructor can visualize the procedure or procedures which will best serve the purpose. However, a wise teacher will incorporate the interests and ingenuity of the children in the planning and in its implementation. Diversity in teaching methods can mean effectiveness in teaching results.

Selected readings

American Association for Health, Physical Education, and Recreation: School health practices in the United States, Washington, D. C., 1961, The Association.

Association for Supervision and Curriculum Development: Toward better teaching, a report of current practices, 1949 Yearbook, Association for Supervision and Curriculum Development.

American Association of School Administrators: Choosing free materials for use in the schools, Washington, D. C., 1955, National Education Association.

Bayles, E. E.: Democratic educational theory, New York, 1960, Harper & Brothers.

Beyrer, Mary K.: The significance of current trends in school and college health programs (doctoral dissertation), 1959, The Ohio State University, Columbus.

Brood, H. S.: Building a philosophy of education, New York, 1954, Prentice-Hall, Inc.

Brown, J. W., Lewis, R. B., and Harcleroad, F. F.: A-V instruction: materials and methods, New York, 1959, McGraw-Hill Book Co., Inc.

Brubaker, J. S.: Eclectic philosophy of education, New York, 1951, Prentice-Hall, Inc.

Brubaker, J. S.: Modern philosophies and education, Chicago, 1955, University of Chicago Press.

Burton, W. H.: The guidance of learning activities, ed. 3, New York, 1952, Appleton-Century-Crofts, Inc.

Byrd, O. E. School health sourcebook, Stanford, Calif., 1955, Stanford University Press.

Cantor, N.: The teaching-learning process, New York, 1953, Holt, Rinehart & Winston, Inc.

Curriculum and Instruction Committee of the Rocky Mountain Study Council: Guidelines for the selection of programed materials, University of Denver.

Dale, E.: Audio-visual methods in teaching, New York, 1954, Holt, Rinehart & Winston, Inc.

Dent, E. C.: The audio-visual handbook, ed. 6, Chicago, 1949, Society for Visual Education, Inc.

Educational Policies Commission: Education for all American children, Washington, D. C., 1948, The Commission.

Finn, J. B., Perrin, D., and Campion, L.: Studies in the growth of instructional technology. I. Audio-visual implementation for instruction in the public schools, 1930-1960, Paper no. 6, Washington, D. C., 1961, National Education Association.

George Peabody College for Teachers, Division of Surveys and Field Services: Free and inexpensive learning materials. Nashville, Tenn., published annually, The Division.

Gladston, I.: Motivation in health education, American Journal of Public Health 39:1276, 1949.

Grout, Ruth E.: Health teaching in schools, ed. 4, Philadelphia, 1963, W. B. Saunders Co.

Haag, Jessie H.: School health program, New York, 1958, Henry Holt & Co., Inc.

Haas, K. B., and Packer, H. G.: Preparation and use of audio-visual aids, ed. 3, New York, 1955, Prentice-Hall, Inc.

Harnett, A., and Shaw, J.: Effective school health education, New York, 1959, Appleton-Century-Crofts, Inc.

Kilander, H.: Evaluating health teaching, Journal of Health, Physical Education and Recreation 32: Nov., 1961.

Kinder, J. S.: Audio-visual materials and techniques, ed. 2, New York, 1959, American Book Co.

Lysaught, J., and Williams, C.: Guide to programed instruction, New York, 1963, John Wiley & Sons, Inc.

Mayshark, Cyrus: Critical analysis of attitude measurement in health education, Research Quarterly 29: April, 1959.

Moore, J., and Smith, W. I.: The role of knowledge of results of programmed instruction, Lewisburg, Pa., 1962, Bucknell University.

Mort, P. R., and Vincent, W. S.: Modern educational practices, New York, 1950, McGraw-Hill Book Co., Inc.

National Education Association and American Medical Association: Health education, Washington, D. C., 1961, National Education Association.

National Society for the Study of Education: Learning and instruction, the forty-ninth yearbook, Part I, Chicago, 1950, University of Chicago Press.

Noar, Gertrude: Freedom to live and learn. Techniques for selecting and developing units of learning in the modern classroom, Philadelphia, 1948, Franklin Publishing & Supply Co.

Nolen, J.: Personal hygiene guides, Minneapolis, 1955, Burgess Publishing Co.

Richardson, C. E.: Three test instruments for measuring health attitudes of college students, Los Angeles, 1959, University of California Press.

Ridenour, Nina: The children we teach, New York, 1960, Mental Health Materials Center.

Sands, Lester B.: Audio-visual procedures in teaching, New York, 1956, The Ronald Press Co.

Schneider, R. E.: Methods and materials in health education, Philadelphia, 1958, W. B. Saunders Co.

Silvern, C.: Introducing and operating programed instruction in large-scale systems, Los Angeles, 1962, Hughes Aircraft.

Spence, K. W.: Behavior theory and learning, Englewood Cliffs, N. J., 1960, Prentice-Hall, Inc.

Starr, H. M.: Today's pupil, health-informed or health-educated? Journal of Health, Physical Education and Recreation 25:18, 1954.

Steinhaus, A. H.: More firepower for health education, Washington, D. C., 1945, United States Government Printing Office, Office of Education Bulletin no. 2.

Strickland, Ruth G.: How to build a unit of work, Washington, D. C., 1946, United States Office of Education.

Tape recording in the classroom. In Handbook for teachers and administrators, St. Paul, 1952, Minnesota Mining & Manufacturing Co.

The Audio-Visual Research Institute: The audio-visual index, Detroit, 1961, The Institute.

Turner, C. E., Sellery, C. M., and Smith, Sarah L.: School health and health education, ed. 4, St. Louis, 1961, The C. V. Mosby Co.

Zirkes, Laura: Spurs to creative teaching, New York, 1960, G. P. Putnam's Sons.

Habits are first cobwebs, then cables.

—Proverb

Chapter 12

Elementary school health instruction

The school is not the sole agency which contributes to the health education of a child. Yet the core of health instruction must come from the school. Other health instruction should not be considered an embellishment of the program of the school, but an intensification and extension of what the school is doing. This is particularly true in terms of application and verification of what the school is presenting. The school must proceed upon the principle that it will provide optimum health instruction for the pupils and that other sources of health instruction will add to that optimum. This is altogether sound because some children have limited opportunities for health instruction outside of school.

In the elementary school, health instruction should be a meaningful experience of permanent value, not just an activity to occupy time. Learning does not have to be painful in order to be beneficial. Effective learning can be highly enjoyable. However, in our efforts to make health interesting and enjoyable, the means should not detract to the extent that it obscures the path of learning and distracts from the real purpose of the activity. Poster construction, puppet shows, and plays can be effective vehicles for health instruction, but, when the poster, the puppets, or the play "is the thing," little in the way of health education is derived. Health instruction must be an effective experience, not a delightful diversion. An elementary school teacher should resolve to affect the health of each child favorably.

Organizing for effective health instruction

Once the health curriculum or course of study has been established, the next logical step is the organization of the implementation of the curriculum. Health instruction must be fitted into the total school schedule. More than time is involved. Effective instruction requires that all possible teaching opportunities be included in the class organization. The schedule for health instruction should allow for planned teaching, incidental learning, correlation, and integration. Though flexible, the schedule must be sufficiently definite to ensure effective health instruction. Certain current practices in education indicate the principles which will guide scheduling for health instruction.

1. A weekly schedule provides for extended time periods and allows for necessary flexibility.
2. A daily health period is not required for health instruction.
3. Two fairly extended periods per week may be sufficient for health instruction in the primary grades and three periods a week will serve the intermediate grades.
4. A flexible schedule allows for continuation of an activity which is particularly challenging.
5. Opportunities should be provided for the varieties of activities health instruction entails.
6. When special health needs or interests require it, the schedule should be rearranged. Extra time invested in health instruction during one week can be followed by incidental instruction in the following week or weeks.
7. Opportunities for incidental and integrated health instruction should not be sacrificed to maintain a rigid schedule.
8. Correlation of health with other areas, to be effective, must be given a definite place in the organization for health instruction.

Health director's role. Properly the health director should be thought of primarily as a supervisor. Recent studies reveal that competent supervision more than justifies its cost in the added effectiveness which it gives to the school program. A supervisor who can help each teacher improve her services by 5% has made a considerable contribution. From the recognized past neglect of supervision, one very definite trend in education is the increase in supervision.

As a supervisor the health director helps the teacher to do a more effective job. In helping the teacher organize her health instruction program, the director gives her the benefit of his own professional preparation and experience as well as his knowledge of the total school health program. He becomes the key to the grade-to-grade integration of health instruction. He also is familiar with state requirements and resources. The health director does not hand the classroom teacher a schedule or plan for organization. He works the plan out with her or reviews her proposal with her and makes suggestions for improving the program. An experienced health director recognizes individual differences in teachers and accordingly recognizes that each teacher tends to organize her program in a pattern which best fits her particular abilities. Variation from grade to grade in the organization of health instruction is an indication of a vitalized program.

During the course of the year the director serves as a consultant for the teacher, aids in working out problems, and suggests new approaches which might be introduced. The director appraises the program both during the year and at the conclusion of the year.

Administrator's responsibility. If there is no health director, the principal should serve as a resource person for organizing health instruction. Some elementary school principals have an excellent health background and can provide highly valuable health supervision. However, principals with a very limited health background can be of assistance to the classroom teacher in resolving specific problems which may be particularly vexing.

Health resource person. Some elementary schools have regular staff members serve as resource people in music, art, geography, health, and other areas. Elementary school graduates with a minor in health are prepared for this. Other elementary teachers return to college during summer sessions to obtain a minor in health. This health resource person serves as a health consultant for the other teachers in the building. In some school systems such a resource person may serve more than one building, and some have eventually become health directors for the whole school system. The advisability of such a health resource person in an elementary school is obvious. If the present trend continues, most elementary schools will have a recognized health resource person on their staffs.

School health coordinator. An extension of the concept of a resource person in health is the creation of the role of school health coordinator, more generally for the elementary school, but applicable to the junior high school and the senior high school. The role arises from the recognized need to provide leadership to coordinate all school activities in the area of health. A coordinator in the building will make it possible to use more effectively all health resources and facilities in the school, the home, and the community.

A health coordinator is appointed by the principal or other administrative head of the school. In a large school the coordinator may have no other major responsibility. Or the coordinator may have regular classroom responsibilities, perhaps dividing the time between teaching and coordinator duties.

A health coordinator serves directly under an administrator (usually the principal) and frequently works with a health council or committee which assists in formulating general policies and which aids in the solution of problems requiring group consideration. Certain functions usually are the direct responsibility of the health coordinator.

1. Structure a coordinated over-all health program for the school
2. Furnish the staff with all necessary information regarding the total school health program
3. Serve as the line of communication between the school, the home, the health department, and the other sources in the community which contribute to child health
4. Develop a plan for keeping health records
5. Arrange for school health services

6. Provide procedures by which classroom teachers observe and report departures from normal child health
7. Assist teachers in assessing health needs of pupils and in interpreting policies and procedures to be followed in the event of pupil injury and illness
8. Provide specific procedures for effective referrals and follow-ups
9. Arrange for in-service health preparation for the teaching staff
10. Obtain and distribute to the teachers recommended health instruction materials
11. Arrange for the coordination and progression of health instruction from grade to grade
12. Provide for health counseling
13. Provide leadership in the promotion of healthful school living
14. Provide leadership in the promotion of safety practices and sanitation in the school
15. Arrange for periodic evaluations of the over-all school health program

A health coordinator should have academic preparation in personal, school, and community health, experience in health education, and, above all, a sincere interest in health promotion. On-the-job experience fanned by enthusiasm can flare into a highly effective health coordinator with a complete school health program which meets the present and future needs of the pupils.

In several states the use of health coordinators has become a well-established practice. It is of interest and significance that the State Board of Education in Oregon has passed a regulation that all schools *shall* appoint a health coordinator.

Classroom teacher's function. The classroom teacher is the key person in the organization and implementation of elementary school health instruction. Others may advise the teacher and assist in other ways, but, because of her strategic location, only the teacher is in a position to appreciate the total situation and the health implications inherent in it. Because she will direct children in learning, it is essential that she have a complete grasp of the health instruction plan and organization. If an inflexible plan and organization are handed to her, she is not likely to do an effective job of health teaching. On the other hand if she has been a prime figure in the development of a health instruction plan and organization, her familiarity with the *what, how,* and *why* of the program should make her contribution a more meaningful and effective one.

When the teacher is left to her own resources, she is justified in utilizing plans and programs which have been developed by others and then modifying and adapting them to her own classroom situation. These standard or developed programs should be a guide, not the inflexible unalterable procedures to be accepted *in toto.* The use of several sources may provide the teacher with the substance from which to organize her own health instruction. Whatever the approach or source of reference, the health needs and interests of the children in a particular classroom should be the focal center from which the program emerges. The health concerns and outcomes, in terms of the students, is the vehicle which propels the program. The guiding motive in the organization of health instruction is to provide students with opportunities to explore health concerns and to solve vital health problems.

Certain universal health needs and interests of pupils make it possible for a teacher to utilize available materials and apply them effectively to the immediate situation. Yet each group of children has need for special health emphasis or the consideration of a different type of health problem. For this reason, in a new situation an elementary school teacher might consider the organization of health instruction for a half year. A reappraisal at that time will indicate the strengths and weaknesses of the program and the modifications which are in order.

Classroom instruction

To motivate pupils sufficiently so that they want to establish desirable health practices is the ingredient which must run through all health instruction. Motivation is the catalyst of all teaching, but most essentially so in health teaching. Yet in a complementary vein health instruction lends itself rather readily to motivation when the established devices are employed.

Basic to motivation in elementary school health instruction is to give each pupil status in the classroom. A *team* concept, *us, we, all of us,* must permeate the atmosphere. This relationship within the group should be supported by a strong teacher-pupil relationship. Active participation in health projects is the need for all pupils. Neither passive nor vicarous participation will establish heath practices. Above all, an organic relationship of pupil to group and group to pupil must be maintained for effective health instruction.

Pride in oneself, in one's own accomplishments, and in one's own progress is in the nature of all of us. To fan this pride is to use a most effective means for initiating a health practice and for continuing the practice until it becomes ingrained in the pupil's mode of life. Appeal to pride in personal appearance can be as effective at the elementary school level as at adolescence if attention and praise are properly distributed.

Self progress reinforced by an understanding of that progress motivates the pupil in his quest for advancement. Competition with himself can be wholesome motivation for the pupil when realistic standards are the guide and he is guided in his appraisal of his advances, his plateaus, and his failures. Achievement which is visible to the child can stimulate him to further achievement. It may be necessary to help him see his achievement.

Unless the child identifies the matter of health instruction with himself, the whole opportunity for education has been missed. He must be the center of action, the vital element of greatest consideration. Moreover, he should feel this and be stimulated by it. This is germane for any teaching situation to be effective.

At all times the elementary school teacher should direct health instruction toward the establishment of certain desirable health practices. Knowledge and attitudes can grow out of the establishment of health practices and contribute to the formation and permanence of these practices. These practices should be related to recognized factors in health such as play and rest, vision promotion, hearing protection, care of the teeth, cleanliness, general appearance, use of the toilet, avoiding infection, work practices, sleep, safety at school, safety at home, going to and from school, bicycle safety, fire safety, water safety, courtesy, self-reliance, self-discipline, and social adjustment. Specific practices will be listed in units and other sources which follow, but the teacher with some degree of ingenuity can develop a list of practices suited to the particular group of youngsters in the room.

In a well-organized system-wide health program certain specific health practices should be common to all elementary schools as a guide in health education. This common core of practices will provide continuity and intensification. It will assure some measure of permanence in health practices. In an elementary school in which teachers are in agreement on what health practices should be established, the health program is assured of reasonably effective long-time results. Besides the reinforcing effect of such an established program, the likelihood of omissions is reduced if not virtually eliminated.

Various approaches to health instruction are in general use. Each has merit and can be used to advantage when adapted to particular needs and situations. Four approaches are of special interest.

1. Integrated living as health instruction
2. Direct planned formal and informal instruction
3. Incidental instruction
4. Correlated health instruction

Since all four approaches have special attributes and merits, the prudent elementary school teacher utilizes all four in conducting an effective health instruction program. Together the four approaches tend to ensure the maximum in effective health instruction.

Integrated living as health instruction

Life is not cast in a mold of isolated islands or separate compartments. Interwoven in each child's daily activities are health implications, values, and factors. All adaptation that pupils make has implications of either mental or physical health. In some activities health occupies a prominent role and in others assumes a lesser role. Yet whether it occupies a major or minor role, if the opportunity for health instruction is fully developed, the resulting health education can be both effective and lasting. If learning is a meaningful functional experience, it becomes an established integral part of the mode of living of a child—the true goal of the school.

Pupil-teacher relationships. No one has objectively measured the specific influence of a particular teacher upon a given pupil. Yet there is ample evidence that the teacher can tangibly modify the child in a beneficial way. Perhaps no phase of the school health instruction program can have a more beneficial lasting effect than the teacher's interest in and encouragement of each child's health. The approval of his teacher in matters of health can develop the self-interest in health which is so necessary to the promotion of personal health. From such experiences will develop worthy health goals which, because of self-esteem, each person will strive to maintain. A teacher makes a lasting wholesome impression when she recognizes and commends the child's cleanliness, appearance, dental care, posture, safety measures, dietary practices, courtesy, thoughtfulness, social adjustment, vitality, bouyancy, and general development. To the child, health truly becomes a matter of personal concern and gratification. It is the seed from which will develop a life-long interest in personal health promotion.

Most teachers are vitally interested in the well-being of school children. However, it is a passive lazy interest and should be replaced by a positive attitude which is expressed by interest in the child's health and his efforts in its behalf. Could there be a more worthy outcome of the total program of the school than students with a wholesome concern for their own health and with the necessary preparation to make the decisions which relate to their health and that of their families? Pupil-teacher relationships provide the most effective means for motivating children to accept responsibility for the promotion of their own health.

School experiences. Many school activities with health aspects provide opportunities for effective education. Quite often the instructional opportunities are missed completely. Perhaps more frequently, the experience is given cursory treatment. An alert teacher not only utilizes the unusual event for instructional purposes, but also recognizes opportunities for health instruction in the regular program.

There are many opportunities in daily school experiences to apply health knowledge. The acts of coming to school and going home involve problems in safety for pedestrians, for bicycle riders, for the general traffic, and for bus riders. Within the school, safety is an ever-present problem. Lighting, ventilation, cleanliness, dental health, posture, activity, rest, lunchroom practices, and social problems provide a diversity of opportunities for learning and its application.

Unusual experiences can have health implications of instructional value. The illness of a child can have learning value for classmates if the teacher directs the learning into constructive channels. An appendectomy can be discussed in terms of early indications, the desirability of avoiding self-diagnosis and self-medication, the need for immediate medical care, the effectiveness of modern medicine, and the importance of relying upon the physician to restore health. Thus the fact that it is the individual who

Fig. 43. The positive and negative. Mental health can be portrayed pictorially with a little ingenuity. This bulletin board is more than clever. It is intensely meaningful as well as artistic. (Courtesy Corvallis Public Schools, Corvallis, Ore.)

promotes health and the physician who restores health can be re-emphasized.

If one child in the class wears glasses because a physician has advised him to, the wisdom of wearing glasses can be emphasized by a wholesome class study of the problem. If the situation is dealt with openly, the supposed onus which youngsters may associate with glasses is removed. The children can learn that wearing glasses is not a stigma, but the badge of a person who is wise enough to use the fruits of modern science, just as a wise persons uses other modern inventions.

Occasionally sensitive circumstances which relate to health arise in the school. If the teacher is not sure what to do, discretion would dictate that she do nothing. After extended deliberation she may devise a means of using the event for instructional purposes. Perhaps the solution will be to consider related problems rather than the specific event. If a child has been hospitalized with tuberculosis, a discussion of the measures for control of communicable disease rather than of tuberculosis alone may be less disturbing but educationally just as valuable.

Many school experiences merit repeated consideration. A single discussion may create an interest, but not result in effective learning. Correlation of the factors in two or more experiences adds interest to the discussion and provokes thinking.

Fig. 44. Statistical presentation. To make comparisons and percentages more meaningful, the use of figures can be effective. Using a main hallway display case adds to the interest. (Courtesy Salem Public Schools, Salem, Ore.)

Community experiences. Events in the community may be a concern of school children. In the primary grades a pupil has only slight community interest, which tends to expand as he reaches the intermediate grades. If he does not have an interest in community events, it should be cultivated. If he does have a community interest, it should be propagated. Expansion of the municipal water facilities, construction of a sewage disposal plant, restaurant inspection, control measures for communicable disease, medical services, air pollution, safety programs, industrial health, recreation, and special health drives should be of interest to the future adults of the nation. Community health personnel can serve as a resource for stimulating the interest of children in community health.

Interest in local health can be projected to the state and nation. Children can acquire health understanding from epidemics, disasters involving health problems, new health experiments and discoveries, reports on the conquest of disease, extension of life expectation, and population growth. Indeed international health can be of interest to them.

Planned direct instruction

With the elementary school program fragmented as it tends to be, one wonders whether the situation might not be relieved by assigning no scheduled time for health instruction. Doubtless a few teachers, highly skilled in incidental, correlated, and integrated health instruction, may do an effective job of health teaching without a scheduled period for health, but most teachers will need definite scheduled time to provide the necessary core instruction. A daily period is not necessary, but a fairly extended period of thirty minutes twice a week for primary pupils and three periods a week for intermediate children should serve as a minimum for core health instruction if supplementary health teaching makes a reasonably strong contribution. Such scheduling does not make an inordinate demand upon school time. It would indeed be a dismal example of health instruction which would not justify this minimum amount of time. Usually time alloted to health is well invested, even with mediocre teaching.

If one seeks assurance that the health instruction program be effective, then one logically should make direct teaching the core of the instructional program. Other procedures can supplement direct teaching advantageously, but the base of the instruction pyramid would be direct teaching. It serves many purposes and has definite advantages.

1. It gives status to health as a subject area.
2. There is assurance of at least a minimum of emphasis on teaching.
3. Direct teaching provides an organized approach.
4. It deals with realistic specific needs.
5. A teacher of average ability can attain effective results.
6. Direct teaching tends to give emphasis to the positive aspects of health.
7. Direct teaching can be applied even with incidental teaching.
8. It can emerge from correlated teaching.
9. It can be channeled into integrated and other approaches.
10. Direct teaching provides for outcomes in terms of interpretations, values, and other attributes.

Planned direct teaching need not be drab and uninteresting. The imaginative teacher can use direct teaching as an adventure in health education. It can be as effective as it can be interesting.

Allocation and gradation. Emphasis for areas of special teaching should be allocated in the over-all plans for health instruction. The barometer must be the interests and needs of the children at each age level. This is especially important in health teaching because health instruction is effective when it begins with the child and a concern or problem of his. If he can conceive of a health problem as his, he will associate himself with it and it has a personal meaning. The most effective health education is achieved when a child considers it to emanate from him rather than to be imposed from above. Complexity of treatment is adjusted to the psychological level of the pupils. Interests of the students indicate levels of maturity.

Areas of emphasis. A teacher can obtain an overview of the health needs, interests, and problems from observing the children, from their questions, from observing school, home, and community life, from statements of parents, from the suggestions of health personnel, and from the school records. She will note that the tendency of a child in his early years to be very much an individualist is reflected in his health interests. Beginning in about the fifth grade, the tendency toward gangs begins to be expressed in an interest in group and community health.

Several studies have revealed the almost universal health interests and needs of children at various levels. An elementary school teacher can be guided by these studies if no other data are available. Where allocations of areas have been made on a school basis, results of these studies have frequently been used as a guide. Usually kindergarten and grades one, two, and three are grouped and grades four, five, and six given individual assignments of areas. It will be noted that the health of the individual is emphasized in the early years and community health is emphasized beginning with the fifth grade. Repetition and duplication are not necessarily objectionable. Certain duplications are inevitable, even desirable, but specific emphasis changes with the maturity of the pupil. Nutrition in the primary grades deals with a few simple dietary practices. In the intermediate grades an understanding of the *how* and *why* of certain nutritional needs are of interest to the pupils (see Table 18).

Motivation. A cue to all motivation in education is the natural human desire for self-gratification. Each pupil seeks self-status through attention, achievement, advancement, improvement, superiority, praise, and recognition. Motivation in health instruction should be relatively simple because health deals directly with a pupil's own welfare, but the whole experience must begin within the child if force and direction are to be given to him.

To promote self-identification in health, effort should be made to introduce each topic as a problem which is the concern of all who are present. By using a question as the vehicle, the problem should be launched with emphasis on *you, we, all* of *us,* or *you* and *I.* The question should include or imply self-improvement. How can *we* keep clean so that *we* always look nice? Out of this appeal to appearance and improvement will emanate subquestions of keeping the hair nice, having clean fingernails, and other specific activities of cleanliness. How can *you* keep *your* teeth healthy and looking nice? The approach can apply equally to *our* school, *our* community, and *our* nation.

Questions can serve various purposes in making the instruction effective.

1. Arouse curiosity, stimulate interest, and develop purpose
2. Prepare the pupil for learning by leading him to draw from his experiences what he needs and is concerned about
3. Cause the student to think and evaluate
4. Understand the pupil's thinking
5. Help the student to discriminate
6. Direct the pupil's attention to significant elements
7. Bring about new concepts
8. Lead the pupils to give expression to their thinking
9. Help pupils see the pathway which might be taken

Table 18. *Areas of emphasis*

Kindergarten and primary grades	Grade 4
Physical health	
Personal cleanliness	Vision and hearing
School cleanliness	Illumination
Rest and sleep	Ventilation
Eating practices	Clothing
Posture	Cleanliness
Play practices	Activity
Dental health	Dental problems
Lighting	Nutrition
Common cold	Preventing infection
Safety to and from school	Illness
Schoolroom safety	Avoiding poisons
Playground safety	Fire prevention
Home safety	Traffic safety
Body growth	
Mental health	
Sharing	Sportsmanship
Working together	Self-direction
Kindness	Confidence
Being friendly	Our friends
Orderliness	Being grown up
Depending on ourselves	Courtesy
Attaining goals	Accepting disappointments
Community health	
Home life	Family health
Sources of water and milk	Helping the neighborhood
Sunshine and health	Improving the neighborhood

Once the project is launched, guidance and particularly recognition are necessary. Since the child is gratified by his achievement, he has something to live up to, something to improve if possible. Self-status becomes a wholesome motivating force. Every child can achieve some degree of success in feeling well, in improving personal appearance, and in following recognized health practices.

Methods. The versatile teacher uses a diversity of methods and adapts teaching to the needs and purposes of the situation. Certain teaching procedures are specially adaptable to the elementary school level. These include group discussion, lecturette, counseling, construction, independent study, oral presentation, problem-solving, project method, reports, demonstration, dramatization, exhibits, field trips, and audiovisual aids.

In the kindergarten and primary grades the health instruction program can be based effectively upon the development of desirable health practices. "Things We Do" is the theme.

1. Wash the face, neck, and ears every morning
2. Wash hands before and after eating
3. Wash hands before leaving the toilet room
4. Keep the fingernails clean
5. Wash the scalp at least once a week
6. Keep the hair well groomed
7. Take a cleansing bath at least once a week

Grade 5	Grade 6
Physical health	
Appraisal of personal health	Bicycle safety
Personal health promotion	Safety patrol
Balanced diets	Health examination
Food preparation and care	Body function
Communicable diseases	Growth and development
Recreation needs	Grooming
Developing skills	Posture
Body development	Rest and sleep
Relaxation	Communicable diseases
Types of school accidents	Home and farm safety
Playground accidents	Emergency care
Fire prevention	First-aid procedures
Fire drills	Safety patrol
Mental health	
Family relationships	Interesting people
Peer groups	Personality
Loyalties	Emotional adjustment
Social status	Life goals
Emotional maturation	Self-improvement
Community health	
Home sanitation	Community disease control
Health advertising	Community water supply
Community safety program	Milk control measures
School sanitation	Community sanitation

8. Stand, sit, and walk tall
9. Get to bed on time each night: kindergarten and first grade, 8:00 P.M.; second and third grades, 8:30 P.M.; fourth grade, 9:00 P.M.; and fifth and sixth grades, 9:30 P.M.
10. Drink at least a half pint of milk with each meal
11. Eat fruit at least twice a day
12. Eat at least one green vegetable each day
13. Eat one other vegetable in addition to potatoes each day
14. Include proteins in each day's dietary
15. Brush the teeth immediately after eating and before going to bed
16. Visit the dentist at least twice a year
17. Keep fingers and other objects out of the mouth
18. Use a clean handkerchief to cover a sneeze or cough
19. Remain at home when ill
20. Be alert for hazards which may cause accidents
21. Follow all safety rules
22. Use proper light for all needs
23. Provide proper ventilation without drafts
24. Keep things orderly
25. Hang up wraps
26. Play out of doors at least one hour each day
27. Work together with others
28. Be friendly
29. Accept disappointments cheerfully
30. Finish tasks which are begun

In the intermediate grades the health instruction program can be effectively incorporated into the general theme of daily living. This is functional instruction at its best.

The use of health texts or health readers and other written materials can be effective when these materials serve as a source of knowledge for pupils and do not constitute the total sum of the health instruction.

Materials. The busy elementary school classroom teacher must obtain instruction materials for a multitude of purposes. To assemble materials for health instruction poses an especially difficult task because of the diversity of topics encompassed by the term health instruction. Because it is known that the busy teacher welcomes direct assistance in finding satisfactory health instruction materials, Appendix A is devoted entirely to resources in health instruction and also lists resource agencies. It is not suggested that these lists are all-inclusive and perfect in all respects. They have been assembled with considerable care and are offered as an aid to the teacher.

Two problems may be especially difficult for the elementary classroom teacher: What text should be used? Should commercially prepared materials for health instruction be used?

A textbook should be regarded as a reference. If textbooks are to be used in health instruction, certain standards in relation to health needs should then be met, in addition to the general criteria for all textbooks.

1. Primary emphasis should be on normal well-being.
2. Health principles should be stressed.
3. Discussion should be directed to the interests and needs of the pupils.
4. Personal appearance, physical health, and mental health are essential in the primary grades.
5. Community health should be included in the intermediate groups.
6. Very little physiology and less anatomy are needed.
7. An overview of each section can be of special value.
8. The literary style should be lucid and interesting.
9. Stimulating examples and original approaches add to the book's value.
10. Vocabulary should be adapted to the grade level.
11. A variety of suggested activities for pupils should be included.
12. Illustrations should be meaningful.
13. Graphs and charts should be such that the pupils can use them.
14. Suggestions for evaluation should be presented.

Commercial firms have turned out mountains of health instruction materials. Obviously the motivating factor has been the promotion of sales for their merchandise. Yet much of this material has been excellent—accurate, reliable, and well presented. If the firm has national operations and promotes its name and sales incidentally, the teacher should feel free ethically to use the material if it serves her purpose. The use of commercial health instruction materials which are produced or distributed locally may lead to certain complications.

Evaluation. In the final analysis the effectiveness of the health instruction program should be measured in terms of improved health of the pupils. This can be done to a limited degree both objectively and subjectively. Beyond this the teacher can observe and measure the effect of health instruction in terms of the child's conduct. Health practices, health attitudes, and health knowledge can be appraised in a practical way. Instruments for measurement will be presented in Chapter 17. Even in considering specific evaluation of the health instruction, the teacher can ask one cardinal question: Is each child building an *estate of health understanding* which will enable him to make the decisions necessary for health?

Resource unit—kindergarten and grade one*

I. UNIT—PERSONAL HYGIENE
II. OVERVIEW

Body care, clothes care, attitudes of self-appraisal to personal practices and posture

It would be difficult to produce valid evidence that personal cleanliness and grooming have specific physical health values. Washing the hands frequently with soap and water during an epidemic does reduce the likelihood of infection. Other than this, there is no acceptable evidence to indicate that daily washing of the hands and face has any physical health effect. Bathing weekly or daily does not have a discernible physical health value. However, concentration on personal cleanliness can be the avenue through which a child will be motivated to develop a wholesome intense interest in his own well-being. Pride in physical appearance is a source from which a whole spectrum of health attitudes can develop. Interest in one's own well-being is invaluable in health promotion and can be sparked through education in personal cleanliness.

Mental health and esthetic implications of bodily cleanliness and care are readily evident. Good appearance gives the child the self-status and self-gratification every normal human being seeks. The esthetic values of cleanliness lift life above the commonplace and give the child an incentive to seek the beautiful and the attractive in life. Establishing recognized practices in body care should be the primary goal in teaching in the area of body care and grooming. Knowledge and attitudes can develop as by-products of activities directed toward the establishment of desirable practices in body care.

III. GENERAL PURPOSE

Establish life-long practices in body care based on authentic knowledge and reinforced by positive attitudes of pride in personal appearance and body care

IV. PROCEDURES

A. Practices and activities
(Consideration should be given to students' ethnic backgrounds, home facilities, family financial means, parental attitudes and ingrained practices, and adjustment of practices and activities made accordingly)

---

*Courtesy Dr. Leon P. Minear, Superintendent of Public Instruction, Oregon State Department of Public Instruction.

1. Practices
   a. Before breakfast wash hands, face, neck, and ears with soap and warm water
   b. Before and after each meal wash the hands with soap and warm water
   c. Wash the hands with soap and warm water before returning from the toilet room
   d. Bathe at least twice a week
   e. Wash the scalp at least once a week
   f. Dry the skin by the proper use of towels and cleansing tissues
   g. Keep the finger nails trimmed and clean
   h. Keep the hair well groomed by using a comb or brush regularly
   i. Wear clothing indicated by weather conditions
   j. Keep clothes clean
   k. Keep clothes orderly
   l. Keep shoes clean
   m. Maintain proper body mechanics while sitting, standing, and walking
   n. Keep desks neat and clean
   o. Put litter in the right places
   p. Keep the school room orderly
   q. Use fountains properly
   r. Teacher appraisal of group practices and progress
   s. Pupil self-appraisal of cleanliness, orderliness, and body mechanics
2. Activities
   a. Washing before breakfast
      (1) Group discussion
         (a) Cleanliness values
         (b) How to wash properly
      (2) Demonstration
         (a) Washing hands, ears, and face
         (b) Drying the skin with towel and with cleansing tissue
      (3) Survey
         (a) Occasional count of how many washed properly that morning
         (b) Plans to improve performance
   b. Washing before and after each meal
      (1) Group discussion
         (a) Importance of washing before and after each meal
         (b) What to do when no washing facilities are available
      (2) Procedures
         (a) Before lunch, providing time for pupils to wash their hands on the way to lunch
         (b) Wash parade before lunch
         (c) Reminders (signs) in the lunch room to wash hands after eating
         (d) Wash more frequently during an epidemic
      (3) Survey
         (a) Spot checks on how many pupils wash their hands before and after all meals
         (b) Keep record on blackboard of improvement of the group
      (4) Construction
         (a) Cards made for pupils on which marks are made for the various cleanliness practices, e.g., washing each morning, before and after each meal, and before returning from the toilet room, cleaning finger nails, bathing, care of the scalp, grooming the hair, and keeping clothes clean and orderly
   c. Washing the hands after using the toilet
      (1) Group discussion
         (a) Importance of washing after going to the toilet

    d. Bathing
      (1) Group discussion
        (a) Importance of bathing
    e. Washing the scalp and grooming the hair
      (1) Group discussion
        (a) Washing the scalp properly
        (b) Combing and brushing the hair
        (c) Attractiveness of hair
        (d) Using one's own comb or brush
      (2) Demonstration
        (a) Proper methods for combing and brushing one's hair
      (3) Construction
        (a) Each child acquire a box or other container for his comb
        (b) Put up a charm corner with a mirror, table top, tissues where pupils may use their own combs, brushes, and nail files or emery board
        (c) Assign monitors to keep the charm corner neat and orderly
        (d) Collect color advertisements on cleanliness
    f. Use and care of clothes
      (1) Group discussion
        (a) Clothes for different seasons and occasions
        (b) Importance of clothing cleanliness
        (c) Care of clothes
        (d) Putting things away
        (e) Being neat, orderly, and attractive
        (f) Change of clothes
      (2) Demonstration
        (a) Hanging clothes
        (b) Folding clothes
        (c) Neatness in dress
        (d) Cleaning shoes
    g. Use and care of drinking fountains
      (1) Discussion
        (a) Proper use of fountain
        (b) Responsibility for neatness
        (c) Reporting fountain out of order
      (2) Demonstration
        (a) Use of the fountain
    h. Keeping desks and floor orderly
      (1) Discussion
        (a) Importance of neatness and cleanliness
        (b) Keeping desks orderly
        (c) Picking up litter from the floor immediately
      (2) Group project
        (a) Before recess, noon, and dismissal put desks in order
        (b) Pick up litter immediately and put in receptacle
B. Evaluation
  1. Teacher self-appraisal of procedures
    a. Am I helping pupils to recognize and accept responsibility for cleanliness?
    b. Am I helping pupils accept group responsibility?
    c. Am I providing pupils with opportunities for planning and participating in practices and activities relating to cleanliness?
    d. Are students manifesting the necessary pride in their own cleanliness and appearance?
    e. Are students making progress in their desire to improve themselves?

2. Student self-evaluation procedures
   a. On blackboard have "These things we do." At two-week intervals go over the list with the class. Use yes, no, or other rating such as dates instead of yes and no.

Yes	No	These things we do
_____	_____	1. Wash the hands, face, neck, and ears each morning
_____	_____	2. Wash the hands before and after eating
_____	_____	3. Wash the hands before leaving the toilet room
_____	_____	4. Keep the fingernails trimmed and clean
_____	_____	5. Wash the scalp at least once a week
_____	_____	6. Keep the hair combed or brushed
_____	_____	7. Take a bath at least once a week
_____	_____	8. Wear clean clothes
_____	_____	9. Keep clothing orderly
_____	_____	10. Keep shoes clean
_____	_____	11. Keep desks neat and clean
_____	_____	12. Keep floor free from litter
_____	_____	13. Keep the school room orderly
_____	_____	14. Use the drinking fountain properly

Resource unit—grade 2

As a vehicle for direct health instruction the integrated unit permits the use of various teaching procedures which grow out of recognized interests and needs of the pupils. If the unit is constructed for the primary purpose of establishing certain health practices, it will inherently include health attitudes and knowledge. The representative unit presented here is designed primarily to establish certain nutritional practices, but cleanliness, dental health, and table manners are associated with the experiences in eating which can fortify the nutrition practices and, in turn, can be established as part of a total aspect of life.

The unit can be introduced by questions which deal with feeling well, looking well, and growing. Out of the preliminary discussion will evolve the question, What foods help us feel best and grow best?

UNIT TITLE—WHAT FOODS HELP US FEEL BEST AND GROW BEST?

Objectives

Establish practice of washing hands before and after eating

Keep fingernails clean

Establish importance of regularity of mealtime

Practice drinking at least a half pint of milk with each meal

Eat fruit at least twice a day

Eat one green vegetable each day

Eat other vegetables every day

Eat whole-grained cereals and bread

Eat meat, eggs, or dairy products each day

Brush the teeth immediately after each meal and before going to bed

Visit the dentist at least twice a year

Choose a wholesome breakfast, lunch, and dinner

Use proper table manners

Promote an active interest in personal growth in height and weight

Create a pride and interest in personal well-being, appearance, and conduct

Activities
Group discussion

Why we all like to feel well
Why we all want to look nice
Why we all should learn to do things correctly
Getting ready for a meal
Why we should always try to be clean
Eating meals at regular times
Mealtime
Milk and growth
Milk and feeling well
Amount of milk to drink with each meal
Why coffee and tea are not good for children
Source of milk for each home
Care of milk
Cereals and whole-grained bread
Kinds of fruits—name all we know
Favorite fruits
Amount of fruits we should have each day

Learning about new fruits
Why babies should have orange and tomato juice
Kinds of green vegetables
Other vegetables
Favorite vegetables
Vegetables which should be eaten each day
Learning about new vegetables
Kinds of meat and dairy products
Meat, eggs, or dairy products every day
Meat, eggs, dairy products, and growth
Weight and height as signs of growth
Foods good for teeth
Why we should brush our teeth right after eating
How to brush the teeth
Toothpaste
How we care for our toothbrushes
Seeing the dentist

Construction

Collecting color advertisements on cleanliness
Color advertisements on milk
Color advertisements on fruits
Color adveriesments on vegetables
Color advertisements on meat, eggs, and dairy products
Color advertisements on care of the teeth
Making posters

Color fruit and vegetable outlined forms
Cutouts of sample meals
Exhibits of fruits and vegetables
Make toothbrush holders
Model of a dairy
Make a clock to indicate mealtime
Make a card shaped like a milk bottle to record height and weight

Dramatization

Wash parade before lunch
Demonstration of handwashing
Clean nails (with toothpicks)
Toothbrush parade
Fruit party
Vegetable party, with raw vegetables which can be eaten

Plan breakfast, lunch, and dinner
Play cafeteria
Play store
Buy food
Have a host and hostess at each table at lunch time

Field trips

Dairy
Grocery

Market
Farm

Evalution

Periodic survey of health practices
Observed attitudes of children toward
  Cleanliness
  Milk
  Fruit and vegetables
  Meat, eggs, and dairy products
  Care of the teeth

Knowledge test
  Oral
  Chalkboard with yes and no answers
  Vocabulary

Fig. 45. Selecting food for a balanced diet. A grocery store mock-up gives practice in the primary need in nutrition education—the selection of food. (Courtesy Portland Public Schools, Portland, Ore.)

Fig. 46. Study of a community, including produce from the farm to the consumer, foods in the store, and safety measures. Integrated teaching can be incorporated into broad interest units, as well as correlated teaching. (Courtesy Portland Public Schools, Portland, Ore.)

Many elementary schools are departing from the practice of using one central lunch room, and instead all children eat their lunches in their respective classrooms. This arrangement has excellent possibilities for health instruction. A wash parade before lunch, white napkins at the table or desk at lunch time, and a host and hostess each day have a marked effect upon table practices.

Resource unit—grade 4*

An excellent example of an integrated unit has been developed through the curriculum laboratory of the Portland, Oregon, Public Schools. With health programs as the core it provides for the integration of various subject areas which are normally included in the curriculum for the intermediate grades. The unit centers on problems with suggested activities and materials. Besides an evaluation and realistic outgrowth activities, the unit encompasses a considerable variety of suggestions for the classroom teacher.

UNIT TITLE: HOW SHOULD A TEN-YEAR-OLD CHILD MEET HIS HEALTH NEEDS?†

Overview

This unit has been prepared as resource material for the fourth-grade teacher. The problems and activities listed are suggestions to aid pupil-teacher planning in making the fourth-grade student aware of what he can do to meet his own health needs.

In this unit the child gains a knowledge of what constitutes good health practices. Through group planning he is able to face problems and arrive at a method of attack which thus enables him to assume more responsibility for his personal health and safety.

The subject of health constitutes an excellent center of interest for integrating arithmetic, language, reading, art, physical education, music, spelling, science, and social studies which are listed in the scope of the curriculum for intermediate grades. While learning about his nutritional needs, the student has an opportunity to gain a knowledge of the food habits in other cultural backgrounds. He learns to appreciate and to respect the culture of children of other nationalities who may be a part of his social group. Through home room activities he participates in preparing for picnics or parties and thus has opportunities to gain a positive approach to food, to know how interesting food can be, and to have the fun associated with purchasing, preparing, and eating food. He learns that good manners and happy living constitute a phase of healthful living. The problems and activities of the unit offer opportunities for the child to understand what people in the community are doing to safeguard his health and to appreciate

---

*This unit was developed by Mrs. Violet Jaross, with the help of the consultants and the supervisors.

†Courtesy Portland, Oregon, Public Schools.

their efforts in his behalf. The following quotation is an expressive summary.

> Wherever you are in the world,
> No matter who you are in the world,
> You must have the things you need;
> A home where your family can be,
> Friends to talk to,
> Food to keep the body strong,
> Clothing to keep the body warm,
> Work to make you of use to the world,
> Play to make your heart more gay.

Objectives

The child begins to realize the importance of the role of good health in daily living.

The child develops habits, attitudes, and understandings that lead to healthful living practices in the home, school, and community.

The child understands what helps him to grow.

The child understands the importance of nutrition, exercise, rest, fresh air, cleanliness, and posture.

The child understands how proper clothing, housing, and medical and dental care contribute to healthful living.

The child learns what the community is doing to safeguard his health and safety, and he understands his responsibility as a citizen.

The child learns the value of scientific contributions in the field of health.

The child understands the importance of health services available—weighing, measuring, dental inspections, physical examinations, and vision and hearing tests.

The child learns how to care for and to protect the special sense organs.

The child learns what to do in case of emergencies.

The child learns to understand where he can get help to meet his personal health problems.

The child accepts his share of responsibility in safeguarding his own health.

The child develops skills in the use of resource material—using books, reading for information, relating it to the problem involved.

The child becomes more skillful in expressing himself in reports, demonstrations, and stories; he broadens and enriches his vocabulary and spelling achievement.

The child participates in group planning, learns to appreciate the contributions of others, and develops intelligent self-direction in meeting problems of growth and development.

Concepts

Useful personal health habits are basic to the development of the individual in order that he may participate in and enjoy life.

Activities in health and safety provide opportunity to learn and to practice intelligent self-direction.

Personal and community health are interrelated, and each individual has responsibility for both.

Carelessness endangers life and health.

People have the same basic needs.

Community health services help to promote and protect the health of the people.

People depend upon others as they meet their health needs.

It is important to have clean safe places in which to live and play.

Our health needs include adequate food, shelter, clothing, rest, sanitary conditions, adequate medical and dental care, and recreation.

Great progress in the field of health has been made since the time of the Indians and
pioneers.

We all have responsibility in contributing to happy and effective community living.

A new traffic light in the neighborhood shows community growth in awareness of the
importance of safety in the neighborhood.

Initiating the unit

Through arrangement of the room including
  Specially arranged bulletin boards
  Attractive library arrangement featuring books on health and safety
  Centers of interest to stimulate discussion
    Exhibits
    Pictures
    Models
Through sharing experiences relating to health
  Discussion of visits to the family physician or dentist
  Discussion of home practices in eating, resting, sleeping, cleanliness, and recreation
  List ideas regarding safety
Demonstrations of handwashing procedures by public health nurse
Through related activities
Show films or slides, followed by discussion which leads to need for more information
  Art work expressing health ideas
  List health questions which need answers
Discuss current health practices such as program for vaccination for poliomyelitis or
  other scientific discoveries
Listen for questions that children ask or things that they discuss during any of the
  class activities

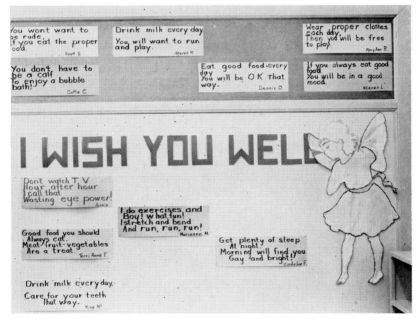

Fig. 47. Correlation of health with composition and art. A three-in-one project provides opportunities to emphasize health practices and fun in trying a hand at being a
rhymster.

Problems	Activities	Materials
I. How do we grow?	Ask three children volunteers to be weighed and measured and compare with their last record.	*How Your Body Works*
What do we need to help us to grow?	Talk about what may contribute to differences in height—illness, rate of growth, heredity, etc.	*Two Little Rats and How They Grew* *Growing Up*
Why are some fourth grade children sometimes taller than others?	Discuss rate of growth of different children. Why are they different? (Work on attitudes toward and understanding of stature and figure.)	*The Girl Next Door*, pp. 140-143 *Healthful Ways*, pp. 75-81
What foods help us grow?	Discuss and make reports on topic *How We Grow*. Read reference material on foods.	*Discovering Our World*, Book I, pp. 166-167
	Place Basic 7 chart on bulletin board. Discuss chart.	*Food for Health*
	Make pictures and charts.	*Good Eating Habits*
	Compare the foods of today with those of the pioneers and Indians.	*Fuel Foods* *A Clean Plate*
How does our school cafeteria plan a well-balanced meal?	Post daily cafeteria menu in room and discuss the menu in the classroom. Visit cafeteria.	Posters—dairy booklets
	Make posters of balanced meals and display in the cafeteria.	
	Have a talk by the cook of the cafeteria.	*Healthful Ways*, pp. 135-152
	Discuss the value of a host or hostess at the table.	*Safety Everyday*, pp. 26, 28, 30, 32, 40, 42
	Discuss and demonstrate approved table manners.	
	Dramatize pleasant conversation at a meal.	Dairy council materials
Why should we limit the amounts of sweets we eat?	Discuss why too many sweets may help promote dental caries.	*Useful Plants and Animals*
	Give a Bunny Party (children bring lettuce, carrots, celery, turnips).	*Milk We Drink*
What foods help us grow?	Discuss why coffee, tea, and soft drinks do not aid body growth.	*Growing Your Way* *Among Friends*
II. How should a fourth grade student care for his body?	Make a good grooming chart for classroom use.	*All Aboard for Health*
	Place a mirror at eye level in the classroom for self-inspection by pupils.	*Good Health Is Fun*, p. 1-58
Why should we keep our bodies clean?	Discuss being ready for school.	*Safety Everyday*, pp. 148-159

Problems	Activities	Materials
	Stress use of soap, water, and clean towels.	*The Pet Show*
		Care of the Skin
	Ask public health nurse to discuss importance of and show a good method of washing hands.	*Care of the Skin*
		Daily Health Inspection
	Demonstrate care of fingernails.	
	Keep individual cleanliness charts for two weeks.	*Care of Hair and Nails*
	Organize a 4-H health club.	*Billy Keeps Clean*
	Discuss availability of soaps and facilities for keeping clean now as compared with pioneer times.	*Public Health Nurse Dental Counselor*
		How We Are Built
How can we care for our teeth?	Ask the dental counselor to demonstrate the correct way to brush the teeth.	*Healthful Ways*, p. 95
	Talk about foods that help build strong teeth.	*Good Health Is Fun*, pp. 123-143
	Discuss teeth and how they grow.	
	Discuss the importance of regular visits to the dentist.	*The Girl Next Door*, pp. 122-132
	Discuss the reasons for dental inspection and how the dental counselor helps us.	
	Plan and give plays and dramatizations about visiting the dentist.	
		Visual aids
	Read stories of foods.	
How can our eyes do their best for us?	Show model of the eye.	*Safety Everyday*, pp. 92-115
	Discuss the reasons for the visual testing program.	
	Interview the public health nurse regarding care of the eyes.	
	Invite the public health nurse to talk about caring for and wearing glasses when necessary.	*The Girl Next Door*, pp. 150-153
	Discuss correct lighting and rest for eyes.	*Let's Look Inside Your House*
	Make a list of ways to protect the eyes.	
How can we best care for our ears?	Discuss structure and care of the ears.	*Safe and Sound*, pp. 164-174
		Sound
	Check out science kit on heat, light, and sound.	
	Make a simple drawing of the ear.	*Everyday Machines and How They Work*

Problems	Activities	Materials
	Use of tuning fork to demonstrate sounds.	*Good Health Is Fun,* pp. 172-174
	Discuss reasons for and cooperation necessary when when hearing tests are conducted with the audiometer.	*Public Health Nurse*
III. Why are exercise and rest helpful in building strong bodies?	List the games we play and the games we are going to learn to play.	*Physical Education in Elementary Schools*
		Healthful Ways, pp. 111-117
How does playing games help us grow?	Show how running, jumping, skipping rhythms, and other forms of play give us needed exercise.	*The Girl Next Door,* pp. 166-171
Why do we use various postures?	Discuss and dramatize postures for health and appearance.	*Stand Tall*
	Discuss dressing appropriately for the weather.	*Posture*
	Use shadow pictures to show good postures.	*Posture Habits*
	Check desk for size.	*Straight and Tall*
	Emphasize stand tall and sit tall. Make a poster.	*Health at Home and School,* pp. 22-45
	Discuss why we get tired.	
	Have demonstrations of useful postures.	*Growing Your Way,* pp. 11, 17, 157, 66-67, 238-156
How do we relax?	Play rag doll.	*All Aboard for Health,* pp. 114, 126, 127, 186, 187, 102
	Discuss how change in activity is restful.	
How can we tell when we're tired?	Discuss how we can tell when we are tired.	*Among Friends,* p. 155
	Discuss how pets play hard, then rest when tired.	*Safety Every Day,* pp. 56, 109, 11
How much sleep do children our age need?	List some reasons for getting enough sleep.	*Good Health Is Fun,* pp. 76-79
	Keep track of sleeping time for a week.	
	Plan dramatizations.	*The Girl Next Door,* p. 183
	Write short stories about the fun we can have at home, in the park, on a picnic, at school, etc.	*Sleep for Health*
		Sleep and Health
		Getting Ready for Bed
		Early to Bed

Problems	Activities	Materials
		Magic of Sleep ✓

IV. What do we do for recreation?

How can we spend our free time?	Make a list of recreational possibilities	
What books can we read?	Give book reports of favorite books. Secure and use a community library card.	Library
What are some interesting hobbies we might enjoy?	Plan a hobby show. Why do we have mountains, streams, and other natural areas?	*Good Health Is Fun,* p. 8
How did our scenery come to be the way it is?		*Health at Home and School,* pp. 133-142
What kinds of recreation do we have in our parks?		*The Girl Next Door,* p. 183
What are some radio or television programs that will bring us information, real pleasure, and enjoyment	Discuss enjoyable programs for fourth grade children. Discuss how frightening stories and strenuous games before bedtime may interfere with restful sleep.	*Healthful Ways,* pp. 60-61; 78, 43-45, 91 *All Aboard for Health,* pp. 113-116, 118 *Safety Every Day,* pp. 12, 15 *Among Friends,* pp. 239-241, 243-248, 89-92 *Growing Your Way,* pp. 28-29; 238, 169 *Safe and Sound,* pp. 268-269
V. What health services do we have?	Discuss the city and state bureaus of health and their services. Tell how immunization is part of a plan to control communicable disease.	*Safety Every Day,* pp. 50, 60, 66 *Growing Your Way,* pp. 165, 167-169, 171
What official services are provided for us?	Discuss the individual cooperation necessary to make it successful.	*Among Friends,* pp. 26, 42, 85, 86, 233-236
Why should we keep our streams clean?	Discuss why we should never say "just a cold."	
Should we swim in the river?	Read *Naughty Little Foxes* in *Stories We Like,* p. 53.	*Safe and Sound,* pp. 226-229, 234
What do various departments in the bureau of health do to help us?	Tell why one should be willing to give up some personal liberties for the protection of his own health and that of others.	*Health at Home and School,* pp. 200-204, 206-208

Problems	Activities	Materials

Good Health is Fun, pp. 228-230, 231-232

What school health services do we have?

Have a panel discussion on the topic *Clean Streams for Oregon.*

All Aboard for Health, pp. 217, 211, 65, 160

What personal health services are available to us?

Discuss the responsibility of official health agencies for maintaining health in the community.

Healthful Ways, pp. 195, 87, 95-100

What is our responsibility for keeping our surroundings clean?

Discuss how to help keep our homes, our classroom, and our school grounds clean.

The Girl Next Door, pp. 88-89, 59-62, 68-81, 107, 111, 129, 139

Make posters to discourage litterbugs.

Discuss the individual's responsibility for contributing to community health.

Naughty Little Foxes (colds), In *Stories We Like,* p. 53

Invite the health educator of the bureau of health to speak to class.

Pueblo Indian Stories
  Housing, pp. 2, 3
  Play, p. 6
  Water, pp. 15-16

Discuss sanitation in the state, city, and home. Tell how each one can contribute to healthful living.

Discuss reasons for inspection of milk, meat, and other foods.

On We Go
  Home With Mumps, pp. 22-41

Discuss reasons for mosquito control.

Discuss the functions of the public health nurse and the dental counselor. Invite representatives to speak to the class.

Compare these present services with those available to the pioneers.

Discuss part played by the family physician and dentist.

Discuss how we can cooperate with our family physician and dentist to maintain and improve our health.

Discuss how personal health contributes to community health.

Resources

Contact the city bureau of health and learn about the services available through:
  Division of food and sanitation
  Division of laboratories
  Division of meat inspection
  Division of milk sanitation
  Division of public health nursing
  Division of tuberculosis control
  Division of school health
  Bureau of insect control

City bureau of health

Sewage treatment plant

Municipal incinerator

Bureau of water works

Problems	Activities	Materials
	Visit the sewage treatment plant.	State board of health
	Visit the municipal incinerator.	
	Ask a representative from the water bureau to discuss the city water supply and show pictures describing it.	
VI. Why is safety a public health problem What organizations help to promote safety? How can we practice safety in our home? How can we be safe at school? How can we practice bicycle safety? How can we practice safety when riding on a bus? How can we practice safety on the street? How can we practice safety in our work and in our play?	Discuss service of the police department. Ask a police officer to speak to the class. Take field trip to police station. Discuss fire department. Work with the department's home check list. Discuss annual house-to-house inspection of fire department for fire hazards. Learn how to secure a permit to burn bonfires. Invite firemen to speak to class and demonstrate use of fire extinguishers. Discuss the function of the city traffic and safety commissions. Invite speaker. Discuss services of city and state bureaus of health. Write a skit showing cooperation necessary for real safety in the community. Conduct a panel discussion on responsibility for safety. Appoint a room steering committee to discuss ways to improve safety practices. Discuss safety in the home. List safe practices for the home. Make a mural of ways to prevent accidents. Draw posters and write slogans. Make individual maps showing the safest way home. Invite a speaker on home safety. Plan for a 4-H safety program.	*All Aboard for Health,* pp. 221-225, 199-201, 217, 194-207, 223-224 *Growing Your Way,* pp. 230-233, 224, 228-229, 225-227, 223-229 *Safety Every Day,* pp. 54-55, 16-17 *The Girl Next Door,* pp. 22-24, 14-21, 105, 25-30, 220 *Good Health Is Fun,* pp. 249-260, 239-240 *Safe and Sound,* pp 256, 258 *Health at Home and School,* pp. 31-35, 112-114 *Healthful Ways,* pp. 208-220, 206-207 *Among Friends,* pp. 72-76, 114-123, 26-28, 84-87, 33-34, 37, 140-142, 144, 212-216, 217, 249

Problems	Activities	Materials
	Invite parents to see a home safety skit and to participate in a home safety program.	
	Organize a school safety committee. Discuss safe practices on the school grounds.	
	Make safety posters illustrating do's and don'ts of hall and playground conduct.	
	Make up safety slogans or jingles.	
	Discuss purpose of fire and air raid drills.	
	Discuss function of safety patrol.	
	Make slides illustrating good school safety practices.	
	Write a play or skit.	
	Draw safety posters and pictures.	
	Make a mural showing the school safety program.	
	Invite safety patrol officer to help plan for improved safety practices.	
	Discuss the individual's responsibility for:	
	Proper safety equipment on the bicycle	
	Registration	
	Regular inspection	
	Safe driving of bicycle	
	Make a list of safety rules.	
	Make posters illustrating hand signals. Are there any school rules about bicycles on or around playing areas?	
	Plan a bicycle safety program for school.	
	List bicycle safety rules for streets and schoolgrounds.	**Resources**
	List safety rules for pedestrians.	City traffic safety commission
	Conduct a panel discussion to plan for safety at work and at play.	City bureau of police safety patrol
	Discuss safe swimming practices.	
	Ask a speaker from the American National Red Cross to discuss water safety.	City fire department City bureau of health

Problems	Activities	Materials
	Discuss being a good rider: on a bicycle in a car in a bus on a train on a plane	4-H representative American National Red Cross—Safety, First Aid, and Water Safety State board of health Home safety Home hazard hunt Fire Home homicide

VII. What is our responsibility for keeping our surroundings safe?

How do streams get polluted?

How can we help to keep ourselves and our community safe?

How do our attitudes contribute to safety?

What can we do in emergencies?

VIII. Why do we need to learn about new things?

How do new experience help us grow?

Discuss keeping our outdoor recreation places clean.

Discuss playing on supervised playgrounds.

Report danger spots in the community —holes, electric wires, refrigerators, etc.

Discuss how adequate sleep, rest, and useful health practices affect our safety.

Tell how courtesy can help prevent accidents. Dramatize.

List ways in which a fourth grader can help in an emergency.

Demonstrate first aid and emergency procedures.

Discuss how good mental attitudes help us enjoy new things.

Show why one should understand and obey safety laws.

Discuss how a knowlege of procedures followed in physical and dental examinations help one understand and cooperate.

Discuss the relationship between mental and physical health.

Discuss development of Portland from trading post to the present city.

Discuss need for awareness of change in science, safety rules, and regulations to meet needs of growing community.

Be aware of and ready to accept responsibility for living in a changing community.

Good Health, Good Friends, Good Cheer

See—*Building Our Community*

Evaluation

The teacher may consider the following questions in determining what children are learning through classroom experiences.

1. Do the children understand the general health needs?
2. Have the children gained appreciation of what comprises good health?
3. Have the children indicated an awareness and appreciation of the contribution and interdependence of people in developing useful health habits?
4. Do the children feel that they and their families have definite responsibilities toward their own and each other's health and safety?
5. Have duties and responsibilities of citizenship been developed?
6. Have children developed a willingness to give up some personal liberties for the protection of their health and for the protection of others?
7. Have they learned to share and cooperate in work and play?
8. Have children grown in ability to use many sources of information to answer questions, solve problems, and pursue personal interests?
9. Has there been a definite growth in skills?
10. Has there been definite social growth?
11. Has each child learned what he can do to meet his own health needs?

By teacher

From observation of pupil
By comments made by parents and others
By keeping anecdotal records of progress and behavior

By child

From reports and discussion
By display of work
From outgrowth activities
From daily class records of prograss in form of *Daily News*

Fig. 48. Health project in the intermediate grades. Research, analysis, planning, designing, and artistic effort went into this display, which would reflect credit upon students at the high school level.

Outgrowth activities

Display of work relating to unit
Creative dramatizations of health practices
Planned program for presentation to audience of parents or school mates which
includes
    Talk—reports
    Dramatizations—pantomimes
    Slides by children
    Children's pictures projected on opaque projector
    Demonstrations
    Dances—rhythms
    Songs
    Panel discussions
Plan and eat a meal together
Plan for and have a picnic if the weather is suitable

Resource unit—grade 6

A unit developed primarily to emphasize the prevention and control
of communicable diseases can logically incorporate sanitation practices
in a functional way. Since youngsters in the sixth grade are beginning
to have an interest in group and community affairs, emphasis can be
placed on community and also personal responsibility for disease prevention and control as well as for sanitation.

UNIT TITLE: HOW CAN WE PREVENT DISEASE?

Outcomes

Knowledge

Nature of infectious disease
Characteristics of disease-producing or-
    ganisms
Modes of disease spread
Routes over which diseases travel
Common respiratory diseases and their
    prevention
Common skin infections and their pre-
    vention
Infections of the digestive system
Special infections transmitted by food
Immunization
Isolation and quarantine
Food sanitation
Restaurant sanitation
Milk sanitation
Water purification

School sanitation
Pupil's responsibility in sanitation
    practices
Cooperation in sanitation and preven-
    tion of disease spread
Home sanitation
Boiling and refrigeration as disease pre-
    vention measures
Community disease control problems
    and measures
Value of laboratories in disease control
Responsibility for sanitation in the com-
    munity
Federal control over food, drugs, cos-
    metics, and biological products such
    as vaccine
Effectiveness of sanitation measures

Attitudes as expressed in

Willingness to undergo inconvenience
    for the protection of others
Reliance upon scientific sources of
    knowledge
Willingness to cooperate in disease pre-
    vention efforts
Desire to contribute to the welfare of
    others

Preference for prevention
Pride in a healthy environment
Caution in drinking water or milk from
    unknown source
Need for investing public funds in dis-
    ease control and sanitation
Appreciation that disease prevention de-
    mands constant vigilance

Positive attitude toward community health regulations

Eagerness to cooperate in efforts to improve the health of all

Practices

Avoid exposure to known infection or contamination

Take measures to help others avoid infectious disease

Voluntary isolation when ill

Follow health authorities' recommendations on immunization

Maintain sanitary school environment

Practice approved sanitation in the home

Cooperate in community health efforts

Drink water only from known safe sources

Check on the source of milk before drinking it

Look for sanitation approval certificate in restaurants

Report health hazards to responsible persons

√Read newspaper and magazine reports and articles on communicable diseases

Read available articles on scientific sanitation practices

Activities

Discussion

What is the nature of infectious disease?

What are the characteristics of disease-producing organisms?

How are respiratory infectious diseases spread?

What are some of these diseases?

How can their spread be prevented?

What is the nature of immunization?

What are the dangers of self-diagnosis and self-medication?

Why do we need isolation and quarantine?

What are community requirements for isolation and quarantine?

How can we cooperate as a school?

How can we help as individuals?

How are diseases of the skin acquired?

What are some of these diseases?

How do we prevent skin infection?

How does food transmit these diseases?

What are some other diseases spread by food?

How do we get infections of the digestive system?

What are some of these infections?

What diseases are spread by milk?

What are some diseases water can spread?

How does our community provide water that does not spread disease?

How does sanitation prevent disease spread?

What other purposes does sanitation serve?

Why is restaurant sanitation important?

What does the community do in sanitation measures?

What are good home sanitation practices?

What are the things that make good school sanitation?

What is our part?

What sanitary measures should be taken while camping?

Reports

Respiratory diseases
  Common cold
  Influenza
  Poliomyelitis
  Rheumatic fever
  Sore throat
  Tuberculosis
Skin diseases
  Boils
  Impetigo contagiosa
  Ringworm
  Scabies

Diseases of digestive system
  Dysentery
  Typhoid
Other diseases spread by food
  Trichinosis
  Undulant fever
Special disease
  Tetanus (lockjaw)
Immunization
Isolation and quarantine
Community garbage disposal
Federal control of foods, drugs, and cosmetics

Guest participation

Public health nurse

Sanitarian

X-ray technician

Laboratory technician

Projects

School patrol for school cleanliness

Clean up school grounds

Keep toilet rooms and fountains clean

Keep record of causes of absence

Field trips

Visit to a model home

Locker plant

Water plant

Restaurant

Bakery

Exhibits

Labels on food and drug containers

Communicable disease charts

Tables and graphs on state reported communicable diseases

Posters on sanitation practices

Audiovisual aids

*Body defenses Against Disease**

Body Fights Bacteria†

*Common Cold**

How Disease Travels‡

Prevent Dysentery‡

*Tuberculosis**

Evaluation

To measure the effectiveness of instruction from this unit, the knowledge, attitudes, and practices in the proposed outcomes should be the guide for evaluation procedures. Knowledge can be evaluated in a preliminary way by oral examination of the entire class. Following the oral practice test, written objective and essay tests can give the instructor a more definite evaluation of the knowledge each student has gained. Vocabulary and spelling tests should be included. Attitudes can be judged by the teacher. Practices can be evaluated by surveys or by observation of the youngsters.

In adapting this resource unit to a particular classroom situation, the teacher in charge should be expected to omit, change, and add in terms of the interest and needs of the group. A unit developed for one situation is not likely to be 100% suitable for use in some other classroom. Indeed, for her own classroom needs, the sixth-grade teacher often wisely develops a resource unit which is so broadly inclusive that the person who developed the unit may not use all that the unit provides.

Broad resource unit—grade 6§

A broad resource unit which deals with the personal and community health problems of the countries of the Western Hemisphere has been prepared for use in the sixth grade by a committee of teachers who

---

*Encyclopaedia Britannica Films, Inc.

†Text Film Dept., McGraw-Hill Book Co., Inc.

‡Institute of Inter-American Affairs

§Courtesy of Portland, Oregon, Public Schools.

Fig. 49. Realism in exhibits for health instruction. Highly imaginative intermediate children will create noval displays which will fan health interests.

worked under the supervision of the Curriculum Division of the Portland, Oregon, Public Schools. Perhaps the greatest merit of the unit lies in its inherently wide variety of problems, activities, and resources which can be developed through teacher-pupil planning.

UNIT TITLE: WHAT ARE THE PERSONAL AND COMMUNITY HEALTH PROBLEMS OF THE WESTERN HEMISPHERE?
Overview

This unit is planned to give the pupils an opportunity to study the personal and community health problems of the various countries of the Western Hemisphere. They will learn what the basic requirements for good personal and community health are and will gain an understanding of the need for cooperation in order to make these possible. Physical and mental health, problems of sanitation and safety, and problems of safeguarding community health are included within the study. In order to find information pupils will need to use a variety of texts, supplementary and library books, films and other audiovisual materials and pamphlets, and other materials that are available, which will give them practice in using a variety of materials. A bibliography at the end of the unit lists the materials that have been selected for this study.

The study opens with a question that is of concern to all of the people in the Western Hemisphere—How can we all be healthy and safe?

The following problems are suggested for study:
1. What are the things we all need to be healthy and safe?
2. How are our health needs affected by where we live?
3. How are good health practices promoted?
4. How does the community safeguard our health?
5. How does the civil defense organization protect the health and safety of the community?

Objectives

As a result of their study of the personal and community health problems of the countries of the Western Hemisphere, pupils will achieve the following goals.

Know what being healthy means.

Have a knowledge of the personal health problems of the countries of the Western Hemisphere

Have a knowledge of the community health and safety problems of the countries of the Western Hemisphere.

Realize their responsibility in keeping their community a healthy and safe place in which to live.

Know how their community safeguards health and will use the facilities that are provided.

Avoid careless practices in safeguarding their own health.

Understand the contributions science has made to safeguard health.

Grow in ability to do research and to organize materials.

Grow in ability to use maps, globes, and charts.

Grow in ability not only to work with others, but also to do individual work.

Grow in acquiring the skills necessary for successful participation in group planning and activities.

Develop skills from committee work, group discussions, and class activities.

Develop vocabulary, improve oral and written work, and increase skill and interest in reading, through practice.

Understandings

As a result of the many and varied experiences and discussions in the classroom, students will develop the following understandings.

All communities have some health and safety problems that are similar.

Personal and community health and safety are interrelated.

Each individual is responsible for the health and safety of the community.

Superstitions and ignorance are enemies of good health and good government.

No one is safe from contagious disease as long as one person with the disease exists.

Recreation in a region is determined to a great extent by the natural environment.

Peoples of all races and cultures have the same basic desires and needs.

Differences in customs help to make people interesting.

A knowledge of our neighbors will aid us in understanding them and in interpreting their actions.

Environment affects the needs of health and safety.

Community health services protect the health of all persons.

Fads and fallacies may lead to detrimental health practices.

Science is advancing rapidly in the field of health promotion and protection.

Carelessness endangers health.

Appropriate leisure time activities are important for everyone, young and old.

Persons depend upon one another to meet their needs of health and safety.

Persons must work together cooperatively to provide safe healthful effective group living.

Good personal health and safety practices are basic to the development of the individual in order that he may participate in and enjoy life.

Peoples of all countries have responsibility in helping to solve international health problems.

Suggested approaches

Various approaches can be used to introduce a problem. One type of approach will appeal to one group of pupils; other types are necessary to appeal to other groups. The teacher must evaluate the reaction of the pupils and follow leads in which they indicate an interest in the development of the study of any problem. The following approaches are suggested.

Class discussion of an interesting area of the unit which draws on past experiences of the pupils will arouse interest.

Book displays will attract interest, and free browsing and discussion will stimulate interest.

Discussion of a current article from a newspaper or magazine that is related to the problem stimulates discussion.

Present a pertinent radio or television program, transcription, or film strip.

Conduct a stimulating discussion on a question such as "Is that a fact"?

Begin with a questionnaire to stimulate interest.

Read from an interesting book or a story.

Displays of maps, objects, items from the culture, stamps, etc., will appeal to many students.

Collect material ahead of time for a file and display the material in an interesting manner.

Prepare a collection of mounted pictures for display.

Use opportunities offered by a school assembly to stimulate interest.

Schedule a book review by a pupil.

Discuss the following problem: How do we prepare to visit foreign countries?

Read the following book: *Mosquitoes in the Big Ditch.**

Use Rayoscope and examine drinking water.

Present the following film: *The Winged Scourge (Malaria).*

Ask a guest speaker who has taken an international trip, teachers in building, missionaries, or others who can discuss the problems of personal and community health in various countries to present a talk.

Problems	Activities	Materials
I. What are the things we all need to be healthy and safe?	Discuss basic health needs; list them on the board.	**Books**
	Read for information.	*Habits Healthful and Safe*
	Begin to build a bibliography of resource material (books, audiovisual, aids, etc.).	*Building Good Health*
		Builders of Good Health

---

*Burlingame, L. L.: Mosquitoes in the big ditch, New York, 1931, Henry Holt & Co., Inc.

Problems	Activities	Materials
How do health needs vary according to the individual?	Learn correct bibliography style (see language books).	*You and Others*
Structural defects	Begin a vocabulary chart and add to it as the unit develops.	*Active and Alert*
Individual needs for rest, food, and relaxation		*Growing Healthfully*
		Cross Roads
Individual differences in growth and development		*Safeguards for Your Health*
		Teamwork for Health

Sound films

Guide to Good Eating

Fundamentals of Diet

Exploring Your Growth

Posture Habits

Rest That Builds Good Health

How much rest do we need?		*Whenever You Eat*
How much exercise and what kind do we need?		*Your Cleanliness*
What kinds of clothing are necessary in the various countries of the Western Hemisphere?		*Your Health at Home*
		Your Health at School
	Read in health books and social studies books for information on climate.	*Your Posture*

Film strips

What shelter is required in the various countries?	Study the types of materials that are used for shelter in the various countires.	*Sleep and Rest*
		Care of the Skin
How important are happiness and contentment to the mental health of the individual?	Use science books for information and for suggestions for experiments.	*Save Those Teeth*
	Find the recreational activities in the various countries.	*Food for Health*
		Care of Hair and Nails
Why do we need recreation for mental health?	Use audio-visual material for information. List pupils' questions. (A steering committee may divide these questions into categories for group study).	*Exercise for Happy Living*
		Sleep for Health ✓

Books

What foods do we need, and how does our body use this food? How do the foods differ in the various countries?	Compare and contrast kinds of foods eaten, kinds of shelter, and kinds of clothing among the countries of the Western Hemisphere. Why do these differ in the various countries? Make maps that show the differences and similarities in diagrammatic form.	*Beneath the Skies* *Discovering Our World*, Books 1 and 2

Problems	Activities	Materials
What evidence is there that we need sunshine?	Perform experiments to show effect of sunshine on plants. Learn to spell words that are necessary to communicate ideas in writing; place new words in school spellers.	*New Ideas in Science The How and Why Club* *How and Why Discoveries*
How is posture related to health?	Determine how various postures indicate feelings and problems. Write summaries of reading, class discussions, films, and other materials.	See principal's curriculum file for pamphlets and lists of sources of health materials.
What safety practices should we develop for safety in the home, school, and community?	Prepare oral and written reports based on reading. Begin a class log that will keep a record of what has been learned each day.	**National Dairy Council*** *Guide to Good Eating* (poster)
How do all these needs differ in various countries in the Western Hemisphere?	Discuss the difference climate, culture, and government make in the way needs are met in various countries of the Western Hemisphere. Make a chart, a mural, slides, or a diorama illustrating basic health needs and show how these differ in the various countries. Prepare bulletin board displays of posters and pictures. Arrange book chats based on library books. Discuss materials read and draw conclusions. Plan discussions. Write review of library books. Plan science experiments related to foods, growth rates, safety. Write a radio skit summarizing what was learned about the problem. Invite a speaker who can compare and contrast health factors, such as food and housing, in various countries. Read for information.	*It's Always Breakfast Time Somewhere, Hello South America, Hello Alaska* (unit) **Film strip** *Food in Body,* Parts 1 and 2: *Food We Eat, and Digestion of Foods* **Sound film** *Guide to Good Eating* Radio programs Television programs Commercial radio stations
II. How are our health needs affected by where we live?	Show the effect of climate on activities, clothing, shelter, and foods in various countries.	**Books** *Safeguards for Your Health* *Cross Roads*

*National Dairy Council, 111 North Canal Street, Chicago 6, Ill.

Problems	Activities	Materials
Why do people in some countries take siestas?	Discuss the climates in Canada, Mexico, and South America and compare with the climate in United States of America. How is climate determined by the location of the country?	*Habits Healthful and Safe*
How does climate affect the amount and kind of exercise taken by people who live in the various parts of the Western Hemisphere?		*Working With Science*
	Make murals.	*Tales and Travel*
	Locate transportation routes.	*The Very Good Neighbors*
	Experiment with food spoilage as suggested in *Discovering Our World,* Book 3, pp. 100-103.	*Mexico*
How do varying climates affect available food and water supply, sanitation, production, spoilage, and transportation?		*Our South American Neighbors*
		In Mexico They Says
	Discuss eating habits in various countries. Why do these habits vary?	*Picture Map Geography of Mexico, Central America, and the West Indies*
What is appropriate dress in different sections of the Western Hemisphere as affected by time, custom, available materials, and weather?	Dress dolls to illustrate the theme, *Dressing for the Weather.*	*Central American Roundabout*
	Order doll exhibit from instructional materials department.	*The American Nations*
		American Lands and People
	Write summaries.	*Let's Read About Mexico*
What difference does climate make in the type of homes that are built?	Build model homes of each region. Show why appropriate to the climate. Show differences in safety and health standards.	*Let's Read About Brazil*
		They Live in South America
	Discuss how government, bureaus of health, sanitation, and safety factors differ in these countries.	*Our Southern Neighbors*
		Let's Read About Canada
	Use audiovisual aids.	*Teamwork for Health*
	Learn games and dances of various countries.	**Sound films**
		How Our Bodies Fight Disease
What are the things that affect the types of recreation—jobs, climate, topography, and personal needs?	Show in a mural how different factors such as climate affect jobs, games, and recreation of people in various countries in the Western Hemisphere.	*A. U.S. Community and Its Citizens*
		People of Peru
		Mexican Children

Problems	Activities	Materials
	How are the games that people enjoy alike and different in the various countries?	*Tima, Girl in Mexico*
How is the way we feel and think related to health?		*Farmers of the Andes*
	Discuss ways foods are transported to and from the various countries and regulations necessary for safe delivery.	*Tropical Lowlands, Amazon River*
	Read to learn about importing foods from other countries.	*People of Chile*
		The St. Lawrence Lowland, Quebec
How are various regions of the Western Hemisphere dependent upon one another for food?	Discuss restrictions on foods and why they are restricted.	*Natives of Guatemala*
		French Canadian Children
	Discuss health regulations regarding food importation.	**Resources**
		City bureau of health for field trips and speakers
	Invite guest speaker (city bureau of health).	
III. How are good health practices promoted?		**Sound films**
		City Water Supply
	Find out how our city keeps our water pure. Invite guest speaker (bureau of water works).	*Visit to the Waterworks*
		Invasion
		Defense Against
What are the functions of our bureaus of health?	Secure information on a current local health problem	*Water Supply Immunization*
		The Water We Drink
	Visit the sewage disposal plant.	
		Winged Scourge (Malaria)
How are we responsible for promoting the health in the community?	Do an experiment to find out how water is filtered. (See *How and Why Discoveries*, pp. 290-291.)	*Your Health: Disease and Its Control*
		Your Health in the Community
	How are disease-carrying rodents and insects controlled?	*Defending the City's Health*
		The Housefly
	Observe results of food spoilage under the microscope; write up the experiment. Read textbooks for information.	**Film strips**
How are diseases carried—personal contact and carriers: insects, rodents, persons, impure food, drinks, etc.?		*Insect Pests and Disease*
		Science of Life
	What health precautions are necessary before visiting certain foreign countries? Why different for different countries?	**Transcriptions**
		Mosquitoes and Flies

Problems	Activities	Materials
		How Do You Know Its Safe?
	Write compositions expressing a point of view, an idea about a problem, a summary of a discussion, or a solution to a problem.	**Books** *Discovering Our World,* Books 2 and 3
	Make a time line showing the advances made against disease by science.	*Working With Science*
	Read biographies of great men associated with control of disease.	*Insects and Their Ways*
		Builders of Good Health
		Plant and Animal Partnership
		Habits Healthful and Safe
		Active and Alert
		Growing Healthfully
		You and Others
		Building Good Health
		Builders for Good Health
		New Ideas in Science
		How and Why Experiments
		Cross Roads
		Teamwork for Health
	Discuss growing up, physically and emotionally.	*Safeguards for Your Health*
Why should we accept responsibility for our own health and safety practices?	Write review of films.	**Sound films** *How Friendly Are You?*
	Make posters and charts.	
	Use audiovisual materials.	*The Other Fellow's Feelings*
	Plan panel discussions.	*Words of Courtesy*
		Books
		The How and Why Club

Problems	Activities	Materials
		How and Why Discoveries
		New Ideas in Science
		Discovering Our World, Book 3
		How and Why Experiments
		Working With Science
		You and Others
		Newspaper and magazine articles
		Books *Safeguards for Your Health*
How should one choose his medical and dental adviser?	Invite guest speaker (public health nurse).	*Cross Roads*
	Read in health textbooks for information.	*Habits Healthful and Safe*
What is the advantage of periodic medical and dental examinations?	Discuss what happens when things are out of balance, such as not enough sleep, too much of the wrong kind of food, over exertion, etc.	*Jorge's Journey* *Let's Read About South America*
	Write compositions on the above topics.	*Discovering Our World,* Book 1
		How and Why Experiments
		You and Your Friends
		How and Why Discoveries *Building Good Health*
		Growing Healthfully
How can we secure the things that help to develop healthy bodies and minds, such as adequate nutrition, sleep, recreation, medical care, dental care, etc.	Invite dental counselor and public health nurse to talk to class.	*Builders of Good Health*
	Discuss growth, development, and care of the teeth.	*Let's Read About Canada*
	Discuss accepting personal responsibility for dental care.	**Sound films**
	Use audiovisual material.	*Gateway to Health* (dental)
	Write review of films.	*Two Little Rats and How They Grew*
	Read textbooks and library books.	

Problems	Activities	Materials
		Model
	Discuss material read and reach conclusions.	Tooth; jaw
		Dental health pamphlets
		National Dairy Council
		They're Your Teeth (poster)
		Film strips
		Save Those Teeth
		Sleep for Health
		Books
		Habits Healthful and Safe
		Safeguards for Your Health
How does adequate living space help promote growth?		*Teamwork for Health*
		Cross Roads
		This Useful World
How do living conditions vary throughout the Western Hemisphere?		*Caribbean Lands*
		Mexico
		Let's Read About Mexico
	Read for information.	*The Very Good Neighbors*
How does our use of leisure time affect our health?	Demonstrate favorite leisure time activities.	*Central American Roundabout*
		Neighbors to the South
Do we take time for leisure?	Write summary report of reading (select an interesting problem for the report).	*Our Southern Neighbors*
		Sound film
		Young Uraguay
	Discuss pupils' hobbies. Plan a hobby show.	**Books**
Are there adequate facilities?		*Central American Roundabout*
		Our Southern Neighbors
Do we know how to take advantage of the opportunities?		*Let's Read About South America*

Problems	Activities	Materials
		Let's Read About Canada
Do we know the safest place to play?		*Let's Read About Mexico*
		Growing Healthfully
		Active and Alert
Do we refrain from accepting rides, candy, and money from strangers?	Discuss safest places to play and why one must go directly home from school and other places.	*Discovering Our World*, Books 1 and 3
		Builders for Good Health
	Discuss why we should report loiterers.	*Sky High in Bolivia*
		Nancy Goes to Mexico
		Nick and Nan in Yucatan
		Carribbean Lands
		Mexico
		Wings Over Central America
		French Canadian Children
		Pierre Pidgeon
		Juanita
		Manuela's Birthday
		Watchdog
	Learn dances of the Western Hemisphere.	*Mateo and the Mexican Fair*
	Play games of the Western Hemisphere; list games that are common to all in the Western Hemisphere; list games that are somewhat different in different locales (golf, polo, bowling, etc.).	*Our Little Neighbors at Work and Play: Here, There, Then and Now*
	Discuss why games differ.	*Our Friend and Neighbor, Canada*
	Sings songs of the countries of the Western Hemisphere.	*Children's Games From Many Lands**

*Millen, Nina: From Many Lands, New York, Friendship Press (series 1948, 1951, 1952.)

Problems	Activities	Materials
		Music Everywhere
What safety practices should we develop at home, at school, and in the community?	Listen to music.	**Sound film**
		A City Sings (Canadian Musical Festival)
	Read for information; plan class discussion.	(See audiovisual aids list, instructional materials Department) Rhythm activities
		Books
		Safeguards for Your Health
	Make a list of safety rules for different activities such as riding a bicycle, safety at play, etc.	*Teamwork for Health*
	Write creative stories using characters and situations.	*Building Good Health*
		New Ideas in Science
		Growing Healthfully Active and Alert
		Builders for Good Health
		Discovering Our World, Books 1, 2, and 3
What can be done to help prevent fire and accidents in the home and community?	Read for information.	*You and Others Cross Roads*
		Sound films
		Drive Your Bike
		Mickey's Big Chance
	Study current local efforts in these areas; use newspapers.	*You Can't Stop on a Dime*
		Water Safety
	Use audiovisual aids.	*Safe Living at School*
		Safest Way
	Make a survey of the accidents that happen in school to determine the cause.	*Bicycle Safety*
		Bicycling With Complete Safety
	Make plans for correcting the situation.	*Let's Be Safe at Home*

Problems	Activities	Materials
		Playground Safety
	Invite the safety patrol officers to discuss the problems of crossing streets.	*Safe Swimming*
		Safety in the Home
		Film strips
	Draw a picture map of your home illustrating the danger points as indicated in Building Good Health.	*Safety in the Summer*
		Fire Safety
	Plan and assembly program to show the other students how carelessness endangers our health and what can be done to avoid careless accidents. (Skit, play, shadow box, puppets, etc.).	*In Case of Fire*
		Safety in the Water
		Newspaper articles
		Magazines, papers, radio, and television
How does being adequately informed help us establish good health practices?	Read and discuss information.	**Books** *Teamwork for Health*
	Plan class discussions on this problem.	*Cross Roads*
		You and Others
	Discuss superstitions, patent medicines, advertising, quacks, etc.	*Growing Healthfully*, pp. 229-233
		How and Why Discoveries, pp. 198-199
	Analyze the way in which advertising may mislead us unless we understand a few techniques for evaluating the product. Make a bulletin board display showing the type of information used by Tuberculosis and Health Association. National Foundation, American Cancer Society, American Heart Association, and bureaus of health.	*Habits Healthful and Safe*, pp. 43, 182, 183
		Safeguards for Your Health
		Books *Cross Roads*
	Plan a radio broadcast and write the script.	*Safeguards for Health*
How can one compensate for structural weaknesses and handicaps?		*Health*
		Discovering Our World, Book 1
	Plan recreational activities for people with structural weaknesses and handicaps.	*Growing Healthfully*
		Builders for Good Health
	Plan various types of group discussions based on the subtopics of the problem. Discuss the need to employ the handicapped.	*Building Good Health*
		You and Others

Problems	Activities	Materials
	Read for information.	**Books**
		You and Others
	Plan class discussion.	*New Ideas in Science*
What are the effects of alcohol and narcotics on the body?	Use films for information.	
	Read for information.	*Builders for Good Health*
IV. How Does the Community Safeguard Our Health?	Do an experiment to find out how water is filtered (see *How and Why Discoveries*, pp. 290-291).	*How and Why Discoveries*
		Active and Alert
	Find out how our city keeps our water supply pure.	*Growing Healthfully*
How can we be sure our water is pure (fountains, containers, storage tanks, and source of supply)	Secure maps showing location of storage tanks.	*Cross Roads*
		Newspapers
		National Dairy Council
		Pamphlets, bulletins, charts, etc.
What is the function of the health officer in city, county, and state?	Read for information.	**Film strip** *Inspection and Distribution of Milk*
	Write to the state board of health for information.	**Sound film** *Milk*
		Lantern slides *Butter and Cheese*
What are the functions of the various divisions of the boards of health?	Interview a dairyman and visit a milk-distributing depot to find out about the testing program.	**Books** *Cross Roads*
What steps are taken to assure us of a safe food supply?	Contact city bureau of health for speaker.	*Safeguards for Your Health*
		Teamwork for Health
Why are cows tested?	Watch the newspapers for current news concerning disease control.	*You and Others*
How is the testing program carried on?		*The How and Why Club*
What laws are necessary to prevent people and animals from spreading disease?	Plan a field trip to study the processing, packaging, and distribution of milk.	*Habits Healthful and Safe*
		Building Good Health
	Plan various types of group discussions.	*Builders for Good Health*
What standard must a dairy meet to be licensed to operate?	Plan various types of group discussions. Use audiovisual material.	*Growing Healthfully*
		Discovering Our World, Book 3

Problems	Activities	Materials
	Visit local food dispensers (butcher, grocer, etc.).	*How and Why Discoveries*
How can we get rid of our waste material?	Read for information.	
	Discuss waste material and how it is utilized or disposed of.	**Film strips** *Life of Louis Pasteur*
		Joseph Lister
	Take a trip to the sewage disposal plant.	*Louis Pasteur*
		Madame Curie
	Read science pamphlets and see films; plan experiments in the field of health (see library card catalogues).	*Noguchi*
		Walter Reed
	Write biographies.	*Edward Jenner*
How does science help to protect our health?	Plan dramatizations.	*Florence Nightingale*
		Robert Koch
	Arrange book chats.	*Treadeau*
What contributions have these men made: Koch, Jenner, Pasteur, Lister, and others?	Prepare panel discussion.	Newspapers and magazine articles
	Observe results of food spoilage under the microscope. Write up the experiment.	**Sound film** *Bandages and Bullets*
What inventions have contributed to health protection— microscope, thermometer, x-ray, and others?	Read to find information on the inventions.	*The Community— Our Classroom*
	Make a time line showing the major advances of science in the battle against disease.	(See transcriptions, *Adventures in Research Series,* audio-visual list)
	Hear transcriptions; discuss the information.	(See *Handbook for Health Instruction, State Elementary Schools*)
What diseases have been controlled by vaccination and immunization?	Read local papers and current magazines for material.	
		Film strips *We Have You Covered (Cold)*
How are we able to detect disease in its early stages?	Apply the problems that have been studied to other countries of the Western Hemisphere.	*Community Helpers*
		Human Resources
	Invite a resource person to discuss the community health services available.	**Sound films** *Defense Against Invasion*
What community health services are available—hospitals and clinics, physicians, dentists, nurses, and others?	Discuss difference between communicable and noncommunicable diseases.	*Defending Our City's Health*
		Accent on Use

Problems	Activities	Materials
		Goodbye Mr. Germ
What voluntary health organizations help in the community health program?	Write for information to different organizations.	*From One Cell*
		Sniffles and Sneezes
	Use audiovisual and pamphlet materials.	**Transcription**
		Be Wise, Immunize
What is the work of the TB and Health Association, American Cancer Society, National Foundation, state heart association, and Epilepsy League	Watch for radio and television programs related to the unit study.	(See *Radio Guide* for in-school programs)
	Write reports.	
	Discuss the work of the United Fund in aiding community organizations.	(See principal's curriculum file for pamphlets)
		(See health books)
	List activities of civil defense.	(See science books)
V. How does civil defense protect the health and safety of the community?	Make a chart showing how each individual has a responsibility for knowing civil defense practices and procedures.	(See social studies books)
		Film strip
	Discuss the ways in which knowledge of safety, first-aid, and emergency procedures can make one a valuable member of a team in any kind of an emergency.	*Atomic Energy for Better Health,* Parts 1 and 2: *How to Lessen Chances of Injury From an Atomic Explosion*
How do safety, first aid, and emergency procedures promote and protect personal and community health?		
	Discuss why such knowledge can lead to good mental health practices.	

Outgrowth activities

The purpose of any outgrowth activity is to give the pupils an opportunity to review what they have learned in any given unit of work and to tie all of the parts together. If the activity is planned for a group of parents, guests, or another class, the presence of an audience serves as a motivation for a well-prepared presentation.

Among the activities that may be presented are:

Class and panel discussions	Puppet plays to dramatize events
Reports on topics of the unit study	Class log showing day by day study and
Tape recordings	research
Illustrated maps	Imaginary trip
Folders of work	*You Were There* program
Opaque projections	Time line showing sequence of events
Room displays of projects	Bulletin board displays of mounted pic-
Creative stories and plays	tures and pupils' creative writings.
Dramatizations of events	

Evaluation

Evaluation is a continuous process which lasts for as long as teacher and pupils work together. There should be almost daily pupil-teacher evaluation to determine how well the goals that they have set are being achieved. Two good evaluation and planning questions which should be considered toward the end of each day are "What have we accomplished today"? and "What do we need to do tomorrow"?

Various evaluative procedures may be used, including written tests (both objective and essay types), evaluation of oral and written work, group and individual discussions on what is being accomplished, observation by the teacher, and comments by the pupils that show interest and satisfaction with achievement.

The following questions may help the teacher in evaluating classroom procedures.

1. How am I helping pupils differentiate between group and individual responsibility?
2. Am I helping pupils grow in the ability to evaluate growth in terms of improved accomplishments?
3. To what extent is each pupil trying to work up to his individual capacity—learning, using materials successfully, and working and completing his tasks cheerfully?
4. Am I utilizing the following techniques adequately in evaluating growth: standardized tests, informal tests, outgrowth activities, pupils' conversations, questions, discussions, and parent aand pupil conferences?
5. In what ways do I provide opportunities for the students to aid in planning the daily program which includes time for individual work and group activities?
6. Am I integrating the various subjects when I can do so?
7. Do the pupils frequently experience some type of outgrowth activity to bind all achievements together?
8. To what degree are the pupils applying the skills of writing, spelling, vocabulary building, outlining, and reporting to their work?
9. Has an adequate balance among geography, history, and related content subjects been maintained?
10. Have there been many opportunities for creative expression in art, drama, music, crafts, rhythm, speech, and writing?
11. How adequately am I utilizing the wide variety of source materials—books, encyclopedias, pictures, field trips, audiovisual aids, and community resources?
12. Have I made sure that pupils have a good knowledge of place geography in each area?
13. Are pupils getting a good background of information about our neighboring countries?
14. In what ways are the pupils expressing curiosity?
15. Do pupils try to decide questions according to facts?
16. Are the pupils growing in appreciation of the peoples of our neighboring countries?
17. Will the pupils finish the work with improved attitudes?
18. How much progress are the pupils making in their ability to participate in discussions, conversations, and reports to small groups or the entire class?
19. Have pupils learned to make simple outlines and use them?
20. How effectively are the pupils making progress in reading skills, organizing, summarizing, location of data, dictionary and reference skills, and the development of a broad vocabulary?
21. To what extent are the pupils using the reference skills in the preparation of their lessons?
22. To what degree is each pupil making consistent progress in his desire and ability to write legibly and to speak and write correctly?

23. How am I providing opportunities for creative writing and dramatics?
24. To what extent is each pupil improving in his ability to plan and evaluate?

Incidental instruction

Opportunities and a need for casual or incidental health instruction arise naturally in the course of a school day. Some phases of health teaching may best be handled by such incidental instruction. Problems that are of deep personal concern to a particular pupil or particular types of pupils may be dealt with most effectively by incidental treatment. However effective such instruction may be for certain purposes, if the teacher relies entirely upon incidental health instruction, it would result in a decidedly limited health instruction program, regardless of how skillful the teacher may be.

Pupil-teacher conferences and counseling frequently include incidental health instruction. When a teacher discovers the particular needs and problems of a child, the person-to-person relationship promotes a clarifying discussion of the problems. The conference may proceed beyond the original problem and explore related problems of interest and importance.

In class a pupil's question on a health matter may be an occasion for the whole class to learn. At times a discussion of a question considerably removed from health may gradually shift to the health aspects of it. An alert teacher will utilize expressed class interests and explore a whole area of health, perhaps leaving the class with several questions to ponder over, and conclude the discussion on a later date.

Simple incidents in school can have meaning in health terms, and the teacher can make effective use of such realistic teaching situations. Health terms occasionally are used in areas aside from health instruction, and opportunities are presented for the pupils to expand their vocabulary. Examinations usually offer opportunities for incidental health instruction. This is particularly true during the review of the examination after the tests have been scored and returned.

Daily newspaper, radio, and television reports frequently have health topics of interest to the pupils. A new health discovery, an epidemic, a person who has reached the age of 100 years, or a physician who has practiced for fifty years are examples of news items which provide both the opportunity and necessity for consideration in the classroom.

Opportunities are plentiful for the alert teacher who utilizes incidental instruction to fortify and amplify planned health instruction. Spontaneous live instruction is usually most stimulating to the pupils.

Correlated health instruction

Correlation is a reciprocal relationship, and a kindred relationship or alliance exists between health and other cognate areas which provides opportunities for effective instruction. Health aspects can enrich other fields and make experiences more stimulating and rewarding for the child.

Two structures are built simultaneously rather than two birds killed with one stone. While health can very easily be incorporated into other instruction, the teacher must not forget that it is a queer street that does not run in two directions. There are many opportunities in health for instruction in the basic academic skills as well as in the field of life experiences. In health instruction, diction, pronunciation, spelling, coherence, and clarity are important. In a very real sense health involves history, art, and the people of other lands.

Reading. Health readers are available at various levels. They are interesting, are written with regard for comprehension by children, and can be used to encourage general supplementary reading. For the teacher who seeks to enrich the curriculum for the superior pupil, health readers as well as health projects offer a fertile field of exploration.

Language arts. In writing and speaking assignments health topics are a frequent choice of pupils. Reports on special health topics, field trips, and health experiences are used. Articles on health in the school may be written for newspapers. Letters asking agencies for health materials and requests to the health department provide correlated health and writing experience.

Spelling also can be included. Of the 2000 basic words in common usage which are the core of instruction in elementary school spelling, many are in health literature. From classroom health study an instructor can find ample material for spelling purposes.

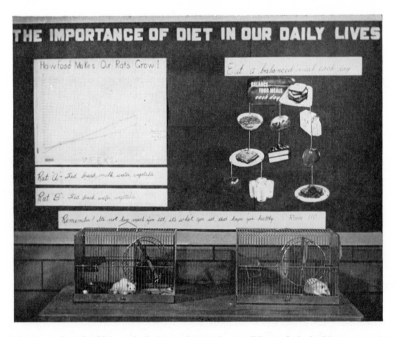

Fig. 50. Science project in fifth and sixth grades. It is possible and desirable to correlate health with other subject areas at all grade levels. (Courtesy Denver Public Schools, Denver, Colo.)

Art. Paper cutting, crayon fill-in, and free drawing can deal with health topics. Paste-on or original posters can be health posters. Health record cards can be a health project.

Music. Implications of mental and physical health in vocal and instrumental music are of interest. Many musical compositions have references to health. Health parodies on recognized songs should be avoided.

Arithmetic. Keeping records of changes in height and weight, attendance, and illness provides problems in arithmetic. Calculation of sleeping time and the amounts of certain foods consumed in a given period of time can be interesting experiences in arithmetic. The intermediate grades may be interested in rates for various health factors.

Geography. Health customs, life span, health problems, and dietary practices of peoples of other lands can be of interest to pupils. How other people live usually interests children.

History. The influence of health and disease upon history challenges the imagination of youth. Health problems of different periods in history and the health problems of famous historical figures are of special interest. Celebrated men and women health heroes live in historical perspective.

Nature study. The life and habits of lower animal forms have health implications. Feeding habits are particularly germane. The interrelationship which exists between man and the plant and animal worlds is a concept that children should acquire as fundamental education.

Children must be helped to see relationships in life. Especially important is the relationship of health to the many aspects of everyday living.

Selected readings

Aids to teaching health in elementary school, grades 1-6, Webster Groves, Mo., 1948, Webster Groves Public Schools.

American Association of School Administrators: Health in schools, twentieth yearbook, Washington, D. C., 1951, National Education Association.

Davis, Roy: Quality in school health administration, National Elementary Principal **39:** Feb., 1960.

Dutton, W. H., and Hockett, J. A.: The modern elementary school, New York, 1960, Holt, Rinehart & Winston, Inc.

Elementary teachers guide to free curriculum materials, Randolph, Wis., published annually, Educators' Progress Service.

Foster, Julia C.: Health activities, ed. 3, Philadelphia, 1954, J. B. Lippincott Co.

Grout, Ruth E.: Health teaching in schools, ed. 4, Philadelphia, 1963, W. B. Saunders Co.

Godshall, Frances R.: Nutrition in the elementary school, New York, 1958, Harper & Brothers.

Haag, Jesse H.: School health program, New York, 1958, Henry Holt & Co., Inc.

Hanna, Lavonne A.: Unit teaching in the elementary school, New York, 1955, Rinehart & Co., Inc.

Health in the elementary school, twenty-ninth yearbook, The National Elementary Principal—Bulletin of the Department of Elementary School Principals, Washington, D. C., 1950, National Education Association, no. 1.

Irwin, L. W., Cornacchia, H. J., and Staton, W. M.: Health in elementary schools, St. Louis, 1962, The C. V. Mosby Co.

Irwin, L. W., Humphrey, J. H., and Johnson, W. R.: Methods and materials in health education, St. Louis, 1956, The C. V. Mosby Co.

Lane, Janet, and Tolleries, Beatrice K.: Planning your exhibit, New York, 1948, National Publicity Council.

Logan, Lillian, and Logan, V.: Teaching the elementary school child, New York, 1961, Houghton Mifflin Co.

Los Angeles City School Districts, California: Health in the elementary schools, Publication no. EC-201, 1959, Office of the Superintendent of Schools.

National Education Association, Department of Elementary School Principals: Instruction materials for elementary schools, thirty-fifth yearbook, Washington, D. C., The Department.

National Elementary Principal: Health in the elementary school, Washington, D. C., 1950, National Education Assoication.

National Safety Council: Safety education methods, elementary schools, Chicago, 1940, The Council.

Ohlsen, M. D.: Modern methods in elementary education, New York, 1959, Holt, Rinehart & Winston, Inc.

Schneider, R. E.: Methods and materials in health education, Philadelphia, 1958, W. B. Saunders Co.

Smith, Helen N., and Wolverton, Mary E.: Health education in the elementary school, New York, 1959, The Ronald Press Co.

Stoddard, M. B.: Unit on teeth, Grade Teacher **72:**59, 1954.

Stoll, Frances A.: Dental health education, ed. 2, Philadelphia, 1962, Lea & Febiger.

Vannier, Maryhelen: Teaching health in elementary schools, New York, 1963, Harper & Brothers.

Virginia State Board of Education: Health education, grades 1-7, Richmond, 1948, Division of Purchasing and Printing.

Walker, H.: Health in the Elementary School, New York, 1955, The Ronald Press Co.

Willey, R. D., Guidance in elementary education, rev. ed., New York, 1960, Harper & Brothers.

Willgoose, C. E.: Health education in the elementary school, Philadelphia, 1959, W. B. Saunders Co.

*No bubble is so irridescent or floats longer
than that blown by the successful teacher.*

—Sir William Osler

Chapter 13

Junior high school health instruction

Junior high school represents a transition from the self-contained classroom in the sixth grade to departmentalized instruction in the seventh grade. It represents a change in the relationship between students and teacher. Teachers in the junior high school who teach subject matter usually do not have the opportunity to establish the degree of rapport with students possible in the elementary grades. However, when the seventh grade curriculum is modified by large core areas, the transition for the students is easier, and teachers have a better chance to establish a close relationship with the students. Unfortunately at the junior high school level the tendency of children to try to identify and classify the Miss Goode and the Miss Meany makes the establishment of the proper kind of student-teacher rapport difficult. This tendency reflects the physiological and psychological characteristics of junior high school students. Obviously health instruction, as all other instruction at this stage in school, must recognize the factors which motivate students and account for their interests and conduct.

Students between the ages of 12 and 15 years in the main include children who are in the homophiliac or gang period, a few who have not yet reached that stage, and perhaps one fifth who can be classed as adolescents. To complicate the picture, physiologically and socially a 12-year-old girl is almost two years in advance of a boy.

During the homophiliac period (11 to 15 years of age), girls are arm-in-arm with girls and boys tend to gang up with boys. Group loyalty is exceedingly important. This tendency toward group action can be an asset in the classroom if it is directed properly. The teacher should capitalize upon the strong desire for approval by their associates and the tendency toward united action by directing all health instruction into channels of group approval and action. A student takes special pride in his health if the group commends him for it. Group interest can mean group accomplishment and community interest.

Basic objectives of health instruction

Health practices previously established will continue to be fortified in the junior high school, and new practices, particularly those associated with group health responsibility, will be established. Knowledge to promote understanding of health measures and procedures will be provided in the junior high school. However, greatest attention should be given to the development of attitudes which are essential to provide the necessary intensity to health practices and to assure the fullest utilization of health knowledge.

Many health attitudes are developed in the junior high school, but attitudes in terms of certain concepts of ideal personal and community attainments will prove to be the most lasting and valuable in terms of the individual's lifelong health measures. Among these will be attitudes which are directed toward the following:

1. Resolution to attain a high level of health
2. Pride in a high quality of well-being
3. Application of reasoning to health problems
4. Conviction that only established health principles should be utilized
5. Acceptance of responsibility for the health of others

Fig. 51. Upgrading the level of health instruction. Junior high school students are not bored by a level of health teaching which challenges them.

6. Ideals of citizen responsibility
7. Cooperation with community health efforts
8. Insistence upon high community health standards
9. Pride in community assets

The knowledge of health which the junior high school student should acquire is expressed in the areas of primary interest at this level.

Areas of primary interest

Certain health interests are virtually universal for children of this age, and instructional planning can be based upon these major interests as the central core. Participation of students in planning the classroom instruction brings out their special health interests. Health needs and interests surveys can be highly revealing.

Physical health

Personal health standards *- 2 wks*
Periodic health examination
Choice of a physician and dentist
Medical and hospital insurance
Biological changes between the ages of 12 and 20 years *- 3 wks*
Adjustment to sexual and reproductive changes *- 2 wks*
Body care and grooming *- 2 wks*
Activity, fatigue, and rest
Tobacco, alcohol, and other harmful drugs *- 2 wks*
Noncommunicable diseases
    Acne
    Anemia
    Cancer
    Diabetes mellitus
    Heart conditions
Tuberculosis

Mental health

Social conduct *- 2 wks*
Personality adjustment
Adapting to common frustrations

Community health

Health superstitions, fallacies, and quackery *- 2 wks*
Fraudulent health advertising *2 - wks*
Patent medicines
Community health services *- 2 wks*
    Water
    Sewage disposal
    Garbage collection
    Insect and rodent eradication
Medical, dental, and hospital services *- 2 wks*
Community health projects
    Helping the disabled
    Mobile x-ray units
    Safety program
    American National Red Cross
Voluntary health agencies

Local health department
State health department
United States Public Health Service ⎤
World Health Organization   ⎦ / wk

Correlation of health and other subject fields

Because of the departmentalized organization in the junior high
school, there tends to be a failure to recognize the correlation between
health and other subject areas. In the self-contained classroom of the
elementary grades it is both easy and natural for the teacher to recognize
and use these correlations for more effective teaching. Yet correlated
teaching is equally as important in the junior and senior high schools
as it is in the lower grades. For that reason Chapter 15 is devoted entirely
to what should be done in health instruction through other subject
fields. The discussion applies to junior and senior high schools alike.

Integrated and incidental health learning

The daily experiences of junior high school students are rich in health
implications. School activities and community events readily interest the
youngster of this age bracket. Opportunities for integrated health instruction are plentiful, but usually only the health instructor capitalizes
on these opportunities. However, if the organized health class does its
work effectively, the students will be alerted to the health significance of
everyday occurrences. If students are stimulated and challenged by a competent health instructor, a considerable amount of integrated health
learning will go on.

In-service preparation of all the school staff in the possibilities and
value of integrated health instruction is an ideal which rarely becomes
a reality. Yet the health director or health instructor may enlist the
cooperation of other staff members, particularly those who have a reasonably good background in health training.

Incidental health instruction arises from student-teacher conferences,
questions from students in the classroom, injuries to students, news
reports, tests, and as an outgrowth of some topic outside of the health
field. Incidental instruction should not be superficial teaching. Any
topic under consideration should be developed sufficiently so that the
students understand and appreciate it.

Various activities in the regular program of the school provide health
learning opportunities. Assemblies, lunchroom service, projects of the
student council, announcements on the bulletin board, saftey drives, and
the health examination all contribute to the understanding, appreciation,
and practice of health.

Organizing for health instruction

Health instruction is a recognized area in the curriculum of the
junior high school, and there are very few junior high schools which
do not offer formal classroom instruction in health. The scheduling of

health instruction follows a variety of patterns. Unfortunately in some junior high schools health can truly be labeled an orphan. It is included if the schedule of a particular section or class has a place for it and someone is available to "take" the class. Under such circumstances there is no teaching; someone is merely holding class. In such schools there is an urgent need to apprise the responsible administrators of the importance of health and what an effective health instruction program can do for students. It is significant that some instructors who are not prepared in the field and resent health classes being assigned to them become enthusiastic about the possibilities of health instruction once they acquire a background in health instruction. Even more interesting has been the skeptical administrator who perhaps covertly has been converted to health in the curriculum, but who now points with professional pride to "my health program."

Few subject areas offer the student as much in a functional way as health. Health instruction properly should not use a disproportionate share of the lesson time of the school. Nor should it be relegated to the second-class status of a fringe subject. Several factors determine the schedule and emphasis assigned to health instruction. The traditional

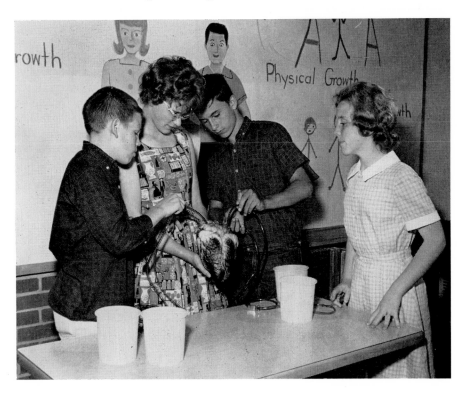

Fig. 52. Demonstration of human circulation. A beef heart, plastic tubes, and red and blue fluids are used to demonstrate the course of blood through the body. (Courtesy Portland Public Schools, Portland, Ore.)

background of the school, state requirements, community demands, the general pattern of the curriculum, the understanding of the administrators, and the competence of the health instructors all affect the nature of health instruction programs.

We can pass by some of the more bizarre arrangements and direct our attention to the more common types of curriculum organization which provide health instruction.

Health incorporated into general science. In a crowded curriculum it is understandable that the uniting of subject areas can be justified for expediency and possible integration. Unfortunately too frequently the marriage of two disciplines is a sort of shotgun wedding which does not turn out too successfully. Usually, biological science instructors who do not have a background in health instruction treat health as a guest, not as a host—nor even a cohost. Biologists frequently regard instruction in physiology as health teaching. It is granted that physiology is a foundation on which to build health instruction, but it is extremely limited in teaching functional health.

A composite course of health and general science can be mutually beneficial. To be successful, such a course must have an instructor interested and professionally prepared in both fields. Some specialists in school health work consider this arrangement the most commendable and satisfactory design for health instruction.

Health incorporated into social studies. A frequent tendency to treat health too superficially and to deal exclusively in the social aspects of health is a common deficiency in this type of arrangement. Even in dealing with community health the social scientist tends to emphasize gov-

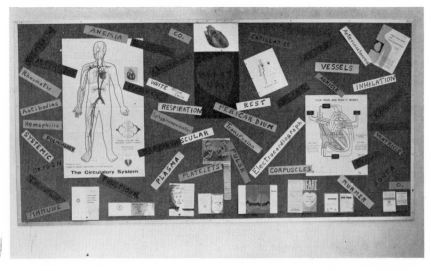

Fig. 53. Vocabulary aid. Novel ideas can help in developing a vocabulary in technical health terminology. Catching the misspellings can add to the interest for the class. (Courtesy Salem Public Schools, Salem, Ore.)

ernment organization and gives very little consideration to real health problems.

An instructor prepared in both social science and health is rather unusual. In a sense public health practice is social engineering, but the type of mind which deals with social engineering has a fundamental interest in the biological aspects as well as the social aspects of human well-being. The combining of health with social studies has been successful. Although the general school situation is significant, it is the individual classroom instructor who is the key to a successful health instructional program.

Health alternated with physical education. As a matter of scheduling convenience, administrators alternate health with physical education. The plan is to teach physical education on Monday, Wednesday, and Friday and health at the same hour on Tuesday and Thursday. During the next week three days are devoted to health and two days to physical education. Unless the instructor in charge is well prepared and highly interested in the health field, health instruction becomes an ugly duckling. Situations of this type have caused students to develop a distaste for health instruction. This is to be expected when one considers the extent to which the attitudes of a teacher are telegraphed to the class. A disinterested instructor leaves the whole class to the students and creates the impression generally that the whole thing is a waste of time and not

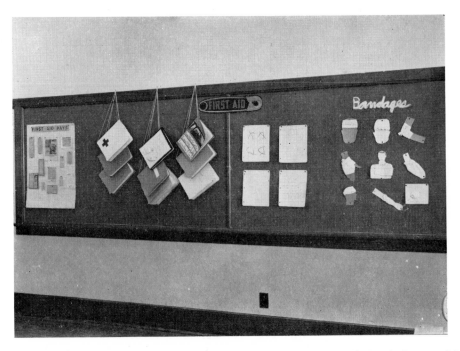

Fig. 54. First aid. Unit on first aid was concluded with a project that displayed the essentials of the facts learned. (Courtesy Salem Public Schools, Salem, Ore.)

worthwhile. It would be better not to schedule health than to foster this type of situation. Even when the instructor is interested in health and is competent to teach it, the three-two scheduling arrangement is generally unsatisfactory.

In some junior high schools physical education is conducted during the fall and spring months. During the inclement weather of winter health is taught.

To schedule health for a half year and physical education for a half year during each of the three years of junior high school is to allot more time to health than is needed or justified. A highly satisfactory plan is to schedule two half years of health instruction on this basis during the junior high school years.

Health as a quarter year-three year course. Too much fragmentation of the health instruction program detracts both from the stature of health as an area and from the effectiveness of the teaching. Rather than integrate health with general science, social science, or any other field, some administrators prefer to assign definite time blocks to health instruction. Occasionally classroom space and available faculty are considerations. A quarter year of health instruction in each grade under the direction of a competent teacher will provide excellent health instruction.

Health as a full-year course. A frequent administrative practice is to schedule health for a full year in the eighth grade. This has proved to be an excellent plan whose excellence is perhaps exceeded only by scheduling a half year of health instruction in each of two years. An ideal schedule of health instruction is to teach it in the second semester in the seventh grade and the first semester in the ninth grade.

Health as a half-year course. The recognized minimum of time devoted to health instruction in the junior high school is a daily period for a half year. When the elementary school has an excellent health program and a full academic credit of health is required in the senior high school, a half year of health instruction in the junior high school can be adequate.

Instructional personnel

Since the recognition of the importance of health instruction, we have seen the abandonment of the unethical practice of assigning teachers to health instruction merely on the expediency of availability. State certification has required preparation for health teaching comparable to preparation in the traditional classical fields. In harmony with state requirements colleges have provided the necessary offerings in their curriculum to prepare the health instructor adequately.

Teachers who are inadequately prepared when first assigned to health instruction have become fully qualified through work in in-service courses, through attending summer sessions at college, and through growth in their classroom role. An interest in health, a good general education background, and good scholastic ability constitute an adequate foundation on which to begin building the necessary qualifications for teaching health in the junior high school.

There is an erroneous impression that a person competent in some other area is not qualified in health instruction. This view has been directed particularly at the physical education instructor. It is true that some physical education majors do a deplorable job of teaching health, but many physical education instructors do outstanding teaching in the health field. Usually these are instructors with a teaching major in physical education and a minor in health. However, some teachers who had very little health preparation originally, through in-service growth and attendance at graduate school, have acquired professional qualifications of the highest order.

Biology instructors, social science instructors, home economics instructors, and other members of the staff may be prepared adequately for health instruction. Competence in one field can be combined with competence in another field. However, deliver a child from the person who, though learned in one field, poses as an expert in all other fields.

Methods of instruction

As in other fields an almost unlimited number of methods and combinations of methods can be used in health instruction, but certain methods appear to be in special favor with health instructors: surveys of health needs and interests, projects, group discussions, panels, symposiums, buzz sessions, lecturettes, reports, demonstrations, presentations of sociodramas, field trips, textbook assignments, reference work, and the use of audiovisual aids. Emphasis on total participation of students, utilization of group interests and recognition, and motivation through self-achievement and self-improvement are the barometers which indicate the essential methods.

Resource unit—what community health resources do we have?

Beginning on a theme of maximum health for every citizen, a well-integrated unit on community resources and services which utilizes the inherent group interests of junior high school students can be evolved. This comprehensive broad unit can be conveniently divided into various areas and thus provide a form of organization which permits easy day-to-day continuity.

UNIT TITLE: WHAT COMMUNITY HEALTH RESOURCES DO WE HAVE?
Preview

The primary responsibility for the promotion of personal health rests upon the individual. Yet in today's complex society no one is totally self-sufficient in attaining and maintaining a desirable standard of health. A reciprocal relationship between personal and community health exists. Frankly in this complex modern life the individual is quite incapable of controlling the many factors which affect his health. The united action of all citizens in the mutual task of health promotion is essential to individual health. Personal and community health have a functional relationship. How the individual lives affects the community, and the health of the community has both direct and indirect effects upon the health of every citizen in the community. Neither the health of the individual nor the community can exist isolated and alone. When the individual fully appreciates these common and interrelated interests, a consciousness of community health emerges.

Few of our citizens have an adequate understanding of the community health resources available to them. An even smaller number appreciates what further community health services are needed and should be made available. If all citizens understood fully how to use community health resources, the quality of the health of the nation would be improved measurably. Those citizens fortunate enough to know the available health services and how to utilize them possess a most valuable asset. The public schools have both an opportunity and an obligation to prepare future adults to avail themselves of community health resources. Even beyond this the adult should understand the further health needs of the community and be willing and eager to initiate and support measures for the extension of the health facilities of the community.

It is equally important that the citizen fully appreciate his obligation

Fig. 55. Health news. To develop the practice of reading articles of health interest, a continuing display of clippings and workbooks of health clippings serve a multitude of educational purposes when the teacher is alert to the many possibilities. (Courtesy Salem Public Schools, Salem, Ore.)

to his community and the health of the people of his community. When each works for the best health of all and all work for the best health of each, everyone is benefitted twofold. This can be attained through an effective program of school health instruction.

The starting point must be an intense interest in one's own quality of health. From this interest a natural transition to an interest in community health is expressed in the question, "What community resources do we have which will protect our high level of health and make it possible to have even better health?" Choosing a physician and dentist and an appraisal of medical, dental, and hospital resources are immediate interests. Consideration of official and voluntary community health services leads logically to a study of existing health problems and projects. State, national, and international health agencies do not touch the citizen directly, but can be of more than academic interest to the student of today whose thinking and interests are much broader than students of previous generations.

Objectives
Knowledge

Quality of health one possesses
Efforts the individual may make in behalf of health
Need for using available community health resources
Need for additional community health resources
Qualifications of a medical doctor
How to choose a physician
Qualifications of a doctor of dentistry
How to choose a dentist
Cost of medical and hospital care
Medical and hospital insurance
All health services provided by the community
Source of the community water supply
Measures to safeguard the water
Fluoridation of water
Community sewage disposal facilities
Disease spread by sewage
Stream pollution as a threat to health
Stream pollution and the destruction of wildlife and stream attractiveness
Individual responsibility for sewage disposal without community service
Relation of garbage and refuse disposal to health and well-being
Community's method of garbage and refuse disposal
Garbage and refuse disposal at a camp or picnic
Insects as a menace to community health

Insect irradication methods
Rodents and community health
Eliminating rodents
Community efforts for the disabled
Needs for further services in aiding the handicapped
Tuberculosis control measures
Community safety program
Services of the American National Red Cross
Medical services in the community
Available dental facilities
Hospital facilities
Importance of adequate medical, dental, and hospital services
Services of voluntary health agencies in the state
How to obtain and use voluntary health agency services
Organization and financing of local public health department
Functions of the health department personnel
Services of the health department
Value of health department services
Organization of the state health department
Services of the state health department
Functions of the United States Public Health Service
Functions of the World Health Organization

Attitudes as expressed in

Appreciation of good health as a personal possession

Constant attention to the promotion of health

Utilizing community health services in promoting personal health

Appreciation of the value of community health resources

Qualifications of a physician and a dentist

Cost of medical and dental care

Medical and hospital insurance

Value of community health services to the individual

Projects

Class make a schedule of qualities essential to health

Each class member appraise and rate his own health

Symposium on topic *Procedures for Personal Health Promotion*

Guest participation by member of local medical society

Guest participation by member of local dental society

Report on cost of medical care

Guest participation by qualified impartial health insurance representative

Report on article *A Quick Look at Some New Directions in Health Insurance Plans**

Show film *Another Light* (community hospital service†)

Show film *Miracle Money* (exposes quackery) ‡

Community health services

Topics

All health services provided by the community

Source of the community water supply

Safeguards to protect the water

Laboratory examinations of water

Effect of fluorides in drinking water

Small water supplies

Dangers of improper sewage disposal

Modern sewage disposal plants

Stream pollution

Preventing stream pollution

Disposing of garbage and refuse in a city

Disposing of garbage and refuse in rural areas

Garbage disposal while camping or on a picnic

Insects as a menace to health

Insects of local importance

Insect breeding areas in the community

Insect control measures

The menace of rodents

Rodent breeding areas

Rodent eradication measures

Projects

Show film *Defending the City's Health*§

Guest participation by city official

Visit community water plant

Show film *City Water Supply*§

Show film *Health and the Cycle of Water*‖

Show film *Safe Drinking Water From Small Water Supplies*¶

Show film *Mr. Farmer Builds a Septic Tank***

Guest participation by health department sanitarian

Survey of garbage and refuse disposal

Survey of insect breeding areas

Show film *Inserts as Carriers of Disease*††

---

*Health Information Foundation.

†Bailey Films, Inc. (25 minutes).

‡Teaching Films Custodian, Inc. (22 minutes).

§Encyclopedia Britannica Films (11 minutes).

‖Louisiana State Board of Health (16 minutes).

¶University of Minnesota (12 minutes).

**Portland Cement Association (19 minutes).

††Institute of Inter-American Affairs (10 minutes).

Report on community sewage disposal and stream pollution

Guest participation by rodent exterminator

Show film *Get Rid of Rats**

Community health projects

Topics

Community efforts for the disabled

Community responsibility

Family responsibility

Further needs for the handicapped

Test programs for tuberculosis

Student participation in test programs for tuberculosis

Other tuberculosis control measures

Importance of tuberculosis program to junior high school students

Community safety program

Statistics on motor vehicle accidents

Regulations governing motor vehicles

Pedestrian and bicycle safety in the community

Citizen cooperation and responsibility motor vehicle safety

Responsibilities in case of an accident

Special traffic safety problems in the community

Services of the American National Red Cross

Blook bank

Disaster relief

Citizen support of all community health projects

Projects

Committee report on crippled children services

Report on community services for the handicapped

Committee to make class plans to have chest x-ray

Guest participation by traffic officer

Guest participation by traffic court judge

Visit traffic court session

Sociodrama to illustrate situation of court trial dealing with violation of pedestrian, bicycle, or motor vehicle

Show film *A Day in Court*†

All students avail themselves of opportunity to have chest x-ray

Guest participation by nurse on tuberculosis control measures

Show film *Lease on Life*‡

Show film *Tuberculosis*§

Show film *Bicycling With Complete Safety*‖

Guest participation by American National Red Cross representative

Visit American National Red Cross blood donation clinic

Panel discussion on topic *Participating in Community Health Projects*

Medical, dental, and hospital resources

Topics

The number of practicing physicians available to the community

Medical specialties

Practicing dentists available to the community

Dental specialties

Available hospital resources in the community

Nursing homes and other similar resources

Future medical and hospital needs

Cost of hospital construction and maintenance

Projects

Survey of physicians and dentists available

Report of committee designated to visit a hospital

---

*National Film Board of Canada (10 minutes).

†Bailey Films, Inc. (10 minutes).

‡National Tuberculosis Association (20 minutes).

§Encyclopedia Britannica Films (11 minutes).

‖Rarig Motion Picture Co. (30 minutes).

Guest participation by member of hospital staff

Guest participation by member of nursing home staff

Panel discussion on topic *Should Hospital Care Be Free to All?*

Voluntary health agencies
Topics

Name and list services of all voluntary health agencies serving the community

Persons in charge of each of the agencies

Name and services of other voluntary health agencies serving the state

How to obtain and use voluntary health agency services

Supporting voluntary health organizations

Value of such organizations to the community and to the individual

Need for such organizations

Health needs not being served which voluntary organizations may fulfill

Projects

Committee survey of community voluntary health organizations

Guest participation by representatives of these organizations

Letters to voluntary agencies in the state but outside of the community

Reports on topic *What Voluntary Health Agencies Can do for Me*

Local health department
Topics

Organization of the local health department

Financing the health department

Staff of the department

Record keeping of the department

Material health services

Infant and preschool services

Child health services

Services to the schools

Adult health services

Communicable disease control activities

Sanitation activities

Importance of continuous health services

Using services to the greatest advantage

Projects

Visit to the health department

Guest participation by member of the health department staff

Symposium on the value of the various activities of the health department

Show film *Defending the City's Health**

Show film *Public Health Service**

State, national, and international health agencies
Topics

Organization of the state health department

Services of the department

The United States Public Health Service

Activities of the United States Public Health Service

The World Health Organization

Promotion of good will in the world through World Health Organization

Projects

Committee report on the state health department

Report on the United States Public Health Service

Report on World Health Organization

Symposium on topic *Health Problems of the World*

Panel discussion on topic *Health as an Agency of Peace*

Class appraisal of America's quality of health

Class appraisal of America's health services

---

*Encyclopaedia Britannica Films (11 minutes; 10 minutes).

Evaluation

That the students should acquire certain knowledge from this unit is quite obvious. Most important, however, is the development of wholesome attitudes toward community health promotion. This means a willingness to cooperate with and contribute to health projects in the community. If a child understands the resources of community health and identifies them with his own welfare at an early age, he is more likely to use these services, support them, and insist on their continuation when he becomes an adult. Practices will consist of using the available community health services and observing the effects of these services on personal and community health.

Resource unit—tobacco, alcohol, and other harmful drugs

Some instructors in the school health program prefer to defer a consideration of tobacco, alcohol, and drugs until the last two years of the senior high school. However, both observation and organized study have revealed that adults who use tobacco, alcohol, and other harmful drugs do not lack knowledge of the effects of these products. They lack the kind of attitudes which will cause them to refrain from the harmful use of these products. If the school is to help individuals acquire certain desirable attitudes toward the use of harmful products, the junior high school will provide the most fertile soil for effective results. Proper attitudes established in the junior high school, fortified by the acquisition of further supporting knowledge in senior high school, would in effect constitute the most effective type of program of instruction about tobacco, alcohol, and other harmful drugs.

Overview

Much of what has been said and written on this subject had been of doubtful value because of the bias of individuals who tend to overstate or understate to serve their own prejudices. Individuals with something to sell or those imbued with a missionary zeal to reform everyone who uses tobacco, alcohol, or other harmful drugs present only one side of the question greatly distorted. The need is for an objective presentation of what is known and what is not known on the subject so that each child can formulate his own conclusions and establish his own values and standards.

Presentation of the subject as a physical, mental, and social health problem primarily, rather than a moral or legal problem, will establish the unit on a sound foundation. Children who have learned to prize their health highly will reject anything which is likely to jeopardize that health. When they understand why people use these products and the psychological aspects of habituation, they will tend to develop attitudes which reject the use of tobacco, alcohol, and other harmful drugs.

The instructor should recognize that many students come from homes in which tobacco and alcohol are used regularly. Data need not be

Fig. 56. A symposium panel in a junior high school health class. In this unusually large class large panel or discussion groups provide for more extensive participation.

feathered for their benefit. These children can face and accept reliable unadulterated data. Yet as health instructors we should not create the impression that all people who drink alcohol will become alcoholics. We also need to make crystal clear that it takes about 20 years for tobacco smoke irritants to have an effect in creating cancer and that, because individuals vary in susceptibility, some persons may be entirely immune to the production of cancer of the respiratory system.

Controversial questions should be analyzed systematically and thoroughly by the whole class. The teacher can help to guide the thinking of the class, particularly in weighing the reliability of data. Not all questions will be resolved satisfactorily. Perhaps further exploration will be indicated.

Junior high school students need and are interested in fundamental questions and problems, not detailed data. It is necessary to guard against consuming valuable class time with questions of minor significance or voluminous details. A straightforward consideration of the main factors in the study will make the unit comprehensible, meaningful, and impressive to the youngsters.

Objectives
Knowledge

Composition of tobacco smoke
Action of nicotine

Week-end and aggressive drinkers
The path of alcoholism

Effect of smoking on respiratory system
Effect of smoking on digestive system
Effect of smoking on circulation
Effects of smoking on circulation
Effects of smoking on thyroid gland
Length of life and smoking
Motherhood and smoking
Why people smoke
Nature of ethyl (grain) alcohol
Absorption of alcohol
Intoxication as indicated by blood-alcohol concentration
Alcoholic malnutrition
Alcohol effect is always narcotic
Effect of alcohol on circulation
Effect of alcohol on nerve conduction
Effect of alcohol on physical health
Relationship of alcohol and mental disorder
Alcohol and the length of life
Absence of a hereditary basis for alcoholism
The social drinker

Why people drink alcohol
Alcoholism as a problem of the individual
Alcoholism as a family problem
Alcoholism as a community problem
Curing alcoholism
Preventing alcoholism
Community responsibility
Marihuana as a threat to youth
Source of marihuana
Methods employed to recruit users
Action of marihuana
Measures to control marihuana
Why people take morphine
Action of morphine
Measures to control morphine
The problem of sleeping pills (barbiturates)
Action of barbiturates
Measures to solve the barbiturate addiction problem
Importance of substituting a healthful practice for an unhealthy one

Attitudes as expressed in

a Desire to conserve and protect personal health
Desire to avoid those factors which injure health
b Conviction that prevention is better than cure
C Recognition that smoking adds nothing of value to a person
Self-reliance in refusing to begin injurious practices
Reliance upon one's own ability to adjust, not on a crutch such as tobacco
d Self-gratification through wholesome achievement
Realization that one must make his own decisions
Insistence upon having facts before making decisions
E Refusal to go along blindly with a popular practice
Pride in the ability to be master of one's actions

Acceptance of inconvenience resulting from nonconformity
Respect for the right of others to choose their practices
Support of worthy recreation outlets for youth
Promotion of wholesome school atmosphere
F Support of community efforts to control use of tobacco, alcohol, and other harmful drugs
Recognition of social pathology of alcoholism and drug addiction
G Acceptance of responsibility for dealing with the problems of smoking, alcoholism, and drug addiction
H Acceptance of the alcoholic and drug addict as an ill person
Need for constant vigilance in preventing marihuana peddlers from recruiting students
I Avoid use of drugs, including barbiturates, except on prescription

Practices

Be guided by established health principles
Engage in wholesome recreation outlets
Conform to community laws and regulations

Follow positive mental health principles
Take drugs only on a physician's prescription

Content and activities

Tobacco

What is the nature and action of nicotine?

What irritants are present in tobacco tar?

What is meant by differences in tolerance?

What causes smoker's cough?

How does smoking affect nutrition?

How does smoking affect the heart and blood pressure?

Why does smoking cause a tremor in some people?

What is the evidence that smoking is related to cancer of the respiratory system?

How does smoking affect the length of life?

Panel discussion on topic *Why Do People Smoke?*

Symposium on topics *Smoking and Athletics, Popularity, and Cost*

Sociodrama to illustrate life situation refusing a cigarette

Ask class to list disadvantages of smoking, with help of chairman and recorder

Panel discussion on topic *Why should the expectant or Nursing Mother Refrain From Smoking?*

Buzz session on topic *How Would You Persuade a Person to Quite Smoking?*

Assignment, written report, on subject *Why I would Be wise Not to Smoke Until I am 30 Years of Age*

Show film *Alcohol and Tobacco: What They Do to Our Bodies* *

Alcohol

Why is alcohol called the benevolent tyrant?

What are some valuable uses of alcohol?

What is meant by ethyl alcohol?

How is a laboratory test of blood used to determine drunkenness?

How does alcohol affect circulation?

Why do alcoholics suffer from poor nutrition?

What effect does alcohol have on general health?

How does alcohol affect the length of life?

Why is alcohol called a narcotic?

What mental changes does alcohol cause?

Why does a person take the first drink of alcohol?

What is a social drinker?

How extensive is the problem of alcohol in the United States?

How does a person become an alcoholic?

What is the community's responsibility to the alcoholic?

Why must alcoholism be regarded as an illness?

Sociodrama to illustrate the situation refusing a drink of alcohol

Symposium on topic *Effect of Alcoholism on the Individual, the Family, the Individual's Employer, the Community*

Guest participation by a representative of Alcoholics Anonymous

Written reports on *Why the Group I Belong to Is So Important to My Health and Well-Being*

Show film *Alcohol and the Human Body*†

Show film *Alcohol is Dynamite*‡

Show film *It's the Brain That Counts*§

Conduct survey on sale of alcohol in the community

Report on community program to reduce consumption of alcohol

Keep a clipping booklet of convictions for drunken driving

Marihuana

From where is marihuana obtained?

Where does the plant grow?

What does the national government do to control marihuana?

---

*Coronet Films (11 minutes).

†Encyclopaedia Britannica Films (15 minutes).

‡Sid Davis Productions (10 minutes).

§Woman's Christian Temperance Union (20 minutes).

How is marihuana used in the United States?

How is it peddled?

How does marihuana affect a person?

How is it related to crime?

Report on topic *Marihuana and Youth*

Obtain a picture of the *Cannabis sativa* plant

Show film *Terrible Truth**

Morphine

What is the value of morphine in medical practice?

What is meant by drug addiction?

How does a person become an addict?

What psychological factors are involved?

What does the national government do about the drug addiction problem?

What does the community do?

Guest participation by member of police department to discuss alcohol and morphine control measures

Sociodrama to illustrate how youth may be lured into the dope habit

Show film *A Story of a Teen-Age Drug Addict*†

Sleeping pills

What are the causes of sleeplessness?

What is the wisdom of consulting a physician?

How do barbiturates affect one?

What kind of people rely on barbiturates?

What measures should these people take for wholesome living?

Conduct survey to determine whether in the community a prescription is needed before obtaining barbiturates

Collect newspaper and magazine clippings of deaths and near-deaths due to an overdose of sleeping pills

Evaluation

In evaluation it is most important to determine whether students have acquired the attitude that drugs are injurious to physical, mental, and social health and should never be used except when prescribed by a physician. Knowledge is important to support these attitudes and prepare the student to evaluate the desirability of never starting an undesirable practice. "This will not be me," should be the cardinal attitude. Knowledge of individual and community responsibility is important. Avoiding certain practices is a negative approach, but has value in this area. Engaging in wholesome activities, following positive mental health principles, and conforming to community laws should be observable outcomes.

Evaluation

The effectiveness of a program for health instruction in junior high school must be measured in terms of the extent to which it has changed the individual student. That change will be in the understanding of health, in health practices, and most important in health attitudes.

Health understanding that is based on fundamental health principles, not infinitesimal detail, is the important knowledge which should be evaluated. Ability to interpret and evaluate health factors is important in understanding. Knowledge of sources of health data, health resources,

---

*Sid Davis Productions (10 minutes).

†Young America Films, Inc. (20 minutes).

and methods for dealing with health problems should be an outcome of health instruction. An understanding of community health and united efforts in behalf of health are important results of effective health instruction on the junior high school level.

Health practices should expand from practices for sheer personal benefit to practices in behalf of the group, the school, and the community as an outgrowth of health instruction in junior high school.

Attitudes which the student acquires are especially important at this level of health instruction. They are difficult to measure objectively, but a discriminating instructor can detect indications of student attitudes. Particularly important are the attitudes toward a high level of personal health, utilization of established health principles, application of reason in matters of health, responsibility for the health of others, and cooperation in community health standards and assets.

In a junior high school in which an effective program in health instruction is in operation, students are conscious of the importance of personal and community health. The vitality of the students and the atmosphere about the school reflect the kind of health program in action. An effective health instruction program does not grow up overnight like a mushroom. It is the product of planned long-range efforts. There will be ample evidence of its effectiveness.

Selected readings

Alberty, H. B.: Developing a curriculum that meets the needs of junior high school youth, Bulletin of the National Association of Principals **31:**69, April, 1947.

Byrd, O. E.: Health instruction yearbook, Stanford, Calif., Stanford University Press.

Denison, L.: Junior high school looks at its school health program, Journal of School Health 25:14, 1955.

Faunce, R. C., and Clute, M. J.: Teaching and learning in the junior high school, Belmont, Calif., 1961, Wadsworth Publishing Co.

Grout, Ruth E.: Health teaching in schools, ed. 4, Philadelphia, 1963, W. B. Saunders Co.

Haag, Jesse H.: School health program, New York, 1958, Henry Holt & Co., Inc.

Harnett, A., and Shaw, J.: Effective school health education, New York, 1959, Appleton-Century-Crofts, Inc.

Health teaching syllabus for junior and senior high schools, Albany, 1949, University of the State of New York.

Irwin, L. W., Humphrey, J. H., and Johnson, W. R.: Methods and materials in health education, St. Louis, 1956, The C. V. Mosby Co.

Joint Committee on Health Problems in Education of the National Education Associa-

tion and the American Medical Association (Bernice R. Moss, W. H. Southworth, and J. L. Reichart, editors): Health education, Washington, D. C., 1961. The Association.

Kellogg Foundation: An experience in health education, Battle Creek, Mich., 1950, The W. K. Kellogg, Foundation.

Kilander, H. F.: School health education, New York, 1962, The Macmillan Co.

National Safety Council: Safety education methods, secondary schools, Chicago, 1939, The Council.

Oberteuffer, D.: School health education, ed. 3, New York, 1960, Harper & Brothers.

Schneider, R.: Methods and materials of health education, Philadelphia, 1958, W. G. Saunders Co.

Suggested teaching units in community health for the junior high school, Bulletin no. 2, Boston, 1940, Massachusetts Department of Education and Department of Health.

Turner, C. E., Sellery, C. M., and Smith, Sara L.: School health and health education, ed. 4, St. Louis, 1961, The C. V. Mosby Co.

Williams, Catherine M.: Sources of teaching materials, Teaching Aids Laboratory Pamphlet no. 1, Columbus, 1958, The Ohio State University, Bureau of Educational Research and Service.

Chapter 14

Senior high school health instruction

Ligh schools no longer devote their major efforts to preparatory education, but deal primarily in terminal education. Graduates leaving the high school today have had the benefit of a curriculum designed to prepare them for the journey of life. They leave with a foundation on which to build life's structure. Surely no course in the high school has more to offer the student for the needs of life than health when it is effectively taught. To be effective health instruction must be adapted to the distinctive characteristics of the high school age.

The high school age represents a transition between childhood and adulthood. In this period of life the individual at times will display the consistency of mature adulthood and at other times will exhibit the inconsistency of childhood. Youth is a period of transition from the dependence of childhood to the independence of adulthood. Self-assertion, determination, and independence reveal the desire of all youth for emancipation from adult domination and for recognition as competent self-reliant individuals in their own right. They want to know the *how* and *why* as well as the *what*. High school students are imaginative, enthusiastic, sensitive, and idealistic. They seek status within their group and try to merit the respect of their instructors. These children need to have a mature standard of values and positive motivation for self-esteem and to experience enjoyment through success. Equally important they must be aware of the growth in their own understanding, viewpoints, standards, and conduct.

In high school the instructor is directing students who have virtually attained the extent of their native intelligence. They lack experience and can acquire a great deal more knowledge, but they do have a near-mature intellect. They have the equipment to profit greatly by experience and to acquire knowledge when the opportunity is available. It is the instructor's task to help them use their native intelligence. The instructor can chal-

377

lenge these young people by providing stimulating opportunities for learning. These experiences can be most meaningful when the students have a role in planning and implementing the instructional program. In education as self-growth, a child must participate actively in creativeness and analysis as well as in sheer memorization. It must develop as growth from within. The instructor guides this growth by providing motivation through wholesome experiences. The student will learn something about health without the assistance of an instructor, but effective instruction will increase his health understanding at least twofold.

Basic objectives of health instruction

A high school student is on the threshold of adulthood. In a few short years he will be relying on his own initiative in a highly competitive social order. To enable this young person to play his proper role in our complex society, the school has an obligation to develop his potential ability to assume the obligations of adulthood. A high school student will learn about health after he graduates. But how observing and discerning he is of health matters, how he interprets and evaluates, and the extent of his health interests will depend upon his health preparation in high school. Thus the high school graduate should have a solid foundation of health knowledge, understanding, values, interpretations, attitudes, and practices which will enable him to evaluate and utilize opportunities for health education. Such a foundation will assure him of the equipment to direct his own health needs, promote his own health, guide the health of his family, utilize health services in the community properly, and make the necessary decisions relating to health.

When the student enters senior high school, he has established certain desirable health practices, developed wholesome health attitudes, and acquired certain health knowledge. These health practices and attitudes should be furthered and fortified in the senior high school by scientific knowledge. The student in high school will be assured that certain practices and attitudes have health value when he has scientifically established knowledge in support of these practices and attitudes. Principal emphasis in senior high school health instruction should be on the acquisition of such knowledge as the adult citizen should have. Health practices and attitudes need not be neglected nor disregarded. Usually they will be by-products of knowledge, but direct attention should be given to health practices and attitudes to ensure the fullest value from the health knowledge. Practices and attitudes are expressions of applied knowledge.

Although the general objective of senior high school health instruction is the acquisition of knowledge, the establishment of practices, and the development of attitudes, the high school health instructor must have certain specific objectives as a guide.

Knowledge related to

Qualities of optimum health	Adjustment in marriage
Methods of personal health promotion	Mental health

Biological bases of health
Heredity and eugenics
Growth and development
Personal grooming
Choice and use of health services and products
Nutrition
Health aspects of activity, fatigue, and rest
Sex and reproduction

Stimulants and narcotics
Common poisons
Communicable and noncommunicable disease control
Community health problems
Community health resources
Sanitation
Health aspects of air and sunlight
Safety
Emergency care and first aid

Attitudes as expressed in

Concern for the quality of one's health
Appreciation of the value of health
Appreciation of moderation and regularity in health promotion
Recognition of the importance of periodic health examinations
Attention to any deviation from normal
Utilization of professional services for restoring health
Concern for having disorders corrected immediately
Interest in new advances in health science
Eagerness to acquire mature understanding of health
Acceptance of only verified health information

Refrain from self-diagnosis and self-medication
Recognition of the value of prevention
Acceptance of responsibility for the health of others
Safety consciousness
Willingness to cooperate in health programs
Support of community health efforts
Appreciation of community health services
Interest in community health problems
Interest in state health problems and programs
Interest in national health promotion
Interest in international health promotion

Practices

Apply health principles to daily living
Apply reasoning to health problems
Use recognized nutrition practices
Engage in moderate activity daily
Avoid overexertion and extreme fatigue
Obtain adequate rest regularly
Refrain from self-medication
Refrain from the use of tobacco, alcohol, and other harmful drugs
Use preventive measures against communicable diseases
Have tests for tuberculosis when available
Self-imposed isolation when communicable disease is suspected

Use recognized safety measures
Make wholesome adjustment to frustration
Participate in normal social activities
Adapt effectively to different individuals and situations
Recover quickly from emotional upsets
Use established sanitary measures
Assume responsibility for improving the environment
Follow all community health laws and regulations
Participate in school and community health promotion
Support special health projects

One might postulate on the quality of the health and life expectancy of the nation if all high school graduates had a health education in terms of these objectives. Perfection in education is not expected, but the goal expressed in these objectives can serve as the ideal. If this ideal cannot be attained, it can be approximated in many individual students. To be classified as successful, a health instruction program need not meet these objectives 100% for every student, but every graduate should have a substantial knowledge of fundamental health principles, a positive health awareness, and established health practices.

Although high school health instruction properly emphasizes the practical aspects of education, opportunities for cultural developments are always present. Pride in high standards of personal cleanliness, grooming, vigor, and appearance promotes the self-esteem which is so essential to a high level of mental health. It expresses a refinement which reflects the personal culture that usually flows over into other spheres of life. If it is properly guided, this application of high standards to personal well-being will be projected to a desire for high environmental standards as well.

Certain factual knowledge may be of academic value only, but frequently is highly interesting to students. A skillful instructor will use this interest to motivate exploration into related practical aspects of the factual material. The fact that in the United States the ratio is seven females to one male at 85 years of age is largely an academic matter, but students' interest in the phenomenon can be directed toward the health implications of the ratio.

Areas of primary interest

In harmony with the modern philosophy of secondary education, so far as possible, the school should prepare the student for the life ahead. In health this would mean an understanding of all possible aspects of health. In a practical sense this is the province of health education in the senior high school. It may not be possible to deal with all aspects of all health areas, but it should be possible to deal thoroughly with the important fundamentals of all areas. In proposing the areas of primary interest to the youth of the nation, it is recognized that local circumstances can account for additional health interests. In some communities certain health factors or areas are of minor interest and significance. The implication is that in any high school it is advisable from a practical standpoint and sound from an educational standpoint for the students to participate in planning the areas to be studied. Special health interests and needs of the group may be discovered through surveys and class discussion. A committee of students can be used to sift out the most generally expressed interests.

Even when class interests are surveyed and used as a guide a core of health areas of general interest to high school students can be of value. Such a core ensures a reasonably comprehensive health instruction program. These areas also express the health education needs of the adult citizen. Modifications and adjustments are in order at any time. Developments and circumstances during the school year may require changes in the original plan and indicate a vital flexible health instruction program. The core of areas of health interest should thus be thought of as the starting pattern (see outline on opposite page).

General areas studied in previous grades are studied in the senior high school also. Reconsideration of these areas again can be highly beneficial if the high school begins where previous instruction left off and proceeds from there. Dealing with these areas from the adult's point of view involves analysis, interpretation, and evaluation of the most significant aspects of health science. Emphasis on the *how* and *why* develops the critical approach which is so important to persons who soon will be personally responsible for their own health problems.

The principal difficulty for the high school health instructor is that he has to open up the gates of opportunity with one hand for the best students while with the other hand he leads the least competent students by a long, long tether.

Physical health

Indices of personal health
Personal health promotion
Extension of the prime of life
Life expectation
Use of medical and dental services
Periodic examinations
Use of health products
Biological bases of health
    Physiology
    Functional anatomy
    Microbiology
Heredity
Eugenics
Physical growth and development
Personal care
    Skin
    Oral health
    Hearing
    Vision
Nutrition
    Dietary practices
Sex and reproduction
Health aspects of activity
Fatigue, rest, and sleep
Stimulants and narcotics
Other poisons
Communicable diseases

Noncommunicable diseases
Health aspects of air and sunshine
Safety promotion
Emergency care and first aid

Mental health

Emotional development
Attributes of a well-adjusted personality
Motivation of human conduct
Adjustment to common problems
Personality adjustment
Adjustment in marriage

Community health

Community health problems
Community health resources
    Official agencies
    Voluntary agencies
Community health services
Special health promotion
Medical and dental resources
Hospital facilities
Health frauds and quackery
State health resources
State health problems
National health promotion
International health programs

Correlation of health and other subject areas

Reciprocal relationships exist between health and other curriculum areas in the high school, but are little used in unifying the student's learning experiences and knowledge. Health is a collective science which utilizes concepts, data, and materials from many sources. It is an applied discipline which devotes itself to human welfare and incorporates biological, psychological, social, economic, and physical aspects of human existence. Too frequently the health instructor does not adequately assist the student to see how knowledge in some other field is applied to health science. To point out such applications is to develop one of the fundamental characteristics of a well-educated person, i.e., the ability to see relationships.

Control of communicable disease is much better understood when the student has a grasp of the characteristics and function of disease-producing organisms. A study of the physiological basis of activity provides an appreciation of the factors of exercise, fatigue, and rest. Social studies reveal the meaning of family relations and economic conditions in health terms. A foundation in nutrition and family life needs are obtained in home economics classes. A study of physical science provides the health field with the fundamentals of light and optics. Mathematical rates permit meaningful presentations of ratios or relationships. It is apparent that in every hour of health instruction material from other fields will be utilized in some form or other. The health instructor should help the students to appreciate this use of knowledge from other areas of instruction.

Viewed from the other direction virtually all subject areas in the high school have opportunities for incorporating health instruction into their classroom activities. Some areas have only occasional opportunities, but other areas have repeated situations in which health applications are directly involved or in which further elaboration will include health aspects of the topic.

To be aware of these opportunities and to utilize them, instructors in fields outside of health must have some preparation. Ideally this should be provided in the instructor's preparation for teaching, but it rarely is. In the absence of such background experience in-service and postprofessional training should be provided. Administrative encouragement and health director leadership and assistance can make the necessary preparation possible.

The incorporation of health instruction into other subject areas is so important that Chapter 15 is devoted entirely to its treatment. If health is to be reflected in a young person's way of life, it should be a part of all possible aspects of his school living. Such a school experience is most likely to provide the complete unified health education which is the goal of all health instruction.

Integrated and incidental health learning

Incidental health learning is a by-product of various school experiences. At times the learning will be minor, but in certain instances the incidental learning will be particularly valuable. The ability of the instructor to guide students in recognizing the health significance of the experience determines the degree of learning they derive from a given opportunity. Incidental health learning can result from accidents, student-teacher conferences, news reports, school and community incidents, and student questions on health and as a development of some question far afield from health. Incidental teaching should not be brushed off lightly. The question under consideration may be of deep concern to one

Fig. 57. Principles of biology applied to health instruction. Correlated teaching can result in more lasting learning.

or all of the students. It is imperative that any health question be pursued to a point at which the students will have a satisfactory grasp of the solution to the question.

Integrated health learning is functional learning. To gain health understanding from participation in the many school activities is to develop a type of ability for learning which should be invaluable in years to come. A person who gains most from the various experiences of life is he with a mind-set which alerts him to the various implications of situations. He is able to gain insight into the operation of health phenomena in a diversity of experiences. Providing these opportunities for integrated health learning in school is half of the task. The other half is to utilize these opportunities to the fullest. Health instructors are expected to make use of the health possibilities in any activity, but ideally all teachers should likewise be alert to the opportunities for health learning. In many high schools this situation exists to an acceptable, not necessarily optimum, degree.

Some of the regular high school activities which provide possibilities for integrated health learning may be enumerated: assemblies, athletics, bulletin boards, proper illumination, lunchroom service, school newspaper, safety drives, student councils, example of teachers, ventilation, and the health council. This does not exhaust the possibilities. An alert health instructor can make a health learning experience out of almost any student activity.

Health council. Under proper supervision a health council can contribute directly and indirectly to student health and school living. Its possibilities for health learning can be visualized by studying the constitution of a typical high school health council or health committee.

High schools which are overorganized may delegate the functions of the health council to a committee of the student council and thus dispense with the health council. Smaller high schools tend to vest these health functions in the student council. Whatever organization is used, high schools will find that these health functions contribute to the school health program, particularly to health learning.

Health Council Constitution

Name	The name of this organization shall be The Health Council of _____High School.
Object	The aim of this council shall be to provide and attain optimum health status, services, and environment for the students, faculty, and staff of this high school.
Functions	The Health Council shall be a planning, coordinating, and executing body.

The Health Council shall direct its efforts to:
1. Providing a healthful school environment
2. Providing a healthful living environment for students in the community
3. Providing services which will maintain and improve various factors which affect the physical and mental health of students
4. Working in close cooperation with health agencies and personnel which have services to contribute to the health of students
5. Coordinating the work of various agencies which affect the health of students and faculty
6. Maintaining relationships with commercial interests in the community which may have contributions to make to school health
7. Providing health counseling and other services to individual students

Membership The Health Council shall include in its membership:
1. Two representatives of the Student Council to be elected annually by the members of that council
2. Three students from each of the three classes to be elected annually at the class election
3. Two faculty members appointed by the principal
4. Director of the school health program, dean of girls, dean of boys, chief custodian, manager of the school lunchroom, and the school nurse

Officers and Executive Committee Officers of the Health Council shall be: Chairman, vice-chairman, and secretary, each to be elected for terms of one year by the council from its own membership at its first fall meeting. The Executive Committee of the council shall consist of the officers and the director of the school health program.

The Executive Committee shall plan and execute the business of the Council in the interim between council meetings.

Policies Such policies as are developed within the Health Council shall be consistent with general policies of the school.

Meetings Regular meetings shall be held during the activity period of the second Wednesday of each month. Special meetings may be called

	by the chairman or upon the request of three members of the Council.
Quorum	A quorum of the Health Council shall consist of a majority of its members.
Governing Authority	The Health Council shall operate in conformity with the latest edition of *Roberts' Rules of Order* unless procedures contrary to that authority are agreed upon by the council.

Organizing for health instruction

Today it is an unusual senior high school which does not offer classroom instruction in health. Some high schools offer health as an elective, but the present trend is to require one credit in health for graduation. In some instances this is a state requirement established by the state board of education or by statutory provision. However, without the benefit of state provisions many local school districts specify one or more credits in health as a requirement for graduation. This recognition of the importance of health instruction is in harmony with the present-day emphasis upon a functional curriculum.

Occasionally health is a phase of a large core area which may be variously titled. Completion of the work in the core area is thus recognized as meeting the health requirement for graduation. Health, which is taught as a phase of a larger area, can be taught effectively as an integrated learning experience. However, usually such instruction deals with only a rather small part of the total health field. Emphasis is placed on one phase of health to the almost complete omission of other phases Social health may be developed fully, but physical aspects of health and even mental health are given cursory consideration. All phases of health should be given adequate emphasis before health instruction is considered satisfactory for graduation purposes.

The separation of boys and girls for health instruction is gradually giving way to the more normal practice of assigning both boys and girls to the same class. When health is paired with physical education, boys and girls are usually separated for health instruction. In some communities boys and girls are traditionally separated for health classes. Thus circumstances may dictate separation of the boys and girls. Such scheduling does not necessarily create a difficult teaching situation. Some excellent health instructors prefer this arrangement. However, there is a serious objection that the students are conditioned to think of health and the separation of the sexes as synonymous.

Should a man teach a health class of girls? Should a woman teach a class of boys? If the instructor is competent, mature, and poised, the answer certainly is yes. Many men have done a superb job of teaching health to a class of girls. Many women have done equally well with a class of boys. Perhaps a mixed class would have all the benefits of such competent instruction without the negative association of health with a separation of the sexes.

Health incorporated into biological science. Unification of health and biological science is entirely logical and could provide an excellent teaching situation for the instructor who is competent in both of the disciplines. Unfortunately when such an arrangement is made, the instructor is professionally trained for teaching biology. He may have little or no interest in health instruction. Even with some background in the health field the biologist frequently tends to treat health as a poor relative. An instructor interested in both fields and prepared in both fields can make the integrated offering an enrichment of both fields. Health provides for the application of fundamental biological principles. In turn biological principles point up the why and how of health principles and practices. Such opportunities for integration of subject fields are few.

Occasionally an instructor prepared in health instruction, but not particularly interested in fundamental biological science, has responsibility for an integrated health-biology offering. Here the fundamental principles of biological science frequently are slighted in favor of the applied health science. Students would lose the value of understanding fundamental biological concepts.

In a few instances one sees a reasonably good balance between the two disciplines when they are combined in a single course. The results range from good to excellent, especially when evaluated in terms of functional learning.

If the two instructors plan and work together, separate courses of biological science and health can be coordinated and will virtually constitute an integrated offering. Such arrangements are not difficult and represent a widely accepted practice. The school should consider this arrangement unless an instructor who is capable of conducting the unified course is available.

Health alternated with physical education. In many high schools health instructors also teach physical education. For this reason health and physical education would be paired when schedules are worked out. Available physical education facilities also affect the scheduling of health. It must thus be recognized that in some situations health class schedules must be adapted to physical education schedules.

One highly undesirable schedule plan is to alternate health and physical education daily. It is commonly referred to as the 3-2 plan. It results in a dilution which makes health instruction a mere veneer. Surveys of entering college freshmen who have had high school health work reveal that those who have been on a 3-2 schedule score lowest as a group on standard health knowledge tests. Even more significant, in a parallel survey this group indicated the least liking for health as a subject in high school. Neither the alibi of limited gymnasium facilities nor the excuse of "making the instructor available" is valid. The same number of hours of gymnasium space is available in the day, regardless of the schedule. An instructor teaches the same number of hours for two classes regardless of how those two classes may be scheduled. Health and physical education can be scheduled more expeditiously than the 3-2 arrangement.

Health on a quarter-year basis. A fairly frequent practice is to schedule health for one quarter in each of the three or four high school years. Usually physical education will be scheduled the other three quarters. A few physical education instructors object to this plan because students will have no physical education during an entire quarter. This objection is not too serious unless the primary objective of physical education is to give the student a workout. Modern physical education is more concerned wtih developing skills and correlated mental health for life's needs than with physical exertion as such.

The scheduling of health classes on a quarter-year basis is acceptable, but not as satisfactory as scheduling for a longer period of time in each year in which health is given. The quarter-year class represents too much segmentation. Certain continuity is possible, but some discontinuity is very likely to occur.

Full-year basis. To schedule health in the junior or senior year on a full-year basis will provide a concentrated study of health. It permits the instructor to give proper time and emphasis to those health interests of most importance to the student. Since a full-year schedule is the usual pattern for traditional courses, the scheduling of health for a full year is tacit recognition of health as a primary subject area.

When full-year scheduling of health is the accepted plan, there is no great choice between the junior and senior years as the preferred time for health instruction. There are advantages in each. Instruction in the junior year permits application of learning for an additional year, and the health instructor is available for health counseling. In the senior year the added maturity and preparation for the years immediately ahead give added force and direction to health instruction. Although either of the last two years is acceptable for full-year health classes, any earlier year should be ruled out except under the most extenuating circumstances.

Full semester in each of two years. Authoritative opinion generally supports the recommendation of the National Commission on School Policies that health be taught one semester in the ninth or tenth grade and another semester in the eleventh or twelfth grade. Experience indicates that three different combinations are satisfactory: ninth and eleventh grades, ninth and twelfth grades, or tenth and twelfth grades. Perhaps the combination of the first semester of the tenth grade and the last semester of the twelfth grade may have a slight advantage over other combinations. Many factors may prevent a school from adopting this specific schedule. One of the other combinations may work out equally well in a given situation. However, a combination of one semester in each of two successive years should be avoided unless extenuating circumstances make the arrangement necessary. Again this arrangement may prove to be highly satisfactory for a particular situation.

Many advantages accrue from dividing health instruction between two years. The foundation laid down in the first semester will carry over into subsequent semesters and can give the student the awareness of health necessary for the fullest realization of health opportunities. The interim experience and maturation between the two semesters of health instruction produce a student who is more able to benefit fully from health instruction in the junior or senior year. Most important, as has been pointed out, the development of a confidential relationship between the teacher and student in the first semester provides a vehicle for health counseling throughout the high school life of the student. This is an important consideration for all students, but it is an invaluable service for students with serious health problems.

It is apparent that in the first semester of high school teaching considerable emphasis must be placed on the importance of health and a person's responsibility for his own health. From this self-interest in health a program of health promotion can be developed. Problems in health promotion will naturally arise. The inevitable sequel is solution of these problems, and application of the solutions is the logical outcome. Periodic evaluations and inventories complete the picture.

In the last semester of health instruction, reappraisal of the previous instructional semester and subsequent experience will lead directly to health needs and interests of deepest concern to the student. Student planning and participation are inevitable in such an approach.

Instructional personnel

An inadequate quality of teaching in any field can be harmful to the students, but incompetent teaching in the health field can actually be injurious. It would be better to cancel a scheduled health class than to turn it over to a person known to be incompetent to teach in the field. This is not to imply that only the great teachers of this generation should be entrusted with health instruction in the high school. Good teachers and fairly good teachers are not only adequate, but also satisfactory if they have the necessary interest and background in health. A recognized health teaching major or minor is acceptable as the initial preparation. The minimum thus is expressed in the minor. An acceptable health minor should include at least 30 term (quarter) hours in the following areas (Table 19).

Table 19. *Recommended health minor*

Area	Hours
Personal health	3
Community health	3
Mental health	3
Family relationships	3
Nutrition	3
School health services	3
School health instruction	6
Safety education	3
First aid	3
Total	30

Supporting preparation in biological science, social science, and psychology is usually an institutional requirement.

As more and more teaching candidates major in the health field, an increasing proportion of teachers come into the field with a major in the

Table 20. *Recommended curriculum for health major (by academic areas)*

Subjects	Term hours	
Humanities—social science		
English composition	9	
Literature	9	
Speaking	3	
American government	3	
Sociology	3	
Anthropology	3	
Economics	3	
Physical education	5	
General psychology	6	
Psychological development	3	
		47
Science		
Physical science	12	
Biological science	12	
Human anatomy	6	
Human physiology	6	
Microbiology	3	
		39
Education		
Educational psychology	3	
Psychology of adolescence	3	
Special secondary methods	3	
Student teaching	12	
Seminar: student teaching	3	
		24
Health		
Introduction to health education	3	
General hygiene	3	
Nutrition	3	
School health services	3	
School health education	3	
First aid	3	
Safety education	3	
Communicable and noncommunicable diseases	3	
Community health	9	
Family relationships	3	
Health of the school-age child	3	
Physical growth and development	3	
Driver education and training	3	
		45
Electives		37
		192

area of health. Others from related fields who have a health interest pursue a major in health on the graduate level. This is particularly true in states where a fifth year of study is required for a life certificate in teaching.

What group of courses constitutes the best major in health raises a question which lends itself to a diversity of proposals. It would be foolhardy to attempt to propose *the* curriculum for an undergraduate health major, but to propose *a* curriculum may be of some value as a guide for the various purposes it might be used.

It must be emphasized that on-the-job professional growth and further formal study should strengthen and extend the qualifications of the health instructor. A considerable portion of the stimulation for growth will come from the students. It is indeed an unresponsive instructor who does not learn from the students. Those who love the teaching profession most and thus are its severest critics would regard such a person as unworthy of the teaching profession.

Should the same instructor teach a class in both semesters of health instruction? There are real advantages to be gained by this policy if the philosophy of the responsibility of the teacher for health counseling is accepted. This philosophy visualizes health instruction as a continuing process. At times various considerations make this arrangement impractical or even impossible. Students may gain some advantage from the benefit of different instructors in their study of health. The influence of the teacher on the student is always an important factor in education.

Perhaps there are advantages in having both men and women health instructors on the staff. These advantages are not readily discernible unless the boys and girls are separated for health instruction and instructors are assigned accordingly. Yet even these schools will find that competent instructors can do an excellent job in teaching a mixed class. Mixed classes in health are both wholesome and challenging. Most of the anticipated difficulties never materialize.

Blights on the high school health program

A variety of malpractices in the school health program tend to have a withering and injurious effect, but the most destructive are those in health instruction. Shortcomings in the health services are usually omissions which persons outside of the health field may not recognize or value adequately. Further as a rule environmental factors must be neglected to a considerable degree before an accusing finger is pointed at the health personnel. It is the instruction phase of the health program which is in the spotlight. It seems that everyone is somewhat of an authority on education, on health, and especially on the combination of health education. Parents, students, and the members of the school staff quickly identify weak, slip-shod, unprofessional, inept, bizarre, and ridiculous procedures in the health instruction program. Ludicrous and unwarranted practices relegate health instruction to a third class status in the school. Fortunately such suspect practices are declining, but are still sufficiently prevalent to merit a listing of the procedures which should be discarded.

1. Assigning the health class to some cubby hole. Although the administrator makes room assignments, certainly the importance of health should give the instructor little difficulty in convincing the administrator that health merits better treatment than assignment to a hide-out. Just as other subjects receive recognition, health should have a recognized classroom acknowledged to be used primarily for health classes. Dedicated health instructors demand and receive proper respect for health in the school. Such respect is always earned.

2. Massing large groups in the gymnasium or auditorium for a series of health lectures

3. Using health as a fill-in during inclement weather

4. Substituting physical education to meet health requirements

5. Excusing students from health classes to engage in extracurricular activities: Occasional excusing of students for such purposes is justifiable, but health should not be singled out as the class from which to call students for extra chores or nonacademic purposes.

6. Presenting lectures on venereal disease as sex education: This applies whether a nonstaff member or the health instructor delivers the lectures.

7. Sensationalism: Health can be made challenging without cheapness.

8. Emphasizing the morbid or the lurid: Some discussion of disorders and diseases is necessary as a practical matter and to make the normal more understandable. However, the normal is primary and abnormal is secondary in health teaching.

9. Prejudice and hearsay: The practice of a critical scientific approach to questions and problems is more important in health than in most other fields. What is the evidence is the question that should be heard frequently in the health classroom.

10. Exclusive dependence upon films for health instruction: Films and other audiovisual aids have a real place in health teaching, but some instructors, without justification, schedule two or more films for each class period. Students will see a lot, but will learn little of lasting functional value from such classes.

11. Promoting commercial advertising: Health materials from commercial firms can be valuable in health instruction, but the advertising should be very incidental. A class demonstration on care of the feet by a highly qualified shoe salesman may be justifiable, but can stir up a hornet's nest in the community.

12. Unrealistic subject treatment and standards: Either medical school or infantile treatment of subject matter are extremes totally unrealistic in any classroom situation.

13. Health competition among students.

14. Improper health practices by the health instructor.

Methods of instruction

An almost unlimited number of teaching methods and combinations of methods are in use in high school health classrooms. It is not necessarily a badge of good teaching to employ a diversity of methods. Methods best adapted to each specific problem or interest are the result of analysis, undertsanding of students, knowledge of the subject, and experience. Effective teaching requires adaptation, improvisation, and experimentation. An instructor who uses the methods with which he has been consistently successful follows a safe course. Perhaps he would be a better teacher, at least an interesting teacher, if he experimented with new procedures and techniques. Certainly many procedures are adaptable to health instruction in the senior high school: surveys of health needs and interests, group discussions, buzz sessions, lecturettes, demonstrations, projects, field trips, reports, panel discussions, symposiums, sociodramas, textbook assignments, reference work, research, and audoivisual aids including classroom and activity tape recordings. Group interests and needs are the hub of the instructional program. Student exploration and participation provide motivation and effective learning. This participation is particularly valuable when applied to student appraisal of progress. To establish the practice of self-inventory or self-appraisal is especially important in the area of health.

Broad resource unit—personal and community health

A committee of health instructors in the Portland, Oregon, Public Schools, has developed a broad unit of student activities for use in senior high school. The approach to health problems, activities, and materials is designed to permit extensive correlated and integrated teaching. All subject fields in the high school can contribute to the solution of the problems as classroom study develops. Each health teacher who uses the unit can expand or limit the various aspects of the unit as dictated by interest of the students and other factors. Only two of the unit sections are presented. The diversity of approach in these two sections serves to illustrate the almost limitless ways in which health can be made vital, stimulating, meaningful, and functional for the high school student.

UNIT TITLE: PERSONAL AND COMMUNITY HEALTH*

Objectives

Students who participate in the development of this unit will have many and varied experiences and will be able to secure pertinent and useful information to share with the members of the class. Through the use of panels, speakers, audiovisual aids, field trips, interviews, reports, reading, and research students will contribute information and develop useful habits and attitudes regarding the promotion and maintenance

---

*This discussion is quoted from mimeographed material. Courtesy J. W. Edwards, Superintendent, Portland, Ore., Public Schools.

of personal and community health. It is desirable that students, through this unit, fulfill the following objectives:

1. Assume responsibility for the optimum development of their health
2. Grow toward physical and emotional maturity
3. Gain an understanding of the various factors which affect one's personal appearance and health
4. Understand why the use of alcohol, narcotics, and tobacco is considered to be a health problem
5. Develop useful health practices and attitudes which will be desirable for their own health and the health of others
6. Understand the necessity for having adequate nutrition
7. Gain a knowledge of dental health problems, dental caries, and preventive measures
8. Appreciate the necessity for and develop good habits regarding sleep, rest, exercise, posture, and use of leisure time
9. Develop an interest in mental health and how it can be achieved
10. Understanding the cause and prevalence of communicable and noncommunicable diseases
11. Gain information regarding the causes of communicable diseases and the program for their control
12. Understand the function of official and voluntary health organizations in the protection, promotion, and maintenance of health in the community
13. Understand and appreciate the contribution of scientific research to health through the ages
14. Understand the effect of advertising on consumer buying habits
15. Gain skill in the choice and use of health services and products
16. Be aware of the mental health problems in the community
17. Assume responsibility as citizens in relation to community health
18. Assume their role in promoting and maintaining health in their home, school, and community
19. Grow in vocabulary, concepts, and study skills which will result in lasting ability to deal with community health problems
20. Develop skill in working with others
21. Increase interest in reading and research in this area of study

Understandings

As a result of the many and varied experiences and discussions organized around these units, the following understandings should evolve. Students should:

1. Understand themselves, how the body works, and their responsibility for maintaining, protecting, and promoting their own health
2. Understand the importance of developing health practices which will contribute to personal well-being and effectiveness
3. Understand that each individual person has the responsibility for promoting and maintaining personal and community health
4. Understand that good posture, exercise, and rest are conducive to satisfactory growth and development
5. Appreciate the importance of good grooming and personal appearance and their contributions to success and happiness
6. Understand that dental health is a problem in our community
7. Assume increasing responsibility for their personal care and appearance
8. Understand the significance of the personal and community problems involving the use of alcohol and narcotics

9. Understand the role of adequate nutrition in growth, development, and the promotion of good health
10. Understand that food fads and patent medicines are usually unreliable and may be dangerous
11. Understand physical and emotional growth and development and the problems of adolescence
12. Understand the many factors which influence the lives of teen-agers
13. Develop wholesome attitudes toward growing up
14. Understand some of the causes of differences in personalities
15. Understand how physical and emotional maturity develop
16. Understand that teen-agers have a responsibility and concern in family affairs
17. Understand where to secure help with their problems
18. Understand that our nation, our state, and our city have major health problems that must be solved by its citizens
19. Understand that official and voluntary health agencies exist to promote and to protect the health of each individual
20. Understand that city and state health officers are charged with the responsibility of protecting the health of the community and guarding it against communicable diseases
21. Know that our nation through research is doing much to control communicable and noncommunicable diseases
22. Know that research is contributing to the improvement of the health of mankind
23. Understand that all people need to make mature choices in the use of health services and products
24. Understand that mental health problems exist in our community
25. Understand that careers in health are open in this community
26. Understand and develop many skills through committee work, group discussion, and class activities
27. Understand how to develop vocabulary, improve in oral and written work, and increase their skill and interest in reading

Suggested approaches

Students will have many suggestions for including topics for discussion in the unit when they learn that through student-teacher planning their ideas will be considered.

The following suggestions for approaching the unit should help stimulate interest:

Ask students to help plan for the unit and suggest topics they wish considered.

Pretest to determine what students already know.

Show an appropriate film. (See film list at end of this unit.)

Evaluate advertisements on products dealing with cosmetics, reducing aids, cure-all medicines, dentifrices.

Discuss recent radio or television programs dealing with personal health.

Invite speaker to discuss specific problems in class such as grooming, care of feet, nutrition, fads and fallacies, epidemics.

The opportunities for the use of resources in our community—field trips, speakers, interviews, reports of research committees—are many and provide excellent enrichment activities for students.

Plan panel discussion on some pertinent problems such as "How do good health practices aid in disease prevention?"

Wide use of the library is desirable. The teacher may make an appointment with

Fig. 58. Using community resources in a high school health class. A specially qualified officer from the traffic safety department of the city bureau of police can contribute to the students' study of a unit on driver education. (Courtesy Portland Public Schools, Portland, Ore.)

the librarian and have her visit the health class and explain library services. The librarian can tell about new materials available, about books of general interest, career reading material, and explain the use of reference resources. She can help the teacher set up magazine, book, or other displays in the library. She can also provide book lists which will be helpful.

Students should use the library to find current, interesting, and challenging material for panel discussions, reports, and general information.

By working with the teacher and the librarian, students learn to consult the card catalog, indexes of books, encyclopedias, pamphlet files, and the *Readers' Guide* for effective use of the library.

During the preplanning and presentation of the topics on personal and community health, or on communicable and noncommunicable diseases, for example, the use of library materials is very helpful. The student may select a particular disease about which he is to report to the class. He will be interested in its discovery and the many research problems involved. He will find out about its prevalence, its cause, and control.

Small committees or work groups may be selected to conduct research on such subjects as personal health as related to community health, community health and sanitation, choice and use of health services and practices, or organization and functions of our city and state bureaus of health. Meat and milk inspection, insect and rodent control, food and drug laws, occupational health problems are also topics of interest. Such subjects as mental health, dental health, alcohol, narcotics, tobacco, nutrition, tuberculosis, structure and functions of the body, exercise, safety and first aid are interrelated and challenge one's ability to keep up to date.

Use posters to promote questions.

Invite public health nurse to talk to class.

Have a display of community resource materials and books.

Have browsing periods in the classroom; in the library.

Have panel discussions regarding the need to carry on research in such fields as polio, tuberculosis, heart disease, and cancer to stimulate interest.

Suggestions for unit development

The following are suggestions for developing this unit.

Teacher activities	Student activities

The teacher "looks ahead" and determines his goals before introducing a unit. He considers the objectives and the concepts as well as the scope, sequence, and content of the unit to be developed.

In formulating these plans the teacher determines the availability of cobasic and supplementary health texts in his building.

In cooperation with the librarian he locates the material available in the school library. He may wish to ask the librarian to set up a shelf of reserve books for students to check out overnight.

He checks the audiovisual handbook, curriculum publications, and units to locate other sources of materials. Community resources and resource people who might be invited to speak to the class are considered.

The teacher aids in evaluating and securing additional materials.

With this preplanning and the security of knowing what materials are available, the teacher is ready to initiate a unit in class.

The teacher checks to see that the psychophysical testing devices are in good working order.

Pupil-teaching planning

1. Help students determine goals to be achieved through study of unit.

2. Guide pupils into possible areas of study.

3. Help students formulate problems to be studied.

4. Help students select their special interest area.

5. Help students divide into work grousps for study of selected problem. Help them to understand their assignments.

1. Determine the goals with the aid of the teacher.

2. Select possible areas for study.

3. Group areas together and formulate problems to be studied.

4. Select special areas or problems of interest for individual study and reports.

5. Divide into committees or work groups for group study and reports. Select chairman and others necessary for the committees to function satisfactorily. Check to be sure each one understands his assignment.

Teacher activities	Student activities
6. Help students plan for individual reports, panels, or other selected means of bringing information to the class.	6. Plan ways to gather information for report and to present it to class.
7. Plan with the school librarian for a visit to the class to explain resources available in the library. Make arrangements for class to spend period in library. Anticipate devoting at least one period to supervised study in the library. This is in addition to supervised study carried on in regular health classroom. The teacher may wish to bring the class to the library to review the use of the card catalog and the *Readers Guide*. If the librarian is not able to give the review, the teacher could assume this responsibility.	7. Class select member of committee to interview school librarian and confirm a date for her to visit the class to tell about the health resources of the library. Plan for a time when the class can go to the library for a period of supervised study.
8. Help students plan field trips to secure information. Use school-approved procedures for being excused for field trips.	8. Plan for a field trip. Decide what information is desired. Develop a list of questions to be asked. Discuss conduct on field trips. Discuss *"Manners and Public Relations."* Secure information to be taken back to class.
9. Help students learn to use the multiple texts available. The problem-solving method of teaching increases understanding, is practical, and encourages students to participate actively. Broad reading, use of many resources, and the stimulation of interest are achieved through the use of multiple texts and many other resources. Help students learn how to take notes.	9. Use multiple texts available to secure information on the problem selected. Use table of contents and index to find sources of information. Use the resources of the school library first. Additional material may be sought in the public library. Discuss how to take notes effectively.
10. Help students select and use other resources.	10. Investigate other resouces where information may be secured on the subjects being studied, i.e., periodicals, radio programs, television, films, film strips, transcriptions, public libraries, interview family and friends, speakers, official health agencies, and voluntary health organizations.
11. Help students plan for ways of presenting reports and information to class.	11. Determine how reports or a final presentation of the study might be made. Can they be made by using discussions, dramatization, art exhibits, posters, written reports, displays, exhibits, maps, murals, charts, graphs, a log book, class scrapbook, or demonstrations?

Teacher activities	**Student activities**
12. Help students to evaluate frequently the unit by considering their goals and whether or not they have been met. Help students to understand that broad reading, making reports, and working in groups helps them to improve their ability to speak, write, spell, and solve problems.	12. Evaluate your work in terms of the goals you have set up for yourselves. (a) Have you gained useful information? (b) Have you learned how to budget your time? (c) Have you improved in your ability to organize your work? (d) Have you improved your health habits, your study habits? (e) Have you increased your ability to select useful materials and to evaluate sources of information? (f) Have you increased your ability to read, write, speak, solve problems? (g) Are you able to make practical application of the information you have received? (h) Have you improved your study habits? (i) Are you satisfied with your work?
13. Help students to develop broad concepts included in the unit.	13. Formulate broad statements of fact regarding the information you have received during your study.
14. Help students to: (a) List good study habits (b) List the advantages of good study habits.	14. In terms of efficiency and good health list good study habits which should be developed. Think in terms of study area, lighting, posture, comfort, fatigue, ventilation, noise, pressures, nutrition, attention span, vision, temperature. List the advantages of having good study habits.
15. Help students organize methods for distributing and checking classroom texts and materials in order to keep them in good condition.	15. Accept responsibility for keeping texts, pamphlets, and other materials clean, unmarked, and in good condition.
16. Help students organize a plan for using the psychophysical testing devices. It is desirable for the teacher to demonstrate and use one testing device at a time. Students should be given an opportunity to be tested to show the relationship between physical fitness and safety. The testing devices should be used only under the direct supervision of the teacher. The care of this equipment is important. It should be repaired as soon as it does not function properly. It should be carefully boxed and stored when not in use.	16. Participate in using the psychophysical testing devices. Cooperate with the teacher in carefully using this equipment as necessary repairs are costly and delay your program. Be aware of the relationship of physical fitness and safety.

Teacher activities	Student activities
17. Help the student appreciate the significance of having the Junior Civil Defense Membership Card as an identification and recommendation for services in the community. Emphasize the personal health factors involved in securing this membership card.	17. Understand the significance of your Junior Civil Defense Membership Card and value it as your identification and recommendation for community service.

Problems	Activities	Materials
I. What are the factors which affect my appearance and my health?	Discuss the general factors considered pertinent to one's appearance and well being. As students mention possible factors list them on the board.	*Your Health Today and Tomorrow* *Modern Health*
		Health textbooks
	Begin vocabulary chart and add to it as the unit develops.	*Enjoying Health,* Units 1, 2, 3, 5, 6, 7, 8, 9, 10
	Start a class log or scrapbook which illustrates findings.	*Health in Your Daily Living,* Ch. 1, 2, 4, 6
		Understanding Health, Units 1, 2
	Invite school librarian to visit class to explain resources available in the school library.	*Your Health and Safety,* Ch. 11, 12, 13
		Teen-Agers, Units 1, 2
	Have panel report on grooming, appropriate clothing, posture, and physical and mental health as they relate to personality and appearance.	*Life and Health,* Ch. 2, 8, 9, 10, 11, 12
		Health and Fitness, Unit 2, Parts 7, 11, 17; Unit 5, Parts 29, 30
What factors affect my personal appearance?	Discuss health and oral hygiene as it might affect appearance or personality.	*Health for You,* Ch. 2, 11
	Discuss ways in which posture, mental attitudes, and grooming tell a story about one's self.	*Health Instruction in Oregon Secondary Schools* (State Department of Education, Salem, Oregon)
		State Guide, p. 73
	Discuss how to dress suitably for various types of activities, occasions, and the weather.	*Dental Health Facts*

Problems	Activities	Materials
		Sound films
		Human Skin
	Invite home economics teacher to discuss the above topics.	*Human Hair*
		Film strips
		As Others See You
		You and Your Grooming
	Discuss the use of deodorants.	*Your hair*
	Make self-evaluation check list for grooming and personal appearance: underclothes, shoes, stockings, and socks, outer garments, body cleanliness, face, hair, neck, eyes, ears, hands, nails, mouth, and teeth.	*Your Hands and Feet*
		Pamphlet
		Help Yourself to Health
		Speakers, field trips
	Discuss the types of shoes worn for various occasions and point out how different shapes, kinds of material, heel heights, and construction affect the foot, posture, appearance, and the body as a whole.	*Your Health Handbook*
		Health in Your Daily Living, Ch. 10
		Life and Health
		Health and Fitness
	Demonstrate correct foot position for walking and the effect it has on one's posture, appearance, and shoes.	*Health for You*
		Enjoying Health
	Have a guest speaker on fads and styles for teen-agers.	
	List for further discussion such topics as the following:	
What factors affect my health?	Adequate diet vs. food fads in promotion and maintenance of good health.	*Alcohol Education*
	Committee reports on alcohol, tobacco, narcotics, stimulants, cola drinks.	*Facts About Alcohol*
	The need for wise use of exercise, rest, and leisure time.	Alcohol studies division speaker, films
	Relationship of personal cleanliness to appearance.	
	Community health and safety.	Facts About Narcotics
	Mental health as related to personal health.	**Resources**
	Periodical physical examinations by family physician.	Public health nurse

Problems	Activities	Materials
	Regular dental health care by family dentist.	Dental health counselor
	Immunizations.	Official health agencies
	Disease prevention and control.	
	Occupational health problems.	Voluntary health organization
	Health and safe precautions taken to protect the employed.	
	Accident prevention.	
	Fire prevention.	
	Communicable and noncommunicable diseases.	Pamphlet materials from voluntary agencies
	Tuberculosis, infantile paralysis, cancer, epilepsy, venereal diseases (syphilis, gonorrhea), heart disease, mental illness, senility, schizophrenia.	Hearing aids and their application; speaker
	Care of special sense organs—eyes, ears, nose.	**Psychophysical testing devices**
	Corrective measures for handicaps—glasses, hearing aids, artificial limbs.	Visual acuity
	Use psychophysical testing devices, visual acuity, and field of vision to check vision.	Field of vision
	List additional points for discussion which will help solve some of our problems.	*Life and Health,* Ch. 1
	Review health texts to find additional points of interest.	*Health and Fitness,* Unit 1
	List the various systems of the body as a basis for further discussion.	*Enjoying Health* *Health For You*
II. What are the major community health problems in our city?	Plan with students to list probable areas for research to help them better understand their community health problems and services.	**For information, speakers, and field trips** State board of health: (a) public health laboratory; (b) vital statistics
	Discuss the meaning of community health.	
	Discuss ways in which these problems can be identified.	*Enjoying Health,* Ch. 22
		Health and Fitness, Unit 8

Problems	Activities	Materials
	Visit the local bureau of health to learn about major health and safety problems in our city and list them in importance.	*Health in Your Daily Living*, Unit 8
How can we learn about existing problems?	Bring current events regarding timely health problems to class.	*Understanding Health*, Unit 6
	Have committee or student reports on current health problems.	*Your Health and Safety*, Unit 7, 8
		Health for You, Unit 4
	Invite high school librarian to come to class to discuss materials and plan for class to go to the library.	*Teen-Agers*, p. 269
	Have class, committee, or individual students go to the library to do research for class reports.	*Life and Health* Part 6
		Health Instruction in Oregon Secondary Schools (State Guide) pp. 121-127
	Select field trip or other resources. (See community resources list at end of this unit.)	City bureau of health report
		Pamphlets from official and voluntary agencies are in the health classrooms and in the high school libraries.
	Discuss the prevention of dental caries, including fluoridation.	

Resources

City bureau of health

Discuss constructive use of nuclear substances in the field of medicine.

State board of health

State Tuberculosis and Health Association

People should be made aware of the *constructive* side of the problem.

County Chapter, The National Foundation

American Cancer Society, state division

Examples:

1. Radioactive phosphorus is the first effective treatment for persons whose systems produce too many red blood cells.

State Heart Association

Epilepsy League

2. Radioactive iodine will help in the treatment of inoperable cancer of the thyroid.

Problems	Activities	Materials

| | 3. Nuclear radioactive substances may also be used as a method for tracing water pollution. | **Resources for field trips** |

Why have poisonings become a community health problem?

What official and voluntary health organizations serve our community?

Discuss accidental poisonings and investigate the services and reasons for establishing a Poison Control Registry in the city.

State board of health

City bureau of health report

Discuss household cleaning agents and insecticides as potential hazards and how they should not be kept where children can reach them.

Discuss the differences between the official and nonofficial health organizations and list those which serve our community, such as city bureau of health, state board of health, State Tuberculosis and Health Association, American Cancer Society, Epilepsy League, State Heart Association, and others.

What are the functions and services of official health agencies?

Learn about the functions of official health organizations in the city, county, state, national, and international level.

Discuss the services of the World Health Organization.

Bureau of insect control

Chart the various divisions of city government and locate the place of the city bureau of health in this organization.

Division of civil defense

Division of laboratories

List other departments which function to promote health in the community, i.e., water bureau, sewage disposal, and city incinerator.

Division of meat inspection

Division of milk sanitation

Study the division of school health, bureau of health, and the public health nursing programs.

Division of public health nursing

Division of tuberculosis control

Emergency division

Interview the public health nurse or invite her to speak to the class. Plan questions for her to discuss ahead of time. Interview sanitarian.

Isolation division

Problems	Activities	Materials
		Sound films
	Learn about dental health program in the public schools. Discuss dental health problems with the dental counselor and your dentist to learn why this is a community health problem.	*The Housefly* *Defending Cities' Health*
		Film strips *Health in Your Town*
What are the functions and services of our voluntary organizations?	Name the various local voluntary health organizations and find out how they serve the community.	*Our Nation's Health* Pamphlets from community health agencies
	Invite guest speakers from various organizations to explain their services. Have a committee report on the various organizations while their drive is being conducted.	**Speakers from voluntary health organizations** State Tuberculosis and Health Association
By what means do these organizations finance their services?	See pamphlet, *Agencies of the United Fund,* for descriptions of work of the agencies. (Available in school library.)	American Cancer Society, state division Epilepsy League, county chapter
		The National Foundation
		State Heart Association
		State Mental Health Association
How does our school contribute to the health of the community?	Have students make a survey to determine in which specific areas of the curriculum of our schools health is included. (See chart at beginning of this unit.)	Alcohol studies division *Guide to Better Learning* (Portland Public Schools)
		Directory of services for the handicapped
How does the individual contribute to the health of his community?	Discuss ways in which personal health contributes to community health including immunizations, health examinations, sanitation, and safety.	Community council *Health for You,* Unit 4
	Discuss the role of high school students in community health. Formulate a resolution stating general policies whereby students could aid in the program.	*Health in Your Daily Living,* Ch. 10

Problems	Activities	Materials
	Discuss the function of the health and safety committee of the student council. Organize through the student council drives to promote school health and safety programs, community health and safety programs.	
	Write articles for school paper, prepare and dramatize skits for radio, assemblies, and community organizations showing how teen-agers are community leaders.	*Teen-Agers,* Unit 4
	Participate in the annual tuberculosis press project. Contact journalism teacher regarding the project.	
	Discuss the role of the family in community health. Formulate a check list to be taken home for evaluating own home situation.	Health texts
	Have a committee compile check lists and point up strong and weak areas in a particular community. Organize and do something to raise standards.	*Oregon Trails to Health Careers* *Health Careers* (National Health Council)
	Discuss professional opportunities in the field of health.	*Partners in Health* (National Health Council)
	Discuss the education and training necessary to be a physician, psychiatrist, nurse, lab technician, ophthalmologist, dentist, dental hygienist, social worker, sanitarian, health educator, industrial hygiene engineer.	
	Invite appropriate speakers in to discuss careers in health. Review booklet *Oregon Trails to Health Careers.*	
	Discuss problems of adequate water supply, sewage disposal, rodent control, adequate housing, sanitation, mosquito control, air pollution, and food supplies.	*State Guide,* pp. 31-32 *Insect Control Handbook,* p. 23 (Portland Bureau of Health)

Resource unit—mental health (including family life education)

An interesting unit, combining mental health, sex adjustment, preparation for marriage, and family living has been constructed by the Oregon State Department of Education. Its merit lies in the degree to which it opens up questions and problems which some health instructors find very difficult to introduce effectively. The unit provides ample opportunities for exploration of related problems which students will likely be concerned about. With ingenuity a teacher can develop this framework into a complete structure on personal and family adjustment.

UNIT TITLE—MENTAL HEALTH (INCLUDING FAMILY LIFE EDUCATION)*
Overview of area

The importance of understanding ourselves and others is becoming more obvious and appreciated as our need to get along with others becomes apparent. Young people should be given the opportunity to learn why they and others act as they do in certain situations. All individuals have problems, and the importance of recognizing and understanding these is balanced by the knowledge of what can be done about them.

In this time of speeded up living, our young people need to learn early how to meet their problems. At the same time good mental health should be cultivated in every phase of living. Therefore this unit deals with such psychological concepts as personality development, getting along with ourselves and others, and making future plans.

Some understanding of the effect of family environment upon growth and development will aid youth in understanding themselves. Another important development deals with relationships with the opposite sex. Normal youth want to know how to act, what to say, what is going to happen, and how to control acts and emotions.

High school youth need to develop attitudes and habits and acquire knowledge essential to meet the problems of daily living. The home, the school, the church, and the community share the responsibility of helping youth keep a proper perspective and of preparing them for wholesome living.

The material dealing with more intimate topics is best handled by qualified counselors or on an individual basis. Good results will be obtained by natural unaffected discussion and understandable phraseology and attitude. If handled correctly the study of these topics will be especially significant to teen-aged children.

It is recommended that a minimum of twenty-five class periods be devoted to the teaching of this unit.

Resources

State-adopted texts, as listed in Chapter 11, Health education of the guide to secondary education in Oregon, State Department of Education, Salem, Oregon

Health materials and resources for Oregon teachers, State Department of Education, Salem, Ore.

E. C. Brown Trust, 220 Southwest Alder Street, Portland, Ore.

Mental Health Association of Oregon, 229 Park Building, Portland, Ore.

Department of Visual Instruction, Oregon State University, Corvallis, Ore.

Oregon Sate Board of Health, 1400 Southwest Fifth Avenue, Portland, Ore.

---

*Courtesy Oregon State Department of Public Instruction.

Objectives

The purpose of this unit is to help each student in the following ways:

1. Understand the relationship between mental health, personal fitness, and healthful living
2. Control his emotions in order to achieve more enjoyable and more effective living
3. Understand the common signs indicative of normal mental health
4. Understand the most important factors that affect personality and behavior
5. Understand that normal behavior encompasses a wide range of individual differences
6. Cultivate wholesome attitudes as insurance against mental maladjustments
7. Understand that people with mental disorders are ill people and need professional help
8. Develop a more mature concept of marriage in all of its aspects
9. Understand and participate intelligently in boy-girl friendships
10. Prepare for a successful career and for a happy marriage and family life
11. Realize that love, marriage, and parenthood involve work, responsibility, and sacrifices which require a lifetime of effort by two devoted parents
12. Develop an intelligent attitude toward divorce and the problems it involves

Content and activities

How may I help myself develop and maintain a healthy personality?

Personality

Have the students write a paper on the subject *My Plan of Life*
Discuss the effect of environment and socio-economic factors upon personality
Discuss hobbies and their effect upon personality
Discuss the role of character in personality

Heredity

Discuss the differences between heredity and environment
Discuss the part heredity plays in personality development

Personality attributes

Have the students make out their own personality profile
Have the students hand in their profile without their names and arrange a check list for all the students; discuss this list with the students and try to decide if there is anything they can do immediately to improve personality
Relate the following list of attributes to personality:

Goal in life	Self-reliance
Immediate goals	Adaptability
Confidence	Stability
Concept of humor	Orderliness
Interest in other people	Courage
Self-discipline	

Have the students analyze their own attitudes of generosity, agreeableness, cheerfulness, understanding, dependability, and any other traits they feel are important
Discuss the best methods of developing personality traits that are lacking
Discuss the factors that determine individual differences in personality

Popularity

Discuss the basis of popularity
In this regard, discuss good conversation as the key to popularity

Survey the boys on the qualities they admire in girls, using a rating scale of 1 to 10 to evaluate these traits:

Sincerity and dependability	Friendliness
Congenial companionship	Wit, humor, good nature
Neatness	Good morals
Beauty in form and features	Modesty
Femininity	Good sportsmanship

Survey the girls on the qualities they admire in boys, using a rating of 1 to 10 to evaluate these traits:

Sincerity and dependability	Good manners
Congeniality	Strength and energy
Good sportsmanship	Intelligence
Honesty	Tact
Good morals	Ethics

Behavior

Discuss self-respect and self-reverence as foundations for behavior

Have the students prepare a code of conduct or a set of flexible rules about what to do in various situations

Discuss the effect of tolerance, understanding, temperament, disposition, normal mental health, response to humor, and maturity to behavior

What are some of the factors adversely affecting personality and mental health?

Obtain copies of the pamphlet *Mental Health of Normal Adolescents**

Show film *Emotional Health*†

Discuss the effect of the following factors on emotional health:

Lack of self-control	Anxiety
Self-confidence	Worry
Petty annoyances	Daydreaming
Fear	Insecurity
Feelings of guilt, inferiority	Conflicts
Superiority	Chronic fatigue
Long periods of illness	Disaster, personal and family
Instability	

Obtain copies of the pamphlet, *Nervous Breakdown—A Teen-Age Danger*‡

What are the implications of applied mental health?

Discuss the persons who have most influenced the students' lives

Discuss people who have high levels of mental health

Have the students write a paper on the subject *The Kind of Adult Person I want to Be*

Discuss the topic *Having a Feeling for the Other Individual's Problems or Misfortunes*

Why is it necessary to mature emotionally?

Human relationships

Discuss the value of getting along with family, friends, and teachers

Have the students list emotional problems that might occur and how these problems may be worked out

Discuss the qualities that individuals must have to be a success on a job

Have the students prepare a list of characteristics or qualifications necessary for accepting responsibility

Show the film *Developing Friendship*§

---

*Mental Health Association of Oregon, 229 Park Building, Portland, Oregon.
†Text Film Dept., McGraw-Hill Book Co., Inc. (20 minutes).
‡National Association for Mental Health, 10 Columbus Circle, New York, N. Y.
§Cornet Films (10 minutes).

Community status

Discuss emotional stability as the foundation for successful marriage, being a better parent, and attaining community respect and stature

Discuss the types of people that others look to for leadership

How do feelings affect the mental and emotional health of individuals?

Have each student, without signing his name, write down some of the feelings he has had—at times, not necessarily constantly—such as the following: parents don't love me, teacher is picking on me, I have no friends, no one understands me, I am never asked to go along, etc.

Have the students compile a list of these feelings and discuss them in class

Discuss how "getting something off your chest" helps your feelings

Are good manners a sign of good mental health?

Discuss the characteristics of a well-mannered person

Discuss the subject *It Costs Less to Be Courteous*

What factors in home environment make for a successful future, including marriage and parenthood?

Family history

Study the history of the family since the Middle Ages in relationship to functions, home and job, recreation, and differences between family responsibilities on the farm and in the city

Write the E. C. Brown Trust for their school service on social hygiene and family life education. Also, ask for their material, film, and publication lists; indicate the size, age, and grade level of the class

Discuss the factors that cause the wide variation in family living today

Economic responsibility

Discuss the budgeting of an average salary to cover financial needs

Discuss the value of studying buying guides or charts in purchasing goods

Civic and social responsibility

Discuss the role of parents in regard to life in the community; what obligations do parents have to their children to make the community a better place to live?

Discuss the value of the recreation dollar in family life; discuss the importance of being well-informed on such matters

Have the students survey materials on budgeting and consumer research to learn what helps are available for family planning

Student committees may invite interested citizens such as members of service clubs, physicians, dentists, lawyers, social workers, and city officials to meet with the class and discuss community needs and responsibilities

Discuss the value of parents keeping an active interest in civic affairs

How may wholesome girl-boy relationships be developed?

Distribute copies of the E. C. Brown Trust materials on dating to the students. This and other outside reading will provide background for class discussion.

Discuss the age at which boys and girls should start dating

Check the film catalogues from the Department of Visual Instruction, Oregon State University, Corvallis, Ore.; The E. C. Brown Trust, Portland, Ore.; and The Oregon Mental Health Association, Portland, Ore., for appropriate films to show in the class

Have the students make up questions concerning dating for discussion. Some of them might be as follows: Should a girl ask a boy for a date? How can you let a date know you like him? How often should I go out on dates? How much money should be spent on dates? Should girls contribute to the finances on dates? How about pick-up dates? How about blind dates?

Show the film *Social-Sex Attitudes in Adolescence**

What about petting?

    Assign reading from available resource books such as Landis and Landis and the Duvall texts as listed under state-adopted texts in Chapter 11, *Health Education,* in the *Guide to Secondary Education in Oregon,* State Department of Education, Salem, Ore. The E. C. Brown Trust materials are also readily available.

    Discuss boys' and girls' social standards toward petting

    Discuss whether petting will affect later opportunities for love, marriage, and family life

    Discuss the implications of boys and girls going steady

    Discuss the types of experiences most likely to help boys and girls know each other best

    Discuss how couples may handle problems of petting and kissing when going steady

What should high school students know about love?

    Discuss elements of love such as respect for each other, understanding, affection, willingness to sacrifice, consideration, etc.

    Discuss the difference between love and infatuation

    Discuss things that people should take into consideration in selecting a mate

Why is a courtship and engagement period important before marriage?

Adjustments

    Have the class prepare a list of reasons for the engagement period

    Discuss the pros and cons of long and short engagements

    Discuss whether engaged people should date other than their affianced

    Discuss the part money, hobbies, vocations, and other interests play in deciding upon marriage

Foundations for marriage

    Have the class make a list of the foundation stones that are essential for a happy marriage

    Have a panel discussion centered around such topics as *Attitudes Toward Religion, Goals in Life,* and *Family Background*

    Discuss the subject *What People Need to Know about Human Reproduction in Planning for Marriage,* including the following: function of the female reproductive system, function of the male reproductive system, and heredity as a factor in reproduction

    Show the film *Human Reproduction**

    Invite a doctor or a nurse to meet with the class and discuss human reproduction and prenatal and postnatal care

Marriage

    Discuss the legal requirements for marriage

    Discuss the functions of marriage counselors

    Discuss the major factors which contribute to success in marriage. These should include body processes, attitudes, recognition of individual differences, emotional stability, patience, tact, and sincerity.

In what ways can parents ensure a healthy start in life for their children?

Planning for the baby

    Discuss important factors that parents need to consider in planning for a baby, such as budgeting and changes in social and recreational activities

    Discuss the importance of good prenatal care, periodic medical examinations and

*E. C. Brown Trust, Portland, Ore. (22 minutes).

checkups, and the proper diet, exercise, rest, and clothing during the prenatal period

Invite a nurse to discuss with the class the arrangements prospective parents should make with the hospital for the birth of the baby and postnatal care of the mother

Show the film *Human Beginnings**

Baby care

Discuss the importance of good pediatric care for the baby, including immunization

Discuss the services that are available for babies, such as Well-Child Conferences, Well-Baby Clinics, etc.

Show the film *Care of the New-Born Baby*†

What problems arise when marriages don't work out?

Discuss the factors that contribute to the breakdown of marriages

Invite a social worker or a judge to discuss reasons why marriages break up and the consequences

Discuss the problems couples must face when considering divorce, especially when children are involved, also expense, loneliness, broken homes, etc.

Have a panel discussion on the subject *How Divorce Can Be Avoided*. In this regard mention guidance and counseling, better planning for marriage, the age factor in getting married, and emotional and social adjustments

Have the students report on Oregon laws relating to marriage

Evaluation

Evidence should be available that students have developed the following interests and attitudes:

Have a wholesome attitude toward mental health

Understand better why some people act the way they do

Are developing interest in hobbies and are also interested in wholesome social and recreational activities

Are very much concerned about the "squirrelly drivers" and the "smart alecks" in school

Have a wholesome attitude toward dating, petting, and going steady

Have an open mind toward marriage and realize that a happy family is the basic social unit in our society

Are concerned about the divorce rate and feel that a lot of divorces can be avoided

Resource unit—life adjustment

An experiment with a different type of unit format has demonstrated a unit form which is highly adaptable to an area which requires judgment, values, and standards such as social adaptation, personality development, boy-girl relationships, marriage, and related problems. The basis of the unit is a series of questions obtained from an interest-survey of high school students. If typical students expressed an interest in these questions, there should be little difficulty in evoking a class discussion. In addition to a general class discussion of a question, panels, symposiums, reports, buzz sessions, demonstrations, sociodramas, audiovisual aids,

---

*E. C. Brown Trust, Portland, Ore., or Department of Visual Instruction, Oregon State University, Corvallis, Ore. (20 minutes; 22 minutes).

†Oregon State Board of Health, Portland, Ore. (31 minutes) .

guest participation, and special studies are used to explore any of the questions.

UNIT TITLE–LIFE ADJUSTMENT
Overview

Problems of personality development, social adjustment, boy-girl relationships, preparation for marriage, and family living are of real concern to the juniors and seniors in high school. With some justification students complain that the school teaches them about everything but themselves. Youngsters seek answers to personal problems which the school can help them to find.

The unit may be introduced with a short statement on the value of understanding problems of personal adjustment and the need for each person to work out solutions which best serve his requirements. A survey of class interests will be necessary in order to direct the attention of the study to problems which the students recognize as being important. A free-response survey may be used in which the students are asked to write down questions they wish to have the class consider. From these replies a check list survey form can be constructed, and the students are asked to check those problems they consider most important, of some importance, of little importance, or of no importance. The instructor may contribute items to this check list. Or the instructor may present a check list to initiate the unit.

In the consideration of some questions it may not be feasible nor desirable to arrive at a final conclusion or group unanimity. Each student will appraise the question as it applies to him and draw a conclusion which seems to serve his needs best. The value of the unit comes from the opportunity to discuss these problems, to gain insight into these questions, to understand various ways of dealing with them, and to arrive at a tentative personal decision.

Objectives

1. Knowledge of the attributes of a wholesome personality
2. Understand one's own personality
3. Improve one's own personality through understanding and a planned course of improvement
4. Improve in adjustment to frustration
5. Understand and practice of accepted social conduct
6. Pride in one's own social conduct
7. Recognition of wholesome boy-girl relationships
8. Wholesome respect for members of the other sex
9. Preparation for many problems of marriage
10. Knowledge of sex adjustment
11. Conform to society's moral code
12. Understand personal aspects of marriage
13. Knowledge of social aspects of marriage
14. Recognize the religious aspects of marriage
15. Understand the economic aspects of marriage
16. Knowledge of health aspects of marriage
17. Lay tentative plans for the future

Content

1. What are the most important personal problems of youth?
2. What are the characteristics of an excellent personality?
3. How can we improve our personalities?
4. How does a person get over being timid or shy?
5. How can a person become a better conversationalist?
6. What makes a person popular?
7. How important is personal appearance?
8. How are introductions made?
9. How can one get acquainted with members of the opposite sex?
10. What qualities do boys most admire in girls?
11. What qualities do girls most admire in boys?
12. What are some excellent interests for high school boys?
13. What are some excellent interests for high school girls?
14. How important are skills, e.g., musical, conversational, in the development of personality?
15. What is the obligation of a boy on a date?
16. What is the girl's obligation?
17. Should a girl share expenses on a date?
18. How can a girl get a date she wants?
19. What are some of the traits of maturity in boy-girl relationships?
20. What are some wholesome activities for dates?
21. Do high school students benefit more by dating one person steadily or by dating various persons?
22. Are heartaches and social disappointments inevitable phases of growing up?
23. What is meant by falling in love?
24. Is there such a thing as love at first sight?
25. How would you appraise the quotation, "Man's love is of man's life a thing apart; 'tis woman's whole existence."
26. To what extent is love physical?
27. Why must petting be regarded as an expression of the sex drive?
28. What is the difference in the sex responses of the male and female?
29. Is necking merely an unwholesome form of recreation?
30. What are the dangers of illicit sexual relations?
31. How can illicit sexual relations be prevented?
32. What would constitute wholesome courtship for marriage?
33. What should be the length of the engagement?
34. What besides love is needed for marriage success?
35. How important is the personal and family background of the person one is to marry?
36. To what extent is reasoning used in the selection of a life mate?
37. What are the age and other legal requirements for marriage in this state?
38. What should a husband and wife know about sex and reproduction?
39. Is marriage a fifty-fifty proposition?
40. What personal adjustments are necessary in marriage?
41. What social problems arise in the family?
42. How important is religion in family life?
43. Why are economic matters of family importance?
44. How can a family provide for health needs?
45. What sacrifices does marriage demand?
46. What are the rewards of successful marriage?
47. What educational plans should we make for the future?
48. What are our home and family plans?
49. How can we make social plans for the future?
50. What vocational plans can we make at the present time?

Activities

A class discussion, panel, symposium, or buzz session can be held on any of the suggested questions. Reports on special aspects of a question will frequently add appreciably to student understanding. Other activities may be planned and some are suggested.

Survey boys on the qualities they most admire in girls
Survey girls on the qualities they most admire in boys
Reports on the topic *The Finest Personality I Have Ever Known*
Present sociodrama *Meeting Typical Frustrations of Youth*
Present sociodrama *Adjusting Properly to Various Social Situations*
Report on state marriage laws
Assignment on male reproductive system and female reproductive system
Guest participation by a counselor on marriage, mental health, social conduct, or related areas.
Show film *Understanding Your Emotions**
Show film *Date Etiquette**
Show film *Developing Friendships*†
Show film *Marriage Today*‡

Evaluation

The whole purpose of the study has been to help the student gain an understanding of life adjustment. Consequently not factual knowledge, but attainment of understanding, wholesome attitudes, and changed conduct must serve as the test of the effectiveness of the unit. This can be measured by various devices.

All students write a report on the subject *Adjustment to Life's Problems*
Student reports on topic *My 10 Best Personality Traits*
Student reports on subject *My Plans for Improving My Personality*
Student reports on subject *My Future Educational, Social, Vocational, Home and Family Plans*
Observe student attitudes toward self-improvement
Observe student attitudes toward the opposite sex
Observe student practice of social manners
Observe the application of student learning to school social affairs.

Evaluation

Appraisal of health instruction in the high school should be considered in its broadest sense. What has been the effect of the health program on the health status of the students? What has been the effect on the behavior of the students? What understanding of health have students attained?

Records, pretests, reports, and observations will reveal the health status, health behavior, and health understanding of the student when he first enters the high school health course. Standardized health knowledge tests may serve as pretests of knowledge. Thereafter progress tests, singu-

---

*Coronet Films (13 minutes; 10 minutes).
†Coronet Films (10 minutes).
‡Text Film Dept., McGraw-Hill Book Co., Inc. (22 minutes) .

lar and collective observations, daily contact with the student, and observations by persons outside of the school will indicate the progress in health and health education of the students.

Progress tests should assist the student and his parents to understand his advancement in health education and his further needs. These progress evaluations can be interviews, conferences, surveys, reports, records, questionnaires, self-appraisals, or tests. These tests may be combinations of essay, multiple choice, completion, matching, and other types of objective tests. In addition to evaluating health knowledge the instructor should attempt to appraise health attitudes and practices.

About a week before the end of the semester, achievement tests should be used to assess the final level of health knowledge, attitudes, and practices. As part of the final appraisal, growth in health knowledge may be indicated by repeating the standard health knowledge test. However, a battery of tests will likely yield a better measure of student attainment. Perhaps no better use could be made of the last week of the semester than to review the tests, item by item. Emphasis on the correct concepts by interpreting, evaluating, and expanding these ideas will tend to crystallize the health experiences of the semester for students.

Selected readings

Alberty, H. B., and Alberty, Elsie J.: Reorganizing the high school curriculum, ed. 3, New York, 1962, The Macmillan Co.

Alexander, W. M., and Saylor, J. G.: Modern secondary education, basic principles and practices, New York, 1959, Rinehart & Co., Inc.

American Medical Association, Department of Health Education: Physicians and schools, report of the Eighth National Conference on Physicians and Schools, Chicago, 1961, The Association.

Association for Supervision and Curriculum Development, National Education Association: What shall the high school teach? 1956 yearbook, Washington, D. C., 1956, National Education Association.

Baruch, Dorothy: New ways in sex education, New York, 1959, McGraw-Hill Book Co., Inc.

Biester, Lillian, Griffiths, W., and Pearce, N. O.: Units in personal health and human relations, Minneapolis, 1957, University of Minnesota Press.

Billett, R. O.: Fundaments of secondary school teaching, New York, 1952, Houghton Mifflin Co.

Bossing, N. L.: Teaching in secondary schools, ed. 3, Boston, 1952, Houghton Mifflin Co.

Butler, F. A.: The improvement of teaching in secondary schools, ed. 3, Chicago, 1954, University of Chicago Press.

Byrd, O. E.: Health instruction yearbook, Stanford, Calif., Stanford University Press.

Chenoweth, L. B., and Selkirk, T. K.: School health problems, ed. 4, New York, 1953, Appleton-Century-Crofts, Inc.

Grambs, Jean D., and Iverson, W. J.: Modern methods in secondary education, New York, 1958, Holt, Rinehart & Winston, Inc.

Haag, Jessie H.: School health program, New York, 1958, Henry Holt & Co., Inc.

Hansen, K. H.: High school teaching, Englewood, N. J., 1957, Prentice-Hall, Inc.

Harnett, A., and Shaw, J.: Effective school health education, New York, 1959, Appleton-Century-Crofts, Inc.

Irwin, L. W., and Mayshark, C.: Health in Secondary Schools, St. Louis, 1964, The C. V. Mosby Co.

Kilander, H. (editor): Preparing the health teacher, recommendations from five national conferences on professional preparation, Washington, D. C., 1961, American Association for Health, Physical Education, and Recreation.

Kilander, H. F.: School health education, New York, 1962, The Macmillan Co.

Lantagne, J. E.: Health interests of 10,000

secondary school students, Research Quarterly **23:**330, 1952.

Macomber, F. G.: Teaching in the modern secondary school, New York, 1952, McGraw-Hill Book Co., Inc.

Personal living for senior high school, Salt Lake City, Utah, 1949, Utah Department of Public Instruction.

President's Council on Youth Fitness: Youth physical fitness—suggested elements of a school-centered program, Parts I and II, Washington, D. C., 1961, United States Government Printing Office.

Schneider, R.: Methods and materials of health education, Philadelphia, 1958, W. G. Saunders Co.

Teaching guide for health education, grades 9-12, El Paso, Texas, El Paso Public Schools.

Thut, I. N., and Gerberich, J. R.: Foundations of methods for secondary schools, New York, 1949, McGraw-Hill Book Co., Inc.

Williams, Catherine M.: Sources of teaching materials, Teaching Aids Laboratory Pamphlet no. 1, Columbus, 1958, The Ohio State University, Bureau of Educational Research and Service.

For knowledge, too, is itself a power.

—Bacon

Chapter 15

Health contributions of high school subject fields

Health promotion, like the promotion of citizenship, is a function of all the school. In the high school it is a mistake to assume that the school would meet its health obligations to the students by having merely a health course and a school nurse. Health must be part and parcel of the school community and woven into its everyday fabric. It should be a concern of all the faculty as well as of all of the students. It should be an integrated part of various activities and should be correlated with the several instructional fields. When health weaves a pattern through the woof and warp of the school fabric, it becomes an integrated part of the student's makeup. True education is a garment of seamless cloth. Health is not an accessory to be pinned on the garment where, in someone's opinion, it would look best. It is part of that whole cloth which the loom of education weaves into a complete garment.

If all members of a present-day faculty assume a role in the guidance program, health guidance becomes an integral part of every teacher's efforts to help a youngster acquire self-direction. The over-all purpose of the school, which is the best possible growth and development of all students, encompasses the mental and physical well-being of each student and is both the responsibility and the opportunity for all teachers. The teacher who fulfills his or her proper function in health promotion contributes a valuable service to the students of today and the citizenship of tomorrow.

Most secondary school instructors are willing and even eager to participate in the school health program and to contribute so far as possible to the general well-being of the students. With this potential contribution to the health program ready to be tapped, it would be a short-sighted school administrator or school health director who would not draw on this resource and put it to full use. It will truly yield an integrated over-all health program and a correlated health instruction program.

417

Health preparation of the secondary school staff

Many secondary school instructors have some health background in their preservice professional preparation. In addition to general health they have had work in child growth and development and in the general organization and function of the school health program. Their preparation for teaching frequently includes methods and techniques for correlating subject fields. All secondary school instructors should have a course of study in school health as part of their teaching preparation, which would increase their value to the students they serve.

On any secondary school instructional staff there will likely be some members who do not regard their health preparation as adequate for proper participation in the health program. This group will include some of those who have had course work in school health as well as those who have had virtually no preparation for health work. Thus there is usually a need for an in-service program to give the entire staff the background and confidence necessary for effective participation in the health program.

An in-service program can consist of a regular extension course which has been arranged by the director of health and the school administration. Such a course should not be limited to the instruction phase of school health. Treatment of the entire basic program will give the staff an appreciation of all aspects of the health program. Because the whole staff has a direct contribution to make to the health of the students, the health of the individual child and the school health services aspect of the program should be given particular emphasis.

When an extension course is not available, other provisions can be made. A lecture series may be arranged or a symposium can be scheduled in which several persons present different aspects of the health program. A health institute at the beginning of the school year can emphasize key aspects of services, instruction, and living and provide resource material as a supplement for use by the teachers. These various plans are particularly effective when they are designed to incorporate the problems that are especially important to a particular high school. Visitations to other schools can fulfill the purposes of in-service training, and observation of health work in the schools which are visited should be particularly valuable.

Most important is the inclusion of all staff members in the planning of the health program. All teachers should understand the objectives, organization, and procedures of the health program if they are to be effective in implementing the program. When the staff members understand the plan clearly and their role in the plan, they are more likely to be enthusiastic participants. One should not discount the psychological advantage of adding to the professional and self status of teachers by having them feel they are important to the program.

The administration, perhaps through the health director, should make clear to the staff the importance of student health appraisal, the channels and procedures for referrals, practices for control of communicable diseases, correlation of health instruction, and responsibilities for promoting healthful school living. As a part of the program teachers can bring to the attention of the health administrator certain problems and conditions needing attention. Suggestions of staff members can be exceedingly valuable.

Health responsibilities of all instructors

High school instructors are responsible for many duties other than those related to health. Thus health responsibilities should not impose a burden upon the instructor. Properly conceived, health responsibilities are not burdensome. A staff member who is alert to health needs and opportunities will find that the program requires only a small proportion of time and effort. The teaching staff composes the lookout team for health, not the labor crew to carry out all of the details and time-consuming tasks inherent in the complete program. In practice no time in the instructor's day is more profitably invested than the small amount of time the health program requires.

Cooperation with health program. All aspects of the school health program merit the cooperation of all faculty members. Only through teamwork can an effective program be attained. Occasionally through misunderstanding, an individual staff member fails to cooperate. An obligation rests upon the health director and administration to keep all instructors informed of health plans and developments. Periodic reports and announcements are particularly in order. An obligation also rests on the faculty to inquire of the proper persons when doubt exists about some phase of the program. Misunderstandings and disagreements can be resolved only when there is cooperation between faculty and health personnel.

Health status of students. An instructor who has developed a health awareness will tend to appraise and make a mental assessment of the quality of health of each student. While ideally it would be laudable for every high school instructor to review the health condition of each child in class during the first period of the day, practical considerations rule it out. Constant observation during the day has been found to be an acceptable substitute. Teachers who are with students every day can get a reliable inventory of their level of health and the distinguishing characteristics of their endowment.

Once the instructor has an established assessment of each student's health, he should be able to recognize deviations readily. A slight transitory change may be only a signal to be on the alert for any further developments. Chronic or recurring deviations are the significant sources of concern. A conference with the student may elicit further evidence of a need for a follow-up. When this conference is unproductive, the observations of other instructors may be solicited. The instructor will have discharged his professional responsibility by referral to the director of the program, the school nurse, or the administration. Personal interest may motivate the instructor to pursue the follow-up further.

Health problems of students. By noticing the questions students ask about health and the health problems they have, the instructor can guide students in solving their health needs. The only guidance necessary may be to help find an answer to the questions. Or it may be necessary to work out a projected course of action or refer a student to another person. Whatever the health need, the instructor should interest himself sufficiently to assure the student of a satisfactory solution.

School practices affecting health. Each instructor should be aware of the relationship of the organization of the school day, of rest, relaxation, study, homework, and extracurricular activities to the health of the students. It would hardly be consistent for a school to advocate home practices beneficial to health and itself be guilty of practices inimicable to health. A crowded schedule, constant tension, and chronic fatigue may all be injurious to health. What may be one student's simple sinecure may be another student's oppressive burden. Practical considerations key the school program to the needs and capacities of the general run of students. Yet the program must be adaptable to varying needs. However, both the student who overconscientiously submerges himself in the academic program and the one who escapes into extracurricular activities must be adjusted to the program.

Faculty meetings should consider the relationship of school practices to the health of the students. Homework assignments, class period requirements, and the scheduling program must be worked out by joint faculty action. Student activities outside of school supervision must be considered in appraising the school's program in the light of student health promotion.

Control of communicable diseases. Each instructor should be familiar with the prodromal symptoms of communicable respiratory diseases and the indications of common skin infections and infestations. A tendency of high school students to refuse to accept the first slight symptoms of disease as significant emphasizes the need for staff members to be alert to early indications of respiratory disease. A quiet conference with the student can lead to a friendly suggestion that he lie down in the emergency rest room or go home for the remainder of the day. If these suggestions are not accepted, referral to the nurse, health director, or administration would follow.

When a student has been absent, each instructor routinely should require administrative clearance before readmitting the student.

Healthful school environment. Every conscientious faculty member intends to maintain a healthful environment in the classroom, the laboratory, and elsewhere in the school. Yet unless a planned pointed procedure is established, the instructor can overlook many factors which detract from a healthful environment. A systematic check of lighting practices, ventilation, cleanliness, and orderliness should be made. The mental health aspects of the classroom should be reviewed. Are the students at ease; do they feel they are accepted by others; are they confident they can succeed, attain success, and enjoy their experiences? How can the school life of students be more healthful? These are questions all instructors should ask, answer, and implement.

Healthful student living. Certain children may be in special need of help in health adjustment. A particular example is the student who returns to school after an absence due to illness. The return to school makes many demands on him. Guidance is probably needed, and its cardinal objective must be consideration of the student's health.

Schools can expect to have a few children who for health reasons must be given special consideration. Helping these students to live effectively and enjoyably in terms of their endowment is an obligation of all faculty members. More than this the goal should be to help the child attain the normal level of health and general well-being.

Handling of emergencies. Every classroom teacher should know the basic fundamentals of first aid and emergency care. In practice every instructor encounters emergencies which involve illness or injury. To be prepared for these duties is as logical as to be prepared for the subject field in which one is to teach. Knowledge begets confidence. Confidence is insurance for every student.

Unusual mass emergencies such as fires involve school organization in which every faculty member must have a responsibility. If the teacher is an integral part of the entire school program rather than an isolated classroom drone, the vitality thus derived will doubtless be reflected in the instructional program.

Correlation of subject with health. All aspects of human experience which contribute to the development and maintenance of a high level of physical and mental function must be considered health activities. By their very nature all subject areas in the high school contribute in some form to the health of the student. In addition to the contribution to the student's immediate health through surveillance and guidance from the teacher, health education in some measure grows out of the classroom experiences of the year. Too often the teacher, unaware of the possibilities, passes up excellent opportunities for the development of certain health attitudes and the understanding of health relationships in the particular subject area.

Correlation of health with subject areas is surprisingly simple. It involves no elaborate sideline preparation. It demands no special procedures, calls for no disruption of normal plans, and requires no unusual teaching skill. All high school subject areas deal with the substance of life and living. Living always encompasses health or some phase of mental and physical well-being. It is a matter of the instructor's realizing the health implications and potentialities of the subject. Some subject areas have rather limited contributions to make to the health knowledge of the student, but other areas have extensive opportunities for health instruction as a phase of the subject itself. If health is incorporated in its framework, the subject field is not handicapped nor deprived of anything. The subject itself is enriched from the experiences of the students. By thus revealing its vital applications as related to human health, the subject becomes a more meaningful and personal experience for the student. A greater appreciation of the subject field is a common outcome.

On an all-school basis several plans have been worked out to make correlation effective without unjustified duplications and flagrant omissions. Some schools have used a faculty curriculum committee to carry on the necessary cooperative planning. A modification of this approach is the use of joint curriculum planning by the instructors in the immediate subject areas, with the health director as consultant. In other schools the health instructor serves as an informal chairman of a group which includes instructors in the fields which particularly have contributions to make to health instruction. Out of these groups have come several plans.

Where a core curriculum is in use, health materials are included in the basic studies. New broader courses have made the allotment of health areas a relatively simple problem. Some schools have used the recognized health needs as a guide for all faculty members who thus use their subject field as a vehicle for finding answers to these needs. In other schools instructors have developed units which are then compared for duplications and omissions. Many schools permit each instructor complete leeway in determining the manner in which health is developed in a particular subject field.

Perhaps ideally in harmony with the present trend toward complete integration and correlation of subject fields, a high school course in health could be dispensed with and health instruction be carried out entirely through existing courses and the normal activities of the school. Conceivably such a program may some day be worked out which yields the goals of the school health program. To date, even with outstanding correlation of other subjects with health, a marked deficiency in health education would exist if the health course were not a part of the curriculum plan. The crystallizing effect of the health course is invaluable. To make the health knowledge and understanding of the student complete and functional, the recognized health course in the high school is still the indispensable ingredient, the *pièce de résistance*.

Essential safeguards

In order that misunderstanding be precluded and correlation with health placed in its proper perspective, certain safeguards or limitations should be explored. With the many contributions which other fields can make to health instruction, limitations and even liabilities must be acknowledged. In practice a misuse or abuse of the correlative approach can undo and negate all that the attempt to correlate other fields with health has contributed.

An instructor with a totally inadequate health background would be discreet to limit health instruction in the classroom to the expressed interests and spontaneous activities of the students. Even in this event or situation the faculty member should seek the counsel of the health instructor or director on the appropriateness of the class approach and the accuracy of the content.

Health should not usurp a disproportionate part of the time in a class. Yet in a sense health is the cohost and not the guest in this classroom. Time devoted to a specific health question properly is in proportion to its importance and the interests of the students. In the subject field a topic which has health significance merits the time necessary for its development.

To insert an isolated unit on health in some subject field is not a correlation of health with the subject field. The tie-in which expresses correlation will be the study of health within the subject field, not as an independent entity. The recognized scope of the subject includes areas with health implications or overtones. These areas can be studied and the health aspects developed simultaneously. Frequently the subject is the vehicle for health instruction. The mutual relationship which exists can make the entire activity a more meaningful experience.

Health in English or communication fields

Instructors in English long have recognized the motivating value of student interest in health as a fruitful resource for themes or compositions. A theme on the health of the community requires a preliminary study of aspects of government, social conditions, and public service. Hospital and medical facilities may be studied. Composing the theme is an important experience, but the by-products may be equally valuable. Vocabulary growth is not insignificant. Whether the composition calls for exposition, narration, description, or argumentation, health is a fertile field of subject matter. Every measure should be taken to assure accuracy and soundness in the material the student writes.

In speaking activities which draw on the interests of students for subject matter, children frequently select health subjects for their speeches. Controversial issues in the health field offer much material for both classroom and extracurricular debates. The question of a national health insurance program is an example.

Reading in the biographical field can include assignments on celebrated health figures. The adventures of Walter Reed, Louis Pasteur, Robert Koch, and even Hippocrates can be fascinating to inquisitive youth. Sir Alexander Fleming left a heritage which is stimulating to all who enjoy reading the exploits of the modern scientist.

Instruction in foreign languages can be vitalized and enriched by including the distinctive health problems, customs, and contributions of the nation whose language is being mastered. The language of a nation becomes more functional as it is applied to the people and the problems of that nation. Health is universally both a personal and a public problem.

Physical education

Like other fields physical education makes a considerable contribution to the health program, but physical education per se does not constitute a total health program. On its own, physical education contributes much to education and assumes primary, almost exclusive, responsibility for some contributions because of its distinctive role and position in the school. Other contributions are correlated with other fields or divisions of the school organization.

More opportunities are presented for contributing to the health education of the student than in any other division of the school, with the exception of the health course proper. The list of these opportunities is considerable, and each activity in the list encompasses a number of possible procedures, activities, and outcomes.

1. Mechanics of bodily movement
2. Coordination and efficiency
3. Physiological effects of activity
4. Adaptation of activity to physiological capacity
5. Conditioning
6. Nature of fatigue
7. Rest and sleep
8. Relaxation
9. Nutrition and activity
10. Weight and activity
11. Promotion of personal health
12. Bodily cleanliness and grooming
13. Cleanliness and care of clothing
14. Proper dress
15. Mental health contributions of activity
16. Disease control practices
17. Responsibility for health of others
18. Promotion of safety
19. First aid and emergency care
20. Sanitation of locker rooms, shower rooms, swimming pool, gymnasium, and playgrounds

Any physical educator who does not utilize these opportunities for health instruction lacks a full appreciation of the true role of the physical educator. A unique opportunity is afforded the physical education staff to help the student integrate and apply health knowledge. Actually time and again the physical educator will be called upon for counseling in health problems. The physical education situation provides an atmosphere which lends itself to a highly confidential relationship between student and instructor. Rapport of this type should be utilized in promoting the student's ability to understand and guide his own health.

Biological science

Often regarded as the fundamental science on which health is based in both its fundamental principles and their application, biological science can contribute considerably to the student's understanding and appreciation of health. The very nature of biology implies health. Only guidance by the instructor is needed to help students understand the health implications of fundamental life principles. Teaching biological science as a fundamental health science provides additional motivation for learning. In addition to established biological principles certain specific applications should be especially emphasized.

1. Application of the scientific method to the practical problems of health
2. Contributions of biologists to human welfare
3. Physical growth and development
4. Physiological needs
5. Physiological capacities
6. Biological adaptation
7. Reproduction
8. Genetics applied to health and disease
9. Analysis of fads and quackery
10. Health superstitions and fallacies
11. Biology of infectious disease
12. Biology of disease control
13. Body defenses, including immunity
14. Biological aspects of penicillin, Aureomycin, streptomycin, and other antibiotics
15. Physiological nature of injuries
16. Biological basis of first-aid measures

All of these suggestions represent normal health interests of students. Biology teaching becomes more interesting to the students when it becomes more functional in terms of final outcomes.

Social studies

A field as broad as social studies provides an almost limitless number of health implications. Practically all social problems have health overtones. This is particularly true not only in social pathology, but also in the positive aspects of social progress. Although disease with its social impact is important, the role of health in the social progress of man is at least equally important and interesting.

Health as a social factor can be considered from the standpoint of the individual, the family, the neighborhood, the community, the nation, and the world. Several vital topics are especially interesting to youth.

1. Role of health and disease in history
2. Present health status of the world
3. Health status of the nation
4. Health status of the community
5. Health and its social impact
6. Sociological aspects of disease and disability
7. Spiral of disease-poverty-further disease
8. Community health problems
9. Community health resources
10. Public health organization and service
11. Family health problems
12. Cost of medical care
13. Medical and hospital insurance
14. Sanitation problems
15. Protection of food
16. Patent medicines

Individual, family, and community health needs represent perhaps the core of any study of the sociological aspects of health. Recognizing, understanding, and working out solutions for these needs represent laudable outcomes of classes in social studies. Health problems can have a vital self-identification for the student.

Home economics

Correlation of home economics with health is as logical and natural as correlating play and physical activity. A mutual relationship is inherent in the two fields. Both deal with effectiveness and enjoyment in living and with problems of personal and family concern. Many of the questions and problems of concern in the home economics field are significant in health terms.

1. Nutrition	9. Adjustment in marriage
2. Dietary problems	10. Family life
3. Purchasing food	11. Family resources
4. Food preparation	12. Child care
5. Boy-girl relationships	13. Care of the sick
6. Social behavior	14. Home nursing
7. Personal appearance	15. Consumer education
8. Courtship and marriage	16. Home safety

The present practice of scheduling home economics courses for boys as well as for girls is in harmony with the current philosophy of functional education. Attempts to conceal the true nature of the course under some ingenious title does not fool students. Adolescent boys have a recognized need for education in family life in its broadest sense. That such a course includes health aspects of family living indicates that the course is realistic and the subject matter is integrated.

Physics

Many high schools have developed a broad general course in physical science which integrates physics, astronomy, geology, chemistry, and even mathematics, rather than to offer distinct courses in the various branches of physical science. It is recognized here that such a broad integrated experience has considerable merit, but for the present discussion it is more satisfactory to consider physics, chemistry, and mathematics individually. An individual treatment serves schools with separate distinct courses; yet it permits the integration of material presented here into the integrated general physical science offering.

Normally only a small percentage of the student body tends to enroll in a physics class. Even then it appeals only to those who have a need for physics as preparation for a specific field of study in higher education. In consequence rather specialized aspects of health interests may be explored. Those phases of physics which once were regarded as purely theoretical or academic, but which now serve important uses, appeal especially to the impressionable youth whose interest is in science fields.

1. Light
2. Optics
3. Sound
4. Radioactivity
5. X-ray
6. Electron microscope
7. Electricity
8. Heat
9. Simple diffusion, dialysis, osmosis, and filtration
10. Composition of the atmosphere
11. Atmospheric pressure
12. Caisson disease and its prevention and treatment
13. Altitude sickness
14. Biophysics

All of these topics are important in health. Many of the recent discoveries in health science have been made possible by scientists who have applied the fundamental principles of physics. Special student reports on the application of physics to a health problem can be a fruitful source of investigation.

Chemistry

The revival of interest in chemotherapy is an indication of the health implications in the field of chemistry.

1. Chemotherapy—sulfonamides. arsenic, and bismuth
2. Hormone chemistry
3. Antiseptics
4. Anesthetics
5. Insecticides
6. Detergents
7. Tracers in biochemistry
8. Fats, carbohydrates, and proteins
9. Industrial safety

Instructors in chemistry constantly seek motivating devices in the form of everyday applications. From the work of Paul Ehrlich to the present-day teams of chemists who are employed by pharmaceutical manufacturers or work in clinics or college laboratories, chemotherapy has been a ray of hope for the conquest of tuberculosis and other diseases which thus far have defied the efforts of immunologists. A study of the recent use of radioactive tracers in research will encompass some of the principal health problems of today.

Mathematics

Although at first glance it appears to be a field far removed from health, mathematics can nevertheless deal with problems of concern to human health. Applied mathematics can find a fruitful field in matters of human life, health, illness, and death. Especially challenging to the student is the attempt to project data to the future and work out statistical probabilities. The future is a constant source of interest to idealistic youth.

1. Birth and death rates
2. Disease rates
3. School absence and illness
4. Cost of illness
5. Insurance problems
6. Population curves
7. Human growth curves
8. Life expectation

Summary

Few instructors will exhaust all of the possibilities for correlating their subject field with health. An awareness of the possibilities for correlation and a responsiveness to the health interests, needs, and questions of students will assure a fair degree of correlation. If all members of a high school staff avail themselves of only one fourth of the possibilities, correlation of subject areas with health will be considerable, even adequate. Encouragement and assistance from the director of the health program is all-important.

Selected readings

Alberty, H. B., and Alberty, Elsie J.: Reorganizing the high school curriculum, ed. 3, New York, 1962, The Macmillan Co.

American Association of School Administrators: Health in schools—twentieth yearbook, Washington, D. C., 1951, National Education Association.

Association for Supervision and Curriculum Development, National Education Association: What should the high school teach? 1956 yearbook, Washington, D. C., 1956, National Education Association.

Faunce, R. C., and Bossing, N. L.: Developing the core curriculum, ed. 2, New York, 1958, Prentice-Hall, Inc.

Grambs, Jean D., and Iverson, W. J.: Modern methods in secondary education, New York, 1958, Holt, Rinehart & Winston, Inc.

Grout, Ruth E.: Health teaching in schools, ed. 4, Philadelphia, 1963, W. B. Saunders Co.

Haag, Jessie H.: School health program. New York, 1958, Henry Holt & Co., Inc.

Harnett, A., and Shaw, J.: Effective school health education, New York, 1959, Appleton-Century-Crofts, Inc.

Kilander, H. F.: School health education, New York, 1962, The Macmillan Co.

Meier, F. A.: The study of opportunities in general science as a contribution to health instruction, Bloomington, 1950, Indiana University Press.

Meier, F. A.: Opportunities in general science for health instruction, Research Quarterly 22:91, 1951.

Rugen, Mabel E.: Working together for better health education, Journal of Educational Sociology 22:434, 1948.

Rugen, Mabel E. (editor): The physical educator asks about health. Report of the Joint Committee on Health Problems in Education of the National Education Association and the American Medical Association, Washington, D. C., 1951, the National Education Association.

Schneider, Elsa, and McNeely, S. A.: Teachers contribute to child health, Washington, D. C., 1951, United States Government Printing Office, Office of Education Pamphlet no. 8.

Strang, Ruth M., and Smiley, D. F.: The role of the teacher in health education, New York, 1950, The Macmillan Co.

Wilson, C. C.: Teacher contributions in school health, Journal of Educational Sociology 22:14, 1948.

Wright, Barbara H.: Practical handbook for group guidance, for teacher-advisers of homerooms, common learnings classes, and clubs, Chicago, 1948, Science Research Associates.

Part 5

Healthful school living

Chapter 16

Healthful school

For the student school is a part of his day-to-day living. Merely to erect an attractive sanitary building is not enough. The important thing is the interaction of the environment and the student. Environment is here considered in the dynamic sense. The most important thing in that environment is people, and the most important person is the teacher. But the remainder of the environment is also important. The particular atmosphere created in a school will condition the behavior patterns of a child either favorably or unfavorably. His general school life is an effective learning experience. Whether that learning is a wholesome positive experience or an unwholesome negative one is important in terms of his health education and outlook on personal and community health.

Some children come from homes with a high level of healthful living. This standard should be further fortified by a high level of healthful living in the school. When a child has grown up respecting healthful family and public living conditions, as an adult he will more likely maintain an excellent home life and insist on a wholesome community environment. From such preparation community leaders are developed. Respect for high standards is the requisite of model citizens.

For children whose home life is on a lesser plane from the standpoint of healthful living, the school can serve both as an incentive and an experience in attaining a higher standard of healthful living. From their school experience many persons have received the incentive to establish living conditions in a home of their own which are vastly above those that they experienced in their own childhood. The influence of the school cannot always be measured by standard achievement tests nor, indeed, in terms of dollars and cents.

Architectural, sanitary, esthetic, and social aspects of the school environment must be considered. Perhaps the health implications of school architecture have been overemphasized. Very wholesome living can be experienced in a school of rather poor architectural design. Yet a superbly designed school plant has a greater potential for healthful

431

living than the less well-designed one. Whether the esthetic, social, and functional possibilities are developed is the responsibility of those who live in the building.

Sanitation is dependent upon adequate facilities which are properly utilized through sound housekeeping (or schoolkeeping) practices. All people living in the school should be active participants in schoolkeeping. It would be an injustice to the child to permit him to acquire the concept that the building is kept clean and orderly for him by someone else who is hired for the task. To recruit the youngster's interest and develop his pride in his home away from home is a laudable educational objective. He must participate in the chore of keeping *our* school clean, orderly, and beautiful.

Esthetic and social appreciations are cultivated as by-products of a wholesome respect for beauty and our fellow man. A child acquires an understanding of what is worthwhile; it is not something he is crowned with. The achievement of wholesome relationships in attractive school surroundings is not an accident. It is a creation.

Responsibility for healthful school environment

Theoretically responsibility for initiating and providing for the construction and maintenance of school buildings rests with the board of education. As a matter of practice such action originates with the superintendent who is the professionally qualified expert on such problems.

Administrators. Full-time regularly employed school administrators are constantly appraising the needs of the school district. Classroom enrollments, age-group populations, migrations, consolidations, real estate developments, industrial changes, and other factors that affect present and future school needs are used as bases for constructing new school buildings or remodeling old ones. Knowledge of the present plant, its shortcomings and possibilities, is necessary to the administrator. The economics of building anew or rebuilding will loom as important.

Once administrators have agreed upon the need for plant expansion, a tentative estimate and general plan are developed. The superintendent submits these recommendations to the board for its consideration.

Programs for maintaining the school plant are the responsibility of the superintendent and his administrators, especially the principals. General policies apply to the whole system, and each principal administers the policy to the best advantage for the particular building for which he is responsible. Though the superintendent does not intend to veto or even investigate particular problems or procedures of a particular school, he does need to be informed of unusual situations and circumstances.

Board of education. Sovereignty or ultimate authority rests with the people, but they delegate the exercise of it to the board of education. However, the board does not act upon its own initiative in plant construction, but passes on the merits of recommendations made to it by the professional administrator. It is a wise board which asks a representative community committee to review the plans and make suggestions. This assures adequate study of the plan and community understanding of the proposal. When representative community leaders have approved the plans, the board of education can proceed in the knowledge that the community understands and supports the project.

If the plan is to go forward, an architect is engaged by the board to draw preliminary plans and estimates. The board then takes the necessary steps for financing, which is usually a bond issue for approval by the electors in a regular or special school district election. If the voters approve it, final plans are drawn, bids are called for and opened, and a construction contract is awarded. Because of better school architects, better engineers, illuminating specialists, ventilation experts, and the host of other specialists, school buildings today are a vast improvement over those of a generation ago.

Regulations governing maintenance of the school plant are approved by the board. Often certain board members have an extensive background in the needs and procedures of plant maintenance.

Architect. In recent years school architecture has become a specialty in the architectural profession. As a result school districts are getting better plant designs. Yet even the most competent architect consults the school personnel who will live in the building. For effective school living the plant must be adapted to the recognized needs of the children. Who should know those needs better than the teachers? He is a wise architect who gets the composite judgment of all people who may have something of value to suggest in the planning of the building. In addition to drawing plans the architect has general supervision of construction.

Teachers. Once the structure is completed and furnished, it is the teacher's task to make the building serve the needs of healthful school living.

Student pride in the school is not difficult to develop, but it does require some planning and promotion. Loyalties to the school and what it stands for create a desirable atmosphere for wholesome living. Children do not always develop an appreciation of the meaning of the school in their lives. Under the stimulation and guidance of an understanding teacher, students usually develop a desirable level of appreciation. This can be solidified by having the students assume responsibility for preserving and extending the attractiveness of their common home. Monitors may be designated for specific tasks, but all of the children should feel that they have a responsibility. Procedures for the selection of monitors should be such that every youngster has a regular assignment. None should be excluded, even accidentally.

Within a classroom a wholesome respect for one another fostered by understanding courtesy creates a wonderful atmosphere for intellectual, emotional, physical, and social development. To rise above the commonplace requires a surprisingly small amount of extra effort.

Esthetic appreciation can be fostered through art, music, play, literature, and other creative activities. Recordings can be helpful, but it would be an error to introduce any such opportunity for esthetic appreciation to the exclusion of an appreciation of the beauties of the school and its surroundings. Not until years after they have left a school do some students appreciate the artistic grandeur of the school building, its landscaping, and its accessories.

A teacher who is a one-person schoolkeeper lacks the vision and educational philosophy essential to the best interests of the pupils. The children gain nothing when the teacher assumes full responsibility. Indeed they are the losers. They lose the opportunity for self-growth which comes only with participation.

Students. So far as possible students should assume the primary responsibility for the order and cleanliness of their school. On a cooperative basis some classes undertake to supply additional furnishings for the building. Pictures with a patriotic or story motif, vases, bowls, flower pots, stands, lecturns, and a host of other furnishings have been contributed by classes at various times. On a group basis these projects have merit, but donations from individual pupils should be accepted only under unusual circumstances.

All-school organization for building cleanliness should be administered by a representative council or body under the supervision of a faculty adviser. In the elementary school the primary grades can have responsibility for the cleanliness of halls and stairways. The intermediate grades could supervise cleanliness of toilet rooms and rest rooms. An effective arrangement is to give each grade a month's assignment, with the class organizing for its task. In the high school the student council can assume responsibility for the organization and supervision of the cleanliness program.

Room organization is particularly important in the elementary school. A captain for each two-week period, with necessary assistants, can be a simple form of organization. Division of labor is usually possible. Although the captains and assistants should lead the way, all of the pupils should participate to some degree.

Special projects such as Don't Be a Litterbug Week, special pick-up projects, locker clean-outs, rake-up campaigns, and other activities can add to the interest of the students in maintaining a healthful school environment.

Custodians. The nonskilled janitor has been replaced by the qualified custodian. Besides the mechanical skill needed for the assignment, the custodian should know sanitation, control of communicable diseases, and safety. In-service preparation, usually regional institutes, are provided in most states to assure the schools of well-qualified custodians. In addition to his job know-how the custodian should be in good health and be dependable. A competent custodian can care for ten to twelve rooms properly. Some administrators supply the custodian with a printed list of duties and instructions.

A custodian has many miscellaneous duties, but certain of his duties are of specific health significance. These would include heating and ventilating, dusting, gathering trash and waste paper and burning it, cleaning plumbing fixtures, filling soap dispensers, sweeping floors, mopping, cleaning steps, walls and windows, cleaning chalkboards and erasers, taking care of the school grounds, checking playground apparatus, inspections for safety, and elimination of hazards.

Custodian-staff cooperation is a two-way street. So far as possible the custodian's schedule should be planned not to interfere with the school routine. Time after school and on Saturday is used for dusting, washing walls, and doing other tasks in the classroom. When the students, teachers, and custodians cooperate, everyone's task is lighter, and the whole atmosphere of the school is refreshed.

Although the custodian should be friendly with the children, his is not the role of a teacher or counselor. Nor should the custodian be regarded as a personal servant for any one teacher. When only a small special task for the custodian arises, the teacher may tactfully ask him to do the task. Otherwise such requests should be made to the principal who will inform the custodian of his special assignment. He has specified duties to carry out in the interest of order and cleanliness. A healthful school environment is not solely the responsibility of the custodian.

The principal should make periodic inspections of the work which is the custodian's responsibility. Understanding on the part of the whole staff plus tact on the part of the principal will get the maximum service from the custodial force. An incompetent custodian, like an incompetent teacher, should not be retained in the school.

Lunchroom personnel. Sanitation is more important in the lunchroom than anywhere else in the school. A situation in which sanitation will prevent the spread of disease also provides an opportunity for the children to observe and understand proper conditions and procedures for food handling. Lunchroom experiences integrate health practices and instruction for the children.

The facilities and practices in school lunchrooms are those prescribed by public health departments for the regulation of sanitation in food catering establishments for the public. Observance of these regulations is doubly important in the school.

Lunchroom personnel should feel a special obligation to the children which can best be engendered by a feeling of pride in the importance of the lunchroom work. Personal health habits should be exemplary. If the lunchroom worker suffers from a communicable disease, she should isolate herself voluntarily. The worker who strives for perfection in sanitary measures is an important member of the health instruction team.

Location and plan of school building

Certain factors in the location and plan of a school building are of direct health significance. To these health factors the elementary classroom teacher and the secondary school health instructor should especially direct their attention. It is not suggested that other things about the building are not important, but for present purposes health factors alone will be considered.

Site. School sites should be considered from the standpoint of accessibility, safety, quiteness, cleanliness of the air, adequate drainage, and recreation space. Distance to the school is not so important today as formerly because of means of transportation. Railroad areas, main highways, and through streets are physical hazards to be avoided. Taverns and similar establishments constitute moral hazards. However, city ordinances and state laws usually specify that no alcoholic beverages may be sold within a mile of a school building. For clean air and a quiet neighborhood, residential and rural areas are preferable to industrial or other congested areas. Either natural or installed drainage which will assure dry grounds is important. Adequate play and recreation space can be provided by setting a minimum of five acres for an elementary school, twelve acres for a junior high school, and twenty acres for a senior high school. A standard of 100 square feet of play space per child will be adequate for any situation.

For esthetic reasons the surrounding area should be attractive and the school site itself should be properly landscaped.

Planning of building. A school building should be located on an elevated part of the grounds. Window exposures should preferably be west or east for general classrooms, south or east for kindergarten, science classrooms, and laboratories, north or northwest for art and drafting rooms, and south or east for physical education needs.

Whenever possible, the open-type building plan should be employed. It has many good features.

1. Provides rapid horizontal traffic
2. Reduces fire and other hazards
3. Provides easy access to ground for all parts of the building
4. Reduces disturbing noises and odors
5. Provides for better natural lighting and ventilation

Basement areas should be eliminated because of the unwholesome psychological effect and the poor natural lighting and ventilation.

Corridors usually have a 12 foot unobstructed width. Corridor intersections should be reduced to a minimum. Stairs must be located so as to reduce corridor traffic. An auditorium should be reached by two nonconverging traffic channels.

A kindergarten room is usually 24 × 50 feet and should be a self-contained unit with cloakroom, work sink, fountain, and two toilet rooms. Other elementary school classrooms should be 24 × 40 feet, with work sink and clothes storage. In the high school, classrooms 24 × 36 feet are recommended. Corridor lockers are essential. All classrooms should have walls and ceilings which are treated to absorb noise.

Heating and ventilation

Proper heating and ventilation in the school are not life-or-death matters. Students will not be exposed to a classroom situation in which the oxygen content will not be adequate for survival. Yet for effective and enjoyable school living heating and ventilation are important, and the instructor has an obligation to make every effort to provide a physical atmosphere which is comfortable. It is only a sound educational procedure to enlist the students in the project.

In the heating and ventilating of schoolrooms the entire emphasis must be on physical comfort. Body heat and moisture must be removed. When the elimination of heat and moisture are retarded, students experience drowsiness, lassitude, depression, headache, and loss of vigor. For an alert and stimulating class the room must have proper temperature, humidity, and movement of air.

Standards of physical comfort. For the usual school situation, established standards for physical comfort have been determined by scientific investigation and practical experience. These standards are expressed in terms of temperature, humidity, and movement of air. Properly all three should be discussed together, but practical considerations dictate that they be dealt with one at a time.

Temperature in the schoolroom should be held between 66° and 71° F. In the winter the lower half of this temperature range will feel comfortable. In the hotter seasons a room temperature of 71° F. will feel comfortable.

Humidity or air moisture should be between 30% and 70% of the absolute amount of moisture the air will hold. A humidity of 50% and a temperature of 70° F. are ideal. Several instruments, such as hygrometers and psychrometers, are used for a precise determination of humidity. In the absence of such a device a person may suspect a high degree of humidity when body moisture tends to cling to the body rather than evaporate rapidly. Without an air conditioning unit it is difficult to affect the humidity of a classroom.

Air movement carries away body heat and moisture. To be effective a current of air should be perceptible. The least perceptible current is spoken of as the threshold velocity. Under ordinary room conditions the movement of air should at least be of threshold velocity. A current perceptible at one moment may not be felt a few minutes later. As room temperature declines, the perceptible velocity rises. Since temperature and air movement vary, window ventilation is highly effective because it permits these variations to operate in producing comfortable sensations of the skin. Mechanical ventilating systems do not provide for variations; in this respect they are not so acceptable as the window-gravity method of ventilation.

Heating. Boiler and fuel rooms should be of fire-resistant construction. There is merit in building a brick boiler room separate from the school building.

Radiators and grilles should be placed so that warm air is uniformly distributed without noise or drafts. Heat for each room should be controlled individually. Radiators should be of the wall-hung type and placed beneath windows because this type of radiator is easy to clean.

A thermometer should be placed 5 feet above the floor in each room.

Ventilation. Ordinary window-gravity ventilation can be highly satisfactory if a glass deflector in the window starts the air current upward and an outlet high on the opposite wall permits circulation of the air. Glass deflectors are recommended only because they do not reduce the light from outdoors.

In practice, when there is window ventilation, several purposes are served if specific students are appointed to be responsible for proper ventilation. Someone is responsible for ventilation; the children develop a consciousness of the importance of ventilation; and student participation and responsibility are engendered. Third grade pupils can assume this responsibility although first and second grade children merely participate vicariously since the teacher does the actual chore. If each child is appointed for a two-week period, service opportunities for many pupils, girls as well as boys, are provided.

Mechanical ventilating systems are usually designed to provide 15 cubic feet of air per occupant per minute. Ventilation in one room is not dependent upon ventilation in another room. Zoned ventilation is necessary in large school buildings. The gymnasium, auditorium, shop, and cafeteria usually have independent ventilating units. Cloakrooms have separate ventilation. Toilet rooms have ventilating ducts and fans which are independent of the rest of the system. To remove objectionable fumes or odors, laboratories are provided with special means of ventilation. Chemistry laboratories are provided with fume hoods of acid-resisting construction.

Vent grilles are placed in the walls as far removed from the windows as possible. Neither floor nor ceiling grilles are approved. Fireproof exhaust ducts carry the air outside of the building. Ventilator heads protect the exhaust openings against back drafts and inclement weather.

Air conditioning. The objective of air conditioning is to control the temperature, humidity, movement, and purity of air. The air is filtered and washed to remove dust, smoke, obnoxious gases, and pollen. Temperature is maintained from 68° to 69° F. during the winter and 70° to 71° F. during hot weather. Humidity is maintained from 40% to 45% during winter and from 45% to 50% during hot weather. Air conditioning is used more widely in warmer climates than in colder climates. The primary purpose of air conditioning tends to be temperature control. Air conditioning has much to recommend it, but is not indispensable to good air control in the schoolroom. Air conditioning neither increases nor decreases the incidence of respiratory diseases. The expense is greater than the usual plenum system of ventilation, but in areas with badly polluted air or extremely high temperatures the expense may well be an investment in greater physical comfort and health protection.

Illumination

No one has ever become blind from poor schoolroom lighting, but proper lighting contributes to the effectiveness of students' work and, because it helps prevent fatigue, adds to the enjoyment of the school day. Efficiency and comfort of vision are the major considerations of illumination.

A distinction should be made between the terms light, illumination, and brightness. Light is the source, illumination is the effect, and brightness is the amount of light returned from a surface.

Intensity of visible light is measured in foot-candles. A *foot-candle* is the amount of light received at a point one foot removed from a source of a standard candle power. The universal standard unit of light is at the Bureau of Standards, Washington, D. C. Foot-Candle meters, adjusted to the standard unit, measure the intensity of illumination.

A *foot-lambert* is the brightness of any surface and is the product of the illumination in foot-candles and the reflection factor of the surface. Thus if the light units on a task are recorded as 50 foot-candles and the reflection factor of the task is 70%, the units reflected to the eye would be 35 foot-lamberts. The equation is $F C \times R F = F L$. The foot-lambert must be given major consideration when the environment is conditioned for visual efficiency and comfort.

Three factors in lighting are important—sufficient light, proper distribution of light, and absence of glare. The amount of needed light depends upon the particular activity in which a person is engaged. A corridor requires less light than a reading area where speed of vision is a consideration. Distinctness of vision (visual acuity) reaches its maximum at about 5 foot-candles. Speed of vision attains its maximum effectiveness at about 20 foot-candles. On a sunny day outdoor illumination may be up to 10,000 foot-candles. In a schoolroom the illumination near a window may be above 200 foot-candles.

Proper distribution of light demands that all areas of the vision field have the same approximate intensity. Recognition of the importance of brightness-difference has led to the use of lighter colored chalkboards, woodwork, floors, furniture, and equipment in school rooms. *Brightness-difference* expresses the brightness of the task as compared with brightness of the surrounding area.

Brightness-balance is essential to visual efficiency and comfort. This can be attained by maintaining low brightness-differences between the task and the surrounding area. Absolute brightness-balance in the classroom is not possible as a practical matter. However, the foot-lambert brightness of the best lighted area in the room should not be as much as ten times the foot-lambert brightness of the poorest lighted task where tasks are being performed.

Glare is light that causes discomfort, annoyance, or distress to the eyes. It is annoying to face a window or an uncovered light bulb. Reflected light from a table top produces glare. Contrast in light is disturbing to vision. All of these conditions produce glare and are all too common in schoolrooms.

Classroom factors. Satisfactory illumination in a classroom is more than just the necessary window space and light units. All surfaces should be dull or semiglossy to reduce glare. This means that the furniture must be a light color and have a dull finish. A highly reflective semiglossy paint should be used for the walls and ceiling. Reflective values indicate the colors which should be used in schoolrooms.

It is apparent that the ceiling and the first 3 feet down on the wall should be painted white, ivory, or a light cream color. Attractive pastel tints on the walls provide both attractiveness and good reflective value. Some architects recommend a buff color for the lowest portion of the wall. If this color is used up to the wainscoting, the early appearance of finger marks will be prevented.

Table 21. *Average reflective light of colors*

Color	Per cent of reflected light
Gloss mill white	75–80
Ivory	65–70
Cream	55–70
Yellow	55–65
Buff	45–60
Pastel green	45–60
Light varnish	40–45
Light pink	35–55
Pastel blue	35–55
Pastel gray	15–25
Green	15–25

Table 22. *Recommended lighting levels in schools**

Location	Minimum foot-candles
Classrooms—on desks and chalkboards	30
Study halls, lecture rooms, art rooms, offices, libraries, shops, and laboratories	30
Classrooms for partially seeing pupils and those requiring lip reading—on desks and chalkboards	50
Drafting rooms and typing and sewing rooms	50
Reception rooms, gymnasiums, and swimming rooms	20
Auditoriums (not for study), cafeterias, locker rooms, washrooms, corridors containing lockers, and stairways	10
Open corridors and store rooms	5

*From American Standard Practice for School Lighting, prepared by the Illuminating Engineering Society and the American Institute of Architects, 1948 (approved Acoustical Society of America).

Chalkboards should be dull and light colored, but should never be located between windows. When they are placed in front of the room or on the wall opposite the windows, chalkboards may cause glare. Such glare can be prevented if the lower edge of the chalkboard is pulled out about 2 inches. If the board is tilted thus, the reflected rays are thrown above the heads of the children.

Seats should be placed so that no child faces the window light. By the same token the teacher should not face the light, nor stand in front of the windows so that the children must face the windows in order to see the teacher.

Standards of light. Minimum intensity of light for different purposes has been determined by scientific study and practical experience.

Another set of standards has been set up in terms of foot-lamberts.

Table 23. *Recommended foot-lamberts*

Area	Foot-candles		Reflection factor		Foot-lamberts
Average task	30	×	70%	=	21
Desk top	30	×	50%	=	15
Floor	20	×	30%	=	6
Chalkboard	50	×	30%	=	15
Tackboard	50	×	50%	=	25
Walls	30	×	75%	=	22½

Although sufficient light is important, contrasts should be avoided. The peripheral field and background should be nearly as intensely illuminated as the field of work.

Natural light. Both for the psychological effect and for good visual conditions, natural light should be used to the fullest and most effective extent possible. Window space should be one fifth of the floor area in rooms not more than 24 feet wide. Unilateral lighting or lighting from one side is recommended. The left side is preferred, but the right side is acceptable. Bilateral lighting from one side and the rear is satisfactory and even desirable in large rooms. Cross-lighting is condemned as unhygienic. A bank of windows on one side should cover the back four fifths of that wall, thus leaving the front fifth free of windows. Square-topped windows that extend as close to the ceiling as possible provide a good distribution of light.

Translucent shades diffuse direct sunlight, eliminate glare, and control illumination. If two rollers at the center of the window are used, both rollers can be drawn to allow a foot of clear window space at top and bottom to remain. Shades should be wider than the windows. Venetian blinds, either horizontal or vertical, are satisfactory. Dark lower surfaces of the slats reduce glare. Venetian blinds are durable and do not flap, but are expensive, gather dust, and are hard to clean. Opaque shades can be placed above other shades for movie or other projection activities.

Artificial light. Regardless of the efficacy of the natural lighting in a school, artificial lighting should be planned as a separate system, sufficient within itself. Incandescent lighting is usually semidirect, and the light bulbs are enclosed within Trojan glass units. Indirect lighting is excellent but expensive. Units are concealed in wall recesses, and light is projected to the ceiling where it is reflected to the desks, walls, and other parts of the room. The light is uniformly distributed.

In semidirect lighting the units are dropped about 3 feet from the ceiling to provide more and better distributed light. Units are spaced to give evenness of light. Six or eight units serve the normal sized classroom. The enclosing units should be shaped to throw a great deal of light on horizontal surfaces and should blend in with the ceiling to avoid pronounced contrast. Glass units should be cleaned frequently for maximum efficiency.

Fluorescent lamps are more expensive to install than incandescent lights, but are twice as efficient in converting electric energy into light. Bare fluorescent lamps must be shielded. Louvers, white plastic, and opal glass are most suitable for classroom purposes. White fluorescent lights are recommended for ordinary classroom and shop use. Daylight fluorescent lights are recommended for art rooms, sewing rooms, and other places where color discrimination is necessary. The white fluorescent lamp gives off about 15% more light than the daylight fluorescent lamp.

Fig. 59. School room lighting. A resourceful teacher planned a seating arrangement which eliminated the objectionable features of a single bank of windows for a small classroom.

Fig. 60. Coordinated seating and lighting. Sufficient well-distributed light without glare contributes to more effective enjoyable living. (Courtesy American Seating Company, Grand Rapids, Mich.)

Local lighting units, such as desk lamps, should be used only in very special cases. General lighting should be adequate, without the necessity of installing local units immediately over the field of vision.

Classroom illumination program. So far as possible children should take an active role in the classroom illumination program. An awareness of lighting conditions is best developed through participation. The National Society for the Prevention of Blindness has outlined such a program. Seeing conditions can be improved in the classroom if the following procedures are observed:

1. Keeping upper portions of windows unshaded except when the sun is shining directly on them
2. Drawing shades over the lower portions of the glass area only when necessary to diffuse direct sunlight or to reduce glare from snow, sky, or adjacent buildings
3. Checking illumination levels in all parts of the room periodically with a light meter
4. Making special seating arrangements for left-handed pupils so that light will fall over the right shoulder
5. Keeping window sills free of all obstructions to light
6. Arranging seats and desks so that no pupil will face a window or work in his own shadow
7. Cleaning chalkboards frequently
8. Eliminating books, charts, maps, etc. that are so soiled as to provide poor brightness contrast
9. Providing copyholders and easels to maintain good posture and optimum lighting for close eye tasks

10. Making all board writing large and clear and placing it in the line of vision of the pupils
11. Planning the daily program so as to alternate periods of close eye work with activities less demanding visually
12. Switching on artificial lights whenever brightness levels fall below standard in any part of the room
13. Standing and sitting in positions which direct pupils' vision away from the windows
14. Planning for periodic adjustments of seats and desks to provide for best use of available light
15. Placing pupils with eye difficulties in the best-lighted places from the standpoint of their specific defects
16. Allowing pupils to change their seats whenever they desire more light or less light
17. Selecting work places to make best use of available light
18. Covering chalkboards not being used to conserve the available light
19. Covering glass doors on cabinets and removing pictures covered with glass
20. Selecting and using only those textbooks, maps, charts, posters, etc. that have nongloss surfaces, appropriate type size, and desirable contrast
21. Noting when lamps or tubes become blackened or defective and calling for correction from the custodian
22. Developing in the children a sense of responsibility for assisting in the maintenance of good seeing conditions*

Water supply

School authorities have the responsibility for providing a safe and adequate water supply for school use. When a municipal water supply is used, primary responsibility for its source and purity rests with the municipality and the public health department. Yet the school district is responsible for proper installation and maintenance of water facilities in the school. In addition to being free from contamination, water should be palatable and sufficiently abundant for normal school needs.

Source. Most schools obtain their water from an established public water system. These supplies are under the surveillance of the health department, and the school properly can accept this supervision as adequate. Some schools provide their own water supply, usually by drilling wells.

A shallow well is one which is less than 30 feet deep. Whether dug or driven, shallow wells are unsatisfactory. Public health officials report that most troubles with rural water supplies are caused by shallow wells. A deep (more than 30 feet) drilled well is the recommended water source for a school when no public supply is available.

A well should be located so that it is above sources of contamination from ground water flow. Ground water usually runs toward lakes or rivers, whatever the surface contour may be.

The school district should engage experienced and competent well

*From Classroom lighting, New York, 1950, National Society for the Prevention of Blindness, publication No. 498, p. 14.

drillers. Drilled wells should go down at least 50 feet to a safe water-bearing stratum. This stratum is merely a gravel bed with water in the interstitial spaces. Several impervious layers will lie above the gravel bed and thus prevent contaminated surface water from reaching the ground water stratum. Well casings should be sealed off so that surface water cannot trickle down to the water-bearing stratum. This means that there must be a tight concrete platform as well as sealed-off casing. Chlorination of a ground water supply is usually not necessary, but a sample for bacteriological examination should be taken at least once a month. This test is for the coliaerogenes group of bacteria. Their presence in water indicates that the water has been exposed to contamination from livestock or human beings and may be dangerous for drinking purposes. A positive test thus does not reveal the presence of disease organisms, but the possibility that they may now or later get into the water. One sample is not significant. A number of positive samples, supported by the evidence of a sanitary survey, is the significant source of data. Health department personnel should be consulted. In the meantime water from another source should be used for drinking purposes, or the water should be boiled or chlorinated.

If there is no mechanical chlorinating device, as a temporary measure, a bactericidal chlorine content of water can be obtained by adding 50 drops of 1% chlorine solution to 10 gallons of clear water or by adding 6 teaspoons of 1% chlorine solution to 100 gallons of clear water. A silver spoon should not be used to measure the chlorine solution. The chlorinated water should be well stirred and be permitted to stand for 30 minutes. Individual paper cups should be used for this supply. The labels on Clorox, Purex, and other commercial chlorine products give directions for obtaining at 1% chlorine solution.

Fountains. With running water, fountains provide the most sanitary drinking facilities for the school. One fountain per seventy-five pupils is an acceptable standard. Fountains should be far removed from sinks and washbasins, but should be strategically located. Recesses in corridor walls provide a safety factor. The height of the nozzle should be adapted to the age of the students.

	Height of nozzle
Kindergarten	23 inches
Primary grades	25 inches
Intermediate grades	29 inches
Junior high school	32 inches
Senior high school	35 inches

The nozzle should be above the rim of the bowl and protected by guards. A foot-controlled jet may be more sanitary, but the hand-controlled type is satisfactory. A fountain should be equipped with a flow control valve so that the user merely turns the water off and on and the jet is always the same. The drain pipe should be trapped.

Children ought to have the responsibility for the cleanliness of the

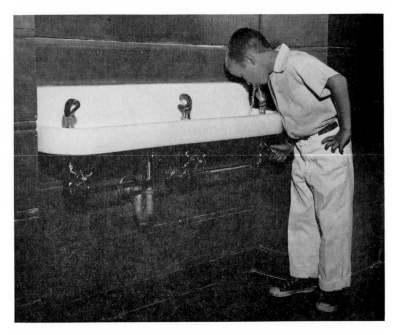

Fig. 61. Multiple fountain. Located in the classroom, this low-cost fountain meets all necessary standards because it is set in for safety and is of the proper height and design.

fountain and the immediate area surrounding it. Opportunities for group organization and discipline have possibilities for training in citizenship.

General toilet room

When general toilet rooms are being located, an outside exposure with direct sunlight should be given preference. Accessibility is important. It is equally important that the girls' and boys' rooms be far removed from each other. Toilet rooms should not be located in the basement.

Ceilings, walls, and floors of toilet rooms should be of washable impervious materials. Uncoated cement floors are not suitable. Impregnated cement, terrazzo, and special tile make excellent floors. Proper drainage is essential, and both hot and cold hose outlets for flushing the floors should be provided. For ventilation provision should be made for exhaust fans with a capacity to remove the room air every 10 minutes.

The students should be responsible for keeping the toilet rooms clean and orderly during the day. In the elementary school the fourth, fifth, and sixth grades can take turns for a month each in being responsible for toilet room cleanliness. While one grade is responsible, other grades will respect its instructions. In junior and senior high schools the health council or student council can provide and administer a plan for orderliness of the toilet rooms. Mopping, scouring, and other cleaning is the custodian's task.

Washbasins. One washbasin or lavoratory for each forty pupils is a recommended standard. Wash fountains can be substituted for washbasins. Height of the washbasins is important.

	Height to rim
Kindergarten	20 inches
Primary grades	22 inches
Intermediate grades	25 inches
Junior high school	28 inches
Senior high school	30 inches

Washbasins should have no stoppers so that students must wash their hands in running water. Each basin should have tempered water which flows through one spigot with hot and cold water valves.

Liquid soap dispensers are preferred. A solution of equal parts of soap and water can be used, which will thus effect a saving. The diluted soap is not as harsh on hands, and students use the same volume from the dispenser. Powdered soap is satisfactory. Bar soap is acceptable. No one has ever demonstrated that disease is spread by a bar of soap. The only real objection to bar soap is that it finds its way to the floor too easily.

Paper towels should be used. Roller towels are not as sanitary because there is no guarantee that a child will turn the roller. When the roll comes to the end, it truly becomes community property.

Waste paper receptacles large enough to hold waste towels for a half day are *musts* if the toilet room is to be orderly. To empty the receptacles is the task of the custodian.

Water closets and urinals. The number of fixtures will vary for different age levels. Any suggested standard may be unsatisfactory for a specific situation.

Elementary school	**Junior and senior high school**
1 water closet to 30 girls	1 water closet to 45 girls
1 water closet to 60 boys	1 water closet to 90 boys
1 urinal to 30 boys	1 urinal to 30 boys

Water closets for elementary schools should be 13 inches to the rim—junior size. Standard size is proper for both junior and senior high schools. Construction should be of porcelain or vitreous china, with flush rim, siphon jet, extended lip or elongated bowl, and open-front seat without a cover. Flush valves and vacuum breakers are preferable to flush tanks. Individual compartments with doors should be provided for each water closet.

Urinals of porcelain or vitreous china of the individual bowl type that are automatically or individually flushed are recommended. Pedestal or wall-hung units are most sanitary. Trough or stall urinals are not acceptable.

Plumbing for sewage disposal. When a municipal sewerage system is available for the disposal of school sewage, the problem which confronts the school is safe and adequate plumbing. Most states have a plumbing code which governs standards for new construction, but is not always applied to buildings already standing, whether they are public or private buildings. Yet older school buildings should be inspected for faulty plumbing.

Back siphonage is the greatest single hazard of faulty plumbing. Back siphonage may be due to cross-connections between water supply systems and sewers, breaks in sewers, or defective water and sewerage piping. Circulating and boosting pumps, water heaters, air compressors, and submerged water inlets in sinks may cause contaminated water to siphon back into the water main. If plumbing installation is not of recent vintage, it would be an investment in health preservation to have a qualified plumber make a thorough inspection of the plumbing. His recommendations should not be neatly filed, but summarily carried out.

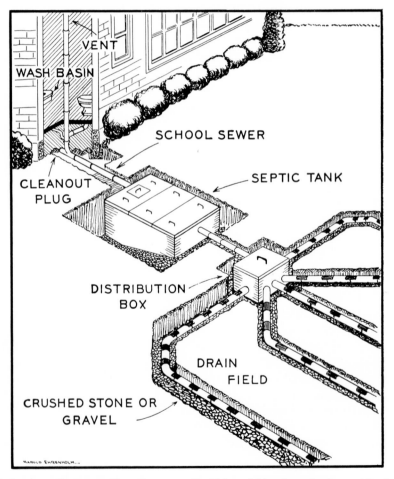

Fig. 62. Septic tank sewage disposal system. Facilities within the school are identical with those in schools connected to a municipal sewer. Wastes settle to the bottom of the tank, and liquid wastes soak into the ground by filtering out of spaces between tile.

Septic tank. Schools without an available municipal sewerage system must provide their own sewage disposal system.

Chemical toilets are used when running water is not available. The vault may be a commercially produced metal one or constructed of concrete. Sodium hydroxide or some other caustic agent is added to the water in the tank. A bottom outlet permits the digested solid matter to be discharged into a soakage pit where the liquid can seep into the soil. Chemical toilets are acceptable if running water is not available, but septic tanks are preferable if water can be provided.

A septic tank of adequate size which is properly designed and installed is entirely satisfactory for school use. Wastes are conducted into a concrete tank which serves as a sedimentation and digestion chamber. Liquids from the tank flow into a distribution box which channels the effluent evenly to the three or four lines of tile buried about a foot under the surface of the ground. A space of ½ inch between the ends of 4 inch field tile permits the liquid to soak into the surrounding gravel and soil. The tank must be cleaned out every two or three years.

The size of septic tank depends upon use. The usual formula is a tank capacity of 15 gallons per student. Most plumbing firms install septic tanks, and some firms make a specialty of their installation.

Special toilet rooms

Kindergartens, locker rooms, faculty lounges, health services facilities, office suites, and other locations in a school building may have special toilet rooms. The number of fixtures in the kindergarten toilet room can follow the elementary school standards. In locker rooms the number of fixtures should be adequate for the enrollment of the largest physical education class. Other special toilet rooms should be equipped with fixtures to meet the maximum needs of the enrollment.

Food service

A food service unit is properly located on the ground floor and is conveniently accessible from the outside. It should be planned to facilitate the most direct route from corridor to serving line, to water cooler, to tables, to soiled-dish counter, and finally to corridor again. A large school will have a serving room, kitchen, and dining room. In smaller schools the serving room is replaced by a serving counter between the kitchen and dining room. Some schools find it necessary to use the dining room for a classroom, for a study hall, and for student activities such as student council meetings. The dining room should be especially pleasant, be well lighted, and have smooth washable walls which are painted in attractive pastel shades.

Facilities. Expenditures on food service facilities represent a long-time investment in the health protection of school children. Dependable equipment costs very little more than inferior questionable equipment.

Storage rooms should be cool (50° to 60° F.), well lighted, adequately ventilated, and vermin free. There should be adequate shelves and clean barrels, boxes, and bins for vegetable and fruit storage.

Refrigeration units should be spacious enough to allow ample room for all foods which need refrigeration. Temperatures must be below 50° F. Dairy products should be kept separate from meats or other foods from which they may absorb odors.

Dishwashing facilities must include an adequate supply of hot water, a wash sink, a rinse sink, and a sanitizing sink that contains a decontaminant or water above 170° F. Use of baskets for the dishes will allow dipping, speed up handling, and make wiping unnecessary.

Dishes and trays should be of smooth nonporous material for easy cleaning. Rusted utensils and cracked or chipped dishes should be discarded.

Handwashing facilities should be available in the kitchen as well as in the toilet rooms. Hot and cold water, soap, and paper towels must be provided. Lockers for storing outdoor clothing and uniforms should be provided for the lunchroom workers.

Practices. The best facilities available would be of little value if the food service personnel did not carry out sound practices. These are simple but important requirements.

1. Food service personnel should meet the same health standards as teachers.
2. The presence of symptoms of communicable disease or open sores should be sufficient cause to remove a worker from duty.
3. A susceptible worker who has been exposed to a communicable disease should have clearance from a physician before reporting for duty.
4. Workers should bathe and change clothing frequently.
5. Workers should wear light-colored washable uniforms while serving food and aprons when preparing food.
6. Caps, bands, or hair nets should be worn.
7. Workers should wash the hands *before* beginning work, *before* handling food, and *before* serving food, and *after* coughing and sneezing, using a handkerchief, returning from the toilet, fixing the hair, and using objects handled by others. Paper towels should be used for drying the hands.
8. Dishes and utensils should be scraped and prerinsed.
9. Dishes and utensils must be washed in hot water (100° to 120° F.) containing a detergent, rinsed, then sanitized for 2 minutes in very hot water (170° F.) or in water containing chlorine or other decontaminant.
10. Glasses and silverware should be wiped with clean dry towels. Dishes should not be wiped.
11. "Tasting" spoons should be used for testing food.
12. Forks, tongs, or spoons should be used for serving.
13. Safety precautions should be taken to prevent the following:

(a) Burns, by using metal match containers, turning pot handles away from workers, using pot holders, opening oven door of gas range before lighting the burner, keeping inflammable materials away from the range, and preventing fat from getting too hot.

(b) Cuts, by providing a holder for sharp implements and by requiring workers to cut away from themselves and to dispose of opened cans, broken dishes and glass immediately.

(c) Falls, by keeping floors dry and free of rubbish, keeping passageways clear, requiring workers to wear low-heeled shoes in of opened cans and broken dishes and glass immediately.

(d) Other hazards, by excluding all but workers from the kitchen, keeping poisons away from the kitchen, not crowding shelves, discarding broken equipment, following recognized practices in operating machines and disconnecting electrical appliances, and turning off gas when not in use.

14. Good storage, including refrigeration, is both sanitary and economical.
15. Tight-covered garbage receptacles should be emptied daily.
16. Ample light in kitchen and dining room is important.
17. Good ventilation is necessary.
18. Floors should be mopped daily.
19. Walls and ceilings should be clean and light in color.
20. Pleasant moderately quiet atmosphere in the lunchroom during the lunch hour is desirable.

In any lunchroom the important factor is competent personnel; this is especially important for the person in charge. If every effort is made to familiarize the students and faculty with the needs and requirements of the lunchroom, understanding will lead to harmonious cooperation. The lunchroom is there for the students and faculty. Respect by the students will most likely come from a realization that this is their lunchroom and they have a joint responsibility in making it a place of which they can be proud. Some noise in the lunchroom is inevitable, but it can be held within bounds without completely restraining the students.

Teachers should correlate the lunchroom experience with the health instruction program. Wash parades just before the lunch hour can establish the practice of washing the hands thoroughly before one eats. When lunch is eaten in the classroom, paper covers for the desks help to create desirable attitudes toward cleanliness at mealtime. Discussions on lunchroom practices and conduct can be fruitful.

Inspections. Administrators are responsible for the sanitation of the food services, and, although health department sanitarians may be asked to make periodic inspections and recommendations, school administrators should provide for in-school inspections. It is a common administrative practice to delegate the task to the director of the school health program. In the absence of a health director the health instructor may be assigned the duty. Such an inspection should be made constructively to improve conditions and encourage the lunchroom personnel in the performance of their duties. A concise practical inspection form, developed jointly by the Oregon State Department of Education and the Oregon State Board of Health, has been highly satisfactory (see accompanying form).

SANITATION REPORT

School and institution food-handling facilities

S Milk, cream _____   Name _____
O Ice cream _____   Location _____
U Cream-filled   No. served daily _____
R pastry _____   Water supply _____
C Meats _____   Sewage system _____
E Shellfish _____
S Ice _____

All items are satisfactory unless otherwise indicated.

Superintendent's name _____ Mailing address _____

Physical plant	*Items*	*Remarks*

1. Floors_____
      Clean and good repair

2. Walls and ceilings _____
      Washable, clean, good repair

3. Doors and windows _____
      Clean screens if needed

4. Lighting _____
      Clean fixtures; adequate light

5. Ventilation _____
      Free from cooking odors (hoods or fans or forced ventilation)

6. Toilet facilities _____
      Clean, good repair; proper vestibules and signs; convenient

7. Lavatory _____
      Located in kitchen and/or toilet room; hot-cold water; soap; paper towels

8. Water supply_____
      Bacteriologically safe

9. Sewage disposal _____
      Adequate

10. Plumbing approved _____

11. Rodent, insect control _____
      Building free of rodent harborage

12. Employees' locker space _____
      Clean, adequate

Equipment

13. Cooking utensils _____
      Good construction; satisfactory condition

14. Work tables _____
       Durable; easy to clean

15. Plates, silverware _____
       Good condition; sufficient for size of operation

16. Refrigeration _____
       Adequate; proper temperature

17. Protected display for exposed foods _____

18. Dishwashing equipment _____
    Approved construction for hand or machine dishwashing; sufficient hot water

19. Storage room _____
       Clean; dry; well-ventilated; vermin-free shelves; racks

20. Garbage cans _____
       Cover; sufficient supply

Operation

21. Dishwashing _____
       Proper washing and sanitizing

22. Food preparation _____
    Proper refrigeration (cream products, etc.); clean and minimum handling

23. Wholesomeness of food _____
    Free from spoilage and contamination; canned foods properly processed
                     from inspected sources

24. Equipment _____
       Power equipment; stoves, utensils, etc. kept clean

25. Storage _____
       Kept clean; food off floor; bulk food in tight containers

26. Employees _____
    Clean uniforms or aprons; hair confined; free from infectious disease; no
                     open or inflamed skin lesions

27. Garbage and refuse handling _____
       Cans kept covered and washed; proper disposal of garbage;
                     no trash accumulation

28. Premises _____
       Kept clean; free from rodents and insects

29. Storage of cleaning supplies _____
       Separate from food storage

30. Cloths _____
       Kept clean

Date of Inspection_____Sanitarian_____

Although this form is designed for use by an outside inspector, it is equally adaptable for use by school personnel.

Gymnasium and activity room

The gymnasium in junior and senior high schools and the activity room in elementary schools should be clean, well lighted, adequately ventilated, and free of all possible hazards. A hardwood floor with a nonslip finish, cleaned daily, keeps dust at a minimum. Windows are often more of a detriment than an asset in a gymnasium. Glass bricks should fill the window space when masonry is used in construction. High windows on both sides may not give adequate light because of the width of the gymnasium. Screens over the windows will reduce illumination, but may be necessary. Artificial lighting as the sole form of lighting can be entirely satisfactory. Forced ventilation is necessary when large crowds occupy the gymnasium. For classes of thirty to forty students, window-gravity ventilation could be adequate. Regular inspections of conditions and practices are essential for the promotion of safety in the gymnasium.

Locker rooms

A well-lighted locker room is usually an attractive and sanitary locker room. Located adjacent to the gymnasium the locker room should provide at least 12 square feet of floor space per student, based on the class with the largest number of students. Floors and walls constructed of nonporous construction promote sanitation. Floors should have excellent drainage and be cleaned daily. A clean well-lighted locker room is usually a tidy one. Adequate heat and mechanical ventilation complete the picture of excellent sanitation.

Shower rooms

Nonslip tile flooring, slightly crowned in the center, is necessary for a satisfactory shower room. On the walls tile wainscot to a height of 5 feet and nonporous material the rest of the way will complete the construction requirements. At least 10 square feet of floor space should be allowed for each shower head. The recognized standard is one shower head for every four students, based on the class with the largest number of students. Shower heads should be at chin height. Different levels of shower heads will provide for the height variation among students. Whether individual or gang showers are used, water-mixing chambers with wheel control valves are recommended. The control of water temperature is quicker and easier with this type of equipment. Compartments for individual showers have largely disappeared. However, drying rooms between the shower and locker rooms have found favor.

In practice, control of fungus infections of the feet is most effective if regular inspections of the feet are made and treatment of all students with the condition is required. Well-lighted locker rooms mopped daily with a detergent complete the picture of easy effective control of the spread of ringworm. The foot bath has many disadvantages and inconveniences and is not essential if other means of control are used.

Swimming pool

Sanitation of the swimming pool is a special responsibility of the physical education staff. Two factors sum up the essence of a sanitary swimming pool—construction and regulation. A properly constructed pool provides for filtration, chlorination, and recirculation and straining of water. A chlorine content of 0.2 to 0.5 parts per million will inactive all pathogenic organisms in the water. Daily samples are taken for determination of bacteriological and chlorine contents. Plans for swimming pools have become so well standardized that schools can now proceed in full confidence that the recommendations of architects and engineers will be totally reliable.

Regulation of a swimming pool has one essential—a qualified person to supervise the use of the pool. Standard regulations are posted governing the users of the pool. Personal cleanliness, freedom from communicable disease, and proper conduct and personal habits in the pool are requisites. It is essential that every one who uses the pool take a cleansing shower, wear a clean suit, and use clean towels. Water temperatures between 72° and 78° F. and room temperatures between 75° and 82° F. are maintained. The pool is drained and scrubbed with a decontaminant about once a week. Frequency depends upon the load the pool carries.

Housekeeping

The actual housekeeping of the school should be done by the custodial staff. However, the students should cooperate in all possible ways to make the task of the custodian easier and more effective.

It is the custodian's responsibility to clean chalkboards and erasers, and it should be done when students are not present. If damp cloths for chalkboards and vacuum cleaners for erasers are used, dust in the school will be reduced. It is equally essential that furniture and fixtures be dusted with a treated cloth. Sweeping or any other activity should be planned to cause a minimum of dust.

The key to good schoolkeeping is the work done during vacation periods. Schools in superb condition before the session for the year begins are easy to keep clean. Painted and washed walls and woodwork, refinished floors, renovated fixtures and furniture, general repair, and replacement of all defective equipment are the prelude to healthful school living.

Healthful mental environment

Important as the physical environment is, the mental environment is even more important because it is less tangible than the physical environment and thus more difficult to control. A healthy mental environment must be built up and maintained by recognizing the factors which favorably or unfavorably affect each child's adjustment.

Characteristics. There are certain attributes or characteristics of a healthy mental environment in the schoolroom which one can readily identify.

1. The children are relaxed and at ease.
2. They feel that the teacher and their classmates regard them highly. Their age-mates become their peer group, and approval of their peer group becomes progressively more important, even to such a

degree that some high school students will rate peer approval to be more important than parental approval.

3. They have a high level of self-esteem.
4. They are challenged by the situation.
5. They are confident that they can succeed.
6. They experience success.
7. They receive adequate personal gratification from their success.

To attain this atmosphere in the classroom, the school has certain responsibilities:

1. Recognize and identify in children those deviations in emotional adjustment which fall out of the normal range and undertake re-education
2. Provide all children with experiences which will stimulate the progressive development of desirable patterns of emotional behavior
3. Provide students with esthetic experiences which will develop an awareness of beauty in life and will identify them with cultural groups
4. Provide opportunities for the development of concepts of values and for practices in conduct arising from these concepts

Role of the teacher. A teacher must be realistic and deal objectively with student adjustment. She should know more about the child than he knows about himself. All school activities directly or indirectly contribute to the personality growth of the students. Because each child is unique, it is necessary to provide for all types and degrees of participation.

To create a hygienic mental environment, a teacher can make many contributions to the adjustment of the student.

1. Adjust the difficulty of the curriculum to the mental capacity of the student
2. Adjust the curriculum to the educational maturity of the student
3. Make special provisions for specific deficiencies and thus fortify the weaknesses
4. Develop high ideals and good habits of conduct as by-products of reading, discussion, visual aids, and other procedures
5. Utilize the social influence of the group to aid in developing a child
6. Give students opportunities to make decisions
7. Develop responsibility and leadership
8. Develop a wholesome interest in law and order within the classroom, the school, and the community
9. Provide desirable social experiences
10. Create a desire in each child to participate in extracurricular activities
11. Instruct pupils in extracurricular activities
12. Restrict or extend extracurricular functions in keeping with the needs of each student

13. Give due encouragement and credit to each child for each accomplishment
14. Be an understanding listener
15. Make assistance as real as possible by helping the pupil to help himself
16. For the poorly adjusted child find the group and teacher to which he will best adjust
17. Help the parents to know the child better
18. Help the parents develop a wholesome attitude toward a child's ability
19. Help the parents to acquire a sensible attitude toward success in school
20. Help the parents to give the child the most wholesome environment possible
21. Supplement the home environment so far as possible

Healthful school living is an environment in which students effectively and enjoyably carry out a self-gratifying program of activities in a school plant which provides for the highest possible level of physical health. A school provides healthful living when students can develop a high level of physical and emotional well-being in an atmosphere in which there develops a high level of self-esteem growing out of self-gratification in accomplishment.

Selected readings

Aaron, J. E.: Are you a safety educator? Safety Education 39: March, 1960.

American Academy of Pediatrics: School health policies; report of the Committee on School Health, Pediatrics 24: Oct., 1959.

American Association of School Administrators: American school buildings, twenty-seventh yearbook, Washington, D. C., 1949, National Education Association.

American Association for Health, Physical Education, and Recreation and National Education Association: Health aspects of the school lunch program, Washington, D. C., 1956, National Education Association.

Association for Supervision and Curriculum Development: Fostering mental health in our schools, Washington, D. C., 1950, National Education Association.

Bernard, H. W.: Mental hygiene for classroom teachers, ed. 2, New York, 1960, McGraw-Hill Book Co., Inc.

Bryan, M. de G.: School cafeteria, ed. 2, New York, 1958, Appleton-Century-Crofts, Inc.

Committee on School Sanitation: School sanitation, American Journal of Public Health 39:111, 1949.

Environment and health, Washington, D. C., 1951, United States Government Printing Office, United States Health Service Publication no. 84.

Hickols, J. E.: School building codes, New York, annual, American School Publishing Corp.

Hopkins, E. S., and Schulze, W. H.: The practice of sanitation, ed. 3, Baltimore, 1958, Williams & Wilkins Co.

Illuminating Engineering Society: American standard practice for school lighting, New York, 1948, Illuminating Engineering Society.

Jacobs, L.: Mental health in the school health program, Journal of School Health 22:288-295, 1952; 23:79-86, 1953.

Kleinfeld, H. J.: Dishwashing practice and effectiveness, American Journal of Public Health 37:379, 1947.

Kotinsky, R.: For every child a fair chance for a healthy personality, Educational Leadership 7:524, 1950.

Linn, H. H., and Helm, L. C.: Check list forms for rating school custodial service, New York, 1940, Columbia University Press.

Linn, H. H., and others: The school custodian's housekeeping handbook, New York, 1948, Columbia University Press.

United States Office of Education: Making school lunches educational, Washington, D. C., 1944, United States Government Printing Office, Pamphlet no. 5.

Menninger, W. C.: Mental health in our schools, Educational Leadership 7:510, 1950.

Mensh, I. N., and Mason, E. P.: Relationship of school atmosphere to reactions in frustrating situations, Journal of Educational Research 45:275, 1951.

National Education Association: Common sense in school lighting, Washington, D. C., 1956, The Association.

National Education Association: Our schools plan safe living, Washington, D. C., 1956, The Association.

National Education Association: Planning America's school buildings, Washington, D. C., 1960, The Association.

Pearson, E. M., and Sauer, M.: Guiding the emotionally disturbed child in a normal school environment, National Elementary Principal 34:76, 1954.

Perkins, L. B.: Workplace for learning, New York, 1957, Reinhold Publishing Corp.

Redl, F., and Wattenberg, W. W.: Mental hygiene in teaching, ed. 2, New York, 1959, Harcourt, Brace and Co.

Sanitation in urban and rural schools, Topeka, Kans., 1946, Kansas State Policy-Making Commission on Health Education.

Stack, H. J., and Elkow, J. D.: Education for safe living, New York, 1957, Prentice-Hall, Inc.

Weeden, Vivian: Beware the ides of April, Safety Education 40: April, 1961.

Wisconsin Cooperative School Health Program: Guides for better school health (publications on surfaces, lighting, heating, and ventilation and water supply) Madison, Wis., 1950, State Board of Health.

Part 6

Appraisal in school health practice

Quality, not quantity, is my measure.

—Douglas Jerrold

Chapter 17

Evaluation

H ow much has the school health program improved the health status of the children? How effective is the school health program? Does it measure up to the recognized standards? Is the health instruction effective? Does the school meet standards for healthful living? All of these are inevitable and logical questions for those who concern themselves with the school health program. To what extent school health work is meeting the general and specific objectives of the health program is of concern to the students, the parents, the community, the school administration, and particularly the health instructors.

Evaluation may be considered an appraisal, assessment, or measurement in its *broadest* and most complete sense. In school health, evaluation is a process of determining the effectiveness of the program and its several phases through the measurement of its progress and the extent to which the health objectives of the school are being achieved. It encompasses the purely subjective transient judgments incidental to health activities as well as the highly objective scientific measurement of factors affecting health. Thus evaluation is inherent in the teacher's observation of a child's attitude toward the dental examination and in the audiometrist's determination of a child's hearing acuity by means of a pure-tone audiometer. Evaluation includes a wide range of activities.

In appraising the health work of a school one must still rely a great deal upon subjective judgments. These have particular value when they are made by prepared and experienced personnel and should be used in the absence of anything more precise. Singular and collective observation by teachers, daily contact with the student, observations of people outside of the school, and other subjective judgments have value. Proper interpretation and weighing of these judgments can make them highly meaningful. However, standardized and adequately objective devices are being developed for measuring different aspects of school health. These devices are not necessarily instruments of precise measurement, but they are more accurate than personal judgment. Their use is analogous to the use of a yardstick to measure the distance between two school buildings. The figure thus obtained will not be precisely correct, but will be more so than the estimate of some individual.

Purpose of evaluation

In general terms health evaluation is both a progress report and an inventory. It tells what is, what should be, and what should not be. It reveals many things and serves various general purposes.

1. Inventories the present status of child health and the health program
2. Appraises the health of the individual child
3. Appraises all aspects of the health program
4. Measures progress
5. Points up strengths in the program
6. Reveals places where emphasis is needed
7. Assists children in understanding their health condition and progress in health education
8. Helps parents understand the health of their children and the school health program
9. Gives the school a basis for revising both its health program and general program
10. Provides a basis for public support and funds for school health work

Time of evaluation. Different conditions require different treatment, but a general pattern of evaluation suggests itself in almost all school health situations which merit measurement.

1. Pretest or a measurement before an activity begins to set up a marker for future comparisons
2. Progress tests to determine the degree and direction of gain from a particular project or activity
3. Verification study when it is doubtful that the activity is effective or is going in the direction expected
4. Special measures to determine whether certain by-products are being achieved
5. Achievement or end result measure of the final status of the condition or factor being developed

Evaluation procedures

Because of the number of factors in the health program which must be evaluated and the variety of conditions and situations under which evaluating must be done, it is obviously not possible to set up a step-by-step procedure which will serve all purposes. Yet certain elements in evaluation must be recognized if the evaluative procedures are to be orderly and meaningful.

1. Broad general objectives of the activity to be evaluated must be clearly conceived as the aims of the enterprise.
2. Specific objectives as stepping stones or component parts of the

broad objectives must be sufficiently definite and meaningful to serve as measurable outcomes.

3. All products, records, and by-products of the activity should be preserved. They can be highly meaningful as evidence that the project was an enriching experience for the participants.

4. Determine what in the situation merits measurement and the devices which will best evaluate these elements.

5. Ascertain how these elements can be measured so that their true significance will be revealed.

6. Construct or select a measuring tool which will likely give the data essential to evaluation.

7. Utilize the measuring tool to the best advantage by adapting it, if necessary, to the specific situation.

8. Analyze the results carefully. Face the task realistically and strive to reduce subjectivity. Note the strengths and weaknesses as revealed by the results.

9. Draw a specific, though tentative, conclusion. The term conclusion should never be written with a capital letter.

10. Apply the results of the evaluation to future situations. A few well-chosen reminders would be helpful for future reference. The appraisal is a means to an end, not an end in itself.

Appraisers. The person who evaluates any phase of the school program varies with the need and the situation. Actually in one way or another many persons are evaluating the health program. Children, parents, and anyone coming in contact with the school are likely to appraise some or all aspects of the health program. However, for specific evaluation the best-qualified person available should do the evaluating. Determining factors are the nature and purpose of the evaluation.

A system-wide or school-wide evaluation of the entire program may be done by outside specialists, the state department of education, the health director of the school, an administrator, a committee of teachers, the school health council, or any combination of these. A special phase of the program may be appraised by one person or a small committee. In practice, evaluation of instruction is done for the most part by the instructor concerned. Occasionally comprehensive health knowledge tests are administered by a testing specialist, a supervisor, or the school health director. Testing is a specialty, but one that a teacher can master by study and application. There are both advantages and disadvantages in evaluations that are made by those closest to the health program and most concerned with its success. Critical self-analysis on the part of the tester will help to eliminate the disadvantages of subjectivity and still retain the advantages of first-hand knowledge.

Evaluation devices

Very few things in this life can be proved. The best we usually can do is present evidence. This should be kept in mind as a guide in the selection and use of any evaluation instrument because the instrument is merely a device for obtaining evidence. Some human being must interpret and weigh the evidence. Some devices provide fairly precise data, whereas others yield only general tendencies or relative differences. Many evaluating devices that have recognized mechanical faults and qualitative shortcomings may nevertheless serve worthwhile purposes in certain situations. A critical analysis should be made of every measure used, but the device should also be appraised in terms of the service it performs and of the purpose for which it is used.

Statistical measures. Statistical methods have long been applied to measurement in education. Their special appeal lies in the facility with which they permit the establishment of norms and thus provide a standard for comparison. Numerical scores suggest precision and are clear-cut and definite. Averages, deviations, variabilities, and consistencies can be determined with a high degree of accuracy. Tests of health knowledge are particularly amenable to statistical treatment. Raw scores can be made more meaningful if an analysis is made of the scores in specific sections of the test and of the types of errors which have been made. When statistical methods are applicable in the evaluation of health factors in the school, they should be given preference. However, care should be taken in the interpretation of statistical results as well as of other data. A high correlation does not establish a cause-and-effect relationship.

Clinical appraisals. Clinical evaluations are less precise and standardized than statistical evaluations. Yet clinical evaluation is the only means we have for appraising some activities in health. The determination of the health status of a child does not lend itself readily to statistical treatment. The findings of the physician and dentist, the observations of the nurse and teacher, the personal history of the child, and the report of the parents can be adequate for clinically evaluating the health status of the child. Perhaps statistical precision is lacking, but the purpose is served. No one has developed a satisfactory standardized test of health attitudes which would lend itself to statistical treatment. Yet teachers have a need for some sort of appraisal of the health attitudes of students. Perhaps the teacher's study of a child's reactions to a given situation is not the most scientific, but it does have value because it provides some appraisal of his health attitudes. Norms cannot be determined and perhaps are not necessary. Too many health activities and objectives are multiphased and involve too many intangible values to be gauged with available statistical instruments. Until statistical measures are available, clinical appraisals will have to be utilized to attain a general evaluation of various health factors.

Types of instruments. A variety of devices is available for health evaluation purposes.

Observations. The most frequently used instrument in all school appraisal—observations—can be both meaningful and valuable in health evaluation. To be most effective observation must be critical and precise.

By using self-discipline and self-direction in observation, a teacher can develop a highly accurate level of discrimination.

Interviews and conferences. Interviews reveal many things other devices cannot elicit. Conferences involving parents and others who know a child are highly productive in disclosing health information.

Self-appraisal. Appraisal by students of their own health discloses information and stimulates interest in their health. A check list combined with original comments will be highly meaningful.

Questionnaires. A list of a series of specific questions can be helpful in obtaining information on health practices and problems of deepest personal concern. Several standard health questionnaires are in general use.

Check lists. Check lists which usually consist of yes-or-no or check-off items are used for studies of sanitary conditions and health practices.

Surveys. A survey can use observations, a check list, interviews, or records to obtain a general report of a situation or phenomenon.

Records. Family and personal health records can be fertile sources of data. School health records should be sufficiently complete to be a dependable source of information.

Reports. Accounts, descriptions, or statements, either incidental or developed for a special purpose, have value especially when correlated with other data.

Tests. The most commonly used form of measurement in the school, written or oral tests are adaptable to health instruction. They are particularly effective in revealing the nature and extent of learning.

Criteria. The mechanics of all evaluation instruments should measure up to the usual obvious criteria of clarity, brevity, administrative efficiency, and adaptability. In addition objectivity, validity, and reliability should command attention, especially in the clinical appraisal.

Objectivity implies the elimination of personal bias, self-interest, or judgment. It is the converse of subjectivity which denotes that one's personal interest colors his decision or choice. Certain laboratory tests that the physician uses in his examination may be totally objective. An electrocardiograph gives an objective measure of the frequency and rhythm of the heartbeat and the nature of the action of the heart. Perhaps the recording of blood pressure is considered objective although human judgment and a subsequent though minor error can creep in. Whenever human judgment is involved, the evaluation cannot properly be termed totally objective.

Perhaps no test used by the teacher to measure learning is totally objective. Even a mathematics test with ten problems, each of which properly can be worked only one way and have but one correct answer, is dependent upon someone's judgment that these were good problems. To that extent the test would be subjective. If one hundred specially trained people agree on the items, personal bias, and thus subjectivity, would be reduced. The practical approach in evaluation is to reduce subjectivity to a minimum and use the subjective approach only when no objective device is available.

Validity is the extent to which a test measures what it attempts to measure. When tests for the busy teacher are constructed, perhaps the best means for establishing a reasonable degree of validity is to depend upon the collective judgment of several qualified people. Other standard tests may also be used as a basis for comparison. Analysis of particular items will help to indicate validity. The frequency with which an item is answered correctly and the distribution of the selection of each of the foils or incorrect answers can be meaningful. Validity implies a balance in the test comparable to the weighing of the material (e.g., as used in a course) which is to be measured. Concealed factors in responses may make invalid an apparently valid test. This factor occurs in health attitude tests. Instead of recording his predisposition to react to an item, the person being tested reponds in terms of his knowledge of what the most desirable response should be.

Reliability is the consistency of measurement. Retesting, testing comparable groups, and treating the results statistically will yield a measure of group and individual consistency. If they are highly similar or correlated, two sets of scores obtained from two similar tests covering the same field indicate a high degree of reliability. The busy teacher hardly has the time needed to go through all the procedures necessary for establishing reliability. The stock in trade of the classroom teacher is to construct tests that her experience indicates will obtain meaningful results and to supplement these with standardized tests.

Evaluation of change in health status of child

Since the present-day school health program places great emphasis upon building up and maintaining the highest possible level of health in every child, a reliable means for measuring health status change would be extremely valuable. No single scale or measure has been devised, but a combination of various available tests and methods can be used to obtain a workable profile of a student's health level.

A recent thorough health examination will obviously give a clear picture of the child's health. Comparison with previous examinations will be relatively simple for children who have had defects corrected during the interim. However, for the vast number of youngsters no such corrections have been necessary, and to make an evaluation of change in health status commands the best analysis and judgment of the physician.

In the absence of a health examination the teacher's own assessment or appraisal of a child's level of health will be of value. Though highly subjective, the appraisal considers buoyancy, pleasure in activity, vigor, zest, endurance, recovery from fatigue, ability to relax, steady weight increase, absence of defects, and social adjustment. The appraisal can be supplemented by the child's school health record. Dental corrections, vision tests and corrections, hearing tests, weight and height changes, and records of illnesses may be significant sources of information. The Wetzel Grid could be helpful by indicating the youngsters' developmental course.

If the teacher's appraisal is supplemented by the judgment of other teachers who have had ample opportunity to observe the child and the assessment of the parents, the subjective factor will be reduced. Whether the evaluation will be of value is secondary to the importance of interesting the child in his own health status. If the child has had the benefit of good health guidance and instruction, his assessment of his own health will be worthy of inclusion in the evaluation.

Evaluation of administrative practices

School health work is advanced or retarded in terms of administrative policies and practices which relate to the health program. An insight into the success or failure of the health program of a school may well be gained by a survey of administrative practices. The usual survey is made by means of a check list of the widely accepted health responsibilities of the school administrator.

1. Recognize health as a basic objective of education
2. Secure and budget adequate funds for the health program
3. Keep parents informed of the health program
4. Cooperate with all health agencies
5. Maintain communication with community organizations
6. Employ qualified health personnel
7. Know the health problems of the school
8. Arrange the school day in accord with sound health practice
9. Establish an effective system for keeping health records
10. Establish a definite health examination program
11. Provide for health observations by the teachers
12. Establish a systematic referral program
13. Promote measures to ensure corrections for every child
14. Establish a program for control of communicable diseases
15. Procure necessary materials, facilities, and equipment for health instruction
16. Provide time and facilities for health instruction in the secondary school
17. Appoint only qualified teachers for health instruction
18. Provide a healthful physical environment
19. Provide a mentally hygienic environment
20. Establish and promote a safety program
21. Provide facilities, personnel, and an established plan to meet emergencies
22. Provide health services for professional personnel
23. Provide in-service health instruction for teachers
24. Provide for faculty sick leave and require that ill teachers remain home

This check list does not include all of the health responsibilities of the administrator, but by specifying the essential minimum practices it serves as a practical realistic measuring stick of the administration's contribution to the school health program.

Evaluation of the school health program

Appraisal of the over-all school health program is necessary as a measure of the completeness of the program, its function, and its effectiveness. A valid evaluation of the program would point up its strengths and weaknesses. Despite the recognized need for such an evaluation instrument, very few appraisal forms are available. In consequence most program evaluations are either general surveys or evaluations of specific phases of the program, notably the health instruction phase.

Available standard forms differ in purpose, scope, and composition. They can be used to advantage, particularly if supplemented by other evaluative devices to serve specific situations and needs.

The following sources for use in evaluation are suggested:

1. American Public Health Association: Evaluation schedule. This publication has a section which evaluates school health as a phase of community health.
2. Rogers, J. F.: Safety and health of the school child, Washington, D. C., United States Office of Education Pamphlet No. 75.
3. Grout, Ruth E.: School health inventory. In Handbook of health education, New York, 1936, Odyssey Press, Inc. Although it is directed to the needs of rural schools, this inventory is of value in appraisal of the health program of any school.
4. Texas Education Agency: A checklist: Appraising the elementary and secondary school health program, Austin, Texas, 1951, Bulletin No. 519. The information in this publication is directed toward state use, but is applicable in other situations.
5. Phelan, Annette M.: A study of school health standards, Menasha, Wis., 1934, George Banta Publishing Co. This book provides a basis for evaluating the health program in a school and also for appraising the quality of the health program.

Oregon State University developed a School Health Program Evaluation Scale which was completed as it now stands in 1959. Perhaps ideally a scale should measure the results of the health program, but the inherent difficulties are obvious. However, the use of inference tests in psychology has been highly successful, and this scale is based upon the same principle. Studies have revealed that when school health programs attain their basic objectives, certain practices, procedures, standards, activities, and facilities are usually present. This scale was developed in terms of recognized procedures, practices, standard facilities, and activities. The inference is that, if a school health program possesses certain attributes, the health objectives will be attained. Every effort has been exerted to make the scale applicable to urban and rural schools alike, to the small school system as well as medium sized and large school systems. A certain amount of subjectivity is inherent in some of the items; yet the total scale is reasonably objective. A member of the school staff can use the scale, or an independent outside person may rate the program with this instrument.

The scale appraises the various aspects of the health program and permits numerical scoring by providing for 1000 possible points. Weighting is done by allocating 350 points to school health services, 400 points to health instruction, and 250 points to healthful school living. The scale has a two-fold purpose. It is of value to the teacher, health educator, and administrator in measuring the attainment and progress of the health program in terms of a recognized standard. It will indicate strengths and weaknesses. The second purpose is to furnish a means for comparing school health programs. The complete scale is given in Appendix C.

A review board of twenty-four experienced health educators critically analyzed all aspects of the scale. Their independent criticisms and suggestions were incorporated into the next draft of the scale. The final form thus represents extended study, review, and experience. The scale must be a functional organ that undergoes constant growth and refinement in harmony with changes in the school health program.

Some health educators are apprehensive of any attempt to measure school health in terms which are too precise. Yet if we are to have tangible meaningful evaluations of school health work, our procedures must be well defined, clearly set forth, and definite. The field of school health has come of age sufficiently to accept discriminating detailed examination rather than high-sounding generalities.

Evaluation of health services

Circumstances may make it desirable to evaluate health services independently of other phases of the health program. Such an evaluation would include the nature and frequency of health examinations; dental examinations; screening of vision, hearing, weight, and height; and the teacher's appraisal of the child's health. The follow-up program and correction of defects must be included. Prevention and control of diseases, emergency care, and first-aid provisions are part of the health services to be appraised.

1. Weatherby, H. R.: A check list for school health services, Stanford, Calif., 1952, Stanford University Press. This publication is highly recommended because it represents both accepted standards and established practices and can be applied to a diversity of school situations and serve the several purposes of appraisals.
2. Oregon State University: School health program evaluation scale, Part I, School health practices. This section can be used independently of the remainder of the scale. In addition to weighting the different items the section points up the different phases of health services which are recognized as essential.

Evaluation of healthful school living

Any assessment of the school environment must extend beyond the mere static physical environment. It must encompass the activities and practices in the school which affect health promotion, disease prevention, safety, social adjustment, and esthetic appreciation. Evaluation must include factors affecting physical and mental health in terms of dynamic school living. The construction of the school plant and sanitation facilities are important, but an evalaution of healthful school living must be extended to the total school program and the people who are part of the child's environment.

No phase of the school health program is as easy to appraise as the physical environment. Sanitary facilities are tangible, can be counted or tabulated, and involve very little analysis or decision. Even the safety elements of the school environment are amenable to easy identification and tabulation. Perhaps for these reasons sanitary surveys of schools have long been a common routine in school practice. Certainly the sanitary survey should be continued, but it should be expanded into an evaluation of total healthful school living.

Most forms developed for use in making evaluations of the school environment are survey check lists which require either yes or no answers, check marks, or X marks. Such survey forms have merit because of their directness, simplicity, and utility. Such a check list is presented in Appendix D, which deals in definite terms, not relative ones. Either the school has thirty or more foot-candles of light on working surfaces or it does not. Either the fire extinguishers are properly distributed or they are not. This type of survey has value in the present status of the school environment and what should be done. It can serve as an incentive for improvement and, in subsequent appraisals, reveal improvement in conditions. Most state departments of education have similar check-list forms.

Perhaps a more functional evaluation of healthful school living can be made if Part III in Appendix C is used. In this section the school is visualized in action as a dynamic community of people. The various forces and factors which affect the well-being of the child are included and evaluated in terms of their influence upon his total health. In addition to its appraisal of school life in action this scale can serve as a stimulating instructional instrument. The students can benefit from the opportunity to participate in the evaluation if a scale of this type is used.

Evaluation and health instruction

Two aspects of evaluation are applied to health instruction. An evaluation *of* the health instruction program differs from evaluation *in* health instruction though the former carries a connotation of the measurement of the effectiveness of the health instruction activities.

Evaluation of the health instruction program. What should be included in a health instruction program? What subject areas should be included? What objectives should be recognized? What time allotment is made? What facilities, equipment, and material are available? What methods are being used? To what extent do integration and correlation take place? What training do the health instructors have? These are questions which must be answered in an evaluation of the school health instruction program.

Because schools vary markedly in what they regard as the cardinal aims of their health instruction, to develop a scale which would be universally applicable would be a near impossibility. Any form devised which is broad enough to encompass all purposes and situations would be so all-inclusive as to be virtually impractical. The problem becomes one of determining the primary essentials of the health instruction program and constructing a scale based on these as a foundation. In using such a scale, each school can thus rate itself in terms of these basics and then implement the rating with an evaluation of the special features of its own program.

In Part II, Health instruction, of the School health evaluation scale in Appendix C, the recognized essentials of school health instruction are presented. Since it measures procedures and activities, it must necessarily be based upon the inference that these procedures and activities yield the desired end result in terms of health knowledge, attitudes, and practices. Whether a correlation exists can be determined statistically by testing the change in children which result from these procedures as compared with other types of health instruction programs.

An individual health instructor or any other person can use the section on health instruction as a suggested approach to health instruction. It can indicate strengths in the present program and possibilities for improvement. If it is used for a second evaluation, progress in the interval between appraisals will be indicated. A health instruction program which includes all of the items in the scale and goes beyond these is basically likely to be an effective program, even an outstanding one.

An evaluation of a health course per se can be done by use of a check list in question form which includes the important criteria of classroom practice applied to health.

HEALTH COURSE INVENTORY

1. Is the general classroom atmosphere one of vitality and purpose?
2. Do students exhibit an alert interest?
3. Is the emphasis on the individual and *his* health?
4. Does the class deal with real student health needs and interests?
5. So far as possible is the scientific approach used?
6. Is a diversity of instructional methods utilized?
7. Is a variety of materials and teaching aids used?
8. Is subject matter accurate?
9. Are provisions made for differences in student ability?
10. Are opportunities provided for full student participation?
11. Are generalizations channeled to practical applications?
12. Are abstractions vitalized in meaningful terms?
13. Is understanding emphasized?
14. Are health practices developed?
15. Is essential terminology made clear?
16. Is experience in discovery provided?
17. Is class experience integrated with general experience?

18. Is health instruction correlated with other instruction?
19. Do students have opportunities to discover sources of health knowledge?
20. Are frequent reviews held?
21. Are examinations challenging?
22. Do tests measure student progress?
23. Are tests reviewed by the group?
24. Is the course analyzed periodically in the interest of improvement?
25. Does the course undergo modification?

Evaluation in health instruction. The development of instruments for evaluating the effectiveness of health instruction requires an understanding of the subject field, a grasp of the outcomes toward which health instruction is directed, competency in test construction, and a willingness to put forth the effort which creativeness demands. Whether a teacher needs a simple survey of health practices or a complex objective test to measure students' understanding and appreciation of health values, demands on time, patience, ingenuity, and energy are involved.

Test construction and testing are competencies which every classroom teacher should strive to master. Standard tests have their place and have value, but constant reliance on such tests indicates a limited classroom testing program. Standard tests cannot replace teacher-made tests. A rich meaningful evaluation program means tests and testing which are integrated with the objectives, procedures, activities, experiences, techniques, concomitant learning, skills, and values developed in the class. Like other teaching competencies, testing is not something mysterious and beyond the ability of the typical health teacher. Testing can be mastered by study and practice. A teacher need not attain the competence of a specialist to do an acceptable job of testing. In addition to its contribution to the instructional program, competency in testing is a source of personal professional gratification to the teacher.

Tests are used for a diversity of purposes. They can be used for diagnostic purposes, to determine progress, and to measure final achievement. In all cases they should reveal the nature and extent of learning. They can be tailormade to fit each situation. They can be enjoyable and stimulating. Tests should be considered a means to facilitate learning. A student thinks of a test as an opportunity to demonstrate knowledge and skill. Fear that students may have of tests can be overcome by using this positive approach and by giving frequent, though short, tests. Skill in testing includes putting students in a proper frame of mind before the test.

Procedure in test construction is most productive when it is well organized. A logical procedure can be followed.

1. Formulation of basic objectives
2. Specific aspects of each objective
3. Outline of material in topic form
4. Objectives or abilities to be tested
    (a) Information—terminology, general principles, and facts
    (b) Reasoning—deduction and induction

    (c) Skills

    (d) Practices

    (e) Technical performance

    (f) Location of relevant data

    (g) Interpretation

    (h) Point of view

    (i) Making decisions

    (j) Drawing conclusions

    (k) Accepted values

5. Collection of situations in which pupils will deal with objectives
6. Determination of type of test
7. Determination of difficulty of test
8. Ascertaining desirable length of test

In developing the test the teacher may find it necessary to include several types of test forms. To get meaningful responses in one area of the subject may require one set form, whereas another area of the subject lends itself more readily to another type of test pattern.

Health practices tests should do more than measure the pupils' knowledge of health practices which should be followed. Such tests have decidedly limited value. The pertinent question is whether this knowledge is being applied.

Since health practices are greatly stressed in the primary grades, adequate evaluation of the health instruction program at this level must be concerned with the extent to which health practices are established. Daily observation by the teacher is an acceptable, though not completely satisfactory, means of determining child health practices. The health practices of the children can be surveyed by orally asking the class to indicate how many drank milk for breakfast, how many brushed their teeth after breakfast, and how many carried out other health practices. Group discussion will logically follow the tally, and group motivation can be utilized advantageously. Successive surveys will reveal group progress. Opportunities are present for teaching honesty, self-descipline, and self-reliance.

Some teachers develop a short *health practices questionnaire* for parents which asks them to indicate the health practices of the child. A brief form indicates the nature of this type of questionnaire.

THINGS OUR CHILDREN DO FOR HEALTH

Our first grade is working hard to do the things that will mean better health. Would you help us by checking the practices of your first grade child?

My child _____

Check
here

    1. Washes clean before each meal

    2. Keeps fingernails clean

    3. Helps with own grooming

    4. Takes a bath at least once a week

5. Has milk each breakfast
6. Has fruit for breakfast
7. Has breakfast cereal at least four times a week
8. Eats an adequate evening meal
9. Eats fruit between meals but no candy
10. Brushes teeth thoroughly after each meal
11. Keeps all possessions in good order
12. Helps with tasks about the home
13. Is considerate of others
14. Has a happy disposition
15. Goes to bed early
16. Is improving in health practices

_____   _____
Parent   Date

The questionnaire is obviously slanted to interest the parent in the child's health practices and in the school health program. Items are relatively simple and easily scored. If a scoring is done after the class program has been in operation for two or three months, it will not preclude a follow-up survey with the same form several months later.

A *health practices inventory* is a satisfactory instrument for calling the teacher's attention to the progress of the program in general and specific practices in particular. It depends upon the teacher's observation, but it is a directed observation on an item-to-item basis. In practice this type of evaluating device has served its intended purposes.

HEALTH PRACTICES INVENTORY

Pupils
1. Come to school rested
2. Come with hair combed
3. Have clean faces, ears, and necks
4. Have clean hands and nails
5. Brushed teeth
6. Have neat and clean clothing
7. Remove and hang up outdoor wraps when indoors
8. Take off rubbers indoors
9. Keep all possessions orderly
10. Use a clean handkerchief properly
11. Cover coughs and sneezes
12. Keep their fingers and other objects away from mouth
13. Wash their hands before eating
14. Are cheerful and orderly at lunch time
15. Have a hot dish (not cocoa) and milk with lunch
16. Have fruit with lunch
17. Eat no candy at school
18. Brush their teeth after lunch
19. Participate in organized play at noon and recess
20. Wash their hands after lunch and recess
21. Maintain good posture at all times
22. Work in good light
23. Hold their work in correct position
24. Wear glasses when prescribed
25. Follow good work practices
26. Accomplish their tasks
27. Display cheerfulness and vitality
28. Adjust well to each other
29. Experience and enjoy success
30. Are at ease in the classroom

Several health practices inventories are available from which the teacher may select the forms she needs rather than construct an original form. The following sources are suggested.

1. Johns, E. B.: Health practice inventory, Stanford, Calif., 1943, Stanford University Press. This is a well-constructed inventory for school use.
2. National Safety Council: National Safety Council tests, Chicago, 1946, The National Safety Council. This publication consists of one-page tests for use in specific grades.
3. Neher, G.: Health Inventory for High School Students, Los Angeles, 1942, California Test Bureau. The first part of this book deals with health information and the second part with health practices.

Health attitudes tests have challenged the most skilled experts in test construction. Since attitudes are abstractions, they are intangible and thus not readily amenable to precise measurement. Indirect questioning, inference items, duplicate techniques, repetition of similar yet distinctive items, and comparative choices have been used in the construction of attitude tests, but without too much success. Still to be solved is how to distinguish between a testee's own attitudes and his knowledge of the responses which are approved by society. Whether the item measures a predisposition or a considered judgment is always a moot question. The dividing line between traits and attitudes poses an additional problem.

Psychophysical methods which measure responses to sensory stimuli, such as weight differences, can be applied with limitations to certain social phenomena such as attitudes. However, certain assumptions are necessary. The primary assumption here must be that an opinion is a symbol or an expression of an attitude. Thus opinions would be the means by which attitudes would be measured.

How reliable is an opinion? Intentionally or unintentionally the subject may distort his true attitude or reaction. However, a person's actions also may belie his true feelings. The real discrepancy between expressed opinions and actual attitudes may be revealed or at least minimized if the same test is repeated at intervals. In the evaluation of health attitudes degrees of preference such as more or less may be used, or absolutes such as yes or no can be employed.

If opinions on health are the means employed for discovering health attitudes, statements must be definite and clear. They should be brief, and each item should deal with only one factor. In verification of the reliability of responses, it can be helpful to duplicate the opinion in several different sentence forms. In any event the interpretation factor will be all-important in any attempt to determine health attitudes.

Among the health attitudes tests available, three may be of use to the teacher who seeks to evaluate the effectiveness of the health instruction program in developing health attitudes.

1. Byrd, O. E.: Health attitudes scale, Stanford, Calif., 1941, Stanford University Press. This scale was prepared for use at high school and college levels.
2. Franzen, R. H., Derryberry, M., and McCall, W. A.: Health awareness test, New York, 1941, Bureau of Publications, Columbia University Press. This test is to be used at the junior high school level.
3. Southworth, W. H., Latimer, J. V., and Turner, C. E.: A study of the health practices, knowledge, attitudes, and interests of senior high school pupils, Research Quarterly, American Association for Health, Physical Education and Recreation, May, 1944. This article includes tests for use by health instructors.

In actual practice the teacher's own evaluation, subjective as it is, can adequately serve to indicate the predispositions of children to react to health situations and values. The evaluation of several teachers would have additional significance.

Health knowledge and understanding tests constitute the health teacher's principal evaluation need and implement. Knowledge as a recognized objective of health is amenable to fairly precise measurement, and many test forms can serve this purpose. Understanding is equally important as an objective and, though more difficult than knowledge to measure, can be evaluated by means of tests built on recognized principles of test construction.

Certain forms and criteria are recognized in test item construction. They are helpful guides in aiding the health teacher to develop classroom tests which are challenging to the students and which truly evaluate aspects of health education.

Essay tests. The essay examination has considerable merit. It can reveal a student's general grasp of a subject and his ability to organize and express his understanding of the subject. These are skills or attitudes that the whole school program seeks to develop. The essay test is especially valuable for diagnostic purposes. An essay question should call for a sequence of ideas, for the development of logical thinking, or for support for an idea.

Some suggestions for the construction, use, and scoring of essay tests can be channeled to the needs of the teacher of health.

1. Questions should elicit reactions to a situation, not merely a description of it.
2. Most valuable questions are those based on how, why, or of what significance. Mere restatement of facts by the student in response to what, or who, or when is of little value. How can you help to protect the health of others? is a better question than When should the health department isolate a child?
3. Call for definite precise points and ask that the most important points in the answers be underlined.
4. Work out several model answers for use in grading and set up certain pertinent points.
5. To give uniformity to grading, read the first question on all papers, then the second on all papers, and on through the last. Subjectivity can be reduced by taking the average score of several qualified graders, but there is not likely to be such a luxury as several graders in the usual school situation.
6. Two devices can be used in scoring. The first is the positive approach of adding points for each contributing statement. The second is the negative approach of starting the reading by giving the question an arbitrary value (e.g., 20) and then deducting from the maximum score as the answer is deficient in meeting the model or standard answer.

7. If selected answers are read in class, students will be helped to evaluate their own performance and understand what a topflight answer is.

True-false test. To many people an objective test means only one thing—a true-false test. Most widely used, most abused, and most maligned, the true-false test can be highly discriminating and useful. It is easy to construct, is useful in testing for misconceptions, is especially suitable for situations involving just two alternatives, such as infectious or noninfectious, provides for wide sampling, and is easy to score.

Testing as well as teaching should discourage rote learning without understanding. For that reason if the number of wrong anwers are subtracted from the number of right ones $(R - W = S)$ in obtaining the score, both rote memorizing and guessing will be discouraged. For a single test, correction for guessing $(R - W = S)$ will produce a different distribution of letter grades than when no penalty is received for an incorrect answer. In addition, substracting the number wrong from the number right produces a greater spread in numerical scores. However, over a period of time (e.g., a semester) in which several tests are involved, the final distribution of letter grades will be pretty much the same under either plan.

A good test uses new terms and phrases, cast in a new mold, and avoids common word associations and textbook statements. A good test will favor the student whose preparation has been thorough and who understands. It will penalize and confuse the student whose preparation has been superficial and who tries to get by through cleverness and outguessing the tester. A few suggestions may be helpful.

1. Use true and false statements approximately in equal proportions.
2. Make the important factor in the statement apparent to the student.
3. Use straightforward statements, not confusing or trick statements.
4. State exactly what is meant and avoid ambiguity (perhaps this can be avoided if another instructor reads the statements).
5. Quantitative terms should be used rather than qualitative terms. Great, small, or many can be misleading.
6. Whether the statement is true or false should not depend upon recalling a precise figure or word.
7. The longer the statement, the more likely it is to be true.
8. About 9 out of 10 statements with the word *only* are false.
9. About 3 out of 4 statements which use the words *never* or *always* are false.
10. About 4 out of 5 statements with the word *all* are false.
11. Statements with terms such as *usually, frequently,* and *almost always* are far more often true than false.
12. About 4 out of 5 sentences with the words *not* or *none* are true.

Thus, though all of these terms can be used, care must be exercised in constructing statements which contain them.

A modified true-false item is one in which one or more key words are underlined. If the statement is correct, it is marked true. If it is incorrect, the underlined term is crossed out and a correct substitute term is written in the blank space.

Other variations of the true-false type are the use of S and U for satisfactory and unsatisfactory or the use of A, D, and U to designate agree, disagree, and undecided.

Sample true-false items will illustrate some of the enumerated suggestions.

Items 1 to 10 are true-false questions. If the statement is true, circle the T; if false, circle the F.

T	F	1.	Health means more than being out of a sickbed.
T	F	2.	There is no single index of the quality of a child's health.
T	F	3.	Large persons always have good health.
T	F	4.	A person who inherits a good constitution will usually have good health.
T	F	5.	A mentally healthy person never gets angry.
T	F	6.	Fatigue and hunger can affect a person's mental health because they tend to be upsetting
T	F	7.	A balanced diet is one having the same number of calories each meal of the day.
T	F	8.	Overweight is due primarily to a glandular condition.
T	F	9.	The best position in which to sleep is the most comfortable one.
T	F	10.	Tooth paste is better for bleeding gums (pink toothbrush) than oranges.

11. Alcohol is always a stimulant to the human body.   narcotic

12. The most harmful substance in cigarette smoke is the *irritants*.   T

Some common errors in item construction have been purposely included.

Material which lends itself to modified true-false items can usually be converted to simple true-false or short-answer items.

Multiple-choice tests. Superficially all multiple-choice questions appear to be similar, but a wide variety of items is included. Most satisfactory is the five-response multiple-choice item. It yields a greater dispersal of scores and is adaptable to many situations. Several forms can be used.

The first type is a direct question followed by five possible responses, one of which is correct or the best answer. Some examples will illustrate.

Items 13 to 35 are multiple-choice questions. From the key select the best answer to each item. Place the *letter* of the best answer in *front* of the number of the item.*

_____13. The statement "In solving one problem we often create a new problem" is best illustrated by which of the following?

    A. The discovery of penicillin put the producers of tincture of iodine out of business.

    B. Controlling infectious diseases has made new immunization methods necessary.

    C. Prolonging the length of life has resulted in new economic and social needs.

    D. The decline of infectious disease has created the problem of an oversupply of physicians.

    E. The discovery of the electron microscope has added new diseases to be conquered.

_____14. Which of the following statements have no scientific basis?

    A. Smoking irritates the respiratory tract.

    B. Smoking has a stimulating effect on some people.

*If machine-scored, numbers may be used for responses in place of letters.

C. Smoking has a soothing effect on some people.
D. Smoking stunts growth.
E. Smoking is usually a release mechanism.
_____15. What tends to promote drowsiness?
A. Reading while lying down
B. Warm lunch
C. Lack of air movement
D. Lukewarm bath
E. All of the above four

In the second type of multiple-choice test, the items are stated as incomplete sentences; there are five proposed completions, one of which is the best.

_____16. The expression "Nature grants biological function without social favor," means
A. Reproduction is solely a function of socially well-adjusted people
B. Only responsible people should have children
C. Some people, capable of being fathers and mothers, are incapable of being proper parents
D. The ability to reproduce is independent of economic or educational level
E. Sterility does not occur among the more socially fortunate
_____17. With recent health advances we can now logically abandon
A. Sanitary measures
B. Program to prevent childhood diseases
C. Immunization programs
D. Health research programs
E. None of the above four
_____18. The usual sequence to chronic alcoholism is
A. Week-end drinking, solitary drinking, alcoholism
B. First drink from curiosity, alcoholism, social drinking
C. Curiosity, social drinking, to relieve tensions, alcoholism
D. To relieve tensions, social drinking, alcoholism
E. Curiosity, aggressive drinking, social drinking, alcoholism

In the third type of multiple-choice test, one key with five responses for a series of statements is used.

Key for items 19 to 23
A. Favorable for prevention of respiratory infection
B. Unfavorable for prevention of respiratory infection
C. Not related to prevention of respiratory infection
D. Favorable for prevention only when a person is under 10 years of age
_____19. Vigorous exercise
_____20. Avoiding crowds
_____21. Avoiding night air
_____22. Fatigue
_____23. Taking a laxative

Another example of the same type of multiple-choice test which has some characteristics of a matching test is as follows.

Key for items 24 to 30
A. An *A* level of mental health
B. A *B* level of mental health

    C. A *C* level of mental health
    D. All of the above levels
    E. None of the first three

_____24. Improvement in mental health possible
_____25. Alcoholic
_____26. Never gets angry
_____27. Minimum of friction; maximum of enjoyment
_____28. Uninspired, everyday boredom
_____29. Perfect mental health
_____30. Constructive, effective adjustment

Another design of multiple-choice test may stimulate analytical thinking.

Key for items 31 to 35
A. Statement is correct; reason is correct.
B. Statement is correct; reason is incorrect.
C. Statement is incorrect; reason is correct.
D. Statement is incorrect; reason is correct

_____31. All overweight people should exercise vigorously because exercise increases metabolism.
_____32. Drinking fluids before or during a meal will stop digestion because water will dilute stomach acid.
_____33. Regularity is favorable to good digestion because it permits a cycle or rhythm in the function of the digestive system.
_____34. Dentifrices should be used in brushing teeth because dentifrices are antiseptics.
_____35. Fluorine prevents decay for adults because it destroys bacteria.

Another variation in multiple-choice tests is a chart on which designations are used as the key and the items refer to the designations on the chart.

In the construction, use, and scoring of multiple-choice items, certain safeguards are suggested.

1. There should be only one correct or best answer.
2. The position of the correct response should be changed from item to item. There is a tendency to make the second response the correct one more frequently than the other four positions.
3. Skill in constructing foils is the key to good multiple-choice test construction.
4. Foils should be attractive and vary in degree of plausibility.
5. One item may ask the student to select the exception to the other four items.
6. Direct statements are preferable to incomplete sentences.
7. If incomplete sentences are used, the responses should come at the end of the sentence.
8. All responses to incomplete sentences should be grammatical completions of the sentence.
9. Responses should be as homogenous as possible.
10. When multiple-choice items are placed in a block, the student is aided and scoring is more simple.
11. Avoid words in the response which repeat words in the sentence, except when inserted as foils to counter attempts to outguess the test.
12. Correct responses should not be conspicuous by being long or short.
13. Avoid the use of direct phrases from the text.

14. If the five-response items are well constructed, deducting ¼ point for each error (R − ¼W = S) will spread the scores and reduce guessing.
15. The multiple choice test lends itself to the effective measure of understanding.

Matching tests. Matching tests are really a modification of the multiple-choice test. In this type of test two columns are used; one column consists of either incomplete statements or a list of questions and the other column of a list of responses. An example will illustrate.

From the key at the right, select the best response to each statement in the column to the left. Place the *letter* of that response in *front* of the number of the statement.

_____36. Health of the gums	A. Vitamin A
_____37. Important for thyroxin production	B. Vitamin B
_____38. Elevates a school child's intelligence	C. Vitamin C
	D. Vitamin D
_____39. Necessary mineral for red corpuscles	E. Fat
	F. Iodine
_____40. Helps prevent infection	G. Iron
_____41. Bone growth and development	H. Protein
_____42. Growth and repair of tissues	I. None of the above
_____43. Citrus fruits	

Another form of matching test consists of parallel columns, as illustrated in the following example.

Statements in items 44 to 47 are to be compared quantitatively.
    Key for items 44 to 47
    A. Statement M is *greater than* statement N.
    B. Statement M is *less than* statement N.
    C. Statement M is *the same* as statement N.

Statement M	Statement N
_____44. Number of chromosomes in a sperm	Number of chromosomes in a mature ovum
_____45. Number of ova in the newborn girl	Number of sperms in newborn boy
_____46. Rate of maturation in the male	Rate of maturation in the female
_____47. Action of progesterone before ovulation	Action of estrone before ovulation

Matching tests are quickly constructed and require little space. For large subject areas they are satisfactory, but are not readily adaptable to small subject areas. Matching tests are excellent for testing knowledge and association, but have limited value for testing analysis and interpretation.

In the construction, use, and scoring of matching tests, certain suggestions are helpful.

1. Avoid the same number of terms in each column.
2. Statements should be in the left column and responses in the right column.
3. It is highly acceptable to use the same response more than once.
4. Each statement should have at least two plausible answers which serve as foils in addition to the correct response.

5. A single block should contain only homogeneous material from a single area.
6. Sentence structure and the form of the responses should be consistent.
7. The students should understand the mechanics of the test.

Deduction for errors presents a problem. If a deduction is to be made, the number of possible choices must be considered. An arbitrary formula of $R - \frac{1}{4}W = S$ serves in most instances since usually no more than four foils would likely apply to the statement.

Completion tests. In completion tests incomplete statements are supplied, and the student either chooses the correct responses from a list or writes in the appropriate terms. This test is not too satisfactory for grading purposes, but has diagnostic value. It is used to excess almost, largely because it is easy to construct. It is convenient for small areas of subject matter and can be objective if terminology is not a major consideration. These tests are inclined to be tests of sheer factual material. Sentence structure may cause confusion. However, if care is used, satisfactory items can be developed.

For items 48 to 59 in each blank space place the letter of the term which best completes the statement.

Key for items 48 to 59

A. Age	E. Fat	I. Regulation
B. Building	F. Height	J. Sex
C. Carbohydrate	G. Organic	K. Upkeep
D. Energy	H. Protein	L. Weight

A food is any substance which provides cells with (48)____, materials for (49)____ and (50)____, or which provides for the (51)____ of functions. Only (52)____ foods are digested and these are of three classes, (53)____ the sugars and starches, (54)____ which contains nitrogen, and (55)____. Placed in alphabetical order, four factors are important in determining a person's basal metabolic rate: (56)____, (57)____, (58)____ and (59)____.

There is merit in using more responses than blanks. However, that style was not followed in the example. This type of test can be challenging, even taking on some of the aspects of a puzzle. Deduction for errors is difficult to determine.

A simple type of completion test is one in which a short key applies throughout.

Key for items 60 to 64
A. Increase (increased)
B. Decrease (decreased)
C. Not change (not changed)

Regular exercise may (60)____ one's resistance to disease and (61)____ one's immunity to infection. Regular exercise will (62)____ one's predisposition to a particular disease. Regular exercise will (63)____ the output of the thyroid. According to present studies, an athlete's life expectancy will (64)____ as a result of athletics.

Short-answer tests. In short-answer tests the student completes the statement by writing in a short answer. Space should be left for the student's answer. Credit should be given for reasonably correct responses. Textbook sentences should not be used in the items. Care must be taken to avoid revealing the correct response. Sentence structure is highly important. The shorter the answer required, the less the subjective judgment of the grader will enter into the scoring. A few examples of short-answer items illustrate this type of test.

> Items 65 to 70 are short-answer questions.
> In your words complete the following sentences with a brief statement.
>
> 65. A food is any substance which _____
> 66. The most nearly perfect food is _____
> 67. The best way for a person to lose weight is _____
> 68. Infection is _____
> 69. As a cause of death in the United States, communicable diseases are _____
>
> 70. Three of the five leading causes of death in the United States are _____

Limitations inherent in the short-answer tests are obvious, but tests of this type can be used to some advantage. They can be constructed quickly, which is especially helpful when a limited area of material is to be tested.

Summary

Individual instructors find certain types of tests preferable to others. Doubtless the particular skill of the instructor is reflected in the preference. Practical considerations of a busy teacher frequently determine the type of test developed. Ideally test results should be analyzed statistically, but the health teacher has neither the time nor the inclination for such an analysis. For that reason the occasional use of a standard health knowledge test may be advisable. Several standard health knowledge tests are available.

1. Tests of health knowledge, New York, Association Press.
2. Cincinnati Public Schools: Cincinnati health knowledge test, Cincinnati, Ohio, Cincinnati Public Schools. This test is for use in grades eight, nine, and ten.
3. Gates, A. I., and Strang, Ruth M.: Gates-Strang health knowledge test, New York, 1945, Bureau of Publications, Columbia University Press.
4. Gold, Leah: Tests in health knowledge, Northfield, Minn., Carleton College. These are tests for the junior high school.
5. Kilander, H. F.: Kilander health knowledge test, New York, 1936, New York University Press. This test is for use in the senior high school and freshman year of college.
6. Health tests, Bloomington, Ill., Public School Publishing Co. These tests are for use in grades four to eight.
7. Shaw, J., Troyer, M., and Brownell, C. L.: Health education test (Acorn National Achievement Test), Rockville Center, N. Y., Acorn Publishing Co. This test can be used for grades seven to twelve and at the college level.
8. Tressler, V. T., Arnett, C. E. Jr., and Schrammel, H. E.: Health knowledge test, Emporia, Kan., 1940, Kansas State Teachers College. This test is for use in the high school and in college.

To ask for perfection in a health test is to ask for the impossible. These tests depend upon words, and, though words are our best tools for conveying ideas, words themselves are man's biggest obstacle to understanding. Different connotations and shades of meaning are an ever-present difficulty. Health tests need not be perfect to be valuable. A precise measure to the most minute increment is not necessary in the practical affairs of life.

A health test is not the end of health education; it is a record of the past and a barometer for the future. In health evaluation as well as in all other aspects of the school health program, the instructor should keep in mind that the important thing is to plant a seed of health interest, water it with understanding, and nourish it with confidence in its value. Evaluation in health is continuous and never-ending.

Selected readings

American Public Health Association: An appraisal form for local health work (section on school health), New York, 1938, The Association.

Bean, K. L.: Construction of educational and personnel tests, New York, 1953, McGraw-Hill Book Co., Inc.

Byrd, O. E.: Health attitudes scale (secondary schools and colleges), Stanford, Calif., 1941, Stanford University Press.

Cushman, W. P.: Health practice inventory, Columbus, Ohio, 1957, Ohio State University.

Dearborn, T. H.: A check-list for the survey of health and physical education programs in secondary schools, Stanford, Calif., 1940, Stanford University Press.

Evaluation instruments in school health education (a compilation of existing evaluation instruments prepared by a joint committee), Journal of Health, Physical Education and Recreation **26**:13, 1955.

Franzen, R. H., Derryberry, M., and McCall, W. A.: Health awareness test (grades 7-9), New York, 1946, Bureau of Publications, Columbia University Press.

Gates, A. I., and Strang, Ruth, M.: Gates-Strang health knowledge test, New York, 1945, Bureau of Publications, Columbia University Press.

Gold, Leah: New tests in health knowledge (grades 7-9), Northfield, Minn., 1945, Carleton College.

Handbook for health education teachers, Columbus, Ohio, 1947, Ohio Department of Education, Part I, chap. 1.

Health education study, Whittier Elementary School, Minneapolis, Public Schools, 1950.

How is your health programs? Columbus, Ohio, 1952, Ohio Department of Education.

Johns, E. B., and Juhnke, W. L.: Health practice inventory, Stanford, Calif., 1943, Stanford University Press.

Jordan, A. M.: Measurement in education: an introduction, New York, 1953, McGraw-Hill Book Co., Inc.

Kilander, H.: Evaluating health teaching, Journal of Health, Physical Education, and Recreation **32**: Nov., 1961.

Kilander, H. F.: Kilander health knowledge test (secondary school and college), Washington, D. C., 1936, United States Office of Education.

Knutson, A. L.: Evaluating health education, Public Health Reports **67**:73, 1952.

Knutson, A. L.: Pretesting: a positive approach to evaluation, Public Health Reports **67**:699, 1952.

Knutson, A. L., and Shimberg, B.: Evaluation of a school health program, American Journal of Public Health **45**:21, 1955.

Lamkin, Nina B.: Health education in rural schools and communities, New York, 1947, A. S. Barnes & Co.

Los Angeles County Tuberculosis and Health Association: School health education evaluative study (Edward B. Johns, Director), Los Angeles, 1957, The Association.

McCloy, C. H., and Young, N. D.: Tests and measurements in health and physical education, ed. 3, New York, 1954, Appleton-Century-Crofts, Inc.

National Achievement Tests: Health test (grades 3-9), Chicago, Ill., Benjamin H. Sanborn Co.

Neher, G.: Health inventory for high school students. Part I. Personal information; Part II, What you do about health, Los Angeles, 1942, California Test Bureau.

Research needs in school health, American Journal of Public Health (school health sec.) **42:**133, 1952.

Ross, C. C., and Stanley, J. C.: Measurement in today's schools, ed. 3, New York, 1954, Prentice-Hall, Inc.

Rugen, Mabel E., and Nyswander, Dorothy B.: The measurement of understanding in health education, National Society for the Study of Education, forty-fifth yearbook, Chicago, 1946, University of Chicago Press.

Shaw, J. H.: Evaluation in the school health instruction program, American Journal of Public Health 47:582, 1959.

Shaw, J., Troyer, M., and Brownell, C. L.: Health education test (grades 7-12 and college), Acorn National Achievement Test, Rockville Centre, New York, Acorn Publishing Company.

Solleder, Marian K.: Evaluation instruments in health education, Journal of Health, Physical Education and Recreation **32:** Nov., 1961.

Southworth, W. H., Latimer, Jean V., and Turner, C. E.: A study of health practices, knowledge, attitudes, Research Quarterly **15:**118, 1944.

Tyler, R. W.: The place of evaluation of modern education, Elementary School Journal **41:**19, 1940.

University of the State of New York: Evaluation of school health education, Albany, 1952, State Department of Education.

Willgoose, C. E.: Evaluation in health education and physical education, New York, 1961, McGraw-Hill Book Co., Inc.

Appendixes

Knowledge is of two kinds.
We know a subject ourselves,
or we know where we can find
information upon it.

—Samuel Johnson

Appendix A

Resources in health instruction

Textbooks

Elementary school

1. *ABC Health Series:* Brownell, C. L., Evans, Ruth, and Hobson, L. B., New York, American Book Co.

    Grade

1	All Day, Every Day, 1959
2	Blue Skies, 1959
3	Come Rain, Come Shine, 1959
4	Among Friends, 1959
5	Broad Streets, 1959
6	Cross Roads, 1959

2. *The Health Action Series:* Wilcox, Charlotte E., Broullette, Jeanne S., McCall, Edith, and Bolton, William, Chicago, Benefic Press.

    Grade

1	Come On, 1955
2	Here We Go, 1955
3	Step Lively, 1955
4	Good for You, 1958
5	Full of Life, 1958
6	Here's Health, 1958

3. *Health for Young America Series:* Wilson, C., and Wilson, Elizabeth A., Indianapolis, The Bobbs-Merrill Co., Inc.

    Grade

1	Health at School, 1961
2	Health Day by Day, 1961
3	Health and Fun, 1961
4	Health and Growth, 1961
5	Health and Living, 1961
6	Health and Happiness, 1961

4. *Health for Better Living Series:* Hallock, Grace T., Allen, R. L., and Thomas, Eleanor, Boston, Ginn & Co.

    Grade

1	Health and Happy Days, 1958
2	Health in Work and Play, 1958
3	Health and Safety for You, 1958
4	Growing Your Way, 1958
5	Keeping Healthy and Strong, 1958
6	Teamwork for Health, 1957

5. *The New Road to Health Series:* Byrd, O. E., Jones, Edwina, Landis, Paul E., Morgan, Edna, Roberts, Edith, and Shaw, Thelma, River Forest, Ill., Laidlaw Brothers.

    Grade

1	First Steps to Health, 1960
2	Learning About Health, 1960
3	Habits for Health, 1960
4	Building for Health, 1960
5	Your Health, 1960
6	Growing in Health, 1960

6. *The Health, Happiness, Success Series:* Irwin, L. W., Tuttle, W. W., and DeKelver, Caroline (Grades 1-3); Burkard, W. E., Chambers, R. L., and Maroney, F. W. (Grades 4-6), Chicago, Lyons & Carnahan.

    Grade

1	Awake and Away, 1958
2	Growing Day by Day, 1958
3	Keeping Fit for Fun, 1958
4	All Aboard for Health, 1958
5	Better Health for You, 1958
6	Safeguards for Your Health, 1958

7. *The Macmillan Science-Life Series:* Barnard, J. D., Stendler, Celia, and Spock, B., New York, The Macmillan Co.

    Grade

1	Book 1, 1962
2	Book 2, 1962
3	Book 3, 1962
4	Book 4, 1962
5	Book 5, 1962
6	Book 6, 1962

8. *Curriculum Foundation Series:* Bauer, W. W., Baruch, Dorothy W., Montgomery Elizabeth R., Schacter, Helen, Pounds, Eleanore T., Gula, Henrietta, and Wesley, Wallace Ann, Chicago, Scott, Foresman & Co.

    Grade

1	Just Like Me, 1962 (primer)
1	Being Six, 1962
2	Seven or So, 1962
3	From Eight to Nine, 1962
4	Going on Ten, 1962
5	About Yourself, 1962
6	About All of Us, 1962

9. *Winston Health Series Revised:* O'Keefe, Pattric R., Maxwell, C. H., White, Mary S., Zimmer, Louise, and Leader, Barbara, Philadelphia, John C. Winston Co.

Grade

1	From Head to Toe, 1960
2	Side by Side, 1960
3	How We Grow, 1960
4	Bigger and Better, 1960
5	Getting Acquainted, 1960
6	Knowing Yourself, 1960

Junior high school

1. *ABC Health Series:* Brownell, C. L., Evans, Ruth, and Hobson, L. B., New York, American Book Co.

Grade

| 7 | About Your Health, 1959 |
| 8 | Building Better Health, 1959 |

2. *The Health Action Series:* Wilcox, Charlotte E., Broullette, Jeanne S., McCall, Edith, and Bolton, William, Chicago, Benefic Press.

Grade

| 7 | Healthy Days, 1961 |
| 8 | Stay Healthy, 1961 |

3. *Health for Young America Series:* Wilson, C., and Wilson, Elizabeth A, Indianapolis, The Bobbs-Merrill Co., Inc.

Grade

| 7 | Men, Science and Health, 1961 |
| 8 | Health, Fitness and Safety, 1961 |

4. *Health for Better Living Series:* Hallock, Grace T., Allen, R. L., and Thomas, Eleanor, Boston, Ginn & Co.

Grade

| 7 | Exploring the Ways of Health, 1958 |
| 8 | On Your Own, 1959 |

5. *The New Road to Health Series:* Byrd, O. E., Jones, Edwina, Landis, Paul E., Morgan, Edna, Roberts, Edith, and Shaw, Thelma, River Forest, Ill., Laidlaw Brothers.

Grade

| 7 | Improving Your Health, 1960 |
| 8 | Today's Health, 1960 |

6. *The Health, Happiness, Success Series:* Burkhard, W. E., Chambers, R. L., and Maroney, F. W., Chicago, Lyons & Carnahan.

Grade

| 7 | You and Your Health, 1958 |
| 8 | Good Health for All, 1958 |

7. *The Macmillan Science-Life Series:* Barnard, J. D., Stendler, Celia, and Spock, B., New York, The Macmillan Co.

Grade

| 7 | A Search for Evidence, 1960 |
| 8 | A Way to Solve Problems, 1960 |

8. *Curriculum Foundation Series:* Bauer, W. W., Baruch, Dorothy W., Montgomery, Elizabeth R., Schacter, Helen, Pounds, Eleanore T., Gula, Henrietta, and Wesley, Wallace Ann, Chicago, Scott, Foresman & Co.

Grade

7   You're Growing Up, 1963
8   Into Your Teens, 1963

9. *The Macmillan Science-Life Series:* Barnard, J. D., Stendler, Celia, and Spock, B., New York, The Macmillan Co.

Grade

7 and 8   Junior Health Horizons, 1960
8   New Wider Horizons, 1960

10. Jones, Evelyn G.: Enjoying Health, ed. 3, New York, 1959, American Book Co.
11. Rathbone, Josephine L., Bacon, F. L., and Keene, C. H.: Health in Your Daily Living, Boston, 1952, Houghton Mifflin Co.
12. Williams, Dorothea M.: Building Health, ed. 3, Philadelphia, 1959, J. B. Lippincott Co.

Senior high school

1. Brownell, C. L., and Hobson, L. B.: High School Health, New York, 1959, American Book Co.
2. Jones, E. G.: Living in Safety and Health, New York, 1961, J. B. Lippincott Co.
3. Lawrence, T. G. Clemensen, Jessie W., and Burnett, R. W.: Your Health and Safety, New York, 1963, Harcourt, Brace & World, Inc.
4. Meredith, Florence L., Irwin, L. W., and Staton, W. M.: Health and Fitness, ed. 3, Boston, 1951, D. C. Heath & Co.
5. Rice, T. B., and Hein, F. V.: Living, rev. ed., Chicago, 1959, Scott, Foresman & Co.
6. Southworth, W. H., and Davis, Arthur F.: Meredith's Science of Health, ed. 3, New York, 1957, McGraw-Hill Book Co., Inc.
7. Walke, N. W.: Good Health, New York, 1955, McGraw-Hill Book Co., Inc.

Family living

1. Duval, Evelyn M.: Love and the Facts of Life, New York, 1963, Association Press.
2. Duval, Evelyn M.: Family Development, Philadelphia, 1957, J. B. Lippincott Co.
3. Duval, Evelyn M.: Family Living, New York, 1961, The Macmillan Co.
4. Duval, Evelyn, and Hill, R. L.: Being Married, New York, 1960, Association Press.
5. Duval, S. M.: Before You Marry, New York, 1959, Association Press.
6. Landis, J. T., and Landis, Mary G.: Building a Successful Marriage, ed. 3, Englewood Cliffs, N. J., 1958, Prentice-Hall, Inc.
7. Landis, J. T., and Landis, Mary G.: Personal Adjustment, ed. 3, Englewood Cliffs, N. J., 1955, Prentice-Hall, Inc.
8. Osborne, E. G.: Understanding Your Parents, New York, 1962, Association Press.

Pamphlets and films by subject areas*
Body function
Pamphlets

Attractive Teeth for Teen Agers, American Dental Association.   S
Blood Donors, American Medical Association.   S
Blood's Magic For All, Pamphlet No. 145, Public Affairs Committee.   S
Child Who Is Hard of Hearing, U. S. Government Printing Office.   S, T
Dental Caries Prevention and Control, American Dental Association.   S

---

*Level of suitability: E, elementary school; J, junior high school; S, senior high school; T, teacher.

Dental Health Facts for Teachers, American Dental Association. T
Dental Health Program for Elementary and Secondary Schools, American Dental Association. T
Ears That Hear, John Hancock Mutual Life Insurance Co. S
Everybody Smile, American Dental Association. E
Eye Cues for Eye Health, National Society for the Prevention of Blindness. S, T
Eyes That See—And Ears That Hear, John Hancock Life Insurance Co. S
Feet and Shoes, American Medical Association. S
Fluoridation Facts, American Dental Association. S, T
Fluoridation in the Prevention of Dental Caries, American Dental Association. S, T
Fluoride Means Less Tooth Decay, American Dental Association. S, T
Fluorine, Less Tooth Decay for Children, American Dental Association. S
Good Teeth for Young Americans, Church and Dwight Co. S, T
Good Posture in the Little Child, Publication No. 219, Children's Bureau. T
Health Passport, Prudential Life Insurance Co. S, T
Hear Better, Funk & Wagnalls Co. S
High Lights in Low Blood Pressure, American Medical Association. S
Hormones and the Endocrine Glands, American Medical Association. S
How to Tell Your Child About Sex, Public Affairs Committee. S, T
How We See, Better Vision Institute, Inc. S, T
How You Grow, Science Research Associates, Inc. S, T
Human Growth, E. C. Brown Trust. J, S
Know Your Heart, Public Affairs Committee. S
Medical Uses of Blood, American National Red Cross. S
Menstrual Hygiene, Personal Products Corp. J, S
Orthodontics: Questions and Answers, American Dental Association. T
Publications About Your Health, American Medical Association. E, S, T
Signs of Eye Trouble in Children, National Society for the Prevention of Blindness. S, T
Take Care of Your Eyes, National Society for the Prevention of Blindness. S, T
The Care of Children's Teeth, American Dental Association. S
The Liver in Health and Disease, American Medical Association. S
The Story of Blood, American Nationals Red Cross. S
Today's Health, American Medical Association. S, T
Tommy's First Visit to the Dentist, American Dental Association. E
Understanding Ourselves, University of Minnesota Press. S
Understanding Sex, Science Research Associates, Inc. S
Water Fluoridation Facts, Public Affairs Committee. J, S, T
What Teachers See, Metropolitan Life Insurance Co. S, T
Why We See Like Human Beings, Better Vision Institute, Inc. S, T
Why Your Dentist Recommends Fluoridation, American Dental Association. S, T
Wonder Stories of the Human Machine, American Medical Association. S
X-Rays and Your Teeth, American Dental Association. S
Your Child Grows Up, John Hancock Mutual Life Insurance Co. S, T
Your Child's Feet and Footwear, U. S. Government Printing Office. S, T
Your Child's First Visit to the Dentist, American Dental Association. S, T
Your Child's Teeth, American Dental Association. S, T
Your Gallbladder, American Medical Association. S
Your Guide to Dental Health, American Dental Association. S
Your Own Story, University of Minnesota Press. E
Your Teeth—How They Grow, American Dental Association. S
Your Teeth—How to Save Them, American Dental Association. S
Publications About Your Health, American Medical Association. T

Films

A Life in Your Hands, American National Red Cross (10 minutes). S, T
Alimentary Tract, Encyclopaedia Britannica Films, Inc. (11 minutes). J, S

Amoeba, United World Films, Inc. (11 minutes).   S, T
Animal Life, Encyclopaedia Britannica Films, Inc. (11 minutes).   J, S
As Boys Grows, E. C. Brown Trust (15 minutes).   J
Circulation of the Blood, United World Films, Inc. (20 minutes).   J, S
Control of Body Temperature, Encyclopaedia Britannica Films, Inc. (11 minutes).   J, S
Circulation, United World Films, Inc. (16 minutes).   J, S,T
Digestion of Foods, Encyclopaedia Britannica Films, Inc. (10 minutes).   J, S
Elimination, United World Films, Inc. (14 minutes).   S, T
Endocrine Glands, Encyclopaedia Britannica Films, Inc. (11 minutes).   J, S
Explaining Your Growth, Churchill-Wexler Film Productions (11 minutes).   E, J
Growing Girls, Encyclopaedia Britannica Films, Inc. (14 minutes).   J, S
Heart and Circulation Encyclopaedia Britannica Films Inc. (11 minutes).   J, S
Heart—How It Works, Text Film Dept., McGraw-Hill Book Co., Inc. (11 minutes).   J, S
Hemo the Magnificent, Association Films (59 minutes).   J, S
Heredity, Encyclopaedia Britannica Films, Inc. (11 minutes).   J, S, T
How the Ear Functions, Knowledge Builders (11 minutes).   J, S
How We Hear, Bray Pictures Corp. (10 minutes).   J, S
Human Growth, E. C. Brown Trust (20 minutes).   J
Human Heredity, E. C. Brown Trust (18 minutes).   J, S
Human Reproduction, Text Film Dept., McGraw-Hill Book Co., Inc. (20 minutes).   S, T
In the Beginning, U. S. Department of Agriculture (20 minutes).   J, S
Man Is a Universe, National Film Board of Canada (12 minutes).   S, T
Matter of Choice, American Dental Association (27½ minutes).   J, S
Mechanics of Breathing, Encyclopaedia Britannica Films, Inc. (11 minutes).   S
Molly Grows Up, Personal Products Corp. (15 minutes).   J, S
Nervous System, Encyclopaedia Britannica Films, Inc. (11 minutes).   J, S
Nose, Throat and Ears, Text Film Dept., McGraw-Hill Book Co., Inc. (11 minutes).   S
Our Feet, Bray Studios, Inc. (10 minutes).   S
Posture, Encyclopaedia Britannica Films, Inc. (15 minutes).   E, J
Project: Teeth—Dental Health and Classroom Science, American Dental Association. (14½ minutes).   E
Reproduction Among Mammals, Encyclopaedia Britannica Films, Inc. (11 minutes.   S
Teeth: Their Structure and Care, Coronet Films (13 minutes).   J, S, T
The Doctor Examines Your Heart, Bray Studios, Inc. (10 minutes).   S, T
The Human Body, Institute of International American Affairs (9 minutes).   S, T
The Human Foot, Encyclopaedia Britannica Films, Inc. (12 minutes).   J, S
The Human Skeleton, United World Films, Inc. (10 minutes).   J, S
The Human Skin, Bray Studios, Inc. (12 minutes).
The Nose, Throat and Ears, Text Film Dept., McGraw-Hill Book Co., Inc. (10 minutes).   J, S
The Skeleton, Encyclopaedia Britannica Films, Inc. (12 minutes).   J, S
The Story of Menstruation, Kimberly-Clark Corp. (10 minutes).   J, S
The Work of the Kidneys, Encyclopaedia Britannica Films, Inc. (11 minutes).   J, S
There is No Substitute, American National Red Cross (23 minutes).   S, T
What Do We Know About Teeth? American Dental Association (14½ minutes).   E
Wonder Engine of the Body, American Medical Association (11 minutes).   J, S
Your Ears, Young America Films, Inc. (10 minutes).   J, S
Your Children's Eyes, British Information Services (19 minutes).   J, S, T
Your Voice, Encyclopaedia Britannica Films, Inc. (11 minutes).   J, S

Communicable diseases
Pamphlets
Common respiratory diseases

Be on the Safe Side of Diphtheria, Metropolitan Life Insurance Co.   E, J
—Chickenpox, Metropolitan Life Insurance Co.   E, J

Common Cold, Equitable Life Assurance Society.	S, T
Common Sense, Metropolitan Life Insurance Co.	E, J
Control of Communicable Diseases in Man, American Public Health Association.	T
Diversions for the Sick, John Hancock Mutual Life Insurance Co.	S, T
Guarding Your Family's Health, John Hancock Mutual Life Insurance Co.	S, T
Health Hero, Metropolitan Life Insurance Co.	S, T
Health Through the Ages, Metropolitan Life Insurance Co.	S, T
Home Care of Communicable Diseases, John Hancock Mutual Life Insurance Co.	T
Influenza, U. S. Department of Health, Education and Welfare.	S
Let Your Cold Alone, American Medical Association.	J, S
Measles, Metropolitan Life Insurance Co.	E, J
Mumps, Metropolitan Life Insurance Co.	E, J
Respiratory Diseases, Metropolitan Life Insurance Co.	S
Rocky Mountain Spotted Fever, U. S. Government Printing Office.	S, T
Scarlet Fever, Metropolitan Life Insurance Co.	E, J
Smallpox Is Still Here, Metropolitan Life Insurance Co.	E, J
The Science Book of Wonder Drugs, Pocket Books, Inc.	J, S, T
Tularemia, U. S. Government Printing Office.	S, T
Whooping Cough, Oregon State Board of Health.	S, T
Whooping Cough, U. S. Department of Health, Education and Welfare.	T
Winter Enemies, John Hancock Mutual Life Insurance Co.	S, T

Poliomyelitis

A Message About Polio, The National Foundation.	S
Doctor, What Can I Do, The National Foundation.	S
Polio and Salk Vaccine, Public Affairs Committee, Inc.	S, T
Polio Pointers, The National Foundation.	S, T
Polio Poster, The National Foundation.	S, T
Poliomyelitis, The National Foundation.	S
Polio Vaccination and Your Small Child, The National Foundation.	S, T
Publications of The National Foundation, The National Foundation.	S
Schools Help Carry the Ball in the Fight Against Polio, The National Foundation.	S
So You Don't Scare Easily, The National Foundation.	S, T
Story Behind the Polio Vaccine, The National Foundation.	S, T
Teacher's Guide to Be Used With Poliomyelitis, The National Foundation.	S, T
The Research Story of Infantile Paralysis, The National Foundation.	S, T
Vaccination Before Vacation, The National Foundation.	S, T
What You Should Know About Polio Vaccine, The National Foundation.	S, T
When the Polio Patient Is Cared for at Home, The National Foundation.	S, T

Tuberculosis

Climate and TB, The National Tuberculosis Association.	J, S
Crusade of the Christmas Seal, National Tuberculosis Association.	J, S
Facts About TB, National Tuberculosis Association.	S, T
Help Fight Tuberculosis, National Tuberculosis Association.	E
How Your Body Fights Tuberculosis, National Tuberculosis Association.	J, S
I Went to the Sanitarium, National Tuberculosis Association.	S
Rest to Beat Tuberculosis, National Tuberculosis Association.	S
The News About Tuberculosis, John Hancock Mutual Life Insurance Co.	S, T
The Tuberculin Test, National Tuberculosis and Health Association.	S
Tuberculosis, World Health Organization.	S, T
Tuberculosis—How Your Body Fights Tuberculosis, National Tuberculosis Association.	S
Tuberculosis From 18 to 80, National Tuberculosis Association.	S
Tuberculosis Through the Teens, National Tuberculosis Association.	J, S
TB—Basic Facts in Basic English, National Tuberculosis Association.	J, S
TB—The Killer Cornered, National Tuberculosis Association.	S, T

The High School's Part in Tuberculosis Control, National Tuberculosis
    Association.   S

Tuberculosis—How It Spreads, National Tuberculosis Association.   S

Ways to Keep Well and Happy, National Tuberculosis Association.   E

What You Need to Know About TB, National Tuberculosis Association.   J, S

What You Can Do About Tuberculosis, John Hancock Mutual Life Insurance
    Co.   J, S

Venereal diseases

Cause, Spread and Cure of Syphilis, U. S. Government Printing Office.   T

Controlled Prostitution? American Social Hygiene Association.   T

For the Carriage Trade, American Social Hygiene Association.   T

Gonorrhea, Its Cause, Spread and Cure, U. S. Government Printing Office.   T

Journal of VD, U. S. Department of Health, Education and Welfare.   T

Management of VD, U. S. Department of Health, Education and Welfare.   T

Protecting the Unborn Baby From Syphilis, U. S. Government Printing Office.   T

Some Questions and Answers About VD, American Social Hygiene Association.   T

Syphilis, the Invader, Public Affairs Committee, Inc.   T

Wedding Plans, U. S. Government Printing Office.   T

Why a Blood Test, American Social Hygiene Association.   S

Why Let It Burn? American Social Hygiene Association.   T

Miscellaneous communicable diseases

Athlete's Foot, American Medical Association.   J, S

Mad Dog, American Medical Association.   J, S

Rabies, Metropolitan Life Insurance Co.   J, S

Typhoid Fever, Metropolitan Life Insurance Co.   J, S

Undulant Fever, U. S. Department of Health, Education and Welfare.   J, S

What Is Known About Brucellosis, United States Livestock Sanitary Association.   J, S

Films

Antibiotics, Encyclopaedia Britannica Films, Inc. (14 minutes).   S

Are You Positive, National Tuberculosis Association (13½ minutes).   S, T

Billion Dollar Malady, The Common Cold, Bray Studios, Inc. (15 minutes).   J, S

Birthright, Center for Mass Communication, Columbia University Press
    (45 minutes).   J, S

Body Defenses Against Disease, Encyclopaedia Britannica Films, Inc. (10
    minutes).   E, J

Body Fight Bacteria, Text Film Dept., McGraw-Hill Book Co., Inc. (15
    minutes).   S

Common Cold, Encyclopaedia Britannica Films, Inc. (11 minutes).   J, S

Confessions of a Cold, National Motion Picture Co. (13 minutes).   E, J, S

Defense Against Invasion, Department of State, New York (10 minutes).   E, J, S

Feeling All Right, Center for Mass Communication, Columbia University Press
    (25 minutes).   S, T

How Disease Travels, Institute of Inter-American Affairs (10 minutes).   E, J, S

How Our Bodies Fight Disease, Encyclopaedia Britannica Films, Inc. (8 minutes).   E, J

How to Catch a Cold, Kimberly-Clark Corp. (10 minutes).   E, J, S

I Never Catch Cold, Coronet Films (10 minutes).   E

Immunization, Encyclopaedia Britannica Films, Inc. (11 minutes).   J, S

Interim Report, The National Foundation (15 minutes).   S, T

Joan Avoids a Cold, Coronet Films (10 minutes).   E

Kill the Louse, Institute of Inter-American Affairs (8 minutes).   J, S

Lease on Life, National Tuberculosis Association (20 minutes).   E, J, S

Let's Have Fewer Colds, Coronet Films (10 minutes).   E

Man Against Microbe, Metropolitan Life Insurance Co. (10 minutes).   J, S

Message to Women, U. S. Public Health Service (20 minutes).   S, T
New Frontiers of Medicine, March of Time (17 minutes).   S
Our Job to Know, American Social Hygiene Association (18 minutes).   S, T
Pneumonia, Encyclopaedia Britannica Films, Inc. (10 minutes).   J, S
Polio Vaccine News Report, Eli Lilly & Co. (13½ minutes).   S, T
Prevent Dysentery, Institute of Inter-American Affairs (7 minutes).   E, J, S
Preventing the Spread of Disease, National Motion Picture Co. (14 minutes).   E, J, S
Sixteen to Twenty-Six, National Film Board of Canada (18 minutes).   S
Smallpox, Brandon Films, Inc. (9 minutes).   J, S
Sneezes and Sniffles, Text Film Dept., McGraw-Hill Book Co., Inc. (10 minutes).   J, S
Story of Dr. Jenner, Teaching Film Custodians, Inc. (10 minutes).   E, J, S
Striking Back Against Rabies, U. S. Public Health Service (12 minutes).   S, T
The Invader, Center of Mass Communication, Columbia University Press (40
   minutes).   J, S
The Magic Touch, Avis Films (14 minutes).   E, J
This Is TB, National Tuberculosis Association (11 minutes).   S
Tracking the Sleeping Death, Teaching Film Custodians, Inc. (10 minutes).   E, J, S
Tuberculosis, Encyclopaedia Britannica Films, Inc. (11 minutes).   J, S
Unconditional Surrender, The National Foundation (25 minutes).   S, T
VD Sport Films, Center for Mass Communication, Columbia University Press (5
   minutes each).   J, S
Very Dangerous, National Film Board of Canada (18 minutes).   S
Yellow Jack, Teaching Film Custodians, Inc. (29 minutes).   J, S
Your Health: Disease and Its Control, Coronet Films (11 minutes).   J, S
With These Weapons, American Social Hygiene Association (11 minutes).   S

Community health and sanitation
Pamphlets

A Dental Health Inventory for Maintown, American Dental Association.   S, T
Better Health Through Fluoridated Water, U. S. Department of Health, Edu-
   cation and Welfare.   J, S
Clean Water Is Everybody's Business, U. S. Department of Health, Education
   and Welfare.   J, S
Feed People Not Rats! U. S. Department of the Interior.   S
Fluorine, Less Tooth Decay for Children, American Dental Association.   S, T
Food Hygiene, World Health Organization.   S, T
From Hand to Mouth, U. S. Department of Health, Education and Welfare.   S, T
Home Sanitation, U. S. Department of Health, Education and Welfare.   J, S
How to Obtain Fluoridation for Your Community, American Dental Association.   S, T
Key to Community Health, American Medical Association.   S, T
Let's Fight Rats, U. S. Department of the Interior.   J, S
Louse Infestation, U. S. Government Printing Office.   S, T
Maintown Dental Health Project, American Dental Association.   S, T
Milk Pasteurization, World Health Organization.   S, T
Pesticides: Insect Control, World Health Organization.   S, T
Rat Control, Farmers Bulletin No. 1533, U. S. Fish and Wildlife Service.   J, S
Rat Proofing Buildings and Premises, U. S. Department of the Interior.   S
Safe Water, U. S. Department of Health, Education and Welfare.   J, S
The Cold Facts About Safe Food, Equitable Life Assurance Society.   S, T
The Lamp Is Lit, The Story of WHO, World Health Organization.   J, S
Water Fluoridation: Facts Not Myths, Public Affairs Committee, Inc.   S, T

Films

A Drop in the Bucket (fluoridation), U. S. Public Health Service (13 minutes).   J, S
Another Light, International Film Bureau, Inc. (25 minutes).   J, S
A Place to Live, Dynamic Films, Inc. (33 minutes).   T

Basic Sanitation—Community Fly Control, McGeary-Smith Laboratories (10 minutes). — S, T

Behind the Menu, National Film Board of Canada (10 minutes). — J, S

Camp Sanitation, National Motion Picture Co. (15 minutes). — J, S

City Water Supply, Encyclopaedia Britannica Films, Inc. (11 minutes). — E, J

Clean Waters, General Electric Co. (21 minutes). — J, S

Community Health and You, Text Film Dept., McGraw-Hill Book Co., Inc. (10 minutes). — J

Community Health in Action, International Film Bureau, Inc. (22 minutes). — J, S

Community Health Is Up to You, Text Film Dept., McGraw-Hill Book Co., Inc. (18 minutes). — S

Contamination of Drinking Water by Back-Siphonage, University of Minnesota (18 minutes). — S, T

Control of Mosquito-Borne Diseases, Educational Film Dept., United World Films, Inc. (19 minutes). — S

Crusade, American Cancer Society (11 minutes). — J, S

Defending the City's Health, Encyclopaedia Britannica Films, Inc. (11 minutes). — J, S

Environmental Sanitation, Institute of Inter-American Affairs (10 minutes). — E, J, S

Fly About the House, Center for Mass Communication, Columbia University Press (9 minutes). — E, J, S

For Us the Living, Visual Training Institute (20 minutes). — S, T

Get Rid of Rats, National Film Board of Canada (10 minutes). — S, T

Guardians of Our Country's Health, U. S. Public Health Service (16 minutes). — J, S

Health for Defense, Teaching Film Custodians, Inc. (9 minutes). — S, T

How Disease Travels, Institute of Inter-American Affairs (10 minutes). — E, J, S

In Daily Battle, The National Foundation (26 minutes). — J, S

Insects as Carriers of Disease, Institute of Inter-American Affairs (10 minutes). — E, J, S

Let's Look at Water, National Film Board of Canada (22 minutes). — J, S

Meats With Approval, U. S. Department of Agriculture (20 minutes). — J, S

Miracle of the Meadows (milk), Bailey Films, Inc. (19 minutes). — E, J

Mosquito, Encyclopaedia Britannica Films, Inc. (10 minutes). — E, J, S

Multiple Screening, Center for Mass Communication, Columbia University Press (8 minutes). — J, S

Problems of Housing, Encyclopaedia Britannica Films, Inc. (10 minutes). — J, S

Rat Destruction, British Information Services (10 minutes). — S, T

Rescue Party, National Film Board of Canada (29 minutes). — S

Safe Drinking Water From Small Water Supplies, University of Minnesota (12 minutes). — J, S

Sanitary Market, Institute of Inter-American Affairs (9 minutes). — E, J, S

Sanitation and the Rural Home, National Motion Picture Co. (10 minutes). — J, S

The Danger Point, Association Films, Inc. (12 minutes). — S, T

The Eternal Fight, American Medical Association (22 minutes). — S

The Housefly, Encyclopaedia Britannica Films, Inc. (11 minutes). — J, S

The Life Cycle of the Mosquito, Young America Films, Inc. (12 minutes). — S, T

Wastage of Human Resources, Encyclopaedia Britannica Films, Inc. (10 minutes). — S

Water—Friend or Enemy, Precision Film Laboratories (12 minutes). — E, J, S

Your Health Department, National Motion Picture Co. (20 minutes). — J, S

Your Health at Home, Coronet Films (11 minutes). — J, S

Your Health at School, Coronet Films, (11 minutes). — J, S

Your Health in the Community, Coronet Films (11 minutes). — J, S

Health services and products

Pamphlets

A Quick Look at Some New Directions in Health Insurance Plans, Health Information Foundation. — S

Absent From School Today, Metropolitan Life Insurance Co. — J, S

Basic Principles of Medical Economics, American Medical Association. — S

Blue Cross Bulletin, American Hospital Association. ..... S
Caring for the Sick in the Home, John Hancock Mutual Life Insurance Co. ..... S
Does Your Town Gamble With Your Life? Redbook Magazine. ..... S, T
First Steps in Health Education, Metropolitan Life Insurance Co. ..... S
Food and Drug Administration, Federal Security Agency. ..... S, T
Guarding Your Family's Health, John Hancock Mutual Life Insurance Co. ..... S
Health Aspects of the School Lunch Program, National Education Association and American Medical Association. ..... S
Health Bulletin for Teachers, Metropolitan Life Insurance Co. ..... S, T
Health Councils, Ohio State Medical Association. ..... S, T
Health Through the Ages, Metropolitan Life Insurance Co. ..... S
How Shall We Pay For Health Care? Public Affairs Committee, Inc. ..... S
Meeting the Costs of Medical Care, Public Affairs Committee, Inc. ..... S, T
Profile of the Practicing Physician, Metropolitan Life Insurance Co. ..... S
Publications of the Council on Medical Service, American Medical Association. ..... T
Stepping Stones to a Health Council, National Health Council. ..... S, T
Suggested School Health Policies, National Education Association and American Association for Health, Physical Education and Recreation. ..... T
That Extra Something, National Health Council. ..... S, T
The Cost and Quantity of Medical Care in the United States, American Medical Association. ..... S
The Doctor Prescribes, American Medical Association. ..... J, S
The Nurse in the School, American Association of Health, Physical Education and Recreation. ..... T
The School Administrator, Physician, and the Nurse in the School Health Program, Metropolitan Life Insurance Co. ..... T
Your Best Buy, U. S. Department of Health, Education and Welfare. ..... S

Films

Another Light, Bailey Films, Inc. (25 minutes). ..... S
Capitol Story, Castle (20 minutes). ..... S, T
Consumer Protection, Coronet Films, (10 minutes). ..... J, S
Choosing a Doctor, Text Film Dept., McGraw-Hill Book Co., Inc. (11 minutes). ..... S

Doctor in Industry, General Motors Corp. (60 minutes). ..... S, T
For Us the Living, Visual Training Institute (20 minutes). ..... S, T
Fraud Fighters, Text Film Dept., McGraw-Hill Book Co., Inc. (17 minutes). ..... J, S
Health Careers, National Health Council (15 minutes). ..... S, T
Journey Into Medicine, Castle (39 minutes). ..... S, T
Miracle Money, Teaching Film Custodians, Inc. (22 minutes). ..... S
Modern Surgery, March of Time (18 minutes). ..... S, T
Mr. Williams Wakes Up, North Carolina Board of Health (28 minutes). ..... E, S, T
Quacks and Nostrums, Text Film Dept., McGraw-Hill Book Co., Inc. (19 minutes). ..... S
Triumph Without Drums, Teaching Film Custodians, Inc. (10 minutes). ..... S
What's Under the Label, National Film Board of Canada (11 minutes). ..... J, S

History of health

Pamphlets

Great Achievements in Medicine, American Medical Association. ..... J, S
Health Heroes Series (Louis Pasteur, Edward Livingston Trudeau, Edward Jenner, Walter Reed, Florence Nightingale, Robert Koch, and Marie Curie), Metropolitan Life Insurance Co. ..... J, S
Health Through the Ages, Metropolitan Life Insurance Co. ..... J, S
Light and Shade, (Chart for Health Through the Ages), Metropolitan Life Insurance Co. ..... J, S
Outstanding Medical Advances, American Medical Association. ..... J, S

The Endless Frontier (medical research), Health Information Foundation.　　J, S

X-rays in the Sciences and the Arts, American Medical Association.　　S

Films

Man Against Microbe, Metropolitan Life Insurance Co. (10 minutes).　　J, S

Man's Greatest Friend (Louis Pasteur), Teaching Film Custodians, Inc. (10 minutes).　　J, S

New Frontiers of Medicine, March of Time (17 minutes).　　S

Story of Dr. Jenner, Teaching Film Custodians, Inc. (10 minutes).　　E, S, T

They Live Again (discovery of insulin), Teaching Film Custodians, Inc. (11 minutes).　　J, S

Triumph Without Drums (history of pure food and drug law), Teaching Film Custodians, Inc. (10 minutes).　　J, S

Mental health and family living

Pamphlets

A Pound of Prevention, New York State Society for Mental Health.　　T

Activities of a Mental Health Nurse, U. S. Public Health Service.　　T

Adolescent and the Family, New York State Society for Mental Health.　　S

Allied Youth? Allied Youth, Inc.　　S

An Approach in Schools to Education for Personal and Family Living, American Social Hygiene Association.　　T

Are We Helping or Hindering Our Children? National Committee for Mental Hygiene, Inc.　　S

Baby and Child Care, Pocket Books, Inc.　　S, T

Baby Book, Health Publications, Inc.　　S

Betrothal, Publication No. 972, American Social Hygiene Association.　　S

Between One and Five, John Hancock Mutual Life Insurance Co.　　S

Boys on the Beam, American Social Hygiene Association.　　S

Building Sex Into Your Life, American Institute of Family Relations.　　S, T

Building Your Marriage, Public Affairs Commitee, Inc.　　S

Children Are Our Teachers, Federal Security Agency.　　T

Children of Divorce, Federal Security Agency.　　S, T

Choosing a Home Partner, American Social Hygiene Association.　　S

Comics, TV, Radio, Movies—and Children, Pamphlet No. 148, Public Affairs Committee, Inc.　　S

Dates and Dating, American Social Hygiene Association.　　S

Dating Do's and Dont's for Girls, American Social Hygiene Association.　　S

Deciding What Is Best for the Retarded Child, New York State Society for Mental Health.　　S, T

Easy Answers to Your Child's Sex Questions, American Society Hygiene Association.　　T

Emotional Maturity, New York State Charities Aid Association.　　S

Emotions and Physical Health, Metropolitan Life Insurance Co.　　S, T

Enjoy Your Child (ages 1, 2, 3), Public Affairs Committee, Inc.　　S

Expecting a Baby, John Hancock Mutual Life Insurance Co.　　S

For Good Mental Health in Your Community, National Association for Mental Health.　　S, T

Forgotten Children, National Association for Mental Health.　　S

Framework for Family Education, American Association for Health, Physical Education and Recreation.　　T

From Boy to Man, Social Hygiene Association.　　S

Growing Up and Liking It, Personal Products Corp.　　S

Guarding Your Family's Health, John Hancock Mutual Life Insurance Co.　　S

Guiding the Adolescent, Federal Security Agency.　　S, T

Healthy Personality for Your Child, U. S. Government Printing Office.　　S, T

Help Yourself to Health, Metropolitan Life Insurance Co.	S, T
Helping Children in Trouble, Federal Security Agency.	S
High Schools and Sex Education, Public Health Service.	T
How Do You Know You're in Love? American Institute of Family Relations.	S
How Does Your Baby Grow, Maternity Center Association.	S
How Is Your Mental Health? Health Publications, Inc.	S
How Old Are You? Metropolitan Life Insurance Co.	J, S
How to Discipline Your Children, Public Affairs Committee, Inc.	S
How to Live With Parents, Science Research Associates, Inc.	S
If the Child Is Slow, National Association for Mental Health.	S
In the Teens, John Hancock Mutual Life Insurance Co.	S, T
It's So Much Easier When You Know, Personal Products Corp.	S, T
Keeping Up With Teen-Agers, Public Affairs Committee, Inc.	S
Keystones in Psychological Thinking About Young Children, National Association for Mental Health.	S, T
Know Your Daughter, American Social Hygiene Association.	S, T
Know Your Son, American Social Hygiene Association.	S, T
Leisure Time, Equitable Life Assurance Society.	S, T
Life Situations. Emotions, and Disease, National Association for Mental Health.	T
Live Long and Like It, Public Affairs Committee, Inc.	S
Looking Forward to School, Equitable Life Assurance Society.	S, T
Making the Most of Maturity, John Hancock Mutual Life Insurance Co.	S
Marriage and Parenthood, American Social Hygiene Association.	S
Maternal Care and Mental Health, World Health Organization.	S
Mental Health and the World of Today, National Association for Mental Health	S
Mental Health—Everybody's Business, Public Affairs Committee, Inc.	T
Mental Health Is a Family Affair, Public Affairs Committee, Inc.	S
Mental Health Is One, Two, Three, National Association for Mental Health.	S, T
Mental Health in Review, National Association for Mental Health.	T
Mental Hygiene in the Classroom, American Medical Association.	T
Mental Hygiene Problems of Youth Today, National Association for Mental Health.	S
Mental Illness: A Guide for the Family, National Association for Mental Health.	S
Mind, The John Hancock Mutual Life Insurance Co.	S, T
Needlepoint, Connecticut Mutual Life Insurance Co.	S, T
Normal Personality Development, National Association for Mental Health.	S
Occupational Therapy, American Occupational Therapy Association.	S
Overweight and Underweight, Metropolitan Life Insurance Co.	S
Parents Book, Health Publications Institute.	S, T
Personality Counts (self-evaluation chart), National Dairy Council.	J
Preparing for Parenthood, Metropolitan Life Insurance Co.	S, T
Preparing for Marriage, American Institute of Family Relations.	S, T
Preparing for Your Marriage, American Social Hygiene Association.	S, T
Pre-School Years, Health Education Service.	S, T
Psychiatric Aspects of Juvenile Delinquency, World Health Organization.	T
Psychological Care of the Physically Handicapped, The National Foundation.	S
Public Health Approach to Improving Community Mental Health Through the Schools, U. S. Public Health Service.	T
Relax, You're a Bundle of Nerves, Consumers Services.	S, T
Scattered Showers (script for play), National Association for Mental Health.	S
Seriously Retarded Child, New York State Society for Mental Health.	S, T
Sex Education Series, American Association for Health, Physical Education and Recreation.	T
Six to Twelve, John Hancock Mutual Life Insurance Co.	S, T
Social Hygiene Materials for Teachers, E. C. Brown Trust.	S

Straight From the Shoulder (for boys), National Dairy Council.   S
Teachers and Behavior Problems, Commonwealth Fund.   T
Teacher Listen—The Children Speak, New York State Society for Mental Health.   S, T
Teaching Guide, Menstrual Education, Kimberly-Clark Corp.   T
Teamwork for Maturity, National Association for Mental Health.   S
This Is the Adolescent, National Association for Mental Health.   T
The Family—A Focal Point in Education, American Social Hygiene Association.   T
The Retarded Child in the Community, New York Society for Mental Health.   S
The Shy Child, Public Affairs Committee, Inc.   T
They Call Them Crushes, American Institute of Family Relations.   J, S
Three to Six: Your Child Starts to School, Public Affairs Committee, Inc.   S, T
Toward Mental Health, Public Affairs Committee, Inc.   S, T
Understanding Your Child From Six to Twelve, Public Affairs Committee, Inc.   S, T
Understanding Ourselves, University of Minnesota Press.   S
Understanding Your Teen Ager, Metropolitan Life Insurance Co.   S, T
Understanding Your Young Child, Metropolitan Life Insurance Co.   S, T
Understanding Yourself, National Association for Mental Health.   S, T
Wanted: A Pattern for Modern Man, Naional Association for Mental Health.   S
What Can the Public Health Nurse Do in Mental Hygiene? National Association
    for Mental Health.   S
When You Grow Older, Public Affairs Committee, Inc.   S
Who Should Marry? American Institute of Family Relations.   S
Worry Go-Around, Connecticut Mutual Life Insurance Co.   S, T
You and Your Baby, John Hancock Mutual Life Insurance Co.   S
You and Your Contented Baby, Carnation Co.   S, T
You Don't Have to Be Perfect—Even If You Are a Parent, National Association
    for Mental Health.   S
Your Child Grows Up, John Hancock Mutual Life Insurance Co.   T
Your Mind and You, National Association for Mental Health.   S
You're a Big Girl Now, American Social Hygiene Association.   S
You're a Young Lady Now, Kimberly-Clark Corp.   E
Your Child From One to Six, U. S. Department of Health, Education and Wel-
    fare.   S, T
Your Child From Six to Twelve, U. S. Department of Health, Education and
    Welfare.   S, T
Your Child's Emotion Health, Public Affairs Committee, Inc.   T
Your Child's Questions, American Social Hygiene Association.   T
Your Contented Baby, Carnation Co.   S, T
Your Future and You, Metropolitan Life Insurance Co.   S, T
Your Inferiority Complex, American Institute of Family Relations.   S, T
Your Teen Years, Metropolitan Life Insurance Co.   J, S
Your Premature Baby, U. S. Government Printing Office.   S, T
Your Mind and You, National Association for Mental Health.   S
Your Own Story, University of Minnesota Press.   T

Films

A Child Went Forth, Brandon Films, Inc. (18 minutes).   E, J, S
Act Your Age, Coronet Films (13 minutes).   J, S
A Family Affair, International Films Bureau, Inc. (31 minutes).   S
Age of Turmoil, National Association for Mental Health, Inc. (20 minutes).   S
Am I Trustworthy, Coronet Films (10 minutes).   E
Angry Boy, International Film Bureau (33 minutes).   J, S
Answering the Child's Way, Encyclopaedia Britannica Films, Inc. (13 minutes).   J, S
Appreciating Our Parents, Coronet Films (10 minutes).   E
Attitudes and Health, Coronet Films (10 minutes).   J, S

Benefits of Looking Ahead, Coronet Films (10 minutes). J, S
Better Use of Leisure Time, Coronet Films (10 minutes). J, S
Boy With a Knife, International Film Bureau (24 minutes). S
Breakdown, Text Film Dept., McGraw-Hill Book Co., Inc. (41 minutes). S, T
Control Your Emotions, Coronet Films (13 minutes). J, S
Date Etiquette, Coronet Films (10 minutes). J, S
Dating: Do's and Don'ts, Coronet Films (13 minutes). J, S
Developing Friendships, Coronet Films (10 minutes). S
Developing Imagination, Coronet Films (10 minutes). J, S
Developing Leadership, Coronet Films (10 minutes). J, S
Developing Responsibility, Coronet Films (10 minutes). E, J
Developing Self-Reliance, Coronet Films (10 minutes). J, S
Don't Be Afraid, Encyclopaedia Britannica Films, Inc. (12 minutes). E, J
Don't Get Angry, Encyclopaedia Britannica Films, Inc. (12 minutes). E, J
Emotional Health, Text Film Dept., McGraw-Hill Book Co., Inc. (20 minutes). S
Everyday Courtesy, Coronet Films (10 minutes). E, J, S
Families First, New York Youth Commission (17 minutes). S
Family Circles, National Film Board of Canada (31 minutes). S, T
Farewell to Childhood, Bailey Films, Inc. (23 minutes). S
Feeling Left Out, Coronet Films (12 minutes). S, T
Feelings of Hostility, Text Film Dept., McGraw-Hill Book Co., Inc. (27 minutes). S, T
Friendship Begins at Home, Coronet Films (15 minutes). J, S
From Sociable Six to Noisy Nine, Text Film Dept., McGraw-Hill Book Co., Inc. (22 minutes). S, T
From Ten to Twelve, Text Film Dept., McGraw-Hill Book Co., Inc. (26 minutes). S, T
Going Steady, Coronet Films (10 minutes). J, S
Good Sportsmanship, Coronet Films (10 minutes). E
Good Table Manners, Coronet Films (10 minutes). E, J
He Acts His Age, Text Film Dept., McGraw-Hill Book Co., Inc. (15 minutes). S, T
Head of the House, Bailey Films, Inc. (40 minutes). S
Helping the Child to Accept the Do's, Encyclopedia Britannica Films, Inc. (11 minutes). S, T
Helping the Child to Face the Don'ts, Encyclopedia Britannica Films, Inc. (11 minutes). S, T
How Do You Know It's Love, Coronet Films (13 minutes). S
How Friendly Are You, Coronet Films (10 minutes). E, J
How Honest Are You, Coronet Films (13 minutes). E, J
How to Remember, Coronet Films (10 minutes). J, S
How to Say No, Coronet Films (10 minutes). S
How We Cooperate, Coronet Films (10 minutes). E
Improve Your Personality, Coronet Films (10 minutes). J, S
It's Wonderful Being a Girl, Personal Products Corp. (20 minutes). J
It Takes All Kinds, Text Film Dept., McGraw-Hill Book Co., Inc. (20 minutes). S
Judging Emotional Behavior, Churchill-Wexler Film Productions (20 minutes). J, S
Know Your Baby, National Film Board of Canada (10 minutes). S, T
Let Us Grow in Human Understanding, Harmon (30 minutes). J, S
Let's Play Fair, Coronet Films (10 minutes). E, J
Life With Baby, Contemporary (18 minutes). J, S
Make Your Own Decisions, Coronet Films (11 minutes). J, S
Making Life Adjustments, Text Film Dept., McGraw-Hill Book Co., Inc. (20 minutes). S
Marriage Today, Text Film Dept., McGraw-Hill Book Co., Inc. (22 minutes). S
Mental Health, Encyclopaedia Britannica Films, Inc. (12 minutes) S
More Dates for Kay, Coronet Films (10 minutes). S

Overcoming Fear, Coronet Films (14 minutes).   J, S
Overcoming Worry, Coronet Films (10 minutes).   J, S
Over-Dependency, Text Film Dept., McGraw-Hill Book Co., Inc. (32 minutes).   S
Preface to a Life, U. S. Public Health Service (30 minutes).   S
Retire to Life, International Film Bureau (23 minutes).   S, T
Right or Wrong, Coronet Films (10 minutes).   J, S
Search for Sanity, Smith, Kline & French Laboratories (30 minutes).   S, T
Self-Conscious Guy, Coronet Films (13 minutes).   J, S
Shy Guy, Coronet Films (13 minutes).   J, S
Shyness, Text Film Dept., McGraw-Hill Book Co., Inc. (13 minutes).   S, T
Sibling Relations and Personality, Text Film Dept., McGraw-Hill Book Co., Inc.
 (22 minutes).   S, T
Sibling Rivalries and Parents, Text Film Dept., McGraw-Hill Book Co., Inc. (11
 minutes).   S, T
Snap Out of It, Coronet Films (13 minutes).   J, S
The Baby Sitter, Young America Films, Inc. (15 minutes).   S, T
The Feeling of Depression, Text Film Dept., McGraw-Hill Book Co., Inc. (32
 minutes).   S, T
The Feeling of Rejection, Text Film Dept., McGraw-Hill Book Co., Inc. (21
 minutes).   S, T
The Fun of Being Thoughtful, Coronet Films (10 minutes).   J, S
The High Wall, Text Film Dept., McGraw-Hill Book Co., Inc. (31 minutes).   S, T
The Lengthening Span, Smith, Kline, & French Laboratories (30 minutes).   S, T
The Meaning of Adolescence, National Association for Mental Health, Inc. (16
 minutes).   S
The Other Fellow's Feelings, Young America Films, Inc. (8 minutes).   E, J
The Outsider, Young America Films, Inc. (10 minutes).   E, J
This Charming Couple, Text Film Dept., McGraw-Hill Book Co., Inc. (19
 minutes).   S
To Serve the Mind, National Film Board of Canada (25 minutes).   S
Understand Your Emotions, Coronet Films (13 minutes).   J, S
Ways to Settle Disputes, Coronet Films (10 minutes).   E
We, the Mentally Ill, Smith, Kline, & French Laboratories (30 minutes).   S, T
What About Juvenile Delinquency, Young America Films, Inc., (10 minutes).   S, T
What to Do on a Date, Coronet Films (10 minutes).   J
What's on Your Mind, National Film Board of Canada (10 minutes).   S, T
When All the People Play, National Film Board of Canada (27 minutes).   S
When Should I Marry? National Association for Mental Health, Inc. (19
 minutes).   S
You and Your Attitudes, Association Films, Inc. (10 minutes).   S
You and Your Parents, Coronet Films (14 minutes).   J, S, T
You Are Not Alone, Association Films, Inc. (33 minutes).   S
Youth and the Law, National Association for Mental Health, Inc. (36 minutes).   S

Noncommunicable diseases
Pamphlets
General diseases

About Muscular Dystrophy, Muscular Dystrophy Association.   S, T
Allergy, U. S. Department of Health, Education and Welfare.   T
Anemia, U. S. Department of Health, Education and Welfare.   T
Answers to Some Questions About Allergy, American Foundation for Allergic
 Diseases.   S, T
Appendicitis, Metropolitan Life Insurance Co.   E, J
Arthritis, U. S. Department of Health, Education and Welfare.   T
Arthritis and Rheumatism, U. S. Government Printing Office.   S, T

Asthma, U. S. Department of Health, Education and Welfare.	T
Be Smart, Protect Your Heart, American Heart Association, Inc.	S
Birth Defects, National Foundation.	S
Breast Self-Examination, U. S. Superintendent of Documents.	S
Cancer Is a Killer, American Cancer Society.	S
Cancer—When Days May Count, John Hancock Mutual Life Insurance Co.	S
Cell Examination—New Hope in Cancer, Public Affairs Committee, Inc.	S, T
Concerning Diabetes, John Hancock Mutual Life Insurance Co.	S
Diabetes, Health Publications Institute, Inc.	S
Diabetes, Metropolitan Life Insurance Co.	S
Diabetes, U. S. Department of Health, Education and Welfare.	S
Facing the Facts About Cancer, American Cancer Society.	J, S
Facts About Rheumatic Fever, Children's Bureau.	E, J
Foes After Forty, John Hancock Life Insurance Co.	S
Heart Diseases at All Ages, Metropolitan Life Insurance Co.	S
Heart Diseases in School Life, American Heart Association, Inc.	E
Heart Quiz, American Heart Association, Inc.	S
High Blood Pressure, American Heart Association, Inc.	S
How to Help Your Handicapped Child, Public Affairs Committee, Inc.	T
How to Make Your Own Take—A Part Model of DNA, The National Foundation.	S
How Your Doctor Detects Cancer, American Cancer Society.	J, S
If You Suspect Cancer, John Hancock Life Insurance Co.	J, S
Know Your Heart, American Heart Association.	S
Leukemia, U. S. Department of Health, Education and Welfare.	T
Light and Shade, Metropolitan Life Insurance Co.	S
Malaria, World Health Organization.	S, T
Medical Uses of Blood, American National Red Cross.	S, T
Most People Don't Know About Cancer, American Cancer Society.	J, S
Muscular Dystrophy—the Facts, Muscular Dystrophy Association.	T
101 Answers to Your Questions About Cancer, American Cancer Society.	J, S
Pinworms, U. S. Government Printing Office.	S, T
Publications About Your Health, American Medical Association.	S, T
Rheumatic Fever—Childhood's Greatest Enemy, American Heart Association.	E, J
Ringworm, U. S. Government Printing Office.	S, T
Ringworm, Including Athlete's Foot, U. S. Department of Health, Education and Welfare.	S, T
Self-Examination of the Female Breast, The Cancer Bulletin.	S, T
Something Can Be Done About Chronic Illness, Public Affairs Committee, Inc.	S
Tapeworm, U. S. Government Printing Office.	S, T
Tetanus, U. S. Government Printing Office.	S, T
The Case of the American People vs. Heart Disease, American Hearth Association.	S
The Child With Cerebral Palsy, U. S. Government Printing Office.	S, T
The Heart of the Home, American Heart Association.	S
The Traitor Within, American Cancer Society.	S
The Truth About Cancer, Health Publications Institute, Inc.	J, S
Third of the Day, Equitable Life Assurance Society.	S, T
Trichinosis, U. S. Government Printing Office.	S, T
Undulant Fever, U. S. Department of Health, Education and Welfare.	S, T
What You Should Know About Cancer, Metropolitan Life Insurance Co.	S
What About Your Heart? American Heart Association.	S
What Teachers Should Know About the Child With Cerebral Palsy, National Society for Crippled Children and Adults.	T
What the Classroom Teacher Should Know and Do About Children With Heart Disease, American Heart Association.	T

What You Should Know About Rheumatic Fever, American Heart Association.	E, J
When Days May Count, John Hancock Mutual Life Insurance Co.	S, T
Your Blood Pressure and Your Arteries, American Heart Association.	S
Your Heart, Metropolitan Life Insurance Co.	S

Rheumatic fever and heart disease

Foes After Forty, John Hancock Mutual Life Insurance Co.	S, T
Heart Disease—A Story of Progress, U. S. Government Printing Office.	S, T
Heart Diseases in School Life, American Heart Association.	E
Heart Quiz, American Heart Association.	S
High Blood Pressure, American Heart Association.	S
Know Your Heart, Public Affairs Committee, Inc.	S
Rheumatic Fever, Public Affairs Committee, Inc.	J, S
The Case of the American People vs. Heart Disease, American Heart Association.	S
The Heart of the Home, American Heart Association.	S

Films

At Our House (health screening), Columbia University Press (9 minutes).	S
A Way in the Wilderness, Teaching Film Custodians, Inc. (11 minutes).	S
Be Your Age (heart), Metropolitan Life Insurance Co. (11 minutes).	S, T
Breast Self-Examination, American Cancer Society (16 minutes).	S, T
Cancer, Encyclopaedia Britannica Films, Inc. (12 minutes) .	J, S
Challenge: Science Against Cancer, International Film Bureau (36 minutes).	S
Choose to Live, U. S. Public Health Service Communicable Disease Center (11 minutes).	S, T
Common Heart Disorders and Their Causes, Text Film. Dept., McGraw-Hill Book Co., Inc. (17 minutes).	S
Crusade, American Cancer Society (11 minutes).	S
From One Cell, American Cancer Society (12 minutes).	J, S
Man Alive, American Cancer Society (12 minutes).	J, S
Man's Greatest Friend, Teaching Film Custodians, Inc. (10 minutes),	J, S
Multiple Screening, Center for Mass Communication (8 minutes).	J, S
The Traitor Within, U. S. Public Health Service Communicable Disease Center (11 minutes).	S
The Warning Shadow, American Cancer Society (17 minutes).	S, T
They Live Again, Teaching Film Custodians, Inc. (11 minutes).	J, S
Time Is Life, American Cancer Society (16 minutes).	J, S
You Are the Switchman, American Cancer Society (8 minutes).	J, S

Nutrition

Pamphlets

A Nutrition Guide, General Mills, Inc.	T
And in Food, Balance Is Everything, Aetna Life Insurance Co.	S
Basic Facts About Enriched Bread, American Institute of Baking.	S
Bread, A Visit to a Modern Bakery, American Institute of Baking.	E
Bread in the Making (for intermediate grades), American Institute of Baking.	E
Breast Feeding, U. S. Government Printing Office.	S, T
Canned Food Tables, National Canners Association.	S
Classroom Food Facts and Fun (for elementary grades), Wheat Flour Institute.	T
Classroom Weight Record, The Borden Company.	T
Design for Better Living, Wheat Flour Institute.	S, T
Diet and Dental Health, American Dental Association.	S
Diets to Fit the Family Income, Farmers' Bulletin No. 1757, U. S. Department of Agriculture.	J, S
Eat a Good Breakfast to Start a Good Day, Cereal Institute, Inc.	E

Eat to Live, Wheat Flour Institute.	J, T
Educational Materials on the Good Breakfast and Cereals, Cereal Institute, Inc.	T
Feeding Little Folks, National Dairy Council.	S, T
Food and Nutrition News, National Livestock and Meat Board.	S
Food and Science, Public Affairs Committee, Inc.	J, S
Food for Children, Farmer's Bulletin No. 1674, U. S. Department of Agriculture.	S
Food for Families With School Children, U. S. Department of Agriculture.	S
Food for Health, United Fruit Co.	E
Food for the Family, Metropolitan Life Insurance Co.	S, T
Food for the Family With Young Children, U. S. Department of Agriculture.	S
Food Guide for Older Folks, U. S. Department of Agriculture.	S, T
Food Value Charts, National Livestock and Meat Board.	T
Functions of Food in Nutrition, National Livestock and Meat Board.	E, J
Goals—For Nutrition Education for Elementary and Seconday Schools, Harvard School of Public Health.	T
Good Cooks—Good Eating, American Institute of Baking.	S
Health and Nutrition, United Fruit Co.	S
Health Aspects of School Lunch Program, American Association for Health, Physical Education and Recreation.	T
Information on Bread and Flour Enrichment, American Institue of Baking.	S
Is Yours a Weighty Problem? The Borden Company.	E
Journey of Milk Through a Pasteurizing Plant, The Borden Company.	J, S
Make-A-Meal Picture Book, Wheat Flour Institute.	E, T
Map Your Meals, American Institute of Baking.	J, S
Money-Saving Main Dishes, U. S. Government Printing Office.	S
National Food Guide, U. S. Department of Agriculture.	S
Nutrition Aids, Grades One Through Eight, Kellogg Co.	E
Nutrition and Healthy Growth, U. S. Government Printing Office.	T
Nutrition Ladder, Florida Citrus Commission.	E, S
Nutrition—Up to Date, Up to You, U. S. Department of Agriculture.	S, T
Overweight and Underweight, Metropolitan Life Insurance Co.	S
Publications About Your Health, American Medical Association.	T
Recommended Dietary Allowances, National Research Council.	T
School Lunch Portions, American Dietetic Association.	T
Step Lively, American Dietetic Association.	J, S
Score With Breakfast, American Institute of Baking.	E, J
Teen-Age Food Patterns, Lever Bros. Co.	T
The Cream of Wheat Story, Cream of Wheat Corp.	S
The Family Food Supply, Metropolitan Life Insurance Co.	E, J
25 Ways to Stay on a Diet, Good Housekeeping Institute.	J, S
The Low Calorie Diet, Pocket Books, Inc.	S, T
Waistlines, John Hancock Life Insurance Co.	S
Weight Control in Adolescence, American Dietetic Association.	J, S
We Work Together (chart), Wheat Flour Institute.	T
Well-Nourished Children, U. S. Department of Agriculture.	S
What Foods Do You Choose? Metropolitan Life Insurance Co.	S, T
What to Eat and Why, John Hancock Mutual Life Insurance Co.	S
Wheel of Good Eating (chart), American Institute of Baking.	S, T
Wholewheat Wall Chart, Ralston Purina Co.	S
You and Your Engine, National Livestock and Meat Board.	E
Your Food—How Does It Rate for Health? Metropolitan Life Insurance Co.	E, S

Films

Admirals in the Making, National Dairy Council (13½ minutes).	S, T
And One to Grow On, Social Science Films (12 minutes).	E, T

Choosing for Happiness, Text Film. Dept., McGraw-Hill Book Co., Inc. (14 minutes).   S
Food As Children See It, General Mills Inc., Film Library (18 minutes).   S, T
Food That Builds Good Health, Coronet Films (10 minutes).   E, J, S
Foods and Nutrition, Encyclopaedia Britannica Films, Inc. (11 minutes).   J, S
For Health and Happiness, U. S. Department of Agriculture (10 minutes).   E
Foundation Foods, Avis Films (10 minutes).   E, J, S
Fundamentals of Diet, Encyclopaedia Britannica Films, Inc. (11 minutes).   E, J, S
Fun in Food, Gateway Productions, Inc. (9 minutes).   S
Good Eating Habits, Coronet Films (10 minutes).   E, J
Give Us This Day, American Society of Bakery Engineers (25 minutes).   S
Guide to Good Eating, National Dairy Council (10 minutes).   E, J
Hidden Hunger, American Film Center (22 minutes).   S
It's All in Knowing How, National Dairy Council (13½ minutes).   J, S, T
Magic Foods, General Picture Production (10 minutes).   E
Obesity, Encyclopaedia Britannica Films, Inc. (12 minutes).   S
Proof of the Pudding, Metropolitan Life Insurance Co. (10 minutes).   E, J
Stanley Takes a Trip, National Film Board of Canada (10 minutes).   E
Story of Human Energy, Farm Film Foundation (10 minutes).   E, J, S
The Color of Health, American Bakers Association (11 minutes).   J
The Food Store, Encyclopaedia Britannica Films, Inc. (11 minutes).   E
The Miracle of the Can, Modern Talking Pictures, Inc. (20 minutes).   J, S
The Three Squares, U. S. Department of Agriculture (13¼ minutes).   J, S, T
Understanding Vitamins, Encyclopaedia Britannica Films, Inc. (14 minutes) . S, T
What Makes Us Grow? National Film Board of Canada (11 minutes).   E
Who's Right? Text Film Dept., McGraw-Hill Book Co., Inc. (18 minutes)   S
Why Won't Tommy Eat? National Film Board of Canada (19 minutes).   S, T

Personal health and grooming
Pamphlets

About Us and Our Friends, Metropolitan Life Insurance Co.   E
An Inside Story, National Dairy Council.   T
Answers to Perplexing Skin Problems, Good Housekeeping Institute.   S
Answers to Practical Questions on Menstruation, American Medical Association. S
Are You in the Know? Kimberly-Clark Corp.   S
Attractive Teeth for Teenagers, American Dental Association.   J, S
Basic Rules for Foot Health, National Foot Health Council.   E, S
Care of the Eyes, U. S. Department of Health, Education and Welfare.   J
Caring for the Sick in the Home, John Hancock Mutual Life Insurance Co.   S
Dental Caries Prevention and Control, American Dental Association.   J
Dental Health Program for Elementary and Secondary Schools, American Dental
    Association.   T
Dental Health Teaching Units, Bristol-Myers Co.   E, J, T
Don't Be Misled, American Dental Association.   S, T
Ears That Hear, John Hancock Life Insurance Co.   J, S
Everybody Smile, American Dental Association.   E
Exercise and Fitness, Athletic Institute.   J, S
Fit for Fun (for girls), National Dairy Council.   S
For Good Teeth, Metropolitan Life Insurance Co.   E
14-Day Beauty Success Course, Good Housekeeping Institute.   J, S
Frank Visits the Dentist, American Dental Association.   E
Girls Want to Know, American Social Hygiene Association.   J, S
Good Grooming Teaching Units, Educational Service Department.   J, S, T
Good Teeth for Young America, Church and Dwight Co.   E, J
Growing Up and Liking It, Personal Products Corp.   J

Guide for a Good Grooming Program, Bristol-Myers Co.	E, J
Health and Fitness in the Modern World, Athletic Institute.	J, S
Health Bulletin for Teachers, Metropolitan Life Insurance Co.	T
Healthy Teeth, John Hancock Life Insurance Co.	S
Hearing Is Priceless, Protect It, American Hearing Society.	S
Human Growth, E. C. Brown Trust.	E, J
Medical Uses of Blood, American National Red Cross.	S
Menstrual Physiology, Kimberly-Clark Corp.	T
My Reflections (self-evaluation for girls), National Dairy Council.	S
Overweight and Underweight, Metropolitan Life Insurance Co.	S
Pain—That Is Good for You, John Hancock Life Insurance Co.	J, S
Posture and Body Mechanics, Maternity Center.	S
Postures on Parade (for girls), National Dairy Council.	J, S
Publications, National Society for the Prevention of Blindness, Inc.	T
Publications About Your Health, American Medical Association.	E, S, T
Save Your Sight, Public Affairs Committee, Inc.	S, T
Seven Rules for Shoe Fit, National Foot Health Council.	S, T
Show Off Your Eyes, Good Housekeeping Institute.	S
Sleep and Children, National Education Association and American Medical Association.	T
Sleep, the Restorer, John Hancock Life Insurance Co.	E, J
Sunburn and Suntan, U. S. Department of Health, Education and Welfare.	S, T
Teaching Dental Health, American Association for Health, Physical Education and Recreation.	T
Teaching Guide—Menstrual Education, Kimberly-Clark Corp.	T
The Care of Children's Teeth (questions and answers), American Dental Association.	E, T
The History of Dental Hygiene, Lever Bros. Co.	E, T
The Way to Smile, Procter & Gamble.	J
Toothbrushing, American Dental Association.	E
Today's Health (periodical), American Medical Association.	S, T
Tom Visits the Dentist, Procter & Gamble.	E
Very Personally Yours, Kimberly-Clark Corp.	J, S
Waistlines, John Hancock Mutual Life Insurance Co.	S, T
What Every Teacher Should Know About the Physical Condition of Her Pupils, U. S. Government Printing Office.	E, S
Who—Me? (self-evaluation), National Dairy Council.	S
Why Girls Menstruate, American Medical Association.	S, T

Films

A Drop in the Bucket, U. S. Public Health Service (13 minutes).	S, T
Bathing Time for Baby, Association Films, Inc. (13 minutes).	S
Body Care and Grooming, Text Film Dept., McGraw-Hill Book Co., Inc. (17 minutes).	S
Capitol Story, U. S. Public Health Service, Communicable Disease Center (20 minutes).	S
Care of Hair and Nails, Encyclopaedia Britannica Films, Inc. (11 minutes).	E
Care of Feet, Encyclopaedia Britannica Films, Inc. (12 minutes).	J, S
Care of the Newborn Baby, Castle (31 minutes).	S, T
Care of the Skin, Encyclopaedia Britannica Films, Inc. (11 minutes).	E
Charm and Personality Plus Character, Warren's Motion Pictures (37 minutes).	J, S
Cleanliness and Bathing, Encyclopaedia Britannica Films, Inc. (8 minutes).	E
Cleanliness and Health, Institute of Inter-American Affairs (10 minutes).	E, S, T
Cleanliness—Clean Clothes, Encyclopaedia Britannica Films, Inc. (8 minutes).	J, S
Clean Look, American Film Center (30 minutes).	S

Come Clean, American Dental Association (10 minutes).   J, S
Dental Health: How and Why, Coronet Films (10 minutes).   E, J
Exercise and Health, Coronet Films (11 minutes).   J, S
Eyes Bright, Avis Films (10 minutes).   E
Eyes for Tomorrow, National Society for the Prevention of Blindness (22 minutes). E, J
Fluoridation, U.S. Public Health Service (3 minutes).   S, T
Hear Better: Healthy Ears, Coronet Films (11 minutes).   E
How Billy Keeps Clean, Coronet Films (10 minutes).   E
How to Be Well Groomed, Coronet Films (10 minutes).   S
If It's Health You're Seeking, National Motion Picture Co. (30 minutes).   J, S
Improving Your Posture, Coronet Films (10 minutes).   E, J
Johnny's New World, National Society for the Prevention of Blindness
    (16 minutes).   J, S, T
Keeping Clean and Neat, Encyclopaedia Britannica Films, Inc. (11 minutes).   E
Life of a Healthy Child, Knowledge Builders (12 minutes).   E, J
Losing to Win, Metropolitan Life Insurance Co. (10 minutes).   J, S
Miss Dunning Goes to Town, Association Films Inc. (27 minutes).   S
Modern Guide to Health, Young America Films, Inc. (10 minutes).   E, J
Personal Health for Girls, Coronet Films (12 minutes).   J
Personal Hygiene for Boys, Coronet Films (12 minutes).   J
Posture and Exercise, American Film Center (11 minutes).   J
Posture and Personality, Social Science Films (12 minutes).   J
Posture and Poise, State University of Iowa (22 minutes).   J
Posture Habits, Coronet Films (11 minutes).   E, J
Rest and Health, Coronet Films (10 minutes).   S
Road to Health and Happiness, Knowledge Builders (12 minutes).   S
Save Those Teeth, Encyclopaedia Britannica Films, Inc. (10 minutes).   E
Scrub Game, Modern Talking Picture Service, Inc. (30 minutes).   E, J
See Better: Healthy Eyes, Association Films, Inc. (10 minutes).   E
Sleep for Health, Encyclopaedia Britannica Films, Inc. (11 minutes).   E
Soapy The Germ Fighter, Avis Films (10 minutes).   E
Something to Cheer About, Modern Talking Picture Service, Inc. (20 minutes).   J, S
Target: Tooth Decay, University of Oklahoma (10 minutes).   S
Teeth, Encyclopaedia Britannica Films, Inc. (10 minutes).   E, J, S
Teeth Are to Keep, Encyclopaedia Britannica Films, Inc. (11 minutes).   E, T
The Ears and Hearing, Encyclopaedia Britannica Films, Inc. (11 minutes).   J, S, T
The Eyes and Their Care, Encyclopaedia Britannica Films, Inc. (11 minutes).   J, S
The Foot and Its Problems, National Association of Chiropodists (20 minutes).   S, T
The Human Hair, Bray Studios, Inc. (11 minutes).   J, S
The Magic Pathway, Better Vision Institute (21 minutes).   J, S
The Nose, Throat and Ears, Text Film Dept., McGraw-Hill Book Co., Inc. (10
    minutes).   J, S
The Truth About Fluoridation, Michigan State Dental Association (12 minutes).   S, T
The Walking Machine (foot health), State University of Iowa (14 minutes).   S
Vitamin D, Encyclopaedia Britannica Films, Inc. (15 minutes).   S
Your Cleanliness, Young America Films, Inc. (10 minutes).   E, J
Your Ears, Young America Films, Inc. (10 minutes).   S, T
Your Eyes, Young America Films, Inc. (10 minutes).   J, S
Your Voice, Encyclopaedia Britannica Films, Inc. (11 minutes).   J, S

Safety, first aid, and emergency care
Pamphlets

A Formula For Child Safety, Metropolitan Life Insurance Co.   E
A Guide to Good Driving, Metropolitan Life Insurance Co.   S
A Life in Your Hands, Aetna Life Insurance Co.   S, T

American National Red Cross, Certification Courses in Home Nursing and First
Aid, The American National Red Cross.   S
Annotated Civil Defense Bibliography for Teachers, U. S. Government Printing
Office.   T
Bibliography Elementary Traffic Safety Education and School Patrols Materials,
American Automobile Association.   T
Bibliography of AAA Pedestrian Materials, American Automobile Association.   T
Bibliography of Driver Education Materials, American Automobile Association.   T
Bicycle Care, Bicycle Institute of America, Inc.   E
Bicycle Riding Clubs, Bicycle Institute of America, Inc.   T
Bicycle Safety Aids, Bicycle Institute of America, Inc.   T
Bicycle Safety Quiz, Aetna Casualty and Surety Co.   E
Bicycle Safety Tests, Bicycle Institute of America, Inc.   E
Bike Fun, Bicycle Institute of America, Inc.   J, S
Bike Regulations in the Community, Bicycle Institute of America, Inc.   J, S
Bike Safety Programs, Bicycle Institute of America, Inc.   T
Check Your Home, Prudential Life Insurance Co.   S, T
Child Safety, Purdential Life Insurance Co.   S, T
Civil Defense Education, National Education Association.   T
Civil Defense in Schools, U. S. Government Printing Office.   T
Common Sense Pays Off, Association of Casualty and Surety Companies.   S
Do's and Don'ts of Ladder Safety for Farm and Home, National Safety Council.   S, T
Driver Education in the Secondary School, Association of Casualty and Surety
Companies.   T
Education for National Survival, U. S. Department of Health, Education, and
Welfare.   T
Firearms Safety (outline), National Rifle Asociation.   T
First Aid for Unconsciousness May Save Lives, Aetna Life Insurance Co.   S
Home Hazard Hunt, Center for Mass Communication, Columbia University Press.   E
How's Your Driving? Metropolitan Life Insurance Co.   S
Hunter Safety Handbook, National Rifle Association.   S
Mrs. Hazard's Hunt, Prudential Life Insurance Co.   S, T
N.E.A. Safety Publications, National Education Association.   T
Play It Safe, Metropolitan Life Insurance Co.   E
Poison Ivy, U. S. Department of Health, Education, and Welfare.   S, T
Safe at Home, John Hancock Life Insurance Co.   S
Safety Begins at Home, Metropolitan Life Insurance Co.   S
Safety Education Magazine, National Safety Council.   S, T
Safety Guide for the Farm and Home Front, General Mills, Inc.   S, T
Safety—Your Child's Heritage, Prudential Life Insurance Co.   S, T
Snake Bite, U. S. Department of Health, Education and Welfare.   S
Stop, Look and Live, Metropolitan Life Insurance Co.   E, J
Swimming, U. S. Department of Health, Education and Welfare.   S
Teachers Triptik (guide), American Automobile Association.   T
The Instructional Material Service, National Safety Council   E, S, T
    Accident Facts (annual)
    Congress Transactions
    Introductory Supply of Student Accident Report Forms
    Safety Education Memos
    Safety Sentinel
    Safety Scope (high school)
    School Shop Safety
    Student Safety Organization (high school)
The Safest Route to School, American Automobile Association.   E
The National Material Service, National Safety Council.   T

There's No Place Like Home, U. S. Department of Health, Education, and Welfare. E, S
Traffic Safety Education Films, American Automobile Association. T
When the Unexpected Happens, John Hancock Mutual Life Insurance Co. S
You're in Charge, National Safety Council. S, T
Your Family's Safety, Metropolitan Life Insurance Co. S

Films

A Day in Court, Rarig Motion Picture Co. (30 minutes). J
Anatomy of an Accident, Association Films, Inc. (26½ minutes). S
Auto U.S.A., National Commission on Safety, N.E.A. (27½ minutes). S
Back Pressure Arm Lift Method of Artificial Respiration, Seminar Films, Inc.
    (9 minutes). J, S
Bicycling With Complete Safety, Bailey Films, Inc. (10 minutes). E
Blasting Cap, Modern Talking Picture Service, Inc. (15 minutes). E, S
Care of Minor Wounds, Encyclopaedia Britannica Films, Inc. (5 minutes). E, S
Danger Is Your Companion, American National Red Cross (27 minutes). S, T
First Aid, Encyclopaedia Britannica Films, Inc. (11 minutes). J, S
First Aid in the Prevention of Shock, Educational Film Dept., United World
    Films, Inc. (26 minutes). S
First Aid on the Spot, Encyclopaedia Britannica Films, Inc. (11 minutes). J, S
First Aid: Wounds and Fractures, Encyclopaedia Britannnica Films, Inc.
    (10 minutes). E, J, S
Fundamentals of First Aid, Educational Film Dept., United World Films, Inc.
    (18 minutes). J, S
Help Wanted (first aid), Johnson & Johnson (31 minutes). J, S, T
Home Safe Home, National Safety Council (12 minutes). E, J, S
It Didn't Have to Happen, International Film Bureau, Inc. (13 minutes). S
It's Fun to Swim, American National Red Cross (11 minutes). E, S
Let's Be Safe at Home, Portafilms (10 minutes). E, J, S
Let's Play Safe, Portafilms (10 minutes). E
Let's Stop and Go Safely, Portafilms (17 minutes). E, J
Let's Think and Be Safe, Portafilms (11 minutes). E
Live and Learn, Sid Davis Productions (13 minutes). E, J
Mrs. Hazard's House, Prudential Life Insurance Co. (13 minutes). S, T
Once Upon a Time, Association Films, Inc. (11 minutes). E, S
Operation Doorstep, Educational Film Dept., United World Films, Inc. (10
    minutes). S, T
Outboard Outings, National Commission on Safety, N.E.A. (19 minutes). S
Penetrating Wounds of the Abdomen, Educational Film Department,
    United World Films Inc. (12 minutes). S, T
Respiratory Protection, Castle (13 minutes). S, T
Safe Living at Home, Coronet Films (11 minutes). E, S
Safe Living at School, Association Films, Inc. (10 minutes). E, J
Safety Begins at Home, Association Films, Inc. (11 minutes). E, J
Safety in the Home, Encyclopaedia Britannica Films, Inc. (11 minutes). E, S
Safety on the Playground, Encyclopaedia Britannica Films, Inc. (14 minutes). E
Safety on the School Bus, Young America Films, Inc. (11 minutes). E, J
Safety on the Street, Encyclopaedia Britannica Films, Inc. (11 minutes). E
Safety To and From School, Association Films, Inc. (11 minutes). E, J
Street Safety Is Your Problem, Text Film Dept., McGraw-Hill Book Co., Inc.
    (10 minutes). E, J, S
Sucking Wounds of the Chest, Educational Film Department, United World Films
    Inc. (14 minutes). S, T
That They May Live, University of Toronto (28 minutes). S, T
The Functional Safety Series (seven films), Coronet Films (11 minutes each). E

The Safe Driving Series (three films), Coronet Films (11 minutes each).   S
Traffic With the Devil, Association Films, Inc. (20 minutes).   E, S
What's Your Driving Eye-Q, National Commission on Safety, N.E.A. (13 minutes).   S
Wheel Sense, Association Films, Inc. (20 minutes).   J, S
You Can Take It With You, National Safety Council (13 minutes).   S, T

Sex and reproduction
Pamphlets

Answers to Practical Questions on Menstruation, American Medical Association.   S
Easy Answers to Your Child's Sex Questions, American Social Hygiene Association.   S
Essence of Womanhood, Personal Products Corp.   S
Expecting a Baby, John Hancock Life Insurance Co.   S
Formula for Sex Education, Publication No. 778, American Social Hygiene
   Association.   S
Growing Up and Liking It, Personal Products Corp.   J
Health for Girls, Publication No. A-604, American Social Hygiene Association.   S
Health for Man and Boy, American Social Hygiene Association.   S
High Schools and Sex Education, U. S. Public Health Department.   T
How to Tell Your Child About Sex, Public Affairs Committee, Inc.   S
Sex Education in the Home, American Social Hygiene Association.   S
Social Life for High School Girls and Boys, Publication No. A-349, American Social
   Hygiene Association   S
Sound Attitudes Toward Sex, American Social Hygiene Association.   S
Understanding Sex, Science Research Associates, Inc.   S
When Children Ask About Sex, Child Study Association of America.   T
You're A Big Girl Now, American Social Hygiene Association.   S
Your Own Story (reproduction), University of Minnesota Press.   S

Films

Early Marriage, E. C. Brown Trust (20 minutes).   S
Heredity, Encyclopaedia Britannica Films, Inc. (11 minutes).   J, S
Human Growth, E. C. Brown Trust (20 minutes).   J
Human Heredity, E. C. Brown Trust (20 minutes).   J, S
Human Reproduction, Text Film Dept., McGraw-Hill Book Co., Inc. (20 minutes).   S
In the Beginning, U. S. Department of Agriculture (20 minutes).   J, S
Your Body During Adolescence, Text Film Dept., McGraw-Hill Book Co., Inc.
   (10 minutes).   J, S

Tobacco, alcohol, and other harmful drugs
Pamphlets

A.A.—Helpful Ally in Copying with Alcoholism, Alcoholics Anonymous   S, T
Alcohol and Accidents, School and College Service.   J, S, T
Alcohol and Alcoholism, World Health Organization.   S, T
Alcohol at the Wheel, School and College Service.   S
Alcohol, Cats and People, National Committee on Alcoholism.   S
Alcoholism, a Sickness That Can Be Beaten, Public Affairs Committee, Inc.   S
Alcoholism Is a Sickness, Public Affairs Committee, Inc.   S
Alcoholism: Nature of the Problem and Alcoholism: Its Extent, Therapy and
   Prevention, Rutgers Center of Alcohol Studies.   S
Alcoholism the Illness, Alcoholics Anonymous.   S, T
A Primary Lesson in Narcotic Education, National Women's Temperance Union.   T
Discussion Guides, Rutgers Center of Alcohol Studies.   S, T
Drunks Are Getting Away With Murder, Meredith Publishing Co.   J, S, T
Exploring Alcohol Questions (packet), Rutgers Center of Alcoholic Studies.   E, J, S, T
Facts About Alcohol, Science Research Associates, Inc.   S

First Report on High School Drinking, Meredith Publishing Co.   T
44 Questions and Answers About the Program of Recovery From Alcoholism,
     Alcoholics Anonymous.   J, S, T
Growing Up Socially, Science Research Associates, Inc.   S
Instructor's Guide to Facts About Alcohol, Rutgers Center of Alcohol Studies.   T
Popular Pamphlets on Alcohol, Rutgers Center of Alcohol Studies.   E, J, S, T
Principles of Health Education Underlying Education on Alcoholism, Rutgers
     Center of Alcohol Studies.   T
Recovery From Alcoholism, Alcoholics Anonymous.   S
Studies of Alcohol (supplemental), Rutgers Center of Alcohol Studies   T
     Alcohol and Crime
     Alcohol and Industrial Efficiency
     Alcohol Beverages as a Food and Their Relation to Nutrition
     Alcohol Beverages, Health and Length of Life
     Alcohol, Heredity, and Germ Damage
     Facts on Cirrhosis of the Liver
     Facts on Delirium Tremens
     Government and the Alcohol Problem
     How Alcohol Beverages Affect Behavior
     Moderate and Excessive Users of Alcoholic Beverages
     Production and Properties of Alcoholic Beverages
     The Problem of Alcohol
     What Happens to Alcohol in the Body
Teen Agers and Their Troubles, Allied Youth, Inc.   S
This is A.A., Alcoholics Anonymous.   S
Tobacco and Health, Association Press.   J, S
Understanding Yourself, Science Research Associates, Inc.   S
What Are Your Problems? Science Research Associates, Inc.   S
What Shall Our Schools Teach About Alcohol? Rutgers Center of Alcohol Studies.   T
What We Can Do About the Drug Menace, Public Affairs Committee, Inc.   S, T
Young People and A.A., Alcoholics Anonymous.   S

Films

Alcohol and the Human Body, Encyclopaedia Britannica Films, Inc. (15 minutes).   S
Alcohol and Tobacco: What They Do to Our Bodies, Coronet Films (11 minutes).   J
Alcohol and You (2 parts), Young America Films, Inc.   J, S
Alcohol Is Dynamite, Sid Davis Productions (10 minutes).   J, S
Alcoholism, Encyclopaedia Britannica (22 minutes).   S
Alcoholism: The Revolving Door, Smith, Kline & French (30 minutes).   S, T
Any Boy—U.S.A., Women's Christian Temperance Union (20 minutes).   S
A Story of a Teen-Age Drug Addict, Young America Films, Inc., (20 minutes).   S
Drug Addiction, Encyclopaedia Britannica, Inc. (21 minutes).   S
Drunk Driving, Women's Christian Temperance Union (20 minutes).   J, S
It's The Brain That Counts, Women's Christian Temperance Union (20 minutes).   J, S
Liquid Lore, Women's Christian Temperance Union (20 minutes).   J, S
Narcotics and You (2 parts), Young America Films, Inc.   J, S
Problem Drinkers, Text Film Dept., McGraw-Hill Book Co., Inc. (19 minutes).   J, S
Should You Drink? Text Film Dept., McGraw-Hill Book Co., Inc. (21 minutes).   S
Terrible Truth, Sid Davis Productions (10 minutes).   J, S
That Boy Joe, Women's Christian Temperance Union (20 minutes).   S
The Choice Is Yours, Women's Christian Temperance Union (23 minutes).   J, S
To Smoke or Not to Smoke (19 minutes), American Cancer Society   J, S
To Your Health, Center for Mass Communication, Columbia University Press
     (11 minutes).   J, S, T
What About Drinking? Young America Films, Inc. (10 minutes).   S, T
Where Does It Get You? Film Publishers (16 minutes).   J, S

Pamphlet sources

Abbott Laboratories
14th & Sheridan Rd.
North Chicago, Ill.

Aetna Life Insurance Co.
151 Farmington Ave.
Hartford 15, Conn.

Alcoholics Anonymous, General Board
P. O. Box 459
New York 17, N. Y.

Allergy Foundation of America
801 2nd Ave.
New York 17, N. Y.

Allied Youth, Inc.
1709 M St., N. W.
Washington 6, D. C.

American Academy of Pediatrics
1801 Hinman Ave.
Evanston, Ill.

American Automobile Association
Pennsylvania Ave. at 17 St., N. W.
Washington 6, D. C.

American Can Co.
100 Park Ave.
New York 17, N. Y.

American Cancer Society
521 West 57th St.
New York 19, N. Y.

American Dental Association
Bureau of Health Education
222 E. Superior St.
Chicago 11, Ill.

American Diabetes Association, Inc.
1 E. 45th Street
New York 17, N. Y.

American Diabetic Association
1 Nevins St.
Brooklyn 17, N. Y.

American Dietetic Association
620 N. Michigan Ave.
Chicago 11, Ill.

American Dry Milk Institute, Inc.
221 N. LaSalle St.
Chicago 1, Ill.

American Fire Insurance Companies
Engineering Department
80 Maiden Lane
New York 7, N. Y.

American Foundation for the Blind, Inc.
15 W. 16th St.
New York 11, N. Y.

American Genetic Association
1507 M St. N. W.
Washington 5, D. C.

American Hearing Society
919 18th St., N. W.
Washington 6, D. C.

American Heart Association, Inc.
44 E. 23rd St.
New York 10, N. Y.

American Home Economics Association
1600 20th St., N. W.
Washington, D. C.

American Hospital Association
840 N. Lake Shore Dr.
Chicago 11, Ill.

American Institute of Baking
Consumer Service Dept.
400 E. Ontario St.
Chicago 11, Ill.

American Institute of Family Relations
5287 Sunset Blvd.
Los Angeles 27, Calif.

American Meat Institute
59 E. Van Buren St.
Chicago 5, Ill.

American Medical Association
Bureau of Health Education
535 N. Dearborn St.
Chicago 10, Ill.

American Museum of Natural History
Central Park West at 79th St.
New York 24, N. Y.

American National Red Cross
17th and D Streets, N. W.
Washington 13, D. C.

American Occupational Therapy Association
33 West 42nd St.
New York 18, N. Y.

American Optometric Association, Inc.
Department of Public Information
4030 Chouteau Ave.
St. Louis 10, Mo.

American Physical Therapy Association
1790 Broadway
New York 19, N. Y.

American Public Health Association
1790 Broadway
New York 19, N. Y.

American Seating Company
9th and Broadway
Grand Rapids 2, Mich.

American Social Health Association
1790 Broadway
New York 19, N. Y.

Arthritis and Rheumatism Foundation
535 Fifth Ave.
New York 17, N. Y.

Association of Casualty and Surety Companies
60 John St.
New York 30, N. Y.

Association for Family Living
32 W. Randolph, Suite 1818
Chicago 1, Ill.

Association for the Aid of Crippled Children
345 E. 46th St.
New York 17, N. Y.

Association Press
347 Madison Ave.
New York, N. Y.

Athletic Institute
209 S. State St.
Chicago, Ill.

The Audio-Visual Research Institute
1346 Broadway
Detroit 26, Mich.

Better Vision Institute, Inc.
Suite 3157
630 Fifth Ave.
New York 20, N. Y.

Bicycle Institute of America, Inc.
122 E. 42nd St.
New York 17, N. Y.

The Borden Company
Consumer Services
350 Madison Ave.
New York 17, N. Y.

E. C. Brown Trust
220 S. W. Alder St.
Portland 4, Ore.

California Fruit Growers Exchange
Educational Division
Box 5030 Metropolitan Station
Los Angeles, Calif.

The Cancer Bulletin
1603 Oakdale St.
Houston 4, Texas

Carnation Milk Company
Home Service Department
5045 Wilshire Blvd.
Los Angeles 36, Calif.

Center for Mass Communication
Columbia University Press
1125 Amsterdam Ave.
New York 25, N. Y.

Center for Programmed Instruction, Inc.
365 West End Ave. at 77th St.
New York 24, N. Y.

Cereal Institute, Inc.
Home Economics Dept.
135 S. LaSalle St.
Chicago 3, Ill.

Chicago Heart Association, Inc.
Suite 1608
203 N. Wabash Ave.
Chicago 1, Ill.

Child Study Association of America
132 E. 74th St.
New York 21, N. Y.

Child Welfare League of America, Inc.
130 E. 22nd St.
New York 10, N. Y.

Children's Bureau
Washington 25, D. C.

Cleveland Health Museum
8911 Euclid Ave.
Cleveland 6, Ohio

Commonwealth Fund
41 E. 57th St.
New York 22, N. Y.

Communications Material Center
Journalism Building
2960 Broadway
New York 27, N. Y.

Connecticut Mutual Life Insurance Co.
Hartford, Conn.

Cream of Wheat Corp.
Minneapolis 13, Minn.

Denoyer-Geppert Co.
5235-59 Ravenswood Ave.
Chicago 40, Ill.

Equitable Life Assurance Society of the
    United States
Bureau of Public Health
393 7th Ave.
New York 1, N.Y.

Family Service Association of America
215 Fourth Ave.
New York 3, N.Y.

Fawcett Publications, Inc.
67 W. 44th St.
New York 18, N.Y.

Florida Citrus Commission
Production Dept.
Lakeland, Fla.

Good Housekeeping Institute
57th St. and 8th Ave.
New York 19, N.Y.

Good Teeth Council for Children
17th Floor, Wrigley Building
400 N. Michigan Ave.
Chicago 11, Ill.

Harvard School of Public Health
Cambridge, Mass.

Health Information Foundation
The University of Chicago
Chicago 37, Ill.

Heart Information Center
National Heart Institute
U.S. Public Health Service
Bethesda 14, Md.

Insurance Institute for Highway Safety
1710 H St., N.W.
Washington 6, D.C.

International Cellucotton Products Co.
919 N. Michigan Ave.
Chicago 11, Ill.

Iowa Child Welfare Research Station
State University of Iowa
Department of Publications
Iowa City, Iowa

Kellogg Co.
Home Economics Service
Battle Creek, Mich.

Ladies' Home Journal
The Curtis Publishing Co.
Philadelphia 5, Pa.

Lever Bros. Co.
Public Relations Division
390 Park Ave.
New York 22, N.Y.

The Massachusetts Society for Social Hy-
    giene, Inc.
1145 Little Building
Boston 16, Mass.

Maternity Center Association
654 Madison Ave.
New York, N.Y.

Mental Health Materials Center
104 E. 25th St.
New York 10, N.Y.

Meredith Publishing Co.
Des Moines 3, Iowa

Metropolitan Life Insurance Co.
School Health Bureau
1 Madison Ave.
New York 10, N.Y.

Muscular Dystrophy Associations of
    America, Inc.
Public Information Dept.
1790 Broadway
New York 19, N.Y.

National Association for Mental Health,
    Inc.
10 Columbus Circle
New York 19, N.Y.

National Canners Association
Home Economics Division
1739 H St., N.W.
Washington, D.C.

National Commission on Safety Educa
    tion
National Education Association
1201 Sixteenth St.
Washington 6, D.C.

National Council on Alcoholism
New York Academy of Medicine
2 E. 103rd St.
New York 29, N.Y.

National Dairy Council
111 N. Canal St.
Chicago 6, Ill.

National Dental Hygiene Association
934 Shoreham Building
Washington, D.C.

National Education Association
1201 16th St., N. W.
Washington 6, D. C.

National Epilepsy League
208 N. Wells St.
Chicago 6, Ill.

National Foot Health Council, Inc.
The Phoenix Building
Rockland, Mass.

The National Foundation
Division of Scientific and Health Information
800 Second Ave.
New York 17, N. Y.

National Health Council
1790 Broadway
New York 19, N. Y.

National Health Education Committee,
Inc.
135 E. 42nd St.
New York 17, N. Y.

National Institutes of Health
U. S. Public Health Service
Bethesda 14, Md.

National Live Stock and Meat Board
Dept. of Nutrition, Room 825
407 S. Dearborn
Chicago 5, Ill.

National Multiple Sclerosis Society
257 4th Ave.
New York 10, N. Y.

National Research Council
Food and Nutrition Board
Washington, D. C.

National Rifle Association
1600 Rhode Island Ave.
Washington 6, D. C.

National Safety Council
425 N. Michigan Ave.
Chicago 11, Ill.

National Society for Crippled Children
and Adults, Inc.
2023 W. Ogden Ave.
Chicago 12, Ill.

National Society for the Prevention of
Blindness, Inc.
1790 Broadway
New York 19, N. Y.

National Tuberculosis Association
1790 Broadway
New York 19, N. Y.

National Women's Christian Temperance Union
1730 Chicago Ave.
Evanston, Ill.

New York State Charities Aid Association
105 E. 22nd St.
New York 10, N. Y.

New York State Society for Mental
Health
105 E. 22nd St.
New York 10, N. Y.

Nutrition Foundation
99 Park Ave.
New York 16, N. Y.

Nystrom, A. J. and Co.
3333 Elston Ave.
Chicago 18, Ill.

Ohio State Medical Association
79 E. State St.
Columbus 15, Ohio

Oral Hygiene Publications
1005 Library Ave.
Pittsburgh 22, Pa.

Pepsodent Division, Lever Bros. Co.
390 Park Ave.
New York 22, N. Y.

Personal Products Corp.
Education Dept.
Milltown, N. J.

Pocket Books, Inc.
Rockefeller Center
New York, N. Y.

Procter & Gamble Distributing Company
Public Relations Division
Gwynne Building
Cincinnati 1, Ohio

Prudential Insurance Company of
America
Public Relations and Advertising
Newark, N. J.

Public Affairs Committee, Inc.
22 E. 38th St.
New York 16, N. Y.

Public Health Nursing
1790 Broadway
New York 19, N. Y.

Publications Inquiry Unit
U. S. Office of Education
Washington 25, D. C.

Ralston Purina Co.
Checkerboard Square
St. Louis 2, Mo.

Rutgers Center of Alcohol Studies
Box 566, Rutgers, The State University
New Brunswick, N. J.

School and College Service
Station B
Columbus, Ohio

Science Research Associates, Inc.
57 W. Grand Ave.
Chicago 10, Ill.

Smith, Kline & French Laboratories
1530 Spring Garden St.
Philadelphia 1, Pa.

Society for Visual Education, Inc.
1345 Diversey Parkway
Chicago 14, Ill.

Stanford University Press
Stanford University
Stanford, Calif.

Superintendent of Documents
Government Printing Office
Washington 25, D. C.

Tampax, Inc.
161 E. 42nd St.
New York 17, N. Y.

The Traffic Institute
Northwestern University
1804 Hinman Ave.
Evanston, Ill.

Travelers Insurance Companies
Public Information Dept.
Hartford 15, Conn.

United Cerebral Palsy
369 Lexington Ave.
New York 17, N. Y.

United Fruit Co., Education Dept.
Pier 3, North River
New York 6, N. Y.

United States Department of Agriculture
Washington 25, D. C.

United States Department of Health,
   Education and Welfare
Washington 25, D. C.

United States Government Printing Office
Washington 25, D. C.

University of Minnesota Press
Minneapolis, Minn.

Wheat Flour Institute
309 W. Jackson Blvd.
Chicago 6, Ill.

World Health Organization
Office of Public Information
1501 New Hampshire Ave., N. W.
Washington 6, D. C.

Film sources

Alcoholics Anonymous, General Board
P. O. Box 459
New York 17, N. Y.

American Dental Association
222 E. Superior St.
Chicago 11, Ill.

American Film Center
P. O. Box 363
San Jose 3, Calif.

American Foot Care Institute
1775 Broadway
New York 19, N. Y.

American Heart Association
44 East 23rd St.
New York 10, N. Y.

American Leprosy Missions
4 Garber Square
Ridgewood, N. J.

American Medical Association
Bureau of Health Education
535 N. Dearborn St.
Chicago 10, Ill.

American Petroleum Institute
50 W. 50th St.
New York, N. Y.

American Social Health Association
1790 Broadway
New York 19, N. Y.

American Society of Bakery Engineers
Dept. of Visual Education
208 Third Ave., S. E.
Minneapolis, Minn.

Association Films, Inc.
799 Stevenson St.
San Francisco, Calif.

Avis Films
932 N. LaBrea
Hollywood 38, Calif.

Bailey Films, Inc.
6509 DeLongpre Ave.
Hollywood 28, Calif.

Brandon Films, Inc.
Western Cinema Guild
290 Seventh Ave.
San Francisco 18, Calif.

Bray Pictures Corporation
729 Seventh Ave.
New York 19, N. Y.

British Information Service
30 Rockefeller Plaza
New York, N. Y.

E. C. Brown Trust
220 S. W. Alder St.
Portland 4, Ore.

Castle
7356 Melrose Ave.
Hollywood 46, Calif.

Churchill-Wexler Film Productions
81 N. Seward St.
Los Angeles 38, Calif.

Columbia University Press
Center for Mass Communication
1125 Amsterdam Ave.
New York 27, N. Y.

Contemporary Films
Alvin J. Gordon
1859 Powell St.
San Francisco 11, Calif.

Coronet Films
Coronet Building
Chicago, Ill.

Sid Davis Productions
3826 Cochran Ave.
Los Angeles 56, Calif.

Eastman Films: Eastman Kodak Co.
Informational Films Division
343 State St.
Rochester 4, N. Y.

Educators' Progress Service
Randolph, Wis.

Eli Lilly, Public Relations Dept.
Indianapolis, Ind.

Encyclopaedia Britannica Films, Inc.
Wilmette, Ill.

Farm Film Foundation
1731 Eye St., N. W.
Washington 6, D. C.

Film Publishers
25 Broad St.
New York 4, N. Y.

Gateway Productions, Inc.
1859 Powell St.
San Francisco 11, Calif.

General Motors Corp.
3044 W. Grand Blvd.
Detroit 2, Mich.

General Picture Production
621 Sixth Ave.
Des Moines 9, Iowa

Harmon
Division of Visual Experiment
140 Nassau St.
New York 38, N. Y.

Institute of Inter-American Affairs
499 Pennsylvania Ave., N. W.
Washington 25, D. C.

International Film Bureau
Suite 308-316
57 E. Jackson Blvd.
Chicago 4, Ill.

Johns Hopkins University
School of Medicine
800 Second Ave.
New York 17, N. Y.

Johnson & Johnson
Promotion Dept.
New Brunswick, N. J.

Kimberly-Clark Corp.
Neenah, Wis.

Knowledge Builders
Visual Education Center Building
Lowell and Cherry Lane
Floral Park, N. Y.

March of Time
369 Lexington Ave.
New York 17, N. Y.

McGeary-Smith Laboratories
1905 Fairview Ave., N. E.
Washington 2, D. C.

McGraw-Hill Book Co., Inc.
Text Film Dept.
330 W. 42nd St.
New York 18, N. Y.

Medical Motion Pictures
Committee on Medical Motion Pictures,
    A.M.A.
535 N. Dearborn St.
Chicago 10, Ill.

Modern Talking Picture-Service, Inc.
3 E. 54th St.
New York 22, N. Y.

National Dairy Council
111 N. Canal St.
Chicago 6, Ill.

National Association for Mental Health,
    Inc.
10 Columbus Circle
New York 19, N. Y.

National Film Board of Canada
1270 Avenue of the Americas
New York 20, N. Y.

The National Foundation
800 2nd Ave.
New York 17, N. Y.

National Motion Picture Co.
West Main St.
Mooresville, Ind.

National Safety Council
425 N. Michigan Ave.
Chicago 11, Ill.

National Society for the Prevention of
    Blindness
1790 Broadway
New York 19, N. Y.

National Tuberculosis Association
1790 Broadway
New York 19, N. Y.

North Carolina Board of Health
Film Section
Raleigh, N. C.

Personal Products
Education Dept.
Milltown, N. J.

Portafilms
418 N. Glendale Ave.
Glendale 6, Calif.

Rarig Motion Picture Co.
5514 University Way
Seattle 5, Wash.

Seminar Films, Inc.
347 Madison Ave.
New York 17, N. Y.

Smith, Kline & French Laboratories
1530 Spring Garden St.
Philadelphia 1, Pa.

Social Science Films
4030 Chouteau Ave.
St. Louis 10, Mo.

State Univeristy of Iowa
Iowa City, Iowa

Sterling Television Co.
205 East 43rd St.
New York 17, N. Y.

Teaching Film Custodians, Inc.
25 W. 43rd St.
New York 18, N. Y.

U.S. Bureau of Mines
4800 Forbes St.
Pittsburgh 13, Pa.

U.S. Department of Agriculture
Motion Picture Service
Office of Information
Washington 25, D. C.

U.S. Department of Health, Education
    and Welfare
Washington 25, D. C.

U.S. Public Health Service
Communicable Disease Center
605 Volunteer Building
Atlanta 3, Ga.

United Nations Film Division
Room 1003
1600 Broadway
New York 19, N. Y.

United World Films, Inc.
Educational Film Dept.
7356 Melrose Ave.
Hollywood 46, Calif.

University of Michigan
Ann Arbor, Mich.

University of Minnesota
Minneapolis, Minn.

University of Toronto
Toronto, Canada

Visual Training Institute
40 E. 49th St.
New York, N. Y.

Warren's Motion Pictures
Box 107
Dayton, Ohio

Western Electric Company
Motion Picture Bureau
195 Broadway
New York 7, N. Y.

Women's Christian Temperance Union
1730 Chicago Ave.
Evanston, Ill.

Young America Films, Inc.
18 E. 41st St.
New York 17, N. Y.

Record and report forms

HEALTH EXAMINATION

To be filled in by parent or guardian before the time of the examination.
(please print plainly with ink)

Pupil's name _____ Birth _____ Sex M__ F__
 (Last) (First) (Middle) (Month) (Day) (Year)

Address _____ Phone _____ Parent or guardian _____
 (Street or route) (City)

Family physician's name _____ Phone_____
 (Last) (First) (Initial)

Infancy and preschool history: Record unusual problems, e.g., convulsions, accidents, operations, exposure to tuberculosis, behavior difficulties _____

_____

_____
_____

Past history of illnesses: State the year in which the child had any of the following:

Communicable diseases		*Other diseases*		*Other conditions*	
Chickenpox	19____	Asthma	19____	Constant cough	19____
Diphtheria	19____	Diabetes	19____	Fainting spells	19____
German measles	19____	Hay fever	19____	Frequent colds	19____
Measles	19____	Heart trouble	19____	Frequent sore throat	19____
Mumps	19____	Kidney trouble	19____	Frequent urination	19____
Poliomyelitis	19____	Pneumonia	19____	Hearing difficulty	19____
Scarlet fever	19____	Rheumatic fever	19____	Tire easily	19____
Whooping cough	19____	Tonsilitis	19____	Vision difficulty	19____

History of immunization and tests

Completed booster dose			*Completed booster dose*			*Completed booster dose*		
Diphtheria	19__	19__	Whooping cough	19__	19__	Smallpox	19__	19__
Tetanus	19__	19__	Poliomyelitis	19__	19__	Measles	19__	19__
Other	19__	19__						

 Date Result *Result*

Chest x-ray 19____ ____ Other test 19____ ____

Other information of value to the teacher _____

_____
_____

_____

Front

HEALTH EXAMINATION

To be completed by examining physician

Vision, without glasses, right eye 20/_____, left eye 20/_____
with glasses, right eye 20/_____, left eye 20/_____
Color vision _____ test used _____

Hearing, right ear _____, left ear _____

Eyes	_____	Normal _____	Defect	_____
Ears	_____	Normal _____	Defect	_____
Nose	_____	Normal _____	Defect	_____
Throat	_____	Normal _____	Defect	_____
Thyroid	_____	Normal _____	Defect	_____
Lymph nodes	_____	Normal _____	Defect	_____
Heart	_____	Normal _____	Defect	_____
Lungs	_____	Normal _____	Defect	_____
Blood pressure	_____	Systolic _____	Diastolic_____	
Abdomen	_____	Normal _____	Defect	_____
Genitals	_____	Normal _____	Defect	_____
Posture	_____	Normal _____	Defect	_____
Extremities	_____	Normal _____	Defect	_____
Nervous system	_____	Normal _____	Defect	_____
Skin	_____	Normal _____	Defect	_____
Nutrition	_____	Normal _____	Defect	_____
Musculature	_____	Normal _____	Defect	_____
Other	_____	Normal _____	Defect	_____

Laboratory tests _____

Findings and recommendations _____

_____

_____

Immediate medical referral yes_____ no_____ Dental referral yes_____ no_____
Unlimited activity _____ Limited activity _____

Parent present yes_____ no_____

_____M.D._____

Examining physician   Date

Back

OREGON SCHOOL HEALTH RECORD CARD*
(FOR USE OF CARD SEE HEALTH SERVICES MANUAL, REVISED 1950)

NAME OF PUPIL _____ M___ F___ BIRTH _____ 19___
LAST   FIRST   SEX   MONTH   DAY   YEAR

ADDRESS _____ TEL. NO _____

PARENT OR GUARDIAN _____ OCCUPATION· OF FATHER _____ OF MOTHER _____

A

SCHOOL YEAR	GRADE	SCHOOL	HEIGHT IN INCHES 1ST / 2ND	WEIGHT IN POUNDS 1ST / 2ND	VISION TEST BOTH EYES	R	L	TEETH DECAYED	IMMEC. ULAR	HEARING R	L	ANNUAL HEALTH SUMMARY (SEE HEALTH SERVICES MANUAL FOR INSTRUCTIONS)	DATE PARENT
					W 20/	W 20/	W 20/						
					WO 20/	WO 20/	WO 20/						
					W 20/	W 20/	W 20/						
					WO 20/	WO 20/	WO 20/						
					W 20/	W 20/	W 20/						
					WO 20/	WO 20/	WO 20/						
					W 20/	W 20/	W 20/						
					WO 20/	WO 20/	WO 20/						
					W 20/	W 20/	W 20/						
					WO 20/	WO 20/	WO 20/						
					W 20/	W 20/	W 20/						
					WO 20/	WO 20/	WO 20/						
					W 20/	W 20/	W 20/						
					WO 20/	WO 20/	WO 20/						
					W 20/	W 20/	W 20/						
					WO 20/	WO 28/	WO 20/						
					W 20/	W 20/	W 20/						
					WO 20/	WO 20/	WO 20/						
					W 20/	W 20/	W 20/						
					WO 20/	WO 20/	WO 20/						
					W 20/	W 20/	W 20/						
					WO 20/	WO 20/	WO 20/						
					W 20/	W 20/	W 20/						
					WO 20/	WO 20/	WO 20/						

IMMUNIZATIONS	INITIAL	BOOSTERS			TESTS AND OTHER IMMUN.			AUDIOMETRIC TEST—HEARING LOSS				
SMALLPOX	19	19	19	19	TUBERCULIN	19	RESULT	DATE	SPEECH RANGE		HIGH TONE (DECIBELS)	
DIPHTHERIA	19	19	19	19	CHEST X-RAYS	19	RESULT	19	R L		R L	
WHOOPING COUGH	19	19	19	19		19	19	19	R L		R L	
TETANUS	19	19	19	19		19	19	19	R L		R L	

DATE	PHYSICIAN'S RECOMMENDATIONS AND NURSE'S REPORT NAME OF FAMILY PHYSICIAN _____

Front

REPORT OF SCHOOL DENTAL EXAMINATION

Report of school dental examination

To:_____ Parent or guardian

A dental examination of your child _____

has been made by the school dentist. This examination shows:

☐ 1. Need for dental service. You are advised to consult your family dentist as soon as possible.

☐ 2. No apparent defects.

Signed_____ Date_____

Front

HISTORY OF PAST AND CURRENT ILLNESS, ACCIDENT, DISABILITY, AND ABSENCE

OBSERVATIONS BY TEACHER

B

	SCHOOL YEAR	19	19	19	19	19	19	19	19	19	19	19	19	19	19
	GRADE IN SCHOOL														
EYES	STYES OR CRUSTED LIDS														
	INFLAMED EYES														
	CROSSED EYES														
	FREQUENT HEADACHES														
	SQUINTING AT BOOK OR BLACKBOARD														
EARS	DISCHARGE FROM EARS														
	EARACHES														
	FAILURE TO HEAR QUESTIONS														
ORAL CAVITY	INFLAMED GUMS														
	INFLAM OF LIPS, CHEEKS, PALATE														
	FAULTY ORAL HYGIENE														
NOSE AND THROAT	PERSISTENT MOUTH BREATHING														
	FREQUENT SORE THROAT														
	FREQUENT COLDS														
GENERAL CONDITION AND APPEARANCE	FAILURE TO GAIN WEIGHT														
	EXCESSIVE GAIN IN WEIGHT														
	DOES NOT APPEAR WELL														
	TIRES EASILY														
	POOR MUSCLE COORDINATION														
	POOR POSTURE														
	EMOTIONAL DISTURBANCES														
	SPEECH DEFECT														
BEHAVIOR	TWITCHING MOVEMENTS														
	UNDUE RESTLESSNESS														
	SHYNESS														
	NAIL BITING														
	EXCESSIVE USE OF LAVATORY														
	EXCESSIVE DROWSINESS														
	POOR FOOD HABITS														

CODE   √=DEFECT   T=UNDER TREATMENT   C=CORRECTED   R=REFERRAL   NT=NO TREATMENT NEEDED   STATE PRINTING DEPT.

Back

Report of dental work

This is to report that _____

☐ 1. Needs no dental work at present.

☐ 2. Has all necessary dental work completed.

☐ 3. Is receiving dental treatment.

Recommendation _____

Signed_____ Date_____

(child should return this card to the teacher)

Back

REPORT OF FAMILY DENTIST'S EXAMINATION

Dear Parents: In the interest of better health for your children, the school urges you to have them visit their family dentist at least twice a year. After the family dentist has filled out this card, will you have your child return it to the school?

Sincerely

_____Principal

Front

Report of family dentist's examination

_____ has had a dental examination and

☐ 1. Needs no dental work.
☐ 2. Has all necessary dental work completed.
☐ 3. Is receiving dental treatment.

Recommendation _____

_____

Signed_____ Date_____
(child should return this card to the teacher)

Back

REFERRAL CARD*

Recommended medical or dental consultation

School _____ Date _____

Dear _____

Observation of _____ indicates

_____

_____

The school urges that you consult your physician or dentist.

Sincerely,

_____

Vision screening report

School _____ Date _____

Dear _____

Results of the school vision screening test reveal the possibility that your child _____may be having some difficulty in seeing properly. The school urges you to consult a doctor for a professional examination of your child's vision.

Sincerely,

_____

*Reported after teacher-nurse conference when nurse is available. If there is no nurse, teachers properly should make the report.

Student accident report—Short form   No.____

Name of student _____ Age ____ Grade_____

Time and date of accident _____ Place of accident _____

Cause and nature of accident _____

_____ Injury _____

First aid by _____ Medical care by _____ M.D.

How could accident have been prevented? _____

_____

Reported by _____ Signed _____

              signed   Principal

Student accident report   No.____

Name of student _____ Age ____ Grade _____

Time and date of accident _____ Place of accident_____

Staff member in charge at time of accident _____

Where was staff member at time of accident? _____

Cause and nature of accident _____

_____

Nature of injury _____

_____

First aid by _____ Nature of first aid _____

_____ Medical care by _____ M.D.

Nature of medical care _____

Where was student taken _____ by _____

_____ Parent or guardian notified by _____

Via phone _____ message _____

Witnesses: _____   _____

How could this accident have been prevented? _____

_____

To be added when student returns to school: Days absent _____ Recovery_____

Reported by _____ Signed _____

              signed   Principal

STATE DEPARTMENT OF EDUCATION
Instruction Division
Curriculum and Instructional Services
Salem, Oregon

REQUEST FOR PHYSICIAN'S RECOMMENDATIONS ON
PHYSICAL EDUCATION ACTIVITY

_____19___

Dear Parent:

We have your request that your child_____
of _____School, be excused from physical education.
The activity portion is but a part of the larger health and physical education
program.

The health and physical education program is, however, flexible, since it involves
various forms of activities. In order to comply with your request and in order to
serve best the interests of the child, we ask that you have your physician complete the following statement and return it to the school.

_____   _____
(Signature of person requesting information)   (Position or title)

_____19___

PHYSICIAN'S REPORT

Nature of disability _____

Recommendations:

    ☐ 1. Unlimited activity
          Comment _____

    ☐ 2. Limited activity
          Comment _____

    ☐ 3. No activity
          Comment _____

    ☐ 4. Special recommendations:

          _____

          _____

          I recommend re-examination in _____ weeks.

This statement is valid until_____and does not
extend beyond the current school year.

_____
(Physician's signature)

Form 60—PR

PHYSICIAN'S RECOMMENDATION ON PHYSICAL EDUCATION ACTIVITY
Medford Public Schools
Medford, Oregon

Dear_____:

(Teacher)

_____, a patient

(Student's name)

under my care, should participate in physical education activities to the following extent:

☐ 1. Full activity except for _____

☐ 2. Limited activity

Recommendations _____

_____

☐ 3. Special remedial class (high school only)

Recommendations _____

_____

_____

☐ 4. No activity.

I (will)   (will not)   re-examine the patient in_____weeks.

_____

(Physician's signature)

Date_____

(front)

DESCRIPTION OF PHYSICAL EDUCATION PROGRAM
Medford Public Schools
Medford, Oregon

1. *Full program*

Grades 1-2-3	Grades 4-5-6	Junior high school	High school
Basic rhythms	Folk dance	Folk dance	Track and field*
Active games*	Square dance	Square dance	Field hockey*
Quiet games	Active games*	Exercises*	Touch football†
Basic skills	Relays*	Gymnastics*	Wrestling†
Self-testing*	Sports skills	Trampoline*	Trampoline
Exercises	Tumbling*	Wrestling†	Gymnastics
Fitness tests*	Exercises*	Track*	Weight training†
	Fitness tests*	Basketball*	Swimming*
		Touch football†	Volleyball*
		Softball	Badminton
		Volleyball*	Basketball*
		Soccer*	Softball
		Speedball*	Archery
		Fitness tests*	Tennis
			Exercises*
			Fitness tests*

2. *Limited program*

   Many times the disability is localized and of a nature that permits the use of other parts of the body without detriment. The physician's recommendation in such cases will be faithfully followed.

3. *Special remedial class* (high school only)

   Special classes are scheduled at the high school for students who have problems which require a more individual approach than is possible in the regular class. No medical cases are included in these classes without the recommendation of the physician. The exercises and activities prescribed by the physician will be closely supervised by the physical education teacher.

---

*Strenuous for the grade level.
†Boys' activity only.
Underlined: girls' activity only.

(back)

School health program evaluation scale

Part I. School health services   (350 points)_____

  A. Health appraisal

    1. Frequency of health examinations

      a. Entering pupils examined: 90-100%, 15 pts.; 80-89%, 12 pts.; 70-79%, 9 pts.; 50-69%, 6 pts.; 20-49%, 3 pts.   (15 pts.)_____

      b. New pupils entering the school system examined: 90-100%, 5 pts.; 80-89%, 4 pts.; 70-79%, 3 pts.; 50-69%, 2 pts.; 20-49%, 1 pt. ....   (5 pts.)_____

      c. Pupils examined at least once through grades three to ten: 90-100%, 5 pts.; 80-89%, 4 pts.; 70-79%, 3 pts.; 50-69%, 2 pts.; 20-49%, 1 pt. ....   (5 pts.)_____

      d. Pupils referred by teacher or examined by nurse: 90-100%, 10 pts.; 80-89%, 8 pts.; 70-79%, 6 pts.; 50-60%, 4 pts.; 20-49%, 2 pts. ....   (10 pts.)_____

      e. Interscholastic athletic participants examined: 90-100%, 5 pts.; 80-89%, 4 pts.; 70-79%, 3 pts.; 50-69%, 2 pts.; 20-49%, 1 pt. ....   (5 pts.)_____

      f. Pupils sustaining injuries at school or serious illness necessitating absence of five days or more from school examined: 90-100%, 5 pts.; 80-89%, 4 pts.; 70-79%, 3 pts.; 50-69%, 2 pts.; 20-49%, 1 pt. ....   (5 pts.)_____

      g. Pupils tested with audiometer every three years or more often (elementary schools only): 90-100%, 5 points; 80-89%, 4 pts.; 70-79%, 3 pts.; 50-69%, 2 pts.; 20-49%, 1 pt. ....   (5 pts.)_____

    2. Dental examinations

      Pupils examined by dentist during the year: 90-100%, 5 pts.; 80-89%, 4 pts.; 70-79%, 3 pts.; 50-69%, 2 pts.; 20-49%, 1 pt. ....   (5 pts.)_____

    3. Screening

      a. Pupils' whose height and weight are recorded at least twice a year (elementary only): 90-100%, 5 pts.; 80-89%, 4 pts.; 70-79%, 3 pts.; 50-69%, 2 pts.; 20-49%, 1 pt. ....   (5 pts.)_____

      b. Pupils whose vision and hearing were tested during first two months of school year (elementary school only): 90-100%, 5 pts.; 80-89%, 4 pts.; 70-79%, 3 pts.; 50-69%, 2 pts.; 20-49%, 1 pt. ....   (5 pts.)_____

B. Activities of health appraisal personnel

    1. Physician's examination rated according to time used per child:

      10 minutes or more, 10 pts.; 7-9 minutes, 8 pts.; 5-6 minutes, 6 pts.; 3-4 minutes, 4 pts.; 1-2 minutes, 2 pts. ...... (10 pts.)_____

    2. Nurse's procedures

      a. Obtaining health history* of children examined: 75-100%, 3 pts.; 50-74%, 2 pts.; 1-40%, 1 pt. .... (3 pts.)_____

      b. Making health assessment† of students as requested by teachers .... (3 pts.)_____

    3. Teacher's activities

      a. Elementary school teacher

        (1) Reviewing and using records relating to child's health status .... (5 pts.)_____

        (2) Recognizing outward indices of child health ..... (3 pts.)_____

        (3) Making continuous observations of child's health status and recording appraisal at least twice a year (3 pts.)_____

        (4) Making continuous observations of child's attitudes and social behavior and recording them at least twice a year .... (3 pts.)_____

        (5) Making referrals promptly through available channels

          (a) Child not making satisfactory weight and height gains .... (2 pts.)_____

          (b) Excessively overweight child .... (2 pts.)_____

          (c) Child with defective posture or body mechanics (2 pts.)_____

          (d) Pupil with emotional or personality problems (3 pts.)_____

          (e) Child with apparent hearing difficulties ..... (2 pts.)_____

          (f) Child with apparent vision difficulties .... (2 pts.)_____

          (g) Child with speech difficulties .... (2 pts.)_____

          (h) Child with abnormal skin conditions .... (2 pts.)_____

          (i) Child with low vitality .... (2 pts.)_____

          (j) Child with other symptoms of illness .... (3 pts.)_____

        (6) Preparing pupils for examination through discussion, 1 pt.; review of experience, 1 pt.; evaluation of the examination, 1 pt. .... (3 pts.)_____

      b. Secondary school classroom teachers

        (1) Recognizing outward indices of student health ... (3 pts.)_____

        (2) Making continuous observation of student's health status with referral to health educator or nurse ... (3 pts.)_____

        (3) Making continuous observation of student's attitudes and social behavior, with referral to health educator or nurse .... (3 pts.)_____

      c. Secondary school health educator

        (1) Reviewing and using record's relating to student's health status .... (3 pts.)_____

        (2) Providing for adequate screening of students with emotional or personality problems .... (3 pts.)_____

        (3) Making referrals promptly through teacher-nurse conference regularly scheduled at least once a week (3 pts.)_____

    4. Parent's participation

      a. Making written report of observed practices of child on personal history form .... (2 pts.)_____

      b. Accepting opportunity to confer with physician or nurse (2 pts.)_____

_____

*May be obtained by teacher.

†May be made by health director or other qualified personnel.

5. Child's participation
   a. Discussing health problems with teacher, nurse, or doctor .... (3 pts.)_____
   b. Re-evaluating health status in terms recommended by physician, nurse, or teacher .... (3 pts.)_____

C. Follow-up and counseling procedures
   1. Counseling pupils regarding health status .... (3 pts.)_____
   2. Giving parents adequate information on health status of child within two weeks after examination .... (3 pts.)_____
   3. Giving parents information or other aid in implementing physician's findings and recommendations .... (3 pts.)_____
   4. For teachers, interpreting the physician's findings and recommendations .... (3 pts.)_____
   5. Adapting the school program to meet the needs of handicapped children: 100%, 10 pts.; 75-99%, 8 pts.; 50-74%, 6 pts.; 25-49%, 4 pts.; 1-24%, 2 pts. .... (10 pts.)_____
   6. Making effective use of state and community resources
      a. Consultants: hearing, 2 pts.; vision, 2 pts.; mental health, 2 pts.; dental health, 2 pts.; nutrition, 2 pts.; sanitation, 2 pts. .... (12 pts.)_____
      b. Social workers .... (4 pts.)_____
   7. Aiding in obtaining professional services for children needing corrections but unable to pay: 90-100%, 10 pts.; 80-89%, 8 pts.; 70-79%, 6 pts.; 50-69%, 4 pts.; 20-49%, 2 pts. (10 pts.)_____
   8. Making follow-up survey to determine which corrections have been made: after two months, 5 pts.; after four months, 3 pts.; after six months, 1 pt. .... (9 pts.)_____
   9. Recording corrections on student's health record form.... (3 pts.)_____
   10. Obtaining dental certificates: 80-100% of pupils, 5 pts.; 60-79%, 4 pts.; 40-59%, 3 pts.; 20-39%, 2 pts.; 1-19%, 1 pt (5 pts.)_____

D. Prevention and control of communicable disease
   1. Tuberculosis tests for children exposed to tuberculosis: annually, 10 pts.; biennially, 5 pts. .... (10 pts.)_____
   2. Tuberculosis tests available for all high school students: annually, 6 pts.; biennially, 4 pts.; every three years, 2 pts.; every four years, 1 pt. .... (6 pts.)_____
   3. Spot x-ray surveys: annually, 3 pts.; biennially, 2 pts.; every three years, 1 pt. .... (3 pts.)_____
   4. Tuberculosis tests required of all school personnel: annually, 3 pts.; biennially, 2 pts.; only before entry, 1 pt. .. (3 pts.)_____
   5. Children immunized (elementary school)
      a. For diphtheria: 80-100%, 5 pts.; 60-79%, 4 pts.; 40-59%, 3 pts.; 20-39%, 2 pts.; 1-19%, 1 pt. .... (5 pts.)_____
      b. For smallpox: 80-100%, 5 pts.; 60-79%, 4 pts.; 40-59%, 3 pts.; 20-39%, 2 pts.; 1-19%, 1 pt. .... (5 pts.)_____
      c. For poliomyelitis: 80-100%, 5 pts.; 60-79%, 4 pts.; 40-59%, 3 pts.; 20-39%, 2 pts.; 1-19%, 1 pt. .... (5 pts.)_____
   6. Children with suspected communicable disease reported to the health department .... (5 pts.)_____
   7. Children with symptoms of communicable disease isolated (exclusion of child based on appearance, behavior, and complaints) .... (3 pts.)_____
   8. Parents notified when child appears to be ill .... (3 pts.)_____
   9. Teachers provided with list of characteristics of common illnesses of school children .... (2 pts.)_____
   10. Pupils inspected early morning and before noon during epidemics .... (5 pts.)_____

11. Teacher observation made for symptoms of illness when no epidemic exists .... (3 pts.)_____

12. Pupils absent less than five days checked by nurse or teacher for communicability of disease upon readmission .... (3 pts.)_____

13. Pupils and school personnel absent from school five days or more due to illness with no official isolation, readmitted to school only upon presentation of statement of noncommunicability signed by health department or licensed physician .... (5 pts.)_____

14. Pupils readmitted to school after official isolation for communicable disease only upon release by health department .... (4 pts.)_____

15. Pupils returning to school after serious illness permitted to participate in strenuous activities only by approval of physician or nurse .... (3 pts.)_____

16. Perfect school attendance not emphasized .... (2 pts.)_____

17. Teacher illness reported to principal and recommended control procedures followed .... (3 pts.)_____

E. Emergency and first-aid provisions
1. First-aid training required of every teacher .... (3 pts.)_____
2. Responsibility for care of serious cases assigned to at least one specially qualified person in each building .... (3 pts.)_____
3. Well-planned written procedures giving instructions to follow in case of emergency or disaster reviewed and understood by all school employees .... (3 pts.)_____
4. Emergency and disaster plans rehearsed: six times or more per year, 5 pts.; five times, 4 pts.; four times, 3 pts.; three times, 2 pts.; twice, 1 pt. .... (5 pts.)_____
5. Accidents reported, investigated, and report filed .... (4 pts.)_____
6. Record of family physician of each child kept available .. (2 pts.)_____
7. Adequate first-aid supplies made readily available ...... (5 pts.)_____
8. Telephone made easily available .... (3 pts.)_____
9. Important numbers posted at telephone, e.g., nearest physician, ambulance, police, and fire department .... (2 pts.)_____
10. Fire and emergency alarm systems working efficiently ..... (3 pts.)_____
11. Transportation home provided for ill children .... (3 pts.)_____
12. Rest rooms provided for ill or injured children
    a. Separate rooms for boys and girls .... (3 pts.)_____
    b. At least two cots for boys and two for girls .... (3 pts.)_____
    c. Rooms partially darkened .... (2 pts.)_____
    d. Room temperature and ventilation controlled .... (2 pts.)_____
    e. Responsible person in attendance .... (2 pts.)_____

F. Health room equipment for clinics, conferences, and examinations (table, chairs, good light and ventilation, window shades, scales, measuring rod, and eye charts) .... (5 pts.)_____

G. Records
1. Cummulative health records kept up-to-date, transferrable with other school records .... (3 pts.)_____
2. Cummulative health records made available to administrators, teachers, and medical advisers .... (3 pts.)_____

Part II. Health instruction   (400 points)_____

A. Direct health instruction
1. A general plan of progressive health instruction for all grades used .... (10 pts.)_____

2. Subject areas included in health instruction
   a. Structure and function .... (5 pts.)_____
   b. Personal health .... (5 pts.)_____
   c. Sex education .... (5 pts.)_____
   d. Nutrition .... (5 pts.)_____
   e. First-aid and safety .... (5 pts.)_____
   f. Mental health .... (5 pts.)_____
   g. Control of disease (communicable and noncommunicable .... (5 pts.)_____
   h. Narcotics and other poisons .... (5 pts.)_____
   i. Community health and sanitation .... (5 pts.)_____
   j. Choice and use of health services and products .... (5 pts.)_____
3. Organized course of study for each grade kept on file in principal's office (including aims, objectives, and methods of teaching) .... (5 pts.)_____
4. Course of study reviewed and revised annually .... (5 pts.)_____
5. Health practices, attitudes, and information included in aims and objectives .... (5 pts.)_____
6. Planned instruction in grades one to eight: three or more times a week, 5 pts.; two times a week, 3 pts.; once a week, 1 pt. .... (5 pts.)_____
7. Graduating seniors who have taken high school health instruction: all students, 10 pts.; 80-99%, 8 pts.; 60-79%, 6 pts.; 40-59%, 4 pts.; 20-39%, 2 pts.; 10-19%, 1 pt. .... (10 pts.)_____
8. Scheduled health classes in secondary schools: two semesters during grades nine through twelve, 10 pts.; four quarter years during nine through twelve, 10 pts.; alternating during week with another subject for one year, 5 pts.; one semester during grades nine through twelve, 5 pts. ... (10 pts.)_____
9. Health classes held in standard classroom .... (3 pts.)_____
10. Instruction based on needs and interests of children (as revealed by surveys of their health histories, records, interests, and practices) .... (3 pts.)_____
11. Up-to-date readers or textbooks in health instruction available; all children in health classes, 10 pts.; 80-99%, 8 pts.; 60-79%, 6 pts.; 40-59%, 4 pts.; 20-39%, 2 pts.; less than 20, 0 pts. .... (10 pts.)_____
12. Methods used in teaching health
    a. Discussion (group, buzz sessions, or panels) .... (2 pts.)_____
    b. Reading and study assignments .... (2 pts.)_____
    c. Oral and written reports .... (2 pts.)_____
    d. Lectures .... (2 pts.)_____
    e. Demonstrations .... (2 pts.)_____
    f. Conferences .... (2 pts.)_____
    g. Projects .... (2 pts.)_____
    h. Problem solving .... (2 pts.)_____
    i. Field trips .... (2 pts.)_____
    j. Supplementary aids
       (1) Models, charts, and posters .... (2 pts.)_____
       (2) Lantern slides and motion pictures .... (2 pts.)_____
    k. Plays and role playing.......................... (2 pts.)_____
    l. Health surveys, e.g., practices, illness, medical treatment, immunizations, etc. .... (2 pts.)_____
    m. Experiments .... (2 pts.)_____
13. Both official and voluntary agencies used in health instruction, e.g., literature and speakers .... (5 pts.)_____

14. Health instruction evaluated by
   a. Conferences .... (2 pts.)_____
   b. Objective tests .... (2 pts.)_____
   c. Surveys of health practices .... (2 pts.)_____
   d. Surveys of health attitudes .... (2 pts.)_____
   e. Surveys of health knowledge .... (2 pts.)_____
15. Handicapped children provided with appropriate learning activities .... (3 pts.)_____
16. Students encouraged to evaluate own health behavior and to assume responsibility for improvement .... (5 pts.)_____
17. Supplementary health materials available for student use .... (3 pts.)_____
18. Sufficient facilities provided for adequate health instruction .... (5 pts.)_____
19. Only materials from reliable sources used .... (5 pts.)_____
20. Adult health education program offered .... (3 pts.)_____

B. Correlated health instruction
   1. With art .... (10 pts.)_____
   2. With biological science .... (10 pts.)_____
   3. With physical science .... (10 pts.)_____
   4. With home economics .... (10 pts.)_____
   5. With physical education .... (10 pts.)_____
   6. With social studies .... (10 pts.)_____
   7. With other subject fields .... (10 pts.)_____

C. Integrated health instruction
   1. Health education made functional in classroom activities
      a. Control of heat .... (5 pts.)_____
      b. Control of ventilation .... (5 pts.)_____
      c. Practice of cleanliness .... (5 pts.)_____
   2. Health education made functional in nonclassroom activities
      a. Recreation
         (1) Use of safety precautions .... (5 pts.)_____
         (2) Emphasis on personal adjustment .... (5 pts.)_____
      b. Lunch program
         (1) Selection of food .... (5 pts.)_____
         (2) Adequate time for eating .... (5 pts.)_____
         (3) Time for washing before meals .... (5 pts.)_____
         (4) Favorable lunchroom atmosphere .... (5 pts.)_____
      c. Safety program
         (1) Safety patrol .... (5 pts.)_____
         (2) Traffic patrol .... (5 pts.)_____
   3. Pupils given individualized guidance in evaluating daily health .... (3 pts.)_____
   4. Medical and dental examinations utilized as learning experiences .... (2 pts.)_____
   5. Health instruction integrated with other worthwhile experiences, e.g., field trips, projects, clubs, home and family experiences, etc. .... (5 pts.)_____

D. Preparation of teachers
   1. Areas included in training elementary teacher
      a. Personal health .... (5 pts.)_____
      b. School health services .... (5 pts.)_____
      c. School health instruction .... (5 pts.)_____
      d. Healthful school living .... (5 pts.)_____
      e. Community health .... (5 pts.)_____

2. Training for secondary school health educator
   a. Health teaching major .... (20 pts.)_____
   b. Health teaching minor .... (10 pts.)_____
   c. Ten to twenty quarter hours in health courses .... (5 pts.)_____
   d. Six to ten quarter hours in health courses .... (2 pts.)_____
3. Health education included in in-service program for teachers and principal
   a. Instruction and illustrations of recognizable signs and symptoms of communicable disease given by qualified person .... (3 pts.)_____
   b. Policies and recommendations of health department interpreted to teachers .... (5 pts.)_____
   c. Health information presented through
     (1) Library .... (2 pts.)_____
     (2) Bulletin boards .... (2 pts.)_____
     (3) Faculty meetings .... (2 pts.)_____
     (4) P.T.A. meetings .... (2 pts.)_____
     (5) Radio programs .... (2 pts.)_____
     (6) Newspapers .... (2 pts.)_____

Part III. Healthful school living (250 points)_____

A. Safe and sanitary school facilities
  1. School site
   a. Easily accessible
     (1) Elementary schools not more than one half mile walking distance or thirty minutes riding distance (3 pts.)_____
     (2) Junior high schools not more than one mile or one hour riding distance .... (3 pts.)_____
     (3) Senior high schools not more than two miles on one hour riding distance .... (3 pts.)_____
   b. Free from disturbances
     (1) No distracting noises .... (2 pts.)_____
     (2) No irritating dust .... (2 pts.)_____
     (3) No noticeable smoke .... (2 pts.)_____
     (4) No objectionable odors .... (2 pts.)_____
   c. Well-drained .... (2 pts.)_____
   d. Adequate size
     (1) Elementary school grounds: four or more acres, 4 pts.; three acres, 3 pts.; two acres, 2 pts.; less than two acres, 1 pt. .... (4 pts.)_____
     (2) Secondary school grounds: six acres or more, 4 pts.; five acres, 3 pts.; four acres, 2 pts.; less than four acres, 1 pt. .... (4 pts.)_____
  2. Water supply
   a. Ample .... (3 pts.)_____
   b. Clear and cool .... (2 pts.)_____
   c. Free from undesirable flavors and odors .... (2 pts.)_____
   d. Free from contamination and pollution .... (3 pts.)_____
   e. Adequate in fluorine content .... (2 pts.)_____
  3. Waste disposal
   a. Safe and sanitary garbage disposal .... (3 pts.)_____
   b. Sewage disposal meets state standards .... (5 pts.)_____
  4. Building
   a. Fire protection
     (1) Building constructed of fire-resistant material... (4 pts.)_____

    (2) Fire extinguishers placed conveniently to all parts
of the building .... (2 pts.)_____

    (3) Fire alarms and extinguishers kept in working
order .... (2 pts.)_____

    (4) Fire alarms and extinguishers tested: twice a year
or more often, 2 pts.; once a year, 1 pt. .... (2 pts.)_____

    (5) Fire doors at all stairs .... (2 pts.)_____

    (6) Outside doors open to inside bar .... (2 pts.)_____

    (7) Doors to exits unlocked or chutes open at all times
building is in use .... (2 pts.)_____

    (8) Exits and fire escapes sufficient to empty building
in two minutes .... (3 pts.)_____

    (9) At least two exits from each floor .... (2 pts.)_____

    (10) Exits well marked and lighted .... (2 pts.)_____

    (11) Last section of fire escape stairs left down .... (2 pts.)_____

b. Ventilation

    (1) Controllable in each room .... (1 pt.)_____

    (2) Comfortable circulation of fresh air .... (2 pts.)_____

c. Heating

    (1) Facilities inspected for safety weekly .... (3 pts.)_____

    (2) Classroom temperature range 68° to 72° F. ...... (2 pts.)_____

d. Lighting

    (1) Inspection and approval of electrical wiring at
least once a year .... (3 pts.)_____

    (2) Foot-candles of light available at desk level: 25 or
more, 3 pts.; 15-24, 2 pts.; 5-14, 1 pt. .... (3 pts.)_____

    (3) Uniform light in each room .... (2 pts.)_____

    (4) Absence of glare

        (a) Chalkboards of dull finish not beside windows (2 pts.)_____

        (b) Desks and tables of dull finish .... (2 pts.)_____

        (c) Shades adjustable for maximum light control (2 pts.)_____

    (5) Walls and ceiling of good light-reflecting colors:
white or ivory, 4 pts.; yellow, 3 pts.; light buff,
2 pts.; light gray, 1 pt. .... (4 pts.)_____

    (6) Stairways, entrances, and corridors well lighted:
more than 15 foot-candles, 3 pts.; 10-14, 2 pts.;
5-9, 1 pt. .... (3 pts.)_____

e. Seating

    (1) Individual seats .... (1 pt.)_____

    (2) Movable seats .... (1 pt.)_____

    (3) Regular adjustments to meet the needs of chil-
dren: two or more times a year, 2 pts.; once a
year, 1 pt. .... (2 pts.)_____

    (4) Seat arrangement

        (a) No child facing window .... (3 pts.)_____

        (b) Teacher's desk not facing window .... (2 pts.)_____

    (5) Provision for left-handed pupils .... (3 pts.)_____

f. Drinking fountains

    (1) Type approved by board of health .... (2 pts.)_____

    (2) Adequate number: one or more for 50 children,
3 pts.; one for 60, 2 pts.; one for 70 or more,
1 pt. .... (3 pts.)_____

g. Handwashing facilities

    (1) Type of basin approved by board of health ..... (2 pts.)_____

  (2) Adequate number of washbasins

   (a) Elementary schools: one for each 20 pupils, 3 pts.; one for each 30, 2 pts.; one for each 40 or more, 1 pt. .... (3 pts.)_____

   (b) Secondary schools: one for 50 pupils, 3 pts.; one for 60, 2 pts.; one for 70 or more, 1 pt. (3 pts.)_____

  (3) Hot and cold water available .... (2 pts.)_____

  (4) Paper or roller towels available .... (2 pts.)_____

  (5) Liquid or powdered soap available .... (2 pts.)_____

  (6) Waste basket available .... (1 pt.)_____

 h. Toilet facilities

  (1) Rooms clean, well lighted, and ventilated ...... (3 pts.)_____

  (2) Toilets

   (a) Type meeting state board of health standards (2 pts.)_____

   (b) Number

    1'. For elementary girls: one for 20, 3 pts.; one for 25, 2 pts.; one for 30, 1 pt. ..... (3 pts.)_____

    2'. For elementary boys (toilets and urinals): one for 20, 3 pts.; one for 25, 2 pts.; one for 30, 1 pt. .... (3 pts.)_____

    3'. For girls in grades nine through twelve: one for 45, 3 pts.; one for 50, 2 pts.; one for 55, 1 pt. .... (3 pts.)_____

    4'. For boys in grades nine through twelve (toilets and urinals): one for 60, 3 pts.; one for 65, 2 pts.; one for 70 or more, 1 pt. .... (3 pts.)_____

   (c) Plumbing conforming to state plumbing code (3 pts.)_____

5. Custodial service

 a. Cleaning practices

  (1) Floors cleaned daily with dust-preventive material (2 pts.)_____

  (2) Light fixtures and windows cleaned at least three time a year .... (2 pts.)_____

  (3) Toilet room care

   (a) Swept daily .... (1 pt.)_____

   (b) Scrubbed at least twice a week .... (2 pts.)_____

   (c) Towels, soap, and toilet paper kept available (2 pts.)_____

 b. Building and equipment kept in good repair .... (2 pts.)_____

 c. Building kept free from accumulations of rubbish .... (2 pts.)_____

 d. Inflammable material kept only in tight metal containers .... (2 pts.)_____

 e. Custodian having special training for work .... (2 pts.)_____

6. Lunchroom service

 a. School lunch facilities conforming to standards of state board of health .... (3 pts.)_____

 b. Serving designed to promote good eating practices .... (2 pts.)_____

 c. Sale of carbonated beverages, gum, and candy: prohibited, 2 pts.; restricted, 1 pt. .... (2 pts.)_____

 d. All milk pasteurized .... (2 pts.)_____

 e. All food handlers instructed in sanitary food handling and personal health practices .... (3 pts.)_____

 f. Dishes cleaned and stored in manner approved by board of health .... (3 pts.)_____

 g. Metal garbage cans watertight and rodent-proof ...... (1 pt.)_____

 h. Kitchen well lighted, well ventilated, clean, and attractive .... (2 pts.)_____

    i. Dining room well lighted, well ventilated, clean, and attractive .... (2 pts.)_____

7. Play facilities and practices
    a. Play areas and equipment inspected for accident hazards and such conditions promptly corrected: weekly, 3 pts.; monthly, 1 pt. .... (3 pts.)_____
    b. Adequate indoor play areas with nonslip floors ..... (2 pts.)_____
    c. Adequate outdoor play areas with nonslip surfaces .. (2 pts.)_____
    d. Pupils instructed and supervised in proper use and care of classroom, gymnasium, and playground facilities (2 pts.)_____

8. Safety program
    a. Planned program .... (2 pts.)_____
    b. Responsible supervisor .... (2 pts.)_____
    c. Weekly safety inspections .... (2 pts.)_____
    d. Traffic problems and adequately supervised and controlled .... (3 pts.)_____

B. Healthful school program
1. Teaching methods which promote both physical and mental health
    a. Frequent success experienced by all pupils .... (2 pts.)_____
    b. Mental health of child considered in school discipline (2 pts.)_____
    c. Excessive fatigue avoided .... (3 pts.)_____
    d. Length of school day and frequency and length of recess periods adjusted to age levels .... (2 pts.)_____
    e. Each child encouraged in his special interest .... (3 pts.)_____
    f. Each pupil given opportunity to lead and follow ..... (3 pts.)_____
    g. Each child assisted in development of self-confidence, self-judgment, and good social attitudes .... (3 pts.)_____

2. Good rapport between pupils and teacher
    a. Children feel free to express themselves .... (2 pts.)_____
    b. Pupils are relaxed .... (3 pts.)_____
    c. Pupils feel they are held in esteem by teacher and associates .... (3 pts.)_____

3. Emotional effect on pupils taken into consideration in making decisions .... (3 pts.)_____

4. Teaching staff emotionally well adjusted .... (3 pts.)_____

5. Established standards of health required of all school personnel .... (3 pts.)_____

6. General health examination required of all school personnel: annually, 3 pts.; biennially, 2 pts.; only before entry to school system, 1 pt. .... (3 pts.)_____

7. Teaching load: total work load limited to 40 hours or less per week, 3 pts.; 41-44, 2 pts.; 45-48, 1 pt. .... (2 pts.)_____

8. One week sick-leave granted to school personnel .... (2 pts.)_____

Summary

Part   I. School health services .... (350 points)_____
Part II. Health instruction .... (400 points)_____
Part III. Healthful school living .... (250 points)_____
                                                  Composite score_____

Appendix D

Survey of healthful school living

An inventory of school health practices*

Playground

1. Do teachers supervise playground activities?
2. Are play areas adequately marked out?
3. Is playground space used effectively?
4. Is equipment inspected regularly and kept in repair?
5. At recess, are all children outdoors during nice weather?
6. Do all children participate in activities?

Gymnasinum or activity room

1. Is the gymnasium clean, well ventilated, and well lighted?
2. Does class scheduling allow for effective instruction?
3. Do all children wear proper shoes?
4. Do all children, from the fifth grade on, wear gym suits?
5. Are shower rooms clean and well lighted?
6. Are locker rooms clean, well ventilated, and well lighted?
7. Are lockers orderly and clean?
8. Are effective measures taken to prevent spread of infection?
9. Do students use the scales regularly?

Classrooms

1. Are the cloakrooms or lockers orderly and clean?
2. Is there a mirror in the cloakroom or other convenient place?
3. Is the classroom adequate for the class size?
4. Does the classroom give an appearance of cleanliness and neatness?
5. Are the floors clean and in good repair?
6. Are all chalkboards in good condition and clean?
7. Do chalk trays have a minimum of dust?
8. Are pupils provided seats of the proper size?
9. Are all seats single, movable, and in good condition?
10. Is there an atmosphere of informal good fellowship?
11. Do the children appear to be at ease and relaxed?
12. Do the children have an eager interest in their work?
13. Do children have a high regard for each other and the teacher?
14. Is there evidence that the pupils are being stimulated by their experience?
15. Are there provisions in kindergarten and first grade for students to lie down?

---

*This survey does not include evaluation of the school plant.

Light

1. Do the windows face correctly?
2. Are shades adjusted so top of window is uncovered?
3. Are shades translucent, of light color?
4. Are walls above eye level of light color and the ceiling ivory or white?
5. Is there a good reflecting wall surface opposite the windows?
6. Does artificial lighting provide even distribution of light?
7. Are luminaires above children's vision field?
8. Are luminaires properly covered or shielded?
9. Is working surface light at least 30 foot-candles?
10. Are there provisions for more light as needed?
11. Do walls, ceiling, chalkboards, and furniture have a dull finish?
12. Are windows free from obstruction to light?
13. Are windows kept clean?
14. Are walls, ceiling, chalkboards, and wall displays kept clean?
15. Are work places planned with regard for intensity and direction of light?
16. Are the light needs of left-handed pupils provided for?
17. Are pupils with defective vision placed in the places with best light?
18. Do children adjust to light conditions and needs?
19. Does the teacher stand away from the windows during class discussion?
20. Are illustrative materials placed at the eye level of the pupils?

Heat and ventilation

1. Is the temperature maintained between 66° and 71° F.?
2. Is a thermometer kept at level of pupils' heads and away from heating unit, doors and windows?
3. Do the students keep a temperature record?
4. Do children assume responsibility for regulating heat and ventilation?
5. Is the air in motion properly without direct drafts on pupils?
6. Are window boards or glass deflectors used?
7. Is the classroom aired at least three times daily?
8. Is the air in the classroom always clean and fresh?

Water supply and drinking use

1. Has the water supply been approved by health officials?
2. Is a bacteriological test of the water conducted once a month?
3. Are fountains or other drinking facilities sanitary?
4. Are adequate opportunities for drinking provided?
5. Is the area around the fountain or other facilities neat and sanitary?

Lunchroom

1. Is the lunchroom attractive?
2. Is it arranged most efficiently?
3. Are personnel always neat and clean?
4. Do personnel use sanitary methods in handling and serving food?
5. Are lunchroom facilities inspected each week?
6. Are lunchroom workers courteous to pupils?
7. Are lunchroom regulations posted and understood by pupils?
8. Does the lunchroom schedule work smoothly?
9. Are lunchroom practices a subject of classroom discussion?
10. Are wash parades held before lunch?
11. Do the children take pride in their lunchroom?
12. Is the lunch hour orderly and devoid of rowdyism?
13. Do children assume some responsibility for the lunchroom?
14. Is attention given to conduct and cleanliness when lunch is eaten in the classroom?

Toilet rooms

1. Is sewage disposal approved by health officials?
2. Are toilet rooms adequately ventilated and lighted?
3. Are toilet rooms kept clean and orderly?
4. Do water closets and urinals operate properly?
5. Is adequate toilet paper provided?
6. Are washbasins always kept clean?
7. Is all handwashing done under running water?
8. Is adequate hot water available?
9. Is adequate soap always available?
10. Are paper towels always available?
11. Are large receptacles available for used towels?
12. Is adequate use made of handwashing facilities?
13. Do children assume responsibility for toilet room cleanliness?

Safety and first aid

1. Are regular safety inspections made?
2. Are hazards eliminated or reduced in severity?
3. Are unsafe practices eliminated or modified?
4. Is there an organized continuous safety promotion program?
5. Is there a plan for safety as students go to and from school?
6. Is there an effective school traffic safety program?
7. Do pupils display a safety consciousness?
8. Are horseplay and rough play prohibited?
9. Are inflammable materials stored properly?
10. Are sufficient approved fire extinguishers properly placed?
11. Do older pupils know how to use extinguishers?
12. Do all students understand the approved system of reporting fires?
13. Do fire drills require less than three minutes to evacuate the building?
14. Are student organization and lines of exit well established?
15. Is a thorough study made of each school accident?
16. Is there an organized first-aid service?
17. Is there a well-equipped first-aid cabinet?
18. Do pupils and teachers know first-aid procedures?
19. Are cots and blankets available?
20. Are efforts constantly made to make school life safer?

Index